J. W. HORTON — FUNDAMENTALS OF SONAR

UNITED STATES NAVAL INSTITUTE : ANNAPOLIS

W. HORTON – FUNDAMENTALS OF SONAR

PREFACE

Early in World War II it became apparent that submarine warfare was to require a greatly increased utilization of underwater sound. To this end engineers were recruited from a variety of activities where they had acquired a knowledge of related techniques. These engineers, each making contributions from his own field of applied science, built up the techniques for a new field, now known as Sonar. At the same time scientists, also recruited from many sources, were engaged in studying the physical laws on which these new techniques are based. Driven by necessity, however, the application of the science of underwater acoustics outran its systematic organization. Those responsible for the development of urgently needed underwater sound equipments were forced to make use of widely diversified background information. It is little wonder that the physical relationships which governed their work were not expressed in a consistent manner. The terminology of an engineer from one field was, in fact, often obscure to an associate from another.

The task of achieving unity and coherence of expression is never an easy one for any author. It presents unusual pitfalls for one undertaking to set forth the fundamentals of a subject having a history as confused as that of sonar. It is for such a subject, however, that this effort is most needed.

The organization of the basic relationships of a particular branch of science requires the use of logical and uniform methods of expression. It is not sufficient, however, that these methods be correct within their own boundaries. It is equally necessary that conventions in effect in contiguous fields be adequately observed. The growing complexity of our ever-expanding body of scientific knowledge makes it at once more difficult and more essential that these obligations be met.

The sonar engineer finds his interests joined with those of many others whose daily activities, and whose practices, are quite unlike his own. He must work constantly with the officers and men of his country's naval forces. He must be ready to take advantage of progress made by those skilled in electronics, in acoustics, and in communication theory. He must communicate freely with the oceanographer and with the psychophysiologist. He must never forget that underwater acoustics is but a small portion of the field of general physics; he must not allow his dialect to become too provincial.

It is the purpose of this book to show the relations between those physical factors which are of significance in the employment of acoustic energy propagated through water. An attempt has been made to present these relations in a systematic and general manner and to demonstrate their utility in practical problems. The compilation of previously known relations, and the consideration of increasingly complex problems, have disclosed numerous omissions in otherwise logically ordered sequences. In a number of cases these gaps have been filled by establishing additional relations. Wherever possible this has been done in a manner which conforms to conventions already in use. Unfortunately, strict adherence to this policy could not always be realized. It has occasionally been necessary to choose between the adoption of a coherent general treatment and the retention of a practice having limited utility. In this dilemma the preference has been given to those concepts and to those forms of expression which have the wider applicability. It has been gratifying to find that here, as elsewhere, the more general expressions are usually the simpler. Attention has often been called to the likelihood that this will be true. Descartes, Poincaré, and others have commented at length on its significance.

The material making up this book began to be brought together as notes for use in the instruction of officers of the U. S. Navy taking the Course in Naval Electronics offered by the Massachusetts Institute of Technology, immediately following World War II. These notes were later revised for courses in Sonar given to the technical staff of the U. S. Navy Underwater Sound Laboratory. It is well known that such use provides a healthy environment for the growth of any textbook of a technical nature. Certainly the present book has gained much from the criticisms, too often, alas, well justified, of the many students who have studied it.

There are many others to whom I am indebted for even more tangible contributions. Mr. George W. King, who assisted with the course given at the Massachusetts Institute of Technology, made many welcome suggestions as to how a complex network of interrelations might be untangled for presentation as an appropriate sequence. At the U. S. Navy Underwater Sound Laboratory Mr. William M. Bush and Mr. Louis C. Maples gave much time and thought to questions of terminology and symbols. The clear thinking and encouragement of these two associates have done much to diminish the difficulties of these vexing problems. The labor of preparing the material of this book for the public view has been greatly lessened by the care and patience of Mrs. Alice J. Mabry who made all of the drawings, having first carried out the necessary computations, and who typed the manuscript with a meticulous attention to the many details of form and arrangement. Mr. William R. Ward has demonstrated, by his designs for the cover and dust jacket, that the artist sees things that escape the engineer in a prosaic geometrical figure.

I am most grateful to Captain Edward J. Fahy, USN, formerly Commanding Officer and Director of the U. S. Navy Underwater Sound Laboratory, and to Captain William I. Bull, USN, Assistant Chief of the Bureau of Ships for Electronics, for suggesting that this book be published by the U. S. Naval Institute.

J. WARREN HORTON

New London, Conn.
August 3, 1956

TABLE OF CONTENTS

Chapter 1

INTRODUCTION

Chapter 2

THE NATURE OF UNDERWATER SOUND

Chapter 3

THE PROPAGATION OF UNDERWATER SOUND

Chapter 4

TRANSDUCERS

Chapter 5

TRANSDUCER SYSTEMS

Chapter 6

INDICATORS AND RECORDERS

Chapter 7

DIRECT LISTENING

Chapter 8

FUNDAMENTAL FACTORS IN ECHO RANGING

Chapter 9

ADDENDA

FUNDAMENTALS OF SONAR

CHAPTER 1

INTRODUCTION

Observations of the objects which constitute our environment are made by means of energy radiated from those objects. Man is provided by nature with sense organs which are directly responsive to two forms of radiant energy: light and sound. He has provided himself with instruments by which he may make observations using other forms, such as electromagnetic radiations outside the visible spectrum. By means of light waves observations are made of the incredibly remote or of the incredibly minute. In terms of the quantity and the variety of the information, and of the speed with which it is carried, light is unquestionably our most effective observational agent.

The types of information carried by sound waves are usually quite different from those carried by light waves; in many situations the two agents function in harmonious cooperation. Conditions exist, however, under which paths suitable for light waves are not available; it then becomes necessary to place additional burdens on sound waves. Such occasions arise when information is to be obtained over paths which lead through water. It is with the behavior and utilization of sound waves in such situations that we are here concerned.

1-A THE PURPOSE OF SONAR

Whenever visible signals from lighthouses or other beacons are obscured by rain or fog mariners have, for centuries, relied on audible signals to indicate the proximity or the location of points of which they must have knowledge. Air-borne sound waves are a natural choice for this service. The fact that acoustic paths through the water may, under certain circumstances, be more reliable than acoustic paths through the air led, many years ago, to the development of means for utilizing the former as well. The feasibility of using water-borne acoustic energy as a substitute for electromagnetic energy has, as a result, been long established. When the submarine carried naval warfare beneath the surface of the sea the demands made on water-borne acoustic energy were increased to a new level of severity. These augmented demands are the primary cause of our present interest.

1A-1 Underwater Observational Agents

The sole purpose in building submarines so that they may navigate beneath the surface is to permit them to withdraw to a medium which restricts the propagation of light waves, or, more generally, of electromagnetic waves, to distances of negligible utility. In thus seeking concealment the submarine attempts to deprive its enemies of the usual channels of observation without, at the same time, depriving itself of all access to such channels. Through its periscope the submarine hoped that it might, while impeding attempts at observation by others, maintain a considerable observational advantage for itself. Surface vessels immediately turned to underwater acoustic waves in an effort to correct this unbalance.

In the competition between electromagnetic waves above the water, as employed by the submarine, and acoustic waves in the water, as employed by its enemies, the submarine once showed an appreciable superiority. This has been markedly affected by the development of radar. Limitations imposed by the human eye, or by natural sources of illumination, on which the submarine formerly relied, have been largely eliminated by the facilities thus made available. Any attempt on the part of the submarine to establish contact with the medium of effective electromagnetic propagation immediately exposes it to the risk of almost certain detection, either by day or by night. In restoring the effectiveness of electromagnetic energy, as an agent of the surface craft, radar has, however, by no means decreased the burden on underwater sound. By driving the submarine more completely beneath the surface radar has compelled both of the opponents in subsurface warfare to rely more completely than ever before on those agents which may be propagated through the water of the sea. Having lost one observational advantage, the submarine must now seek another;

where it once attempted to see without being seen it must now endeavor to hear without being heard.

The merit of any observational agent is evaluated in terms of three basic factors: its range of penetration, its velocity of propagation, and its resolving power. We have already seen that light fails, as an underwater agent, because of its low penetration. In other respects sound is definitely inferior to light as a vehicle for carrying information. The velocity of propagation is not of the same order of magnitude for the two; light travels at a speed of 300,000,000 meters/sec; sound in water at 1500 meters/sec. Given a path, an electromagnetic wave can carry a message around the world in less time than an acoustic wave can travel 250 yards through water. Differences between their resolving powers, or between the amounts of information carried by the two, are quite as great as differences in the speeds with which they travel. At the upper end of the visible spectrum the wave length of light, which is the measure of its resolving power, is 0.00004 cm/cyc; at the upper end of the audible spectrum the wave length of sound is 10 cm/cyc. Although the selection of these waves as representative of the two forms of energy is arbitrary they indicate that light has a resolving power some 250,000 times that of sound in water. Light can report the number of bricks in the side of a distant building whereas sound, under comparable circumstances under water, cannot distinguish between a school of fish and the side of a ship; it certainly can make no report on the size of the fish nor of the number of rivets in the ship's plates. It is clearly evident from these facts that the performance of sound in water is far from equivalent to that of light above water.

Certain objects in water may be observed by sound energy which they radiate as primary sources, just as self-luminous objects above the water are observed by light. Above the water, however, the majority of visual observations are made on objects which, receiving energy from natural or artificial primary sources, reradiate this energy as secondary sources. Sonic equivalents of the searchlight have been developed for use under water; there is no sonic counterpart of the sun.

The deficiencies of sound lead us to inquire into the possibilities of other observational agents for undersea duty. Although it is natural, when our eyes fail, to think first of our ears, we need not limit ourselves to forms of energy which may be perceived by our senses.

The first possibility to be considered is that of using electromagnetic waves other than those of the visible spectrum. Can we, in other words, develop an underwater radar? An examination of the quantitative relations having to do with the propagation of such waves shows that the longer electromagnetic waves are, indeed, propagated to greater distances through water than are light waves. This increased range of penetration, however, is still so short as to be wholly inadequate for our purposes. Moreover, in going to the longer wave lengths, the high resolving power which makes light waves so attractive is completely lost; those electromagnetic waves which are propagated to the greatest distances are, in fact, longer than sound waves and hence have an even lower resolving power. Either the low penetration or the poor resolution would discourage attempts to use electromagnetic waves in water.

It is next in order to consider what may be done with electric or with magnetic fields. The possibilities of each of these have been explored and it has been demonstrated that the presence and general location of submerged objects may be discovered by either. Whenever a submarine or other metallic object is submerged in sea water there is always sufficient electrochemical action between different parts to produce lines of current flow in the surrounding water, which acts as an electrolyte. These lines of current flow are accompanied by electric potential gradients from which significant indications may be obtained. This electrochemical action may be detected at ranges of two or three hundred yards. The presence of a submerged object is indicated by a change in the potential between two electrodes rather than by the absolute value of the potential. This requires that either the electrodes or the object be in motion. One weakness of this method is that effects other than those due to submerged metallic objects may cause variations in the indicated potentials. Salinity gradients or temperature gradients in the water, or motion of the electrode system in such manner as to cut lines of the earth's magnetic fields, all produce indications which are more than sufficient to confuse the observer. Exact determinations of the position of an object by this method are so difficult as to be quite unreliable. Electric fields, then, appear to be inferior to sound waves with respect to both penetration and resolution; because of this the speed of transmission is irrelevant.

Objects of magnetic material act, either by their own magnetomotive force or by changing the magnetic permeability of the space which they occupy, to cause irregularities in the distribution of the earth's magnetic field. As with electric fields, these changes in the intensity of magnetization may be detected by moving a suitable coupling device from point to point. This method has an advantage over the electric-field method in that changes in the intensity of magnetization due to objects beneath the surface of the sea may be indicated by instruments above the surface as well as by submerged instruments. This at once leads to the possibility of searching by aircraft, the high speed of which offsets to a considerable extent the short range of possible detection and permits large areas to be covered at a high search rate. This method, like the electric-field method, falls far below the sound-energy method with respect to resolution; neither approaches the requirements which would have to be met for fire control purposes.

In the absence of any known agent of comparable effectiveness it remains to see what can be done to improve the performance of sound waves as observational agents. The velocity of propagation is fixed by laws of nature which all the efforts of science cannot repeal. The resolving power, however, being a function of the wave length, is to some extent at our disposal. It is necessary merely to design equipment for operation at frequencies above the audible spectrum to reduce the wave length by a very considerable factor. Such increase in frequency, unfortunately, is accompanied by an increased absorption of energy by the medium and hence reduces the distance to which the sound may travel. The frequency may, nevertheless, be increased somewhat beyond the limit of audibility. In many applications advantage is taken of the decreased wave length thus obtained to reduce the size of the acoustic generators and receivers, as prescribed by directivity requirements, rather than to increase the actual resolving power of the system. When it comes to increasing the range over which observations may be made by means of underwater acoustic energy we appear to be forced to fall back on the skill and ingenuity of the system designers and on the understanding with which the systems are employed. The factors which must be considered in any effort to extend the performance of underwater sound equipment form the subject matter of this book.

1A-2 The Definition of Sonar

The body of knowledge which has been built up as a result of studies of the nature of acoustic waves in water, and of the manner in which they are propagated through water, is known as underwater acoustics. Systems whereby underwater acoustic energy is used for observation or for communication are known as sonar systems. The word "sonar" has also come to be used to designate the principles and practices employed in the design and operation of these systems and hence with this use of acoustic energy. In addition to the definition given above, then, it would appear proper to say that sonar is a branch of applied acoustics identified with the utilization of water as the propagating medium.

1A-3 The Requirements to be Met by Sonar

The design of any sonar system must inevitably involve some compromise between the operating characteristics desired and the performance characteristics attainable. This is particularly true in military applications where every decision as to methods and means must be made with quantitative exactness. It should be quite apparent from what has been said of underwater sound as an observational agent that it would be futile to attempt to specify the requirements to be met by any sonar system without due recognition of the limitations of this agent. Conversely, it would be shortsighted to undertake any discussion of the factors affecting the performance of such systems without having in mind the uses to which they are to be put. This is desirable if for no other reason than to indicate the most suitable manner in which to describe these factors.

Of the many requirements which may be imposed on any system for making observations of some environment the simplest is that it shall detect the advent of any foreign object. From this they progress to demands that it disclose the position of this object, the direction and rate of its motion, and, finally, its nature. We may say at once that sonar has made little progress toward disclosing detailed information regarding the nature of any target which it may detect or locate. Data as to variations in position may, however, be obtained with considerable accuracy. From these, taken as a function of time, it is possible to derive information as to direction and rate of motion. We may, then, reduce our immediate problem to one having to do with the determination of position. It is important to note, at this point, that while the needs of surface navigation are completely met by the determination of position on a surface, subsurface navigation must recognize the possibility of three dimensional freedom of motion.

It is common practice to express the position of some given subsurface target with respect to a known reference point in terms of cylindrical coordinates by specifying bearing, range, and depth. Actually, position with respect to a single observation point is usually determined in terms of spherical coordinates by measuring bearing, inclination, and range. These requirements are modified when two observation points having known relative positions are used. The general requirement to be met by sonar equipment, however, is that it shall determine the magnitudes of these three quantities.

Although the basic data obtainable with sonar apparatus are in terms of bearing, inclination, and range it is frequently desirable to translate these data into forms more convenient for navigational purposes. This interpretation may often be effected with negligible delay by the sonar apparatus through suitable choice of the method by which its responses are made perceptible to the observer. The apparatus, in other words, may observe target ranges and angles as functions of time and report target position, in terms of any convenient system of coordinates, target course, and target speed.

The first step in undertaking the design of any sonar system is to specify the accuracy required in these reported quantities. These requirements must then be converted into specifications as to the accuracy with which bearing and bearing rate, inclination and inclination rate, and range and range rate must be determined.

1-B THE METHODS OF SONAR

The essential processes on which the art of sonar rests are by no means new. They were, in fact, formulated with astonishing clarity at about the time Columbus was crossing the Atlantic. Near the end of the fifteenth century Leonardo da Vinci made the following entry in his scientific notes. "If you cause your ship to stop, and place

the head of a long tube in the water, and place the other extremity to your ear, you will hear ships at a great distance from you." Any other description of a sonar system differs only by the addition of details. In the four hundred and fifty years since this was written many changes have taken place in the "head" of the tube, in the tube itself, and in the method of observing what happens at "the other extremity." It is still necessary to stop your own ship if you intend to hear "ships at a great distance from you." The one general item found in modern systems which is not included in the above statement is provision for causing an otherwise silent target to become a secondary source of acoustic energy.

Many of the important improvements which have been made in the methods of utilizing underwater sounds are, in one way or another, associated with the electron tube. Although it is unnecessary to resort to electronics to obtain acoustic signals for transmission to the water by conversion from electric signals, or to obtain electric signals for observation by conversion from acoustic signals received from the water, the application of such conversions could never have reached its present state of development without the help of the vacuum tube.

Interesting as it might be to review the major contributions to the art of sonar, we shall confine our historical interlude to the observation that, at the time of Pearl Harbor, submarines of the United States Navy were using listening tubes which differed but little from that of Leonardo. Although the sonar fuse was lighted a long time ago it smoldered, with only occasional brilliant advances, for nearly four centuries; the real expansion has taken place during the past thirty years. Present indications are that the next decade will show comparable progress. There may be definite limits beyond which the performance of sonar systems cannot be carried; the possibilities regarding operations which may be performed within these limits have by no means been exhausted.

1B-1 Acoustical Methods

Although sonar systems which do not employ electroacoustical conversions are now nearly obsolete they are deserving of brief mention. Systems in which the ear of the listener was coupled to the water by wholly acoustic links were used during World War I with much success. The chief advance over the simple listening tube was the development of means for making it directional, thus obtaining two great advantages. Directional systems permit a determination of the bearing of any sound source which may be detected and, by discriminating against sounds on other bearings, reduce the magnitude of interfering disturbances and thereby extend the ranges over which detection is possible. One method by which this was accomplished made use of a number of underwater pick-up points so connected together by ducts of varying length that the several air-borne acoustic responses combined by direct addition for sounds coming from a given direction only. The other general method for obtaining a directional response was to provide a separate listening system for each ear, thus permitting the listener to identify the apparent direction of some definitely localized source by means of his binaural sense.

Virtually all sonar systems in which the energy has been restricted to the acoustic form have been applicable only to situations in which the target to be observed is a primary source of sound. There is no fundamental barrier to the design of a purely acoustic system which will detect or locate a target acting as a secondary radiator, or reflector, of sound generated under the control of the observer or elsewhere. In fact, systems using the reflected energy of explosive sound sources have been shown to be operable. Practical methods for use with silent targets, however, almost without exception include conversions between acoustic and electric forms of energy.

1B-2 Electroacoustical Methods

In spite of the demonstrable fact that sonar systems may be made to give creditable performance without assistance from the electrical engineer such systems have many disadvantages. For one thing, they generally require that the listener be stationed in close proximity to the location of the underwater pick-up system. The inconvenience of this restriction is obvious. Another disadvantage arises from the fact that there are few practical instruments, other than his own ear, for making acoustic energy perceptible to an observer. While the ear is unsurpassed for sensitivity and discrimination, the brain to which it is connected is not always as precise a measuring device as may be required; when it becomes necessary to make accurate quantitative measurements the human mechanism often needs mechanical assist-

ance. If the acoustic energy is converted to electric energy there is immediately made available a great variety of electric indicating and recording instruments. Similarly, in applications where it is desired to transmit an acoustic wave having specified characteristics it is generally more convenient to develop these characteristics in an electric wave, using any of the available techniques of electronics for the purpose, and then to convert the resultant electric energy to the acoustic form.

While it is true that the art of sonar has been able to adapt with little modification many of the electronic circuit designs and many of the developments in recording and indicating instruments which have been made in other fields, it has been obliged to devise its own methods for coupling these electric systems to the water. Transducers, such as microphones, headphones, and loudspeakers, which have been carried to a high degree of excellence for coupling electric systems to air, are quite inadequate for coupling to water. An important difference between the two media, from the standpoint of the sonar engineer, is that the specific acoustic impedance of water is nearly 4000 times as great as the specific acoustic impedance of air. The significance of this is that the efficiency of any electroacoustic transducer designed for coupling to air would drop to something like 0.01 percent of its nominal value if, merely by waterproofing, an attempt were to be made to adapt it to underwater service. The construction of underwater receivers and transmitters has, therefore, called for the employment of wholly different design techniques from those appropriate to the transducers used in telephony and broadcasting. The fundamental physics underlying the two problems is, however, the same, and once the character of the modifications has been understood sonar has profited greatly because of the progress which has been made in the general application of the science of electroacoustics.

At this point it is appropriate to note that the methods used for coupling a sonar system to the observer are no less important than those used for coupling it to the ocean. Much can be done by proper choice of the indicating or recording instrument to enhance any characteristics of the signal which may serve to distinguish it from the inevitable interference. Moreover, the form in which the response of the system is presented for observation determines to a considerable extent the facility with which the information thus obtained may be utilized. In order that full advantage may be taken of the possibilities in this direction it is essential that the sonar designer be informed as to the characteristics of observers as well as to the characteristics of the transmitting medium. Sonar, then, is bounded on one side by oceanography and on the other by psychophysiology.

1B-3 Basic Types of Sonar Systems

The various types of sonar systems may be divided into three basic classifications: direct-listening, echo-ranging, and communication.

In direct-listening systems the target to be observed generates the signal to be received and thus acts as a primary source of sound. Direct-listening systems, then, require only some form of transducer for receiving the acoustic signal present in the water and some means, usually including electronic amplification, for making the energy thus obtained perceptible to an observer. Direct-listening systems may be of many forms. Some are nondirectional and serve only to give warning that a primary source of sound is in their vicinity. Some are directional and permit determinations of the bearing of individual primary sources relative to the listening station. In some cases these determinations of bearing are sufficiently accurate so that observations from two points, having a known relation to each other, may be used to determine the range of the primary source as well as its bearing.

In any direct-listening system the maximum range from which a primary source of sound may be reliably received depends upon two factors: the magnitude of the signal as it reaches the receiving point, and the magnitude of the interfering noise which tends to obscure its reception. There are certain expedients which may be employed to obtain the most acceptable reception under any given set of conditions. Directional discrimination may be used to exclude interference reaching the receiving point from bearings other than that of the signal source. The frequency band to which the equipment is responsive may also be so chosen as to select those components of the signal which are most readily distinguished from the interference. A point is finally reached, however, when the relative magnitudes of signal and of interference fix a limit beyond which satisfactory operation is impossible. Because of the great importance of reliably establishing this limit it is essential that adequate information be available regarding the sound output of ships. This informa-

tion applies to the signal, which is generated by the target vessel, and often to the interference as well, since this may be generated by the listening vessel.

When the target to be detected is not a primary source of sound it is necessary that the generation of the signal be included in the functions of the sonar system. To the receiving apparatus which is sufficient for direct listening, then, there is added some suitable signal generator, usually an electronic circuit, and a transducer by which the energy thus developed is transmitted, in the form of acoustic waves, to the water. In many systems a single transducer is used for both transmission and for reception. Some portion of the energy reaching a target from this transducer is returned to it by reflection, or reradiation, and there received as though the target were a primary, rather than a secondary, source of acoustic energy. By the use of a directional transducer the bearing of the target is determined in the same manner as in direct listening, that is, by noting the bearing at which the maximum response is obtained. The provision of some instrument for measuring the time required for acoustic energy to travel to the reflecting target and back results in an echo-ranging system. In addition to permitting the detection and the determination of bearing of a silent target, a timed echo-signal transmission permits an accurate determination of target range. This requires that the velocity of propagation of sound in water be known. The accuracy of this method of range determination is so great that echo ranging is used against targets which generate sufficient sound for reliable detection, or for bearing determination, as well as against silent targets.

As with direct listening there are several forms of echo-ranging systems. In the simplest form a single short pulse of acoustic energy, generally at an ultrasonic frequency, is directed toward the target and the time required for this single pulse to complete its journey indicated on some suitable instrument. With such a system bearing determinations may be made by transmitting several such pulses and observing the relation between bearing and response. Other systems include means for simultaneous reception by two channels the maximum response bearings of which are so positioned, relative to each other, that bearing, as well as range, may be determined by comparing their responses to a single transmission. In other types of echo-ranging systems, known as scanning sonar systems, the primary signal is transmitted in all directions and the receiving apparatus so operated as to present a plan position indication of all targets within the range of acceptable reception.

Echo ranging, like direct listening, is limited by the relative magnitudes of signal and of interference. In addition to locally generated interference, however, the signal responses of an echo-ranging system may be obscured by the noise developed by the target acting as a primary generator. In some cases the performance of an echo-ranging system is said to be limited by reverberation, meaning by this that energy returned by reflectors other than the target of interest are of comparable magnitude to the energy returned by that target.

The simplest form of underwater communication system is obtained by the joint operation of two echo-ranging equipments, one located at each of the two points between which communication is to be established. In such cases pulses transmitted by one system in a coded sequence are received by the other system, where the message is decoded in the usual manner. In other types of systems an ultrasonic wave transmitted by one station is voice modulated, as in radio broadcasting. This modulated signal is received at the other station and the original voice signal recovered by detection in the same manner as in a conventional radio receiver.

There is a fourth general type of system which should be included in this list, although only a portion of its transmission is under water. This is the system known as radiosonic ranging. Here a pulse of sonic energy, generally developed by an explosive source, activates a radio transmitter at the instant of its initiation and two signals are transmitted simultaneously, one being by acoustic waves following a path through the water and the other being by radio waves traveling through the ether. From the difference between the arrival times at a distant point, and the known velocities of propagation in the two media, it is possible to compute with considerable accuracy the distance between the transmitting and receiving points. The same principle may be applied by using two sonic waves, one in air and the other in water.

1-C THE MEDIUM OF SONAR

The performance of any system whereby information is transmitted from one place to another, using radiated energy as a carrier, is confined within limits imposed by the characteristics of the transmitting medium. During the early stages of the exploitation of some hitherto unused medium, performance is often limited by inadequate equipment as well. As the art develops, however, its boundaries are constantly extended by improved techniques until they reach the barriers set by nature. Sonar has already encountered some of these impassable obstructions.

To insure that the choice of operating methods and of apparatus designs permits the fullest possible utilization of the capabilities of the medium it is necessary that its characteristics be well understood. Since we are here concerned with practical problems, our interest is directed toward the acoustical behavior of water as it exists in oceans and other large bodies rather than with the properties of ideal laboratory samples.

1C-1 The Propagation of Sound in Sea Water

The velocity with which radiated acoustic energy is propagated through water has already been compared with the speeds of other observational agents. This velocity, like other properties of the medium, is a determining factor in many sonar problems. For general purposes its value may be taken as approximately 2900 knots, or about five times the speed of sound in air. Comparisons with the velocity of propagation in air are, however, of little significance since in the everyday use of that medium the distances involved are usually so short that we give little thought to the time required for transmission. In many applications of sonar, on the other hand, the distances may become sufficient to give these travel times appreciable magnitude. When compared with the velocity of propagation of radio waves over comparable distances the speed of sound in water leaves much to be desired. In the use of underwater telephony, for example, an interval of 12 seconds must elapse, at either station, between the conclusion of transmission and the beginning of reception when the two stations are separated by only 10,000 yards.

The known relation between travel time and distance is, it is true, used to advantage in measuring the range of a reflecting target by the techniques of echo ranging. Nevertheless, in the actual operation of an echo-ranging system the time consumed by the transit of the signal makes any attempt to search an area for a silent target a slow process. As a consequence, it has been necessary to devise methods whereby several echo-ranging signals may be in transit simultaneously.

Variations in the velocity of propagation of sound in water have quite as much effect on the performance of sonar systems as has its absolute magnitude. Changes in velocity accompanying changes in temperature, in salinity, and in depth must be taken into account in estimating the range of a reflecting target by measurements on the travel time of an echo-ranging signal. They are of comparable importance in determining direction, particularly in a vertical plane where the most prominent changes in velocity are likely to be found. Here the refraction accompanying changes in velocity may cause sound rays to deviate so far from their nominally straight paths that the apparent direction of their origin is often altogether different from the true direction. Such effects are of little concern in our normal use of air-borne sounds, not because they do not exist but because we rarely attempt to estimate either range or direction by means of sound energy transmitted through this medium; they are of vital significance in many applications of sonar.

In speaking of the velocity with which acoustic energy is propagated through water it must be remembered that only a small portion of the energy which starts out from any given source reaches a given distant point. It is, indeed, constantly diminished in intensity along any path which it may follow. This decrease in intensity is the result of two quite different effects. One is the divergence of the sound rays, as they radiate from the source, which distributes the energy over surfaces of ever increasing area. The other is the absorption of energy by the medium, and the scattering of energy by reflectors contained therein. The first of these introduces what is known as the spreading loss and the second the attenuation loss. The two together constitute the propagation loss, which is characteristic of the medium at a given location and at a given time. There are important differences between these two losses. The spreading loss associated with a given length of sound path depends on the distance of that length from the source but is independent of the frequency of the acoustic wave being transmitted. The attenuation loss, on the other hand, is independent of the distance of the length of path from the source but is a function of the frequency of the wave. The resultant effect of these two types of transmission loss, considered in conjunction with the magnitude of the sonar signal to be observed and the magnitude of the interference which ultimately obscures its observation, determines the range over which acceptable operation of any sonar system may be expected.

Under ideal conditions the spreading loss would be that corresponding to the inverse square law, as a result of which the intensity of the acoustic energy being transmitted is inversely proportional to the square of the distance which it has traveled from its source. Ideal conditions rarely exist in the ocean, however. In this connection, the phenomenon of variable velocity of propagation reappears. The bending of sound rays due to refraction resulting from space variations in velocity modifies the manner in which acoustic energy is distributed and thus modifies the manner in which spreading loss is related to distance from the source. Whenever a ray path crosses a level at which there is a marked change in the rate at which the velocity of propagation varies with depth, due to a change in temperature gradient, particularly if there is a change in the sign of the velocity gradient, there may be a pronounced change in the rate at which the ray paths diverge. After crossing a minimum velocity level the separation between rays in a vertical plane may actually decrease with increasing horizontal distance; after crossing a maximum velocity level the separation may increase much more rapidly with increasing distance than would have been the case had the gradient remained at its original value.

In many situations the effect of refraction may be described qualitatively in terms of the patterns formed by the paths likely to be followed by the sound rays leaving, or reaching, some specified point. In such patterns it is frequently found that there will be certain regions which are not traversed by any ray passing through a given source or receiving point. The spreading loss between the given point and any point in a region of this type is usually so high that it cannot be evaluated, and virtually precludes all possibility of acceptable transmission. Because of this these regions are known as shadow zones. A knowledge of the conditions under which they are likely to exist and methods for determining their probable location are of great value to submarine commanders attempting to avoid detection. Under other conditions the ray patterns may indicate that sound paths through a given point have a tendency to be concentrated in certain regions known as sound channels. Here the spreading loss is more than likely to be appreciably less than would normally be computed on the basis of the known separation between two points and knowledge of the probable location of such regions may be used to advantage without quantitative evaluation of the actual spreading loss. The study of the relations between velocity gradients in the water and the patterns formed by the paths of sound rays, or between these gradients and the spreading loss along some given ray path, has come to be a most important subdivision of the techniques of sonar.

Since the attenuation loss per unit length of sound path is a function of the frequency of the wave being transmitted, it is one of the determining factors in the choice of a suitable operating frequency for any proposed application of sonar. No estimate of the range at which acceptable operation may be expected may be made without taking this quantity into account, together with all other quantities, such as the intensity of the signal or the directional discrimination of the transducer, which also vary in a predictable manner with frequency.

1C-2 Disturbances Interfering with Reception

In addition to the velocity of propagation of acoustic energy and the two types of propagation loss, the contribution of the general sonic disturbances of the water to interfering noise is one of the important characteristics of the medium. Inasmuch as all other interfering noise is, to some extent at least, under control, it is this general water noise which places the ultimate limit below which interference cannot be reduced and which, together with the propagation loss, fixes the range at which the reception of some given signal reaches the limit of acceptability.

———◆———

The four quantities mentioned in the preceding articles represent characteristics of the ocean which have only recently become of interest to mariners. They are, however, of fundamental importance in any consideration of matters having to do with subsurface navigation and have already been recognized as having a place in the oceanography of the future.

In the attempted analysis of any practical sonar problem it is usually a relatively simple matter to work out a general solution based on nominal values for the various factors which influence performance. It is an altogether different matter to obtain an exact quantitative solution by assigning specific values to the various quantities involved. This is particularly true with respect to the physical properties of the ocean. Both the dimensions and the composition of the ocean are subject to wide variation. The only table of physical constants available to the sonar engineer is little more than a list of statistical averages; in the majority of problems it is as necessary to anticipate the consequences of probable departures from these averages as it is to select design constants giving optimum performance under definitely postulated representative conditions. It has been pointed out that the medium fixes boundaries to the performance of sonar equipment which cannot be passed; where these boundaries may be at any time or place can never be forecast with complete assurance. It is, we hope, too much to say that the sonic behavior of the ocean is unpredictable; it is certainly true, however, that the sonar engineer finds the ocean to be as inconstant as does the mariner, and that the predictions of one are subject to as many uncertainties as those of the other.

In the chapters which follow it will be found that much of the discussion is based on the assumption of idealized conditions. In view of the far and frequent deviations from any ideal which characterize all practical applications of sonar it might appear that any deductions based on ideal premises could have no more than academic interest. This is not the case. In the first place, it is necessary that all of the factors which are pertinent to any study which is to be undertaken be rigorously specified. Ideal conditions usually involve few variables and generally permit these few to be described in simple terms. Having determined the performance to be expected under ideal conditions, it is possible to extend the study to include, one by one, the many additional variables associated with anticipated irregularities. Ideal conditions, in other words, represent the most convenient base from which to explore the complex and constantly changing environment of sonar. Such ideal conditions are also a prerequisite in any examination of the comparative performance of different equipment designs, or of different operating methods. Here it is essential that performance variations be those due to the equipment or to the method and not those due to external conditions; the ideal affords the needed stability so sadly lacking in the actual. Additional justification for selecting reference parameters in this manner is to be found in the fact that values characteristic of ideal conditions are, in many situations, also those which statistical surveys show to be the most probable. The reference conditions thus chosen are, in consequence, quite likely to be the most representative as well as the most easily specified and the most stable. In some

situations ideal conditions impose the most exacting requirements on apparatus performance. From every viewpoint, therefore, idealized conditions are the most suitable from which to start in any survey of the capabilities or of the limitations of sonar.

CHAPTER 2

THE NATURE OF UNDERWATER SOUND

The utility of sound waves, not only in sub-surface warfare but in many phases of everyday life, results from the fact that they are a form of energy having certain well-defined character-istics. This energy may be controlled with great accuracy and may be transmitted from place to place. Because of these two properties it may be used as a vehicle for carrying information.

Human beings have occupied themselves, since birth, in the art of interpreting the meaning of variations in acoustic energy existing as sound waves in air, and have acquired more or less pro-ficiency in imparting variations to such waves. Sound waves in water are, generally speaking, something outside their experience. Nevertheless, acoustic energy in water may have quite as much significance as acoustic energy in air. It is our prob-lem here to determine how this energy may most effectively be brought to the attention of our con-sciousness, how we may learn to translate its ob-served variations into terms of the events which produced them, and how we may generate uniquely characterized waves to serve as means for convey-ing specially assigned information. The first step toward a solution of this problem is an examina-tion of the nature and behavior of sound waves in water.

2-A THE PHYSICAL PROPERTIES OF ACOUSTIC WAVES IN WATER

2A-1 The Elementary Equation of Wave Motion

An acoustic wave in water—as in air—results from the motion of some material body. To simplify matters let us consider an entirely imagi-nary body of matter, or a **medium,** which could have no existence outside the realm of mathe-matics. This medium may be assumed to be per-fectly homogeneous, each unit volume having the same mass, for a given temperature and pressure, as all other unit volumes, and each exhibiting the same change in volume for equal changes in pres-sure. Within this medium let us imagine a plane surface of infinite extent dividing the medium

into two portions and moving with pure sinusoidal motion so that each element remains on a straight line perpendicular to the surface.

When we say that the motion of a plane surface is to be sinusoidal we mean that its **displacement** from some fixed position is to vary with time in accordance with the equation

$$\xi_{inst} = \xi_{max} \sin 2\pi(ft) \qquad (2A-1)$$

where

ξ_{inst} = the displacement at any instant (cm)

ξ_{max} = the maximum value of this displacement (cm)

2π = the angle associated with one complete cyclical variation in displacement (rad/cyc)

f = the frequency, or number of complete swings per unit time, with which the plane oscillates (cyc/sec)

t = the time which has elapsed since the be-ginning of the interval covered by the equation, this beginning being at an in-stant when the plane was passing through its mean position in the posi-tive direction (sec)

If we were to plot the displacement as a func-tion of time we would, of course, obtain the familiar sine curve. This curve would complete one cycle of its variation whenever the time, t, reached a value for which the value of the product ft became a whole number. It will be noted from the dimen-sional units given above that the term ft repre-sents the number of cyclical variations, or **cycles,** through which the plane has moved since the be-ginning of the time interval covered by the equa-tion.

The number of cyclical variations, or the frac-tion of a cyclical variation, of a sinusoidally vary-ing quantity which occurs between two events associated with the variation of that quantity is known as a **phase change.** The fraction of a cyclical variation by which some given event follows a reference event, such as the occurrence of a positive maximum value of the variation, is usually spoken of as the **phase** of the variation. The angular magnitude obtained by multiplying a given phase change by 2π radians per cycle is known as a change in **phase angle.** This is in accordance with the requirement that, when the values of a sinusoidally varying quantity are expressed mathematically, as in Eq. (2A-1), each of the complete cyclical variations shall be represented by an angular magnitude of 2π radians.

Portions of the medium immediately adjacent to the plane surface follow its movement almost exactly and oscillate back and forth in such a manner that their movement may be described by the equation given above. A short distance away from the plane, however, this is not true. Here a given small volume of the medium finds itself between a volume on one side which is being moved by the plane and a volume on the other side which, because of the inertia due to its mass, opposes the forces tending to move it. These two volumes, then, exert a pressure on our given small volume and cause it to suffer a slight reduction. This reduction in volume means that the given portion of the medium must exert a pressure of its own; under its influence the volume which, because of its mass, resisted the force exerted by the plane will be caused to move in its turn. The net result of this situation is that any given small volume, or sample, of the medium at a distance from the moving plane is driven to move with a sinusoidal motion. The sinusoidal motion of this distant sample is not coincident with the motion of the driving plane but is delayed in time by an interval the length of which depends upon the separation and upon the physical properties of the medium. The motion of an elementary volume, or particle, of the medium at any distance from the driving plane may be expressed by an equation containing a phase shift term which is proportional to this distance. Thus,

$$\xi_{\text{inst}} = \xi_{\text{max}} \sin 2\pi \left(ft - \frac{S}{\lambda} \right) \qquad (2A\text{-}2)$$

where

$S =$ the distance of the elementary volume in question from the driving plane (cm)

$\lambda =$ the reciprocal of the number of complete cycles per unit distance with which the plane oscillates (cm/cyc)

If we were to plot the displacement as a function of distance for any instant of time—that is, with t equal to a constant—we would, as before, obtain a sine curve. This curve would complete one cycle of its variation whenever the distance, S, reached a value for which the factor $[ft - (S/\lambda)]$ became a whole number. As in the case of the term ft in Eq. (2A-1) it will be seen that the term S/λ represents a number of recurrent cycles in the value of the displacement. Here the term gives the number of cycles appearing, at any instant, in the distance separating the driving plane from the given elementary volume of water. For this reason the quantity λ is known as the **wave length.**

If we were to draw this last sine curve for a succession of values of time we would obtain, in effect, a sine curve moving along the distance scale away from its zero point. For this reason the response of the medium to the movement of the driving plane, which is described by Eq. (2A-2), is said to constitute a wave moving outward from the plane. The equation is, in consequence, known as a **wave equation** or as an equation of **wave motion.**

Because of the specification that our driving plane should be infinite in extent it follows that all elementary volumes at a given distance away, and hence all lying in a parallel plane, have a motion which satisfies this equation. For this reason it is said to be the equation of a **plane wave.** It is quite evident that the sounds encountered in actual experience are never generated by the motion of an infinite plane surface. At a considerable distance from any source, however, the response of the medium is nearly that of a plane wave and the equations given, as well as those to be derived later, are valid. For distances close to a small source, where the response is in the form of a **spherical wave,** equations may be found in texts on theoretical acoustics.

Any constant value of displacement, corresponding to some given point on the moving curve defined by Eq. (2A-2), obviously requires that the value of the factor $[ft - (S/\lambda)]$ be constant. Thus the distance from the point of origin of a condition of constant displacement, considered as a function of time, is $S = S_0 + (\lambda f)t$, where S_0 is the distance at time $t = 0$. The rate at which this condition of constant displacement, or other effect accompanying wave motion, moves away from the origin is the time derivative, dS/dt, of this distance. This rate is known as the **velocity of propagation.** Since both f and λ are constant the derivative is constant and the velocity is

$$\frac{dS}{dt} = c = \lambda f \qquad (2A\text{-}3)$$

where

$c =$ the velocity of propagation (cm/sec)

This is the familiar relation between frequency, wave length, and velocity of propagation.

The simple equations written above have been referred to as wave equations and have been identified with plane waves. These are not the most general form of wave equation but apply only to a single plane wave moving with a definite velocity in an ideal homogeneous medium of infinite extent. In this ideal case the acoustic energy is said to be propagated as **plane progressive waves** under **free field** conditions.

The term $2\pi(S/\lambda)$ appearing in Eq. (2A-2) is required, as we have seen, because of the time delay between the motion of the driving plane and the response of the water at some specified distance. That this is, indeed, a time delay proportional to the distance may be seen by substituting $\lambda = c/f$ into Eq. (2A-2) whereupon there is obtained the expression

$$\xi_{\text{inst}} = \xi_{\text{max}} \sin \omega \left(t - \frac{S}{c} \right) \qquad (2A\text{-}4)$$

Here $\omega = 2\pi f$ as is customary in electrical engineering and other branches of applied physics. The term S/c represents the time required for the effect of motion at the driving plane to travel the distance S at the velocity c.

The instantaneous value of the displacement may also be written as a function of distance by substituting $f = c/\lambda$ into Eq. (2A-2) whereupon there is obtained

$$\xi_{\text{inst}} = \xi_{\text{max}} \sin \frac{2\pi}{\lambda} (ct - S) \qquad (2A\text{-}5)$$

2A-2 Particle Velocity and Volume Velocity

The response of an acoustic medium to the movement of a driving plane may be described in terms of velocity as well as of displacement. The linear velocity with which an elementary volume of the medium moves is known as the **particle velocity.** It will be helpful in evaluating the energy associated with the acoustic wave to have some information about this velocity. This actual movement of the medium must not be confused with the velocity of propagation of the acoustic wave. The difference between the two is the same as the difference between the velocity of the wind during a hurricane and the speed with which the storm center moves across the country. The velocity with which the medium moves depends upon the motion of the driving plane; the velocity of propagation of the wave depends solely upon the physical constants of the medium.

The rate at which the medium as a whole moves across some reference boundary is directly related to the particle velocity. Expressed in terms of the volume passing through some given plane area as a function of time this rate is known as the **volume velocity.** If the plane is taken perpendicular to the direction of propagation of plane waves the motion of a single particle and the motion of a given area parallel to the plane are the same, because all particles making up the area have the same motion. Now the rate at which the volume of the medium flows through this given area of the reference plane is equal to the velocity of linear motion multiplied by the area, since the volume is equal to the linear distance multiplied by the area. In the special case where a unit area is considered it is evident that the volume velocity and the particle velocity are numerically the same. It is also evident that **volume velocity per unit area** and particle velocity are dimensionally the same as well. The volume velocity per unit area, then, is given completely once we have the particle velocity.

Particle velocity may be derived most simply by differentiating, with respect to time, any of the equations for displacement already given. Using Eq. (2A-4) we obtain

$$u_{\text{inst}} = \frac{d\xi_{\text{inst}}}{dt} = \omega \xi_{\text{max}} \cos \omega \left(t - \frac{S}{c} \right) \quad (2A\text{-}6)$$

$$= u_{\text{max}} \cos \omega \left(t - \frac{S}{c} \right) \quad (2A\text{-}7)$$

where

$u_{\text{inst}} =$ the instantaneous value of the particle velocity, or of the volume velocity per unit area (cm/sec)

u_{max} = the maximum value of the particle velocity, or of the volume velocity per unit area
(cm/sec)

The fact that the particle velocity is given as the cosine of an angle and the displacement as the sine of the same angle indicates that the time variations of the two quantities differ in phase by a quarter of a cycle, and that the particle velocity leads the displacement. It is also seen, from the fact that $u_{max} = \omega \xi_{max}$, that the maximum value of particle velocity is proportional to the frequency for a given maximum displacement.

2A-3 Velocity of Propagation in Water

To determine the numerical values of the velocity of propagation and other pertinent constants identified with an acoustic wave in water it is necessary to consider the density and the elasticity of the medium through which the wave is propagated.

The **density** is defined simply as the mass per unit volume. It is written as

$$\rho = \frac{m}{V} \qquad (2A-8)$$

where

ρ = the density
(gm/cm³)

m = the mass of a given volume
(gm)

V = the given volume
(cm³)

The **elasticity** of water, as affecting the propagation of acoustic waves, is defined as the ratio of some given change in pressure to the accompanying fractional change in volume. Thus defined it is known specifically as the **volume elasticity** or as the **bulk modulus**. It is written as

$$E = \frac{p_w - p_{w0}}{(V_0 - V)/V_0} \qquad (2A-9)$$

where

E = the modulus of elasticity
(dyne/cm²)

p_{w0} = the initial value of the total hydrostatic pressure of the water
(dyne/cm²)

$p_w - p_{w0}$ = the change in total hydrostatic pressure (an increase)
(dyne/cm²)

V_0 = the initial volume
(cm³)

$V_0 - V$ = the change in volume (a decrease)
(cm³)

The reciprocal of the elasticity is known as the **compressibility.** Quantitative data relating to the elasticity of various materials may be found in texts and handbooks under either heading.

Although not a physical property of the medium there is another quantity which will be convenient in developing additional relations. This is the **condensation,** which is defined as the ratio of the change in density, accompanying some change in pressure, to the initial density. It is written as

$$\sigma = \frac{\rho - \rho_0}{\rho_0} \qquad (2A-10)$$

where

σ = the condensation
(a numeric)

Since the mass of any given sample of water is constant we may write $m = \rho V = \rho_0 V_0$, whence $\rho/\rho_0 = V_0/V = (1 + \sigma)$, and $\sigma = (V_0 - V)/V$. In any actual case encountered in connection with acoustic waves in water there is little difference between the absolute magnitudes of V and of V_0. It is therefore permissible to write

$$\sigma = \frac{V_0 - V}{V_0} \qquad (2A-11)$$

This equation may be substituted directly into Eq. (2A-9) whereupon there results

$$\sigma = \frac{p_w - p_{w0}}{E} \qquad (2A-12)$$

Let us consider an infinitesimal volume of the medium contained between two planes perpendicular to the direction of propagation of a plane wave. Let this volume have unit cross-sectional area taken perpendicular to this direction. The distances of the two planes from the origin of the wave are S and $S + \delta S$. At any time, t, the displacements of these planes from their normal positions will be ξ_{inst} and $\xi_{inst} + \delta S(d\xi_{inst}/dS)$. The thickness of the sample, and, consequently, its volume, since its cross section is of unit area, is

16

thus changed from δS to $\delta S[1+(d\xi_{inst}/dS)]$. Putting these initial and final volumes into Eq. (2A-11), and combining with Eq. (2A-12), there is obtained

$$\sigma = \frac{\delta S - \delta S\left(1 + \dfrac{d\xi_{inst}}{dS}\right)}{\delta S}$$

$$= -\frac{d\xi_{inst}}{dS} = \frac{p_w - p_{w0}}{E} \qquad (2A-13)$$

Let us now assume the pressure on the surface normally at the distance S to be p_{w1} and the pressure on the surface normally at the distance $(S+\delta S)$ to be p_{w2}. The force tending to move the sample, in the positive direction, is then $F = p_{w1} - p_{w2} = -\delta p_w$. The mass of this sample is $m = \rho(\delta S)$ and the acceleration with which it moves is $a = (d^2\xi_{inst}/dt^2)$. In accordance with the fundamental relation of mechanics, $F = ma$, the force is equal to the product of these two quantities, and we have

$$\delta p_w = -\rho\left(\frac{d^2\xi_{inst}}{dt^2}\right)\delta S$$

or, when δS approaches zero as a limit,

$$\frac{d^2\xi_{inst}}{dt^2} = -\frac{1}{\rho}\frac{\delta p_w}{\delta S} = -\frac{1}{\rho}\frac{dp_w}{dS} \qquad (2A-14)$$

But, from Eq. (2A-13),

$$p_w = p_{w0} - E\frac{d\xi_{inst}}{dS}$$

whence

$$\frac{dp_w}{dS} = -E\frac{d^2\xi_{inst}}{dS^2}$$

therefore

$$\frac{d^2\xi_{inst}}{dt^2} = \frac{E}{\rho}\frac{d^2\xi_{inst}}{dS^2} \qquad (2A-15)$$

The values of the derivatives of displacement, with respect to both time and space, may be obtained, in a form suitable for our present purpose, from Eq. (2A-4). Thus, differentiating with respect to time,

$$\frac{d\xi_{inst}}{dt} = \omega\xi_{max}\cos\omega\left(t - \frac{S}{c}\right) \qquad (2A-16)$$

Differentiating with respect to distance

$$\frac{d\xi_{inst}}{dS} = -\frac{\omega}{c}\xi_{max}\cos\omega\left(t - \frac{S}{c}\right) \qquad (2A-17)$$

Consequently,

$$\frac{d\xi_{inst}}{dt} = -c\frac{d\xi_{inst}}{dS} \qquad (2A-18)$$

By repeating this process, it can be shown that

$$\frac{d^2\xi_{inst}}{dt^2} = c^2\frac{d^2\xi_{inst}}{dS^2} \qquad (2A-19)$$

This is the general differential equation for wave motion. Its chief interest to us is that, by comparison with Eq. (2A-15), it gives the fundamental relation between the velocity of propagation of the wave and the elasticity and density of the water,

$$c = \sqrt{\frac{E}{\rho}} \qquad (2A-20)$$

The theoretical relation stated above was worked out, on a purely mathematical basis, by Sir Isaac Newton[1] many years ago. The velocity of sound in water was first measured experimentally in 1827 by J. D. Colladon and J. K. F. Sturm, in the Lake of Geneva. Their value was reported[2] as 1435 m/sec at 8 °C. At that time there were no data available as to the elasticity of water, consequently these direct measurements could not immediately be checked against the theoretical relation. In 1893 reliable measurements[3] were made of the compressibility of water, which is the reciprocal of its elasticity. When the value thus obtained was substituted into Newton's equation, the computed velocity of sound in water was given as 1430 m/sec at 10 °C. Since that time Eq. (2A-20) has, of course, been repeatedly confirmed, both mathematically and by actual measurement. Today the expression finds considerable utility in permitting a determination of the elasticity of some material in terms of the velocity of sound therein since the latter quantity may, in many cases, be measured more conveniently and more accurately than the former.

Since we are here concerned primarily with the velocity of sound, we shall consider any factor affecting the density or the elasticity only in terms of its resultant effect on the velocity. As a matter of general interest, however, it may be noted that the density of sea water, which is approximately 1.026 gm/cm³, increases with increases in salinity and with increases in pressure, or depth below the surface; in general it increases with decreasing temperature, but in a manner depending on the salinity, it passes through a maximum value at about 4 °C. The elasticity is affected to a much greater proportional degree by these three factors than is the density; consequently, when both vary due to some common cause, the velocity of sound increases or decreases as the elasticity increases or decreases.

In general, temperature has the most important influence on the velocity of sound in water. Obviously this was appreciated by Colladon and Sturm at the time of their first measurement as they were careful to observe and to report the temperature of the water. The velocity of sound in sea water[4] may be written as a function of temperature, depth, and salinity as

$$c = 4422 + 11.25(T) - 0.0450(T^2)$$
$$+ 0.0182(D) + 4.3\,(\text{Salinity} - 34) \quad (2A\text{-}21)$$

where

$c =$ the velocity of propagation of sound in sea water
(ft/sec)

$T =$ the temperature of the water
(°F)

$D =$ the depth below the surface
(ft)

the salinity is given in parts per thousand

Values of the velocity as given by this equation are shown graphically in Fig. 2A-1. In Fig. 2A-2

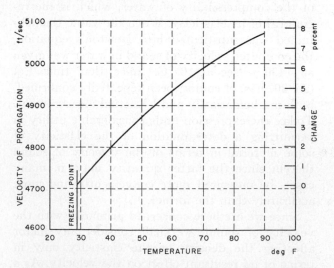

FIG. 2A-1. VELOCITY OF PROPAGATION OF SOUND IN WATER. The velocity of propagation of sound waves near the surface of sea water having a salinity of 34 parts per thousand, as a function of temperature.

FIG. 2A-2. EQUIVALENT VALUES FOR THE VELOCITY OF SOUND IN WATER. The velocity of propagation of sound in sea water, as expressed in various units.

Equivalent Velocities
4935 ft/sec
1645 yd/sec
1504 m/sec
2922 knots

quantitative values, expressed in various dimensional units, are given for the velocity of propagation of sound in sea water, at the surface, for a salinity of 34 °/oo, and for a temperature of 60 °F. For pure water, free from air, the velocity of propagation is 1460 m/sec at the same temperature.

2A-4 Acoustic Pressure

Having established the foregoing relations between the wave and the medium it is now possible to express as a wave equation the changes in pressure accompanying the propagation of an acoustic wave in water. These changes in pressure, which are generally small and superimposed on a much larger **static pressure,** are known as the **acoustic pressure.** To relate acoustic pressure to such quantities as displacement and particle velocity we proceed as follows.

By combining relations given by Eqs. (2A-13) and (2A-17), we may write

$$\sigma = -\frac{d\xi_{\text{inst}}}{dS} = \frac{\omega}{c}\xi_{\text{max}}\cos\omega\left(t - \frac{S}{c}\right) \quad (2A\text{-}22)$$

On the basis of Eqs. (2A-12) and (2A-20), we may write the instantaneous value of the acoustic pressure as

$$p_{\text{inst}} = p_w - p_{w0} = E\sigma = \rho c^2\sigma \quad (2A\text{-}23)$$

whence

$$p_{\text{inst}} = \rho c\omega\xi_{\text{max}}\cos\omega\left(t - \frac{S}{c}\right) \quad (2A\text{-}24)$$

$$= \rho c u_{\text{max}}\cos\omega\left(t - \frac{S}{c}\right) \quad (2A\text{-}25)$$

$$= p_{\text{max}}\cos\omega\left(t - \frac{S}{c}\right) \quad (2A\text{-}26)$$

where

$p_{\text{inst}} =$ the instantaneous value of the acoustic pressure, or the difference between the instantaneous and mean values of the total pressure
(dyne/cm²)

p_{max} = the maximum value of this acoustic pressure
    (dyne/cm²)

This equation shows that variations in acoustic pressure are in phase with associated variations in particle velocity, and that the two are proportional to each other independent of the frequency of the wave. This statement as to phase coincidence applies only to plane waves; it is not true for spherical waves.

2A-5 Acoustic Intensity

Thus far we have spoken of **acoustic energy** without having discussed what we mean by **energy**. This we must now undertake to do, the concept of energy being the foundation of all other concepts, of a physical nature, with which we shall concern ourselves throughout this book. Since it is the most fundamental of these concepts it is obvious that there exist no concepts which are more fundamental by which it may be described. Each of us has, nevertheless, acquired his own personal notion of what is meant by energy through his understanding of the many physical laws which have been stated regarding it. For our present purposes it must suffice to say that acoustic energy is that form of energy which is propagated through a medium having distributed mass and elasticity, and which is made manifest, at any point, as modifications in the mechanical strain and stress which would exist at that point in the absence of this energy. We shall look upon this energy as an imponderable agent, capable of causing force to be exerted, and capable of being transmitted from point to point through solid, liquid, or gaseous media.

The rate of flow of the energy of acoustic waves passing through some given surface is measured in terms of their **acoustic intensity.** Acoustic intensity is defined as the limit approached by the quotient obtained by dividing the power of the acoustic energy being transmitted at a given time through a given area by the magnitude of this area as the magnitude of this area approaches zero. This definition is predicated on the fact that **power** is defined as the limit approached by the quotient obtained by dividing the energy transmitted by a given system in a given time interval by the duration of this interval as the duration of this interval approaches zero. The relation of acoustic intensity to the direction along which the waves of acoustic energy are propagated will be discussed in Art. 2A-7.

To determine the relation between acoustic intensity and the various quantities previously discussed, let us consider the situation at a unit area in a plane surface perpendicular to the direction of propagation of plane waves of acoustic energy. This unit area, as well as those adjoining it, as we have already seen, may be imagined to move back and forth along the direction of propagation with the velocity u_{inst}. This motion may properly be thought of as the direct result of the varying acoustic pressure, p_{inst}, of the medium immediately preceding the plane surface and as the cause of the motion of the medium immediately beyond. It is, in other words, the means by which energy is transmitted through the medium. The energy which flows through unit area of a given fixed surface parallel to the moving plane may, therefore, be computed on the basis of this motion. The amount of work, or energy, associated with a moving force is, by definition, the product of the force by the distance through which it moves. From this it follows at once that the power, or the time rate of flow of energy, is given by the product of the force and the velocity with which it moves. Since the acoustic pressure, which we have already discussed, is the acoustic force per unit area, the instantaneous value of the time rate of energy flow per unit area is the product of the instantaneous acoustic pressure and the instantaneous particle velocity. On multiplying Eqs. (2A-7) and (2A-25), there is obtained

$$I_{inst} = u_{inst}p_{inst} = \rho c u_{max}^2 \cos^2 \omega \left(t - \frac{S}{c} \right) \quad (2A-27)$$

where

I_{inst} = the instantaneous acoustic intensity, or the instantaneous value of the rate of acoustic energy flow per unit area perpendicular to the direction of propagation
    (1 dyne/cm·sec = 1 erg/sec·cm² = 10^{-7} watts/cm²)

By means of trigonometric identities, this may be written as

$$I_{inst} = \frac{1}{2} \rho c u_{max}^2$$

$$+ \frac{1}{2} \rho c u_{max}^2 \cos 2\omega \left(t - \frac{S}{c} \right) \quad (2A-28)$$

The first term on the right in the above equation

does not contain the factor t. It is, therefore, independent of time and represents a constant rate of flow of energy across the fixed plane. The second term is seen to vary sinusoidally with time. For each positive value, therefore, there is an equal negative value and the average value must be zero. The term thus represents energy which surges back and forth across the boundary rather than energy which passes permanently from the medium on one side to the medium on the other. From the foregoing it is evident that the average acoustic intensity is given by the expression

$$I_{aver} = \tfrac{1}{2} \rho c u_{max}^2 \qquad (2A-29)$$

where

$I_{aver} =$ the average acoustic intensity, or average rate of acoustic energy flow per unit area perpendicular to the direction of propagation
(1 dyne/cm·sec = 1 erg/sec·cm² = 10^{-7} watts/cm²)

A second expression for the average acoustic intensity may be obtained by substituting $u_{max} = p_{max}/\rho c$, from Eqs. (2A-25) and (2A-26), into Eq. (2A-29). The resulting expression is

$$I_{aver} = \frac{1}{2} \frac{p_{max}^2}{\rho c} \qquad (2A-30)$$

On substituting $\rho c = p_{max}/u_{max}$, from Eqs. (2A-25) and (2A-26), into Eq. (2A-29) and grouping terms, we obtain a third expression, namely,

$$I_{aver} = \frac{p_{max}}{\sqrt{2}} \frac{u_{max}}{\sqrt{2}} \qquad (2A-31)$$

This shows that the value of the average acoustic intensity is given by the product of the rms values of sound pressure and particle velocity. This is strikingly similar to the case of electric power the value of which is given by the product of the rms values of voltage and current. Since we are primarily concerned with the energy, or power, associated with acoustic waves, it will be convenient hereafter to use rms values for sound pressure and for particle velocity. Whenever, in this book, the terms "particle velocity," "acoustic pressure," or other terms designating quantities which vary sinusoidally with time are not specifically qualified to indicate that instantaneous or maximum values are referred to it will be understood that rms values are designated. Similarly, the term "acoustic intensity" will hereafter be understood to designate an average value unless it is specifically qualified to indicate otherwise. Qualifying subscripts will also be omitted from the letter symbols for these quantities when they represent rms values of amplitude variations or average values of rates of energy flow. In accordance with these conventions, we may write

$$u = \frac{u_{max}}{\sqrt{2}} \quad \text{and} \quad p = \frac{p_{max}}{\sqrt{2}} \qquad (2A-32)$$

where

$u =$ the root-mean-square value of the particle velocity, or of the volume velocity per unit area
(cm/sec)

$p =$ the root-mean-square value of the acoustic pressure
(dyne/cm²)

Also, by substituting Eq. (2A-32) into Eqs. (2A-29), (2A-30), and (2A-31), we may write the average acoustic intensity of plane progressive waves of acoustic energy as

$$I = pu = \rho c u^2 = \frac{p^2}{\rho c} \qquad (2A-33)$$

2A-6 Acoustic Impedance

Any system which responds to a sinusoidally varying stimulus in such manner that the response also varies sinusoidally, and at the same frequency, is characterized by a property known as **impedance**. This property determines both the magnitude of the response relative to the magnitude of the stimulus and the phase of the response relative to the phase of the stimulus. Impedance may be evaluated as a complex quantity having a modulus equal to the maximum value of the stimulus divided by the maximum value of the response, and an argument equal to 2π times the fraction of one cyclical variation of the stimulus by which the positive maxima of the stimulus precede the positive maxima of the response. The response and the stimulus by which the impedance of any system is measured are so related quantitatively that the dimensions of their product are those of a rate of energy flow.

The complex quantity measuring an impedance in the manner described is known as a **phasor**. It may be computed as the quotient of two other complex quantities, which are also called phasors, and which are derived from the sinusoidally varying magnitudes of the stimulus and the response in question. Each of these phasors has a modulus proportional to the maximum value of the sinusoidally varying quantity from which it is derived and an argument which increases at a constant rate equal to 2π times the frequency of that quantity. The expression for the real part of the phasor associated with a given sinusoidally varying quantity and the expression for the instantaneous magnitude of that quantity are identically the same. The expression for the phasor is derived from the expression for the instantaneous magnitude of the quantity by adding an imaginary number of such characteristics that the resulting complex number has a constant modulus equal to the maximum value of the sinusoidally varying quantity.

The property of an acoustic medium which determines the magnitude and phase of the sinusoidal variations in volume velocity per unit area which occur, at any given point and at any given frequency, when an acoustic pressure which varies sinusoidally at that same frequency acts at that same point, falls within the concept of an impedance. For plane waves the acoustic pressure and the volume velocity per unit area are in phase, as shown by Eq. (2A-25). The argument of the phasor representing this impedance is, therefore, zero, and the phasor has no imaginary part. For this case, therefore, the value of the phasor is given completely by the real number expressing the magnitude of the quotient $p_{max}/u_{max} = p/u = \rho c$ shown by Eq. (2A-33). This real quantity is identified with unit area of the medium. The impedance which it measures has been designated as the **specific acoustic impedance** of the medium. Specific acoustic impedance is defined as the quotient obtained by dividing (1) the maximum value of the sinusoidally varying acoustic pressure at a point on a plane surface in a fluid medium due to plane waves of acoustic energy propagated in a direction perpendicular to that surface, by (2) the maximum value of the accompanying sinusoidally varying volume velocity per unit area through the surface at that point. It is understood that the acoustic pressure and the volume velocity per unit area vary sinusoidally at the same frequency. When the acoustic pressure has a maximum value of one dyne per square centimeter and the volume velocity per unit area has a maximum value of one centimeter per second this specific acoustic impedance has a unit value of one **specific acoustic ohm.**

We have now reached the point where it is no longer proper to restrict our attention to plane waves. Having established the nature of the relations between displacement, volume velocity per unit area, acoustic pressure, and acoustic intensity we must next determine how these relations are to be modified to apply to more general cases. These modifications are conveniently examined by means of the concept of impedance.

The impedance which has a modulus equal to the quotient obtained by dividing the maximum value of a sinusoidally varying acoustic pressure at a given point in an acoustic medium by the maximum value of the sinusoidally varying volume velocity per unit area present at that same point, and an argument equal to 2π times the fraction of one cyclical variation of the acoustic pressure by which the maxima of that pressure precede the maxima of the volume velocity per unit area, the two quantities varying sinusoidally at the same frequency, will be designated as the **unit area acoustic impedance** of the medium at the point in question. This unit area acoustic impedance is the quotient obtained by dividing (1) the phasor corresponding, at a given frequency, to the acoustic pressure by (2) the phasor corresponding, at the same frequency, to the volume velocity per unit area.

By a method of analysis[5] which is more general than that of the preceding articles it has been demonstrated that when acoustic energy originates at a point source, thus giving rise to spherical waves, the phasor giving the value of this unit area acoustic impedance is

$$z_A = \frac{p}{u} = \rho c \left[\frac{(kS)^2 + j(kS)}{1 + (kS)^2} \right] \quad (2A\text{-}34)$$

where

$z_A =$ the unit area acoustic impedance of a given acoustic medium to spherical waves of acoustic energy of specified radius and frequency
(spec. acous. ohm)

$p =$ the phasor derived from the sinusoidally varying acoustic pressure of the specified waves
(dyne/cm²)

$u =$ the phasor derived from the sinusoidally varying volume velocity per unit area of the specified waves
(cm/sec)

$\rho c =$ the specific acoustic impedance of the given medium

(1 spec. acous. ohm $= 1$ gm/cm$^2 \cdot$ sec

$= 1$ dyne $\cdot$ sec/cm^3)

$k = 2\pi/\lambda$

= the change in phase angle per unit distance, in the direction of propagation, of the specified waves

(rad/cm)

$S =$ the radius of the specified waves at the point in question

(cm)

It is obvious from this expression that the quantity here in question does not measure a physical property of the medium; its value depends on the medium, on the distance between the sound source and the point at which the force on the medium and its response are observed, and on the frequency of the acoustic waves associated with this force and this response. The factor ρc, on the other hand, represents a quantity which is a unique and important physical constant characteristic of any fluid medium. From Eq. (2A-34) it is seen that this quantity conforms to the official definition[6] of specific acoustic impedance only for the special case of plane waves. It is common practice, however, to speak of the quantity ρc as the specific acoustic impedance and to employ this term as a designation for a property of an acoustic medium. We shall, therefore, throughout the remainder of this book, use this term only in situations where the existence of plane waves may be postulated. For the more general case of spherical waves the more general designation of "unit area acoustic impedance" will be employed. The reason for adopting this particular form of designation will be apparent as we consider other quantities to which related designations have already been officially assigned.

The **acoustic impedance** of a given surface area of an acoustic medium perpendicular, at every point, to the direction of propagation of sinusoidal acoustic waves of given frequency, and having equal acoustic pressures and equal volume velocities per unit area at every point of the surface at any instant, is the quotient obtained by dividing (1) the phasor corresponding to the acoustic pressure by (2) the phasor corresponding to the volume velocity. Acoustic impedance is measured in **acoustic ohms.** One acoustic ohm is equal to one gm/cm$^4 \cdot$ sec, or to one dyne $\cdot$ sec/cm^5.

The **mechanical impedance** of a given surface area of an acoustic medium perpendicular, at every point, to the direction of propagation of sinusoidal acoustic waves of given frequency and having equal acoustic pressures and equal volume velocities per unit area at every point of the surface at any instant, is the quotient obtained by dividing (1) the phasor corresponding to the force, due to the acoustic pressure on the given area, by (2) the phasor corresponding to the volume velocity per unit area. Mechanical impedance is measured in **mechanical ohms.** One mechanical ohm is equal to one gm/sec, or to one dyne $\cdot$ sec/cm.

The mechanical impedance of a given point in a system made up of solids is the quotient obtained by dividing (1) the phasor corresponding to a sinusoidally varying force acting on that point by (2) the phasor corresponding to the sinusoidally varying velocity with which the point moves under the action of the force, force and velocity varying at the same frequency.

If the volume velocity per unit area is u_{inst} throughout a given surface area, A, and the phasor derived from this volume velocity per unit area is u, the phasor corresponding to the resultant volume velocity through that area may be written as Au. Similarly, if the acoustic pressure is p_{inst} throughout the same surface area and the phasor derived from this acoustic pressure is p, the phasor corresponding to the resultant force on that area may be written as Ap. The relations between these phasors and the three impedances which have been defined in the preceding paragraphs, and the relations between these impedances, are given by the following equations.

$$z_A = \frac{p}{u}, \quad Z_A = \frac{1}{A}\frac{p}{u}, \quad Z_M = A\frac{p}{u}$$

and

$$z_A = AZ_A = \frac{Z_M}{A} \qquad (2A\text{-}35)$$

where

$A =$ a given surface area of an acoustic medium, perpendicular, at all points, to the direction of propagation of sinusoidally varying acoustic waves

(cm^2)

$z_A =$ the unit area acoustic impedance at any point of the given surface area

(1 spec. acous. ohm $= 1$ gm/cm$^2 \cdot$ sec

$= 1$ dyne $\cdot$ sec/cm^3)

Z_A = the acoustic impedance of the surface area
(1 acous. ohm = 1 gm/cm⁴·sec
= 1 dyne·sec/cm⁵)

Z_M = the mechanical impedance of the given surface area
(1 mech. ohm = 1 gm/sec
= 1 dyne·sec/cm)

It is at once apparent that the impedance $z_A = p/u$ may properly be described as the **mechanical impedance per unit area** at any point on the area to which the mechanical impedance applies. In such an expression as this the word "per" signifies, unfailingly, that if the magnitude of the quantity for which the expression is a dimensional symbol is multiplied by the magnitude of a quantity having the dimensions specified by the symbols following the word, the resulting product will be the magnitude of a quantity having the dimensions specified by the symbols preceding the word. It is thus evident that the impedance $z_A = p/u$ *cannot* be described as an "acoustic impedance *per* unit area." On the other hand, if the area specified in connection with a given acoustic impedance is of unit magnitude the magnitude of the impedance z_A and the magnitude of the acoustic impedance $Z_A = z_A/A$ will be equal. It is for this reason that the term "unit area acoustic impedance" has been chosen for the impedance defining the relative magnitudes and relative phases of the acoustic pressure and of the accompanying volume velocity per unit area at a point on a surface coincident with spherical waves of acoustic energy.

In general, each of the impedances discussed in the preceding paragraphs, being a complex quantity, has a real and an imaginary component. In each case, following established practice, the real component is designated as a **resistance** and the real part of the imaginary component as a **reactance**. The complex sum of these two components may be written as $z = r + jx$. Resistances and reactances, like impedances, are measured in ohms.

The real component of the unit area acoustic impedance is the **unit area acoustic resistance.**

$$r_A = \rho c \left[\frac{(kS)^2}{1 + (kS)^2} \right] \qquad (2A\text{-}36)$$

The real part of the imaginary component of the unit area acoustic impedance is the **unit area acoustic reactance.**

$$x_A = \rho c \left[\frac{kS}{1 + (kS)^2} \right] \qquad (2A\text{-}37)$$

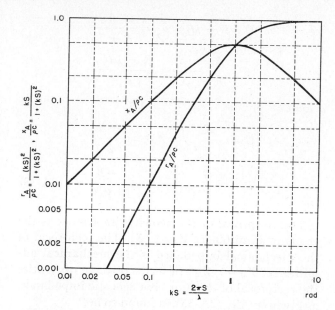

Fig. 2A-3. Acoustic Impedance Components. Graphs showing the relation between the components of the impedance of a fluid medium to spherical waves, plotted as functions of the radius of the waves as measured in radians of phase change.

Values of the quantities in the brackets, plotted as functions of kS, are shown in Fig. 2A-3.

The assumption of plane waves of any frequency is equivalent to the assumption that the factor kS is of infinite magnitude. The real and imaginary components of the specific acoustic impedance of an acoustic medium are therefore obtained by substituting $kS = \infty$ into Eqs. (2A-36) and (2A-37). When this is done it is found that the **specific acoustic resistance** is equal to ρc and that the **specific acoustic reactance** is zero. The ratio of the acoustic pressure of plane waves of specified frequency, on a plane surface perpendicular to the direction in which those waves are propagated, to the accompanying volume velocity per unit area through that surface may, in consequence of the foregoing, be described as the specific acoustic resistance of the medium as well as the specific acoustic impedance.

In accordance with established conventions the reciprocal of an impedance is designated as an **admittance.** Since impedance is a complex quantity admittance must also be a complex quantity. Admittances, like impedances, are evaluated by phasors. The real component of a complex admittance is designated as a **conductance** and the real part of the imaginary component as a **susceptance.** The relations between the components of an admittance and those of an impedance are summarized by the following equalities.

$$Y = G + jB = \frac{1}{Z} = \frac{1}{R + jX}$$

$$= \frac{R - jX}{R^2 + X^2} = \frac{R - jX}{|Z|^2}$$

whence

$$G = \frac{R}{|Z|^2}, \qquad B = \frac{-X}{|Z|^2}$$

$$R = \frac{G}{|Y|^2}, \qquad X = \frac{-B}{|Y|^2} \qquad (2A\text{-}38)$$

The reciprocal of the acoustic impedance is the **acoustic admittance,** $Y_A = 1/Z_A$. The reciprocal of the mechanical impedance is the **mechanical admittance,** $Y_M = 1/Z_M$. In terms of these quantities the reciprocal of the unit area acoustic impedance, as given by Eq. (2A-35), is found to be,

$$y_A = \frac{1}{z_A} = \frac{1}{AZ_A} = \frac{Y_A}{A} = \frac{A}{Z_M} = AY_M \qquad (2A\text{-}39)$$

We have previously seen that the quotient of the phasors corresponding to the acoustic pressure and the volume velocity per unit area might be designated either as the unit area acoustic impedance or as the mechanical impedance per unit area. We now see that the reciprocal of this ratio would, through adherence to the same conventions, be designated either as the **acoustic admittance per unit area** or as the **unit area mechanical admittance.**

The unit area acoustic impedance as given by Eq. (2A-34) is the product of the specific acoustic impedance characteristic of the medium, at the point in question, and a complex factor characteristic of the acoustic waves at the point. The reciprocal of this quantity, or the acoustic admittance per unit area, may be written as

$$y_A = \frac{1}{z_A} = \frac{1}{\rho c}\left[1 - \frac{j}{kS}\right] \qquad (2A\text{-}40)$$

The **specific acoustic admittance** is, by definition, the reciprocal, $1/\rho c$, of the specific acoustic impedance. This is the quantity to which the acoustic admittance per unit area, y_A, reduces for plane waves, when $kS = \infty$. In general, the acoustic admittance per unit area is the product of the specific acoustic admittance characteristic of the medium at a given point and a complex factor characteristic of the acoustic waves at that point.

The real part of the acoustic admittance per unit area is the **acoustic conductance per unit area.**

$$g_A = \frac{1}{\rho c} \qquad (2A\text{-}41)$$

The imaginary part of the acoustic admittance per unit area is the **acoustic susceptance per unit area.**

$$b_A = -\frac{1}{\rho c}\frac{1}{kS} \qquad (2A\text{-}42)$$

The acoustic conductance per unit area is seen to be independent of the curvature or frequency of the acoustic waves. For spherical waves, in other words, the acoustic conductance per unit area and the specific acoustic conductance are equal. These, and other impedance components, are tabulated in Fig. 2A-4.

We are now in a position to compute the average time rate of energy flow per unit area through a surface of an acoustic medium perpendicular, at every point, to the direction of propagation of sinusoidally varying spherical waves of acoustic energy. As in the development of Eq. (2A-31) the instantaneous value of this rate of energy flow is equal to the product of the instantaneous values of the acoustic pressure and the volume velocity per unit area of the acoustic waves reaching this area in the manner postulated. When these two quantities are not in phase their instantaneous values may be written as

$$p_{\text{inst}} = p_{\max}\cos\left(\omega t + \psi_p\right)$$

and

$$u_{\text{inst}} = u_{\max}\cos\left(\omega t + \psi_u\right)$$

Here ψ_p indicates the phase angle of the pressure and ψ_u the phase angle of the velocity, both relative to a common reference. The instantaneous power, which is given by the product of the instantaneous pressure and the instantaneous velocity, is thus

$$I_{\text{inst}} = p_{\text{inst}}u_{\text{inst}} = \tfrac{1}{2}p_{\max}u_{\max}\cos\left(\psi_p - \psi_u\right)$$
$$+ \tfrac{1}{2}p_{\max}u_{\max}\cos\left(2\omega t + \psi_p + \psi_u\right) \qquad (2A\text{-}43)$$

As in Eq. (2A-28), the second term represents energy which crosses the surface in question first in one direction and then in the other. The first term represents energy which flows through the surface at a constant rate. The average rate of energy flow, or the average value of the acoustic intensity, is thus given as the product of the rms

Fig. 2A-4. Acoustic Impedance. The components of the acoustic impedance and of the acoustic admittance associated with unit area of a fluid medium perpendicular to the direction of propagation of acoustic energy.

	Spherical Waves		Plane Waves	
unit area acoustic impedance	mechanical impedance per unit area	$z_A = \rho c \left[\dfrac{(kS)^2 + j(kS)}{1+(kS)^2} \right]$	specific acoustic impedance	ρc
unit area acoustic resistance	mechanical resistance per unit area	$r_A = \rho c \left[\dfrac{(kS)^2}{1+(kS)^2} \right]$	specific acoustic resistance	c
unit area acoustic reactance	mechanical reactance per unit area	$x_A = \rho c \left[\dfrac{kS}{1+(kS)^2} \right]$	specific acoustic reactance	0
acoustic admittance per unit area	unit area mechanical admittance	$y_A = \dfrac{1}{\rho c} \left[1 - \dfrac{j}{kS} \right]$	specific acoustic admittance	$\dfrac{1}{\rho c}$
acoustic conductance per unit area	unit area mechanical conductance	$g_A = \dfrac{1}{\rho c}$	specific acoustic conductance	$\dfrac{1}{\rho c}$
acoustic susceptance per unit area	unit area mechanical susceptance	$b_A = -\dfrac{1}{\rho c}\dfrac{1}{kS}$	specific acoustic susceptance	0

values of acoustic pressure and particle velocity multiplied by the cosine of the phase angle between them. That is,

$$I = pu \cos \psi \qquad (2A\text{-}44)$$

The cosine of this phase angle, which is designated as the **power factor,** may be expressed in terms of the unit area acoustic impedance. If we make the velocity the phase reference quantity and let ψ be the angle by which the pressure leads this velocity, the velocity phasor is

$$u = u_{max}\,(1 + j0) \qquad (2A\text{-}45)$$

and the pressure phasor is

$$p = p_{max}\,(\cos \psi + j \sin \psi) \qquad (2A\text{-}46)$$

The unit area acoustic impedance is then

$$z_A = r_A + jx_A = \frac{p}{u} = \frac{p_{max}}{u_{max}}(\cos \psi + j \sin \psi) \qquad (2A\text{-}47)$$

The ratio of the absolute magnitudes of two phasors is equal to the absolute magnitude of their ratio. Consequently,

$$\frac{p_{max}}{u_{max}} = \left| \frac{p}{u} \right| = |z_A| \qquad (2A\text{-}48)$$

hence

$$\cos \psi = \frac{r_A}{|z_A|} \qquad (2A\text{-}49)$$

The acoustic intensity is therefore

$$I = pu \cos \psi = pu\,\frac{r_A}{|z_A|} \qquad (2A\text{-}50)$$

Since the absolute magnitude of the ratio of the unit area acoustic impedance is equal, as shown by Eq. (2A-48), to the ratio of the maximum magnitudes of the pressure and velocity, it must also be equal to the ratio of the rms magnitudes of these quantities. That is,

$$|z_A| = \frac{p}{u} \qquad (2A\text{-}51)$$

Consequently,

$$I = u^2 r_A = p^2\,\frac{r_A}{|z_A|^2} = p^2 g_A \qquad (2A\text{-}52)$$

From this it is seen that the equality $I = u^2 \rho c$ appearing in Eq. (2A-33) holds only in the special case of plane waves. On the other hand, the equality $I = p^2/\rho c$ holds for spherical waves of any radius or frequency, as well as for plane waves. It must be remembered, however, that here the quantity $1/\rho c$ is the acoustic conductance per unit area. It is incorrect to say that the quantity ρc appearing in this expression is the specific acoustic impedance of the medium; it may properly be so designated in some cases but not here.

The relation between acoustic pressure, acoustic intensity, and specific acoustic impedance is one of great utility in acoustical engineering. It is to be noted that all quantities appearing in Eq. (2A-52) defining these relations are real quantities. It should also be noted that this equation defines the acoustic conductance per unit area as the ratio, I/p^2, of the acoustic intensity to the mean square value of the acoustic pressure. In this respect it is analogous to electric conductance, G, as defined by the relation, $P = e^2 G$, between electric power, P, and electric voltage, e.

The value of the specific acoustic impedance of a fluid medium may be computed from the density and elasticity of the medium. By multiplying Eq. (2A-20) by the density, ρ, it is found that the specific acoustic impedance is

$$\rho c = \sqrt{\rho E} \qquad (2A\text{-}53)$$

At the surface, sea water has a density of $\rho = 1.026$ gm/cm³ for a salinity of 34 °/oo and for a temperature of 60 °F. The velocity of propagation, under the same conditions, is $c = 150,400$ cm/sec. A representative value for the specific acoustic impedance of sea water is, therefore, $\rho c = 154,300$ spec. acous. ohms. For pure air-free water, at the same temperature and pressure, $\rho c = 143,000$ spec. acous. ohms. For air, at a pressure of 760 mm of mercury and a temperature of 20 °C, $\rho c = 42$ spec. acous. ohms. For practical problems relating to sonar it will usually be sufficiently correct to use $\rho c = 154,000$ spec. acous. ohms as a nominal value for the specific acoustic impedance of sea water.

Although we are primarily concerned with the behavior of acoustic waves in water, it is frequently necessary to consider the transfer of acoustic energy between other media and water. The relative magnitudes of the specific acoustic impedances of the two media between which such a transfer takes place is quite as significant as the ratio of the impedances on either side of some junction point in an electric circuit. It is, therefore, desirable to have access to data as to the specific acoustic impedance of any medium through which we may have occasion to transmit a sound wave. Tables of this constant are available in many texts and handbooks. It will help to establish these magnitudes in mind if they are laid off against a suitable scale. Since we are more concerned with relative than with absolute values, this presentation will be most convenient if the scale used is logarithmic, that is, if equal distances are made to correspond to equal ratios. A logarithmic scale is also desirable since it permits impedances of low value to be indicated with the same percentage accuracy as impedances of high value. Such a presentation is given in Fig. 2A-5.

2A-7 Intensity in a Specified Direction

The relations between acoustic pressure, particle velocity, and acoustic intensity have been defined in the preceding articles in terms of plane

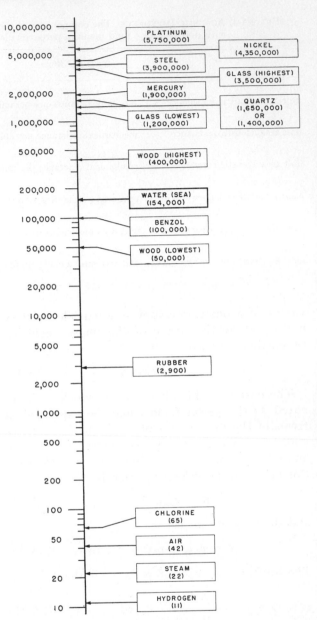

Fig. 2A-5. Specific Acoustic Impedances. The magnitudes of the specific acoustic impedances, in specific acoustic ohms, of various media.

waves of acoustic energy propagated toward some given receiving point from a single source point along a single path. In practice, acoustic energy from a single source point often reaches a single receiving point by a number of paths, along which components of the resultant energy are propagated concurrently. In practice, also, acoustic energy is likely to arrive at a single receiving point from a number of directionally distributed sources, for each of which there may be one or more propagation paths. In either of these situations, the relations between pressure, velocity, and intensity are not the simple relations summarized by Eq. (2A-33).

When acoustic energy reaches a point in an acoustic medium along a number of propagation paths, the instantaneous value of the resultant acoustic pressure is the sum of the instantaneous pressures associated with the several individual energy transmissions. Each of these instantaneous pressures is exerted equally in all directions, in accordance with Pascal's Law. If the individual pressures all vary sinusoidally at the same frequency the resultant pressure will also vary sinusoidally at that frequency. The magnitude of the resultant pressure will then depend on the phases of the component pressures as well as on their magnitudes.

Consider the acoustic energies arriving at a given point along two paths making the angle θ with each other, the two energies being propagated as sinusoidal plane waves of identical frequency. The locus of the end of the vector of sinusoidally varying magnitude representing the instantaneous particle velocity due to the waves of either one of these energies will be a straight line coinciding with the direction of propagation of that energy. The two locus lines will make the angle θ with each other. The vector representing the resultant particle velocity will, in general, be a rotating vector, the locus of its terminal being an ellipse. This will be enclosed within a parallelogram, as shown in Fig. 2A-6. The sides of this parallelogram correspond, in magnitude and direction, to the loci of the terminals of the vectors representing the individual velocities. The exact form of the ellipse within this parallelogram will depend on the phase angle between the phasors representing the magnitudes of these individual velocities. It becomes a straight line, coinciding with a diagonal of the parallelogram, if the two velocities are in

phase or in phase opposition; it is tangent to the sides of the parallelogram at their mid-points, passing through the ends of the loci of the vectors representing the individual velocities, if these velocities are in phase quadrature. For any fixed value of phase angle the vector representing the instantaneous value of the resultant velocity will trace out the corresponding ellipse in a time equal to one period of the sinusoidal variation in particle velocity. The velocity represented by this rotating vector will, at any instant, have a component in any assigned direction. The instantaneous magnitude of this component may be easily computed.

Let the instantaneous magnitudes of the particle velocities due to the energy waves propagated along the two intersecting paths, considered individually, be

$$(u_1)_{inst} = \sqrt{2}u_1 \cos(\omega t + \psi_1) \qquad (2A\text{-}54)$$

and

$$(u_2)_{inst} = \sqrt{2}u_2 \cos(\omega t + \psi_2) \qquad (2A\text{-}55)$$

In these equations $\sqrt{2}u_1$ and $\sqrt{2}u_2$ are the maximum values of the two particle velocities, u_1 and u_2 being their rms values. Each of these instantaneous velocities represents motion in the direction of the path along which the corresponding energy is propagated. Each will have a component along the assigned direction for which the instantaneous value of the component of the resultant velocity is to be computed. If this assigned direction makes the angles θ_1 and θ_2 with the directions of the two propagation paths the instantaneous magnitudes of the two individual components will be

$$(u_{1d})_{inst} = \sqrt{2}u_1 \cos\theta_1 \cos(\omega t + \psi_1) \qquad (2A\text{-}56)$$

and

$$(u_{2d})_{inst} = \sqrt{2}u_2 \cos\theta_2 \cos(\omega t + \psi_2) \qquad (2A\text{-}57)$$

The instantaneous magnitude of the component of the resulting particle velocity in the assigned direction is then

$$(u_{\Sigma d})_{inst} = (u_{1d})_{inst} + (u_{2d})_{inst}$$

$$= \sqrt{2}[u_1 \cos\theta_1 \cos\psi_1 + u_2 \cos\theta_2 \cos\psi_2] \cos\omega t$$

$$- \sqrt{2}[u_1 \cos\theta_1 \sin\psi_1 + u_2 \cos\theta_2 \sin\psi_2] \sin\omega t$$
$$(2A\text{-}58)$$

This may be written as

$$(u_{\Sigma d})_{inst} = A_u \cos\omega t - B_u \sin\omega t \qquad (2A\text{-}59)$$

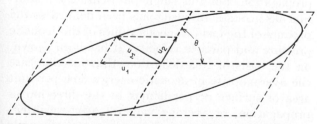

FIG. 2A-6. RESULTANT PARTICLE VELOCITY. The locus of vectors representing the instantaneous values of the resultant particle velocity due to acoustic energies arriving at a given point by propagation paths making the angle θ with each other.

where

$$A_u = \sqrt{2}\left[u_1 \cos \theta_1 \cos \psi_1 + u_2 \cos \theta_2 \cos \psi_2\right]$$

and

$$B_u = \sqrt{2}\left[u_1 \cos \theta_1 \sin \psi_1 + u_2 \cos \theta_2 \sin \psi_2\right]$$

Now let α be an angle defined by the relation $\tan \alpha_u = B_u/A_u$. Then $A_u = \sqrt{A_u^2 + B_u^2} \cos \alpha_u$ and $B_u = \sqrt{A_u^2 + B_u^2} \sin \alpha_u$. Consequently

$$
\begin{aligned}
(u_{\Sigma d})_{\text{inst}} &= \sqrt{A_u^2 + B_u^2}\left[\cos \alpha_u \cos \omega t - \sin \alpha_u \sin \omega t\right] \\
&= \sqrt{A_u^2 + B_u^2}\left[\cos(\omega t + \alpha_u)\right] \\
&= \sqrt{2}u_{\Sigma d}\left[\cos(\omega t + \alpha_u)\right] \qquad (2A\text{-}60)
\end{aligned}
$$

From this it is seen that the resultant particle velocity has a component in the assigned direction which varies sinusoidally at the same frequency, $\omega/2\pi$, as the particle velocities of the waves initially postulated. This sinusoidal variation has a maximum value of $\sqrt{2}u_{\Sigma d} = \sqrt{A_u^2 + B_u^2}$, giving an rms value of

The resultant acoustic pressure, like the component of the resultant particle velocity, varies sinusoidally at the same frequency as the quantities from which it is derived. Its sinusoidal variation has a maximum value of $\sqrt{2}p_\Sigma = \sqrt{A_p^2 + B_p^2}$, giving an rms value of

$$p_\Sigma = \sqrt{p_1^2 + p_2^2 + 2p_1 p_2 \cos(\psi_1 - \psi_2)} \qquad (2A\text{-}67)$$

and a phase angle α_p of such magnitude that

$$\tan \alpha_p = \frac{p_1 \sin \psi_1 + p_2 \sin \psi_2}{p_1 \cos \psi_1 + p_2 \cos \psi_2} \qquad (2A\text{-}68)$$

We have now arrived at some understanding of the acoustic pressure and of the particle velocity at a point receiving acoustic energy by more than one path. The situation which has been examined has been made as simple as possible: it has been restricted to two paths and the waves reaching the point by these paths have been plane waves having sinusoidal variations of identical frequency.

$$u_{\Sigma d} = \sqrt{(u_1 \cos \theta_1)^2 + (u_2 \cos \theta_2)^2 + 2(u_1 \cos \theta_1)(u_2 \cos \theta_2) \cos(\psi_1 - \psi_2)} \qquad (2A\text{-}61)$$

and a phase angle α_u of such magnitude that

$$\tan \alpha_u = \frac{(u_1 \cos \theta_1) \sin \psi_1 + (u_2 \cos \theta_2) \sin \psi_2}{(u_1 \cos \theta_1) \cos \psi_1 + (u_2 \cos \theta_2) \cos \psi_2} \qquad (2A\text{-}62)$$

The acoustic pressures due to the energy waves propagated along the two intersecting paths are each in phase with the corresponding particle velocities, as noted under Eq. (2A-26). Their instantaneous magnitudes may, therefore, be written as

$$(p_1)_{\text{inst}} = \sqrt{2}p_1 \cos(\omega t + \psi_1) \qquad (2A\text{-}63)$$

and

$$(p_2)_{\text{inst}} = \sqrt{2}p_2 \cos(\omega t + \psi_2) \qquad (2A\text{-}64)$$

These pressures are not vectors. Their resultant is thus obtained by direct addition as

$$
\begin{aligned}
(p_\Sigma)_{\text{inst}} &= (p_1)_{\text{inst}} + (p_2)_{\text{inst}} \\
&= \sqrt{2}\left[p_1 \cos \psi_1 + p_2 \cos \psi_2\right] \cos \omega t \\
&\quad - \sqrt{2}\left[p_1 \sin \psi_1 + p_2 \sin \psi_2\right] \sin \omega t \quad (2A\text{-}65)
\end{aligned}
$$

By the same method as that used in deriving Eq. (2A-60), it may be shown that this may be written as

$$
\begin{aligned}
(p_\Sigma)_{\text{inst}} &= \sqrt{A_p^2 + B_p^2}\left[\cos(\omega t + \alpha_p)\right] \\
&= \sqrt{2}p_\Sigma\left[\cos(\omega t + \alpha_p)\right] \qquad (2A\text{-}66)
\end{aligned}
$$

In spite of these restrictions, the conclusions which have been reached will be helpful in studying more complex situations. For the moment, however, we shall continue to examine this simple situation for the purpose of determining the relations between the acoustic pressure and the particle velocity already described and the acoustic intensity.

Acoustic intensity has previously been defined for the elementary case of plane waves having sinusoidal variations in acoustic pressure propagated along a single path. For such waves it has been shown that the variations in particle velocity are also sinusoidal, are in phase with the pressure variations, and apply to motion in the direction of propagation. For this single-path case the instantaneous acoustic intensity has been defined as the product of the instantaneous values of the acoustic pressure and particle velocity. It has been shown, on the basis of this definition, that for this case the average rate of acoustic energy flow per unit area of surface perpendicular to the direction of propagation, or average value of acoustic intensity, is the product of the mean-square acoustic pressure of the waves and the acoustic conductance per unit area of the medium. This has been shown to be true both for plane waves and for spherical waves, even though, in the latter case, the acoustic pressure and the particle velocity are not in phase.

When we come to a situation in which acoustic energy reaches a given point by two or more paths, along which are propagated sinusoidal waves of identical frequency, we find that the particle velocity is, in general, not only displaced in phase with respect to the acoustic pressure, but is no longer restricted to motion in a direction along which waves are being propagated. For such cases, and for more general cases as well, it has been agreed to define an acoustic intensity in terms of the product of the acoustic pressure and a component of the particle velocity having a given direction. Since, for these cases, particle velocity is a vector, acoustic intensity as thus defined is also a vector; at any given point it is not a unique function of the energy actually passing that point but is a function of direction as well.

To cover situations where acoustic energy reaches a given point along a number of paths the **acoustic intensity in a specified direction** has been defined as the average time rate of flow per unit area of the acoustic energy passing through a plane surface perpendicular to this specified direction. It must be understood that this intensity in a specified direction is *not* a measure of energy propagated in the specified direction. This will be evident on examining the case of plane waves passing a given point along a single path. At this point energy is being propagated in one direction, and in one direction only. At this point, however, the particle velocity, although a measure of motion in the direction of propagation, may be considered as having components in other directions. There will be a directionally specified intensity for any direction for which this velocity has a component. Intensity in a specified direction may, in other words, have a value for a direction in which no energy is being propagated. Intensity in a specified direction is a measure of the rate at which energy passes through a surface having a specified orientation, not of the rate at which it is propagated in a specified direction.

With these considerations in mind, we may compute the intensity in a specified direction for the case of acoustic waves propagated along two intersecting paths for which the resultant acoustic pressure and a component of the resultant particle velocity have already been computed. The instantaneous value of the acoustic intensity in the direction for which the component velocity is known is obtained by multiplying Eqs. (2A-60) and

(2A-66). The product thus obtained is

$$(I_d)_{inst} = (p_\Sigma)_{inst}(u_{\Sigma d})_{inst}$$

$$= 2p_\Sigma u_{\Sigma d} \cos(\omega t + \alpha_p) \cos(\omega t + \alpha_u)$$

$$= p_\Sigma u_{\Sigma d} \cos(\alpha_p - \alpha_u)$$

$$+ p_\Sigma u_{\Sigma d} \cos(2\omega t + \alpha_p + \alpha_u) \quad (2A\text{-}69)$$

As with Eqs. (2A-28) and (2A-43), the average value of this intensity, taken over a period of time, is given by the term which does not contain time. It is, therefore,

$$I_d = \frac{1}{t} \int_0^t (p_\Sigma)_{inst}(u_{\Sigma d})_{inst} \, dt$$

$$= p_\Sigma u_{\Sigma d} \cos(\alpha_p - \alpha_u) \quad (2A\text{-}70)$$

where

I_d = the average value, taken over an interval of time t, of the acoustic intensity in a specified direction, at a given point and at a given frequency (dyne/cm·sec)

t = an interval of time equal to one period of a sinusoidal acoustic wave of the given frequency, or a time long compared to this period (sec)

$(p_\Sigma)_{inst}$ = the instantaneous value of the resultant acoustic pressure at the given point and at the given frequency (dyne/cm²)

$(u_{\Sigma d})_{inst}$ = the instantaneous value of the component of the resultant particle velocity in the specified direction at the same point and at the same frequency (cm/sec)

p_Σ = the rms value of the resultant acoustic pressure at the given point and at the given frequency (dyne/cm²)

$u_{\Sigma d}$ = the rms value of the component of the resultant particle velocity in the specified direction at the same point and at the same frequency (cm/sec)

$(\alpha_p - \alpha_u)$ = the phase difference between the resultant acoustic pressure and the component in the specified direction of the resultant particle velocity (radians)

The expression containing the integral sign is a general expression for the average value of the acoustic intensity in a specified direction, taken over a period of time, at a given point. The final expression, on the right of this equation, applies specifically to the plane sinusoidal waves of identical frequency previously postulated.

This expression has the same form as Eq. (2A-50): the average value of the acoustic intensity in a specified direction, at a given point, and taken over an interval of time, due to sinusoidal plane waves of identical frequency propagated along paths intersecting at the given point, is the product of the rms value of the resultant acoustic pressure due to those waves, the rms value of the component of the resultant particle velocity in the specified direction, and the cosine of the angle showing the phase difference between this pressure and this component velocity.

In the case of Eq. (2A-50), it will be recalled, the cosine of the phase angle, which is also called the power factor, may be expressed in terms of the complex unit area acoustic impedance. When the cosine of the phase angle was thus expressed it was found that the acoustic intensity could be expressed as the product of the mean-square acoustic pressure of the acoustic waves and the acoustic conductance per unit area of the acoustic medium. The phase angle between the acoustic pressure and a component of the resultant particle velocity encountered in the case of multi-path transmission cannot be readily expressed in terms of acoustic impedance. For this to be possible it would be necessary to introduce the concept of a directionally characterized impedance. Such an impedance might be defined, for any point and for any specified direction, as the quotient obtained by dividing the phasor derived from the acoustic pressure at that point by the phasor derived from the component of the particle velocity at the same point and in the specified direction. The utility of a quantity defined in this manner is questionable. It will not be considered further here except to note that its value would be no more dependent on the characteristics of the acoustic waves passing the point in question than are the values of the acoustic impedances now in common use.

The intensity in a specified direction given by Eq. (2A-70) may be resolved into components, all of which are in the specified direction, but which are expressed in terms of the acoustic pressures and particle velocities of the individual waves propagated along the intersecting paths. This is done by taking the product of the resultant acoustic pressure and the component of the resultant particle velocity in the specified direction as given by Eqs. (2A-58) and (2A-65). When, in the product thus obtained, those terms which represent sinusoidal variations with time are set equal to zero, the average value of the acoustic intensity in the specified direction is given as

$$I_d = p_1 u_1 \cos \theta_1 + p_2 u_2 \cos \theta_2$$
$$+ \lfloor p_1 u_2 \cos \theta_2 + p_2 u_1 \cos \theta_1 \rfloor \cos (\psi_2 - \psi_1) \quad (2A\text{-}71)$$

The first term on the right of this equation represents the average time rate of energy flow per unit area through the specified surface which would be observed due to one of the two energy transmissions in the absence of the other. The actual direction of this energy flow is along the propagation path of this energy transmission. Similarly, the second term on the right represents the average time rate of energy flow per unit area which would be observed due to the second of the two transmissions in the absence of the first. The direction of this energy flow is along the propagation path of this second transmission.

The final term on the right represents the average time rate of flow of additional energy passing through the surface at the given point when the two transmissions take place simultaneously. It is evident that both the magnitude and the sign of this final term depend on the phase angle between the acoustic pressures, or between the particle velocities, of the plane waves traveling along the two paths. They must, therefore, depend on the lengths of these paths. These lengths vary with the location of the point at which the intensity in the assigned direction is determined. To compute the average time rate of energy flow through some given finite area of plane surface the rate per unit area, for that surface, must be evaluated for each point within the given area. If the dimensions of the area are large compared to the lengths of the acoustic waves it will be found, in general, that the phase angle, $(\psi_2 - \psi_1)$, will vary through all values between 0 and 2π. The average value of $\cos (\psi_2 - \psi_1)$ will then be zero, and the term representing energy in addition to that propagated along the two intersecting paths vanishes.

This demonstrates that the paths along which the energy represented by this term is propagated form closed loops. Energy which passes through the specified surface in one direction at one point returns to this surface at some other point and there passes through in the opposite direction. The final term of Eq. (2A-43) represents energy which flows back and forth past a given point, moving with sinusoidal velocity of propagation along a straight line to give a time average rate of flow past the point of zero. The final term of Eq. (2A-71) represents energy which flows back and forth through a given surface, moving with constant velocity of propagation along closed loops to give an area average rate of flow through the surface of zero.

The intensity, I_d, computed by Eq. (2A-71) for a single point represents the average rate of energy flow per unit area taken over an interval of time which is either equal to one period of the sinusoidal time variation in acoustic pressure or which is long compared to this period. The average value of this time average, when taken over an interval of distance of sufficient magnitude to cause the change in length of one path to exceed the change in length of the other by the length of one cycle of the wave, or by an amount large compared to this length, may be written as

$$\frac{1}{A}\int_0^A (I_d)dA = p_1u_1\cos\theta_1 + p_2u_2\cos\theta_2 \quad (2A\text{-}72)$$

This shows that, for sinusoidal waves of identical frequency reaching a given surface over several paths, the area average of the average time rate of energy flow per unit area is the sum of the averages of the time rates of flow of the energies arriving over the separate paths considered individually.

The expression for average acoustic intensity in a specified direction given by Eq. (2A-71) was derived on the assumption that the energy measured by that quantity was due to sinusoidal waves of identical frequency reaching a given point along intersecting paths. Such a situation is not at all uncommon; multiple paths often exist between a single source point and a given receiving point. When the two transmissions are due to independent sources it is quite improbable that their waves will be of identical frequency. Unless they are identical, however, the final term of Eq. (2A-71) will have an average value of zero if taken over an interval of time of sufficient duration for one transmission to complete one cycle of variation more than the other, or if taken over an interval long compared to this. When acoustic energy from a number of independent sources passes a given point in the ocean, therefore, it is evident that the time rate of flow per unit area of this energy through any plane surface including this point is likely to be the sum of the individual rates of flow per unit area due to the individual transmissions.

2A-8 The Measurement of Acoustic Intensity

The concepts associated with the various quantities which have been described in the preceding articles have been useful in arriving at some understanding of the nature and behavior of acoustic energy propagated through water. When we attempt to observe this energy, however, certain of these quantities are found to be measurable only with great difficulty, if at all. For a quantity to be useful in the application of underwater acoustics it must have practical significance as well as theoretical significance. Before proceeding further, therefore, it appears desirable to examine any restrictions which are likely to be imposed on the physical measurement of acoustic waves in water by the instruments at our disposal.

For this purpose let us consider two sound sources from which are radiated sinusoidal sound waves of identical frequency. Assume these sources to be sufficiently far apart so that, over some finite portion of the line joining them, the magnitudes of the pressure and velocity variations may be considered to be constant. The following discussion will be limited to points on this length of path. Assume, further, that over this increment of path length the pressure which would be developed by one source, if acting alone, is equal to the pressure which would be developed by the other. In this case the velocities due to the two sources acting singly would also be equal.

There will be an instant of time, which will be designated as $t=0$, when for any point the instantaneous acoustic pressure due to waves traveling in one direction will be equal in magnitude and sign to the instantaneous acoustic pressure due to waves traveling in the other direction. At this instant the variations with distance, for waves from either source, will be as shown by the light solid line of Diagram (A) of Fig. 2A-7. At time $t=0$ there will be a point, designated as $S=0$, at which the instantaneous pressures due to the two energy transmissions will both have their maximum values.

The change in phase with position, for either transmission, is

$$\psi = -\frac{2\pi S}{\lambda} = -kS \quad (2A\text{-}73)$$

where S is measured in the direction of propagation. The pressure, at any time and at any point, due to the transmission from one source, may thus be written as

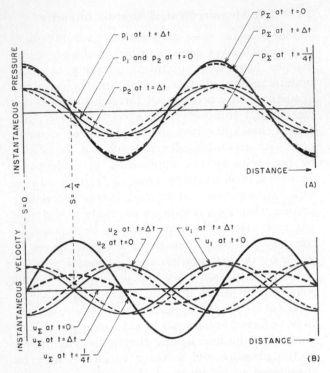

FIG. 2A-7. STANDING WAVES. Resultant values of the acoustic pressure and of the particle velocity of two plane progressive acoustic waves, showing variation with both time and distance.

$$(p_1)_{\text{inst}} = \sqrt{2}p \cos(\omega t - kS) \quad (2A\text{-}74)$$

The pressure due to the second source would be

$$(p_2)_{\text{inst}} = \sqrt{2}p \cos(\omega t + kS) \quad (2A\text{-}75)$$

The positive direction is here assumed to be the direction of propagation of waves associated with the pressure $(p_1)_{\text{inst}}$. The resultant pressure at any time and at any point on the assumed line is thus seen to be

$$(p_\Sigma)_{\text{inst}} = 2\sqrt{2}p \cos kS \cos \omega t \quad (2A\text{-}76)$$

From this equation it is at once evident that at the point for which $S=0$ the resultant pressure is

$$(p_\Sigma)_{\text{inst}} = 2\sqrt{2}p \cos \omega t, \quad (\text{when } S = 0) \quad (2A\text{-}77)$$

At a point one quarter of a wave interval away from this point, in the positive direction, $S=\lambda/4$, $kS=\pi/2$, $\cos kS=0$ and the resultant pressure is zero regardless of the time. When $t=1/(4f)$, $\cos \omega t=0$, and the resultant pressure is zero regardless of position.

These relations are shown graphically in Diagram (A) of Fig. 2A-7. Here the two light dotted lines represent the pressure variations with dis-

tance of the two transmissions at the time $t=\Delta t$. At this time, and at the point for which $S=0$, the two pressures are always of equal magnitude and like sign, and the resultant pressure has twice the magnitude due to either transmission alone. At this time, $t=\Delta t$, and at the point for which $S=\lambda/4$, the two pressures are always of equal magnitude but of unlike sign and the resultant pressure is always zero.

The variations in acoustic pressure here described constitute what are known as **standing waves.** In this particular example, the standing waves are the result of the interaction of **plane progressive waves** of equal magnitude propagated in opposite directions. In standing-wave patterns points at which the acoustic pressure, or other measure of acoustic energy, exhibit maximum values are known as **loops.** Points at which such measures exhibit minimum values, or are zero, are known as **nodes.**

At any time and any point the variation in particle velocity due solely to one of the two transmissions will be in phase with the variation in the acoustic pressure due to that same transmission. At any time and at any point the variation in particle velocity due solely to the other transmission will be in phase opposition to the variation in the acoustic pressure due to that transmission. This follows from the fact that the positive sign for particle velocity is taken in the direction of propagation of the waves with which this velocity is associated, and from the fact that the second of the two transmissions here under consideration is in the negative direction. The magnitude of the particle velocity due to the first transmission, which is in the positive direction, may, for any time and for any point, be written as

$$(u_1)_{\text{inst}} = \sqrt{2}u \cos(\omega t - kS) \quad (2A\text{-}78)$$

The magnitude of the particle velocity due to the second transmission is

$$(u_2)_{\text{inst}} = -\sqrt{2}u \cos(\omega t + kS) \quad (2A\text{-}79)$$

The magnitude of the resulting particle velocity, at any time and at any point, is, therefore,

$$(u_\Sigma)_{\text{inst}} = 2\sqrt{2}u \sin kS \sin \omega t \quad (2A\text{-}80)$$

From this it appears that at the point where $S=0$ the resultant velocity is zero regardless of the time. At the point for which $S=\lambda/4$, $kS=\pi/2$, and $\sin kS=1$ the resultant velocity is

$(u_\Sigma)_{\text{inst}} = 2\sqrt{2}\,u\,\sin\omega t,$ (when $S = \lambda/4$)   (2A-81)

When $t = 0$, $\sin\omega t = 0$, and the resultant velocity is zero regardless of position.

These relations are shown graphically by Diagram (B) of Fig. 2A-7. From the two diagrams of this figure, as well as from a comparison of Eqs. (2A-76) and (2A-80), it is evident that at any point where the magnitude of the resultant pressure variation reaches a maximum the magnitude of the resultant velocity variation is zero; at any point where the magnitude of the resultant pressure variation is zero the magnitude of the resultant velocity variation is a maximum. It is evident, also, that at any point for which $\cos kS$ and $\sin kS$ have like signs the time variation in velocity will lag the time variation in pressure by 90°. At any point for which $\cos kS$ and $\sin kS$ have unlike signs the time variation in velocity will lead the time variation in pressure by 90°. Since the pressure and the velocity variations are always in a quadrature phase relation the intensity in any specified direction computed by the general expression of Eq. (2A-70), for any point, will be zero. This is to be expected since the energy flowing in the assigned direction from one source is equal to energy flowing in the opposite direction from the other source.

There is another measure of acoustic waves which may be considered here. This is the **pressure gradient,** defined as the limit approached, at any given instant, by the quotient obtained by dividing the change in acoustic pressure accompanying a change in distance along the direction for which the change in pressure is a maximum by this change in distance, as this change in distance approaches zero. In the present example, the pressure gradient of the standing waves described may be computed as the derivative with respect to distance of the resultant pressure given by Eq. (2A-76). That is

$$\frac{d\,(p_\Sigma)_{\text{inst}}}{dS} = -2\sqrt{2}\,kp\,\sin kS\,\cos\omega t$$

$$= -\frac{4\sqrt{2}\pi}{\lambda}\,p\,\sin kS\,\cos\omega t \quad (2A\text{-}82)$$

When the acoustic pressure varies sinusoidally with both time and distance the pressure gradient also varies sinusoidally with these variables. This is true for plane progressive waves as well as for standing waves. Since pressure gradient is associated with a definite direction it is, like particle velocity, a vector the magnitude of which is a phasor. The appearance of the wave length, λ, in the coefficient of the term on the right of Eq. (2A-82) indicates that if the magnitude of a pressure variation remains constant as its frequency is varied the magnitude of the associated pressure-gradient variation will increase linearly with increasing frequency. Under these same conditions the magnitude of the associated variation in particle velocity will, like the pressure, be constant.

In the example here under consideration, the positive direction of the vector representing the instantaneous value of the pressure gradient will be in the direction of propagation of the acoustic energy associated with the pressure $(p_1)_{\text{inst}}$. It is evident from Eq. (2A-82) that when $\sin kS = 0$ the magnitude of this pressure gradient is zero regardless of the time. At a point for which $\sin kS = \pm 1$ the time variation in pressure gradient reaches a maximum. Pressure-gradient maxima and velocity maxima are thus seen to occur at the same points. They do not occur at the same times. At any point where there is a velocity variation there will be a pressure-gradient variation, even though the magnitude of the pressure at such a point may, as in the present example, be zero. In the present example, in fact, the pressure-gradient variation is a maximum at any point for which the pressure variation is zero. At any point where there is a time variation in pressure gradient this variation will lag the time variation in velocity by 90°. At any point where there are time variations in both pressure and pressure gradient these variations will either be in phase or in phase opposition.

We may classify the various devices available for measuring acoustic energy in accordance with the manner in which they would behave if moved along the standing wave pattern described above. Practically all such devices operate by converting acoustic energy into electric energy, which is then measured by appropriate electrical instruments. The characteristics of many of these devices are such that the electric energy generated would have maximum power at a point for which the sinusoidal variation in acoustic pressure is a maximum. Such devices are said to be **pressure sensitive.** The maximum electric power of other devices would correspond to a point at which the particle velocity has a maximum variation. Such a device is **velocity sensitive** if, when placed at a point where it and a pressure-sensitive device are simultaneously responsive, the open-circuit voltages of the two are in phase quadrature. It is pressure-gradient sensitive if, when placed at a point where it and a pressure-sensitive device are simultaneously responsive, the open-circuit voltages of the two are either in phase or in phase opposition.

Although any one of these devices is said to respond to acoustic pressure, to particle velocity, or to pressure gradient, each operates because of its ability to withdraw acoustic energy from the medium. In none of the devices described above, however, is the response, either in the form of an open-circuit voltage or of an electric power, a unique measure of the acoustic intensity at the point occupied by the device, except under special conditions.

Devices have been built which do measure acoustic intensity. One is described[7] as an acoustic wattmeter. In this instrument the electric outputs of a pressure-sensitive device and a velocity-sensitive device are combined in an electric circuit in such manner that the resulting electric current is proportional to the value of acoustic intensity in a specified direction given by the general expression of Eq. (2A-70). If placed at any point on the section of line connecting the two sources described in the preceding paragraphs, the response of this instrument would indicate a resultant intensity, in any direction, of zero. In other situations, the indicated intensity in a specified direction would depend on the orientation of the electroacoustic element. In the path of plane progressive waves of acoustic energy propagated along a single path from a single source the magnitude of the response would vary as the cosine of the angle through which this element is rotated from the position at which the response is a maximum.

A second form of instrument[8] measures the rate at which acoustic energy is absorbed by a small sphere of solid material. This device is intended for measurements of water-borne acoustic energy.

2A-9 Equivalent Sine Wave Intensity and Equivalent Plane Wave Intensity

Of the several quantities associated with the acoustic waves at a given point, it is generally agreed that their acoustic pressure is the most conveniently measured. It is often the only quantity which has a scalar value. Particle velocity, pressure gradient, and intensity in a specified direction are, in general, vectors. There are many analytical problems for which acoustic pressure is a significant and useful measure of wave magnitude. There are other problems for which another quantity would be more appropriate.

The instantaneous value of the acoustic pressure at a given point, as we have seen, is the sum of the instantaneous values of the individual acoustic pressures of sinusoidal waves arriving at that point. The rms value of the resultant acoustic pressure is not the sum of the individual rms pressures of these sinusoidal waves. For the case of sinusoidal waves of identical frequency arriving by two intersecting paths the rms value of the resultant acoustic pressure, as obtained from Eq. (2A-67), is

$$p_\Sigma = \sqrt{p_1{}^2 + p_2{}^2 + 2p_1p_2 \cos(\psi_1 - \psi_2)} \quad (2A\text{-}83)$$

where

p_Σ = the rms value of the resultant acoustic pressure at a given point due to sinusoidal waves of identical frequency transmitted along paths intersecting at that point (dyne/cm^2)

p_1 = the rms value of the acoustic pressure which would result from one of these transmissions alone (dyne/cm^2)

p_2 = the rms value of the acoustic pressure which would result from the second transmission alone (dyne/cm^2)

$(\psi_1 - \psi_2)$ = the phase angle between the sinusoidal pressure variations due to the two transmissions (radians)

If the frequencies of the waves arriving over the two paths are not identical, the phase angle appearing in this equation will vary progressively through all values between 0 and 2π. The cosine of this angle will then vary through all values between -1 and $+1$. If taken over an interval of time sufficient for one complete cycle of this variation to occur, or over a time long compared to this interval, the average value of the term $2p_1p_2 \cos(\psi_1 - \psi_2)$ will be zero. When the two transmissions are of unlike frequency, therefore, the resultant mean-square pressure is the sum of the mean-square pressures corresponding to the two transmissions acting singly.

If, instead of two sinusoidal wave transmissions, there are n such transmissions, the resultant mean-square acoustic pressure will be

$$p_\Sigma^2 = p_1^2 + p_2^2 + p_3^2 + \cdots + p_n^2$$
$$+ \sum \left[2p_x p_y \cos (\psi_x - \psi_y) \right] \quad \text{(2A-84)}$$

There will be $(n/2)(n-1)$ terms of the form

$$2p_x p_y \cos (\psi_x - \psi_y)$$

If these transmissions are of unlike frequency the average value of each of these terms will be zero and their sum will be zero. The resultant mean-square pressure will then be

$$p_\Sigma^2 = p_1^2 + p_2^2 + p_3^2 + \cdots + p_n^2 \quad \text{(2A-85)}$$

From the foregoing it is evident that when sinusoidal acoustic waves of unlike frequency reach a given point the mean-square value of their resultant acoustic pressure is the sum of their individual mean-square pressures. For this reason mean-square pressure is, in many problems, a more appropriate measure of wave magnitude than root-mean-square pressure. The quantity most generally used in such problems, however, is not the mean-square pressure but the product of this mean-square pressure and the acoustic conductance per unit area of the medium. This product, it will be recalled, was shown by Eq. (2A-52) to be the average value of the acoustic intensity of sinusoidal plane waves propagated along a single path.

If we multiply both sides of Eq. (2A-85) by the acoustic conductance per unit area of the medium at the point to which this equation applies there is obtained

$$\frac{p_\Sigma^2}{\rho c} = \frac{p_1^2}{\rho c} + \frac{p_2^2}{\rho c} + \frac{p_3^2}{\rho c} + \cdots + \frac{p_n^2}{\rho c} \quad \text{(2A-86)}$$

The acoustic pressures appearing in the terms on the right of this equation are, by hypothesis, all pressures of waves having sinusoidal variations. Each is associated with energy propagated along a single path. Since each of these pressures satisfies the conditions under which Eq. (2A-52) is valid, each of the corresponding terms represents an average acoustic intensity. The resultant pressure appearing in the term on the left is not the pressure of waves having a sinusoidal pressure variation nor is it, necessarily, the pressure due to waves propagated along a single path. It does not, therefore, satisfy the conditions which must be satisfied for Eq. (2A-52) to be valid. We may, however, hypothesize sinusoidal waves which have an rms pressure equal to the rms pressure appearing in this term, and which are propagated along

a single path. Since these hypothetical waves satisfy the conditions for which Eq. (2A-52) is valid they have an average acoustic intensity, the value of which is given by the term in question. This intensity may, therefore, be described as an **equivalent sine wave intensity.** The equivalent sine wave intensity of the acoustic energy passing a given point may be defined as the average intensity of plane waves which have a sinusoidal variation of acoustic pressure, which are propagated along a single path in a medium free of other acoustic waves but having the same acoustic conductance per unit area as the medium containing the given point, and which have a mean-square acoustic pressure equal to the mean-square acoustic pressure of the waves at the given point.

For each of a number of nonsinusoidal wave transmissions there will be an equivalent sine wave intensity which is the sum of the average intensities of the individual sinusoidal components of that transmission. The resultant equivalent sine wave intensity due to all of the nonsinusoidal wave transmissions is the sum of the average intensities of all of the sinusoidal components making up these transmissions. The resultant equivalent sine wave intensity is, therefore, the sum of the equivalent sine wave intensities of the individual nonsinusoidal transmissions. Now, it is self-evident, by definition, that in the case of an energy transmission consisting of sinusoidal waves propagated along a single path the equivalent sine wave intensity and the average acoustic intensity are identically the same. The resultant equivalent sine wave intensity of the acoustic energy reaching a given point is thus seen to be the sum of the equivalent sine wave intensities of the several transmissions contributing to that energy. This is true regardless of whether these individual transmissions are of sinusoidal waves or of nonsinusoidal waves, provided no two arrive along separate paths with sinusoidal variations of identical frequency.

If sinusoidal waves of identical frequency reach a given point by two or more paths the resultant equivalent sine wave intensity will, in general, not be equal to the sum of the individual equivalent sine wave intensities. For example, in the situation illustrated by Fig. 2A-7 the equivalent sine wave intensity due to either transmission alone, which is the same as its average intensity, is $p_1^2/\rho c = p_2^2/\rho c$ at any point on the line interval postulated. Here p_1^2 and p_2^2 are the mean-square acoustic pressures for the two transmissions acting separately. The resultant equivalent sine wave intensity may be computed from the resultant mean-square acoustic pressure given by Eq. (2A-83). When thus computed, it will be found to vary between 0 and $4(p_1^2/\rho c) = 4(p_2^2/\rho c)$, depending upon the point for which the computation is made. It is only when averaged over a length of line equal to one wave interval of the standing-wave pattern that the resultant equivalent sine wave intensity applying to this situation becomes equal to the sum of the equivalent sine wave intensities of the individual transmissions.

In certain situations the resultant acoustic pressure at a given point will have instantaneous values which oscillate between positive and negative values in such manner that successive positive maxima—or negative maxima—vary progressively. When this occurs the equivalent sine wave intensity will also vary in a similar manner.

It is evident from the foregoing that the term "equivalent sine wave intensity" is, in fact, a designation for the product of mean-square acoustic pressure and acoustic conductance per unit area. This product has the dimensions of acoustic intensity. It is thus directly related to acoustic energy, the basic quantity with which we are concerned. It will be found, as we proceed, that this has certain advantages. It must not, however, be allowed to obscure the fact that equivalent sine wave intensity does not necessarily express the time rate of flow per unit area at which acoustic energy actually passes through some given surface.

Much of the acoustic energy with which we shall have to deal reaches a given point in the form of plane waves. For such waves the equivalent sine wave intensity is a true measure of the average time rate of energy flow per unit area of surface perpendicular to the direction along which these waves are propagated. In many situations, however, acoustic energy reaches a point of interest from many sources and along many paths. It is usually not feasible, in such cases, to evaluate separately the energy propagated along any one path. The rate at which energy actually passes through a surface having a given orientation is, therefore, usually unknown. In general, the devices most frequently used for observing this energy are pressure-sensitive. The acoustic pressure at a point, as we have seen, is not dependent on the direction of propagation of the energy to which it is due. When observing the acoustic waves at a single point with a pressure-sensitive device, then,

it is impossible to distinguish between waves which arrive from many directions and plane waves propagated along a single path. The product of the mean-square acoustic pressure and the acoustic conductance per unit area of the medium may thus be considered as representing the time rate of energy flow per unit area of plane waves which have the same mean-square acoustic pressure as that of the waves actually measured. In such cases the equivalent sine wave intensity, computed from data obtained by a pressure-sensitive device, is spoken of as the **equivalent plane wave intensity.**

Throughout the remainder of this book the term "intensity" will, when used in connection with acoustic waves arriving from many directions, be understood to refer to this equivalent plane wave intensity. As such, it designates the time rate of energy flow per unit area of plane surface of hypothetical plane waves. When used in connection with actual plane waves which reach a given point along a single path, the term designates the true time rate of energy flow per unit area through a surface perpendicular to this path.

Later we will come to the study of sound-responsive devices the responses of which are functions of the direction from which acoustic energy reaches them. It will then be necessary to identify an equivalent plane wave intensity with hypothetical plane waves propagated in a specified direction. Unless such a direction is specified, however, equivalent plane wave intensity will be understood to apply to hypothetical plane waves propagated in any direction.

The relations between acoustic intensity and acoustic pressure, which are here under consideration, have been derived in terms of units of the cgs system. For the problems with which we shall have to deal, it will be more convenient if these relations are expressed in terms of practical units. Equivalent plane wave intensity is, therefore, written as

$$I = \frac{p^2 \cdot 10^{-7}}{\rho c} \qquad (2A\text{-}87)$$

where

$I =$ the equivalent plane wave intensity of the acoustic energy passing a given point (watt/cm²)

$p =$ the root-mean-square acoustic pressure of the waves by which this energy is propagated (1 dyne/cm² = 1 μb)

$1/\rho c$ = the acoustic conductance per unit area of the medium at the given point (spec. acous. mho)

The practical unit of pressure, in acoustical work, is the microbar, μb. This is equal to one dyne per square centimeter. The bar, defined by the relation 1 bar = 10^6 dynes/cm^2, has been officially adopted both by physicists and by meteorologists. A pressure of one atmosphere is equal to 1013.3 millibars.

2A-10 Spectra

The sound waves found in the sea rarely have sinusoidal variations in acoustic pressure. They may, however, in many cases, be considered as made up of separate **components,** each of which does have a sinusoidal pressure variation, of fixed frequency. The individual sinusoidal components of a given wave, when considered with respect to their distribution in frequency, are often referred to as the **spectrum** of the wave.

This term does not have a precisely defined meaning, comparable with that which the designation of a physical quantity must have. It is sometimes used in referring to the frequency scale on which the frequencies of the several components of a wave are represented. It is sometimes defined as the distribution in frequency of the wave energy. It is often employed without regard to either the absolute or the relative magnitudes of the wave components.

The word "spectrum" has, of course, been borrowed from optics, where it is applied to electromagnetic energy. If necessary, to avoid ambiguity, the nature of the energy to which the term is applied may be indicated by a qualifying adjective. In sonar we deal chiefly with **acoustic spectra** and **electric spectra.** When an acoustic wave is audible to the ear its components, and the components of electric waves occupying similar positions on the frequency scale, are said to form an **audio spectrum.** The term "spectrum" may also be qualified to indicate the nature of the quantity used for evaluating component magnitudes; we hear of **energy spectra, power spectra,** and **intensity spectra.**

If the frequencies of the sinusoidal components making up a complex wave are separated by intervals on the frequency scale of such magnitude that the magnitude of each component may be independently evaluated, the wave is said to have a **line spectrum.** Such a spectrum may be represented graphically by a series of vertical lines, each being erected at a point on a horizontal frequency scale representing the frequency of the corresponding component and having a length proportional to some measure of its magnitude.

Let us now consider the energy associated with those components of a complex wave the frequencies of which are included between two points on a frequency scale. Such a limited group of components is said to occupy a **frequency band.** When frequency is plotted against a linear scale any interval along that scale measures the difference, $f_b - f_a$, between the frequency of the upper boundary of the band represented and the frequency of the lower boundary. This difference is known as the **band width** of the frequency band. Bands having equal widths are represented on a linear frequency scale by intervals of equal length.

In many problems the ratio, f_b/f_a, between the limiting frequencies of a given band is of more significance than their difference. This ratio, which may be spoken of as the **band ratio,** is represented graphically by an interval on a logarithmic scale of frequency. On such a scale, scale intervals of equal length represent bands having equal band ratios. A band ratio having the value $f_b/f_a = 2$ is the ratio long known to musicians as the **octave.** Physicists and acoustical engineers have now adopted this term. A band having a band ratio of $f_b/f_a = 10$ is properly described as a **denary band.** This band is often spoken of, incorrectly, as a "frequency decade." In accordance with accepted usage a **decade band** is one having a band width of $f_b - f_a = 10$. Decade bands are represented by scale intervals of equal length on a linear scale of frequency.

Frequency bands represented by intervals on either a linear or a logarithmic frequency scale are sometimes spoken of as **spectrum intervals.**

The intensity of a complex acoustic wave having a line spectrum is, as shown in the preceding article, the sum of the intensities of its components. For a complex electric wave having a line spectrum the power is the sum of the powers of its components. For a wave having a line spectrum, therefore, the total intensity, or the total power, of those components within any frequency band is the sum of their individual intensities, or powers.

Let us now assume that two points define a narrow spectrum interval on the portion of a frequency scale between two points corresponding to the frequencies of two adjacent components of a complex wave. The lower bounding frequency of the band thus defined will be designated as f_0 and the upper bounding frequency as f_x. There will be no energy associated with the interval as thus defined. If, however, the frequency f_x is increased progressively finite increments of energy will, from time to time, be included. The power measuring the time rate of energy flow due to all components within the expanding frequency band will change, with increasing band width, only when the increasing frequency coincides with the frequency of a wave component. When such a coincidence occurs, the total power will increase by a finite amount, equal to the power of the component

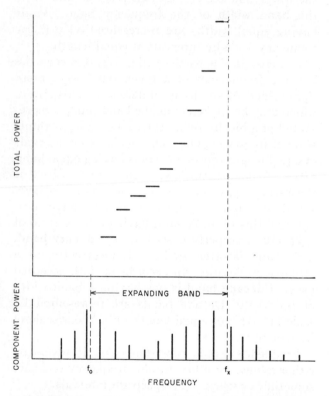

FIG. 2A-8. LINE SPECTRUM. The powers of individual sinusoidal components of a wave having a line spectrum, and the resultant power in an expanding frequency band.

entering the band, for an increase in band width of zero magnitude. The magnitude of the total power in such an expanding frequency band may be considered a function of the frequency of the moving boundary of the band. The fixed frequency is then considered as a parameter. The relations thus expressed are shown graphically in Fig. 2A-8. It is evident that for a complex wave having a line spectrum the power of the components in an expanding frequency band is a discontinuous function of the frequency of the variable boundary.

Complex electric waves in some given circuit, or complex acoustic waves passing through some finite area, often have such a frequency distribution of energy that the total power of the components in a frequency band of varying width appears to be a continuous function of the frequency of the moving boundary. Whether or not the function appears to be continuous depends, of course, on the resolving power of the instruments by which the wave energy is measured. When the power of those components of a complex wave occupying a frequency band of varying width appears to be a continuous function of this width, as observed by instruments of high resolving power, the wave is said to have a **continuous spectrum.** Such a wave may be treated as though it were made up of an infinite number of components, each of an infinitesimal magnitude.

Many of the sounds encountered in air and in water have a frequency distribution of energy which may be described as a continuous spectrum on which is superimposed a line spectrum. This is simply another way of saying that when analyzed by instruments of high resolving power there is evidence of components which are too closely spaced and too small to be measured, and that there is, at the same time, evidence of individual sinusoidal components of measurable magnitude. The spectrum of such a wave may also be described as made up of a sequence of continuous spectra, occupying contiguous portions of a frequency scale, and passing through discontinuous changes in total power at the boundaries between these portions.

2A-11 Power per Unit Band and Intensity per Unit Band

By definition, the components of a complex wave having a continuous spectrum are all of infinitesimal magnitude. Because of this it is not possible, with such a wave, to compute the total power for any given frequency band as the sum of the powers of the individual components in that band. It must, instead, be computed by integration. This requires that we be able to evaluate the derivative of power with respect to frequency. To this end, **power per unit band** is defined as the limit approached by the quotient obtained by dividing (1) the power of the energy being transmitted by a given system, at a given time and in a given frequency band, by (2) the width of this

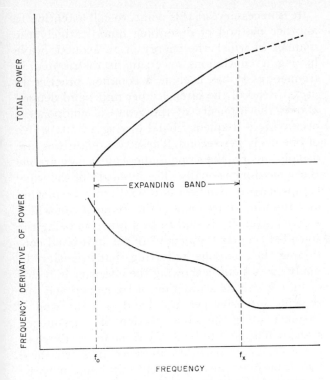

FIG. 2A-9. CONTINUOUS SPECTRUM. The total power in an expanding frequency band of a wave having a continuous spectrum, and the derivative of this power with respect to frequency.

band as the width of this band approaches zero.

In a similar manner, **acoustic intensity per unit band** is defined as the limit approached by the quotient obtained by dividing (1) the intensity of the acoustic energy being transmitted through a given area, at a given time and in a given frequency band, by (2) the width of this band as the width of this band approaches zero. Acoustic intensity per unit band, as thus defined, is also the limit approached by the quotient obtained by dividing the power per unit band of this same acoustic energy by the magnitude of the given area through which it is being transmitted, as the magnitude of this area approaches zero.

The "intensity of the acoustic energy being transmitted through a given area" may be the equivalent plane wave intensity of hypothetical plane waves having a mean-square acoustic pressure equal to the mean-square pressure measured at the given area. In many cases it will be the intensity of plane waves actually passing through the area along a path perpendicular to it.

It must be noted that the concept of power per unit band, or of intensity per unit band, is without significance when dealing with an energy wave

in which all of the energy is carried by a single sinusoidal component. For such a wave we are dealing with a finite power, or a finite intensity, associated with a frequency band of zero width. Such a finite power may be looked upon as the product of a power per unit band of infinite magnitude multiplied by a band width of zero magnitude. This concept is wholly consistent with the principles of dimensional analysis.

It will be at once evident that the two quantities just defined represent additional measures of rate of energy flow. Of the seven possible quantities which may be used for this purpose we shall have occasion to employ four. These are: (1) power, the derivative of energy with respect to time; (2) intensity, the second derivative of energy with respect to time and area; (3) power per unit band, the second derivative of energy with respect to time and frequency band width; and (4) intensity per unit band, the third derivative of energy with respect to time, area, and frequency band width. In this book we shall have no need for the derivatives of energy with respect to area alone, band width alone, or area and band width together. The quantity symbols and unit symbols of the quantities which we do require are tabulated in Fig. 2A-10.

FIG. 2A-10. RATES OF ENERGY FLOW. The derivatives of energy with respect to time, area, and frequency band width which are used in sonar.

Quantity	Quantity Symbol	Derivative	Unit Symbol
Energy	W		joule
Time	t		sec
Area	A		cm²
Frequency			cps
Power	P	$\dfrac{dW}{dt}$	watt
Intensity		$\dfrac{dP}{dA}$	watts/cm²
Power per Unit Band	U	$\dfrac{dP}{df}$	joule/cyc
Intensity per Unit Band	J	$\dfrac{dI}{df} = \dfrac{dU}{dA}$	joule/cm²·cyc

Power per unit band is the rate of change of the total power for a frequency band of finite width with change in the frequency of a moving boundary of that band. For a given wave, and at a given frequency, the value of this rate of change is independent of the frequency of the fixed boundary.

At a specified frequency, therefore, power per unit band is a unique measure of the rate of flow of the energy of a wave having a continuous spectrum. When the power per unit band of a wave having a continuous spectrum is plotted as a function of frequency, a curve is obtained which represents the manner in which the energy of that wave is distributed in frequency. Such a curve may be called a **spectrum characteristic.** It bears the same relation to a continuous spectrum that the vertical line diagram previously described bears to a line spectrum. Spectrum characteristics may be drawn in terms of intensity per unit band as well as in terms of power per unit band.

The curves of Fig. 2A-9 show the total power in an expanding frequency band, and the power per unit band, for a wave having a continuous spectrum, both of these quantities being plotted as functions of the frequency of the moving upper boundary of the band. These curves represent the energy distribution, with respect to frequency, for a wave having a continuous spectrum in the manner that the curves of Fig. 2A-8 represent this distribution for a wave having a line spectrum.

The manner in which the energy of an acoustic wave having a line spectrum is distributed in frequency may be represented by a vertical line diagram in which the heights of the lines are proportional to the acoustic pressures of the components which they represent. A curve may also be drawn for an acoustic wave having a continuous spectrum to show the varying total acoustic pressure for a frequency band of varying width as a function of the frequency of a moving boundary of that band. This total pressure would, moreover, be a continuous function of frequency. Since this is true it is, of course, possible to differentiate this total pressure with respect to frequency. Here the apparent similarity between descriptions of acoustic energy distributions in terms of intensity and descriptions in terms of acoustic pressure ends: the value of the frequency derivative of its acoustic pressure, at any given frequency, is *not* a unique property of an acoustic wave; the frequency derivative of the total acoustic pressure of the wave components in a frequency band having a moving boundary, unlike the frequency derivative of their total intensity, is not independent of the frequency of the fixed boundary of the band. This follows directly from the fact that, although the total intensity of a group of wave components is the sum of their individual intensities, the total pressure is not the sum of their individual pressures.

It is necessary, at this point, to call attention to another method of describing quantitatively the manner in which the energy of an acoustic wave having a continuous spectrum is distributed in frequency. It has become a common practice to use, instead of the intensity per unit band defined above, the intensity of the group of components occupying a frequency band having a finite width of one cycle per second. These two quantities are, usually, nearly the same numerically; they are *not* the same dimensionally. The intensity of the wave components in bands of unit width may be plotted as a function of frequency, the frequency of which a given intensity is said to be a function being the so-called "center frequency" of the unit band containing the components having that intensity. In many cases a curve showing the intensity in bands of unit width as a function of frequency and one showing intensity per unit band as a function of frequency, for the same portion of a frequency scale, will appear to be of the same form. There is, however, an important difference between these two functions: intensity per unit band may be integrated with respect to frequency to yield an intensity; a quantity which is itself an intensity may not be so integrated.

2-B RELATIVE MAGNITUDES AND TRANSMISSION LOSS

The magnitudes of sound waves in water may be expressed in terms of any of the quantities, such as displacement, particle velocity, acoustic pressure, or acoustic intensity, which have been discussed in the preceding section. It has, however, been found advantageous to translate values of certain of these quantities from an absolute magnitude scale to a somewhat different type of scale, which we shall now consider.

2B-1 Relative Magnitudes—The Logit

Experience has shown that the magnitudes of acoustic intensities in water which are of practical significance lie between widely separated limits. The scale of values, in fact, extends from intensities below 10^{-20} watts/cm² to intensities above 100 watts/cm². It is, of course, necessary that we be able to determine the absolute magnitudes of acoustic intensities throughout this entire range. There are, however, situations in which fractional changes in intensity are of primary significance, while absolute magnitudes may be irrelevant or indeterminate. In these cases it is both convenient and necessary to deal with relative magnitudes.

Changes in **relative magnitude** are expressed as ratios, whereas changes in **absolute magnitude** are expressed as differences. The ratios measuring changes in relative magnitude combine by multiplication to produce a similar ratio; the differences measuring changes in absolute magnitude combine by addition to produce a similar difference. Any given change in absolute magnitude is expressed as the number of standard, or unit, differences which must be added together to equal the given change; any given change in relative magnitude may be expressed either as the ratio of the final absolute magnitude to the initial absolute magnitude, or as the number of some specified standard ratios which, when multiplied together, are equivalent to this ratio.

In view of the manner in which relative magnitudes combine, it is evident that any given change in relative magnitude may be written as

$$R = r^m \tag{2B-1}$$

where

R = a given change in relative magnitude
(a dimensionless ratio)

r = a standard ratio, or standard change in relative magnitude
(a dimensionless ratio)

m = the exponent indicating the power of the standard ratio which is equivalent to the given change
(a numeric)

When the value of the standard ratio, r, is fixed the exponent, m, is as unique a measure of a change in relative magnitude as the ratio R. In certain types of problem it is more convenient to use the exponent as a measure of this change than to use the ratio.

The ratio R and the exponent m may be made to conform concurrently to the decimal system if the standard ratio is given the value $r = 10^{0.1}$ $= 1.2589+$. If, when the standard ratio has this particular value, R is expressed as a power of 10 and m as a multiple of 10 the exponent indicating the power and the coefficient indicating the multiple will always be equal. The relation of the quantity $10^{0.1}$ to a scale of relative magnitudes is analogous to that of the unit quantity to a scale of absolute magnitudes; ten of each combine, in accordance with the laws governing their combination, to equal a change represented by the numerical value 10. It has, for this reason, been proposed[9] that this standard change in relative magnitude be designated as a **logit**. The logit may be defined as a standard ratio which has a numerical value of $10^{0.1}$ and which combines by multiplication with similar ratios of the same value. Logits may be used for evaluating absolute or relative magnitudes, the number of logits having a combined value equal to the numerical value of a given magnitude being the exponent indicating the power of the number $10^{0.1}$ which has that value. The relation between logits and **units** may be more evident when it is realized that a unit may be described as a standard difference which has a numerical value of one and which combines by addition with similar differences of the same value. Units may be used for evaluating absolute or relative magnitudes, the number of units having a combined value equal to the numerical value of a given magnitude being the coefficient indicating the multiple of the number one which has that value. The term "logit" may be used for specifying the standard ratio by which generalized relative magnitudes are evaluated. When suitably qualified it may be used, in a similar manner, with the standard relative magnitudes of physical quantities.

The exponent indicating the power to which a standard ratio must be raised to equal some given ratio is computed from the values of the standard and given ratios by solving Eq. (2B-1) for the exponent, m. Thus, in general,

$$m = \log_r R = \frac{\log_{10} R}{\log_{10} r} \tag{2B-2}$$

When the standard change has logit value, $r = 10^{0.1}$, this becomes

$$m = \log_{10^{0.1}} R = 10 \log_{10} R = \text{lgt } R \quad \text{logits} \tag{2B-3}$$

This is the number of logits which are equivalent to the given change in relative magnitude. The process of taking the logarithm to the base $10^{0.1}$ of a given number, or, what is equivalent, the process of taking ten times the logarithm to the base ten of that number, will hereafter be indicated by the operator **lgt**.

It is commonly said that the ratio of two quantities of like kind is dimensionless. What this means is that the numerical value of the ratio is independent of the size of the units by which the two magnitudes are measured, provided, of course, that both are measured in terms of a common unit. The ratio of two lengths, for example, has the same numerical value when both are measured in microns as when both are measured in light years. If, however, ratios are to be expressed in terms of some standard ratio it becomes necessary for the value of this standard ratio to be known. In other words, when the ratio of two absolute magnitudes is considered, the significance which is lost by the size of the absolute magnitude standard is acquired by the size of the relative magnitude standard. Information as to the physical nature of the quantities in question is no less necessary when dealing with relative magnitudes than when dealing with absolute magnitudes. To say that the ratio of two quantities of like kind is dimensionless does not mean that the nature of the quantities thus compared is without significance.

Whenever it is said that any ratio is expressed in logits it is to be understood that the numerical value of the standard ratio is $10^{0.1}$. This information must be supplemented by information as to the physical nature of the quantities. All of this information may be conveyed by suitably qualifying the word "logit." The requirements as to the specification of the nature and magnitude of the standard ratio are fully met by such terms as "energy logits," "length logits," "velocity logits," and so on. Any number expressing the ratio of two physical quantities of like kind must be accompanied by an appropriate symbol conveying this same information. This requires only that the letter "l" be combined with the letter, or symbol, normally used to represent an absolute magnitude of the physical quantity in question. The symbol to be used with a number of frequency logits would thus be "fl," with power logits it would be

"Pl," and so on. Such a symbol serves the same purpose, and has many of the same properties, as the dimensional designations used in connection with statements of absolute magnitude to specify the nature and magnitude of the standard unit used.

The number of logits which are equivalent to a given change in relative magnitude may be computed, using Eq. (2B-3), by means of any table of logarithms or by a slide rule having a log scale. In using either of these when the given change is a ratio less than unity it is necessary that the entire logarithm be considered as a negative number, rather than as a positive mantissa and a negative characteristic. For example:

$$\begin{aligned} \text{lgt } 0.005 &= \text{lgt } 5 + \text{lgt } 10^{-3} \\ &= 6.99 - 30.00 \\ &= -23.01 \end{aligned}$$

A brief table of logit values will be found in the back of this book. A chart showing the relation between the two scales which may be used for expressing relative magnitudes is given in Fig. 2B-1.

Although logits are, by definition, identified with ratios, either abstract or of physical quantities of like kind, they may nevertheless be used for the evaluation of absolute magnitudes. This requires only that, in each case, a definite absolute magnitude be specified as a reference quantity. In other words, if, in the relation $B = \text{lgt } (A_x/A_0)$ a specific value is assigned to the quantity A_0 the quantities B and A_x become uniquely related to each other. The quantity B is then a measure of

Fig. 2B-1. Relative Magnitude Scales. Scales showing the numerical values of ratios measuring relative magnitudes and the corresponding numbers of logits by which these magnitudes may also be expressed. Multiplication of any ratio value by ten requires that ten be added to the corresponding logit value.

the magnitude of the quantity A_x referred to the quantity A_0.

When expressing any absolute magnitude in terms of its value relative to a reference magnitude the reference magnitude must be explicitly specified. It must be stated that the quantity in question is evaluated in terms of logits relative to a known quantity; it is not sufficient to say that it is evaluated in logits. The specification of the reference quantity may be incorporated in symbolic expressions by a simple extension of our conventional notation. For example, to express the magnitude of the frequency f_x in terms of its value relative to the frequency f_0 we may write

$$\text{lgt } \frac{f_x}{f_0} \qquad \text{fl} // (f_0 \text{ cyc/sec}) \qquad (2\text{B-}4)$$

This may be read as, "The magnitude of the frequency f_x is lgt (f_x/f_0) frequency logits greater than the reference frequency f_0 cycles per second." The double solidus (//) indicates that the quantity preceding the symbols with which it is combined is the number of standard relative magnitudes having the nature and value specified on its left which are equivalent to the ratio of the absolute magnitude being evaluated to the absolute magnitude, of a quantity of like kind, having the nature and value specified on its right. It is, therefore, not unrelated to the single solidus (/), which indicates that the quantity preceding the symbols with which it is combined is the number of standard absolute magnitudes having the nature and value specified on its left which are identified with the unit absolute magnitude, of a quantity of unlike kind, having the nature and value specified on the right.

By expressing the absolute magnitudes of related physical quantities in terms of relative magnitudes, referred to suitable reference quantities, it is possible to transform a certain type of equation into a simpler type. The equation $I = k(p^2/\rho c)$ watts/cm², as given by Eq. (2A-87), may be taken as an example. If p is in microbars and $1/\rho c$ in specific acoustic mhos the dimensional coefficient will be $k = 10^{-7}$ watt·sec/erg. This dimensional coefficient is required because we are here dealing with absolute magnitudes. It is possible to select reference quantities for the acoustic intensity, the acoustic pressure, the specific acoustic conductance, and the dimensional coefficient such that $I_0 = k_0(p_0{}^2/\rho_0 c_0)$ watts/cm². The ratio indicating the relative magnitude of the intensity I_x, referred to the intensity I_0, is then

$$\frac{I_x}{I_0} = \left(\frac{k}{k_0}\right)\left(\frac{p_x}{p_0}\right)^2\left(\frac{\rho_0 c_0}{\rho_x c_x}\right) \qquad (2\text{B-}5)$$

If each of these relative magnitudes is now expressed in logits we may write

$$\text{lgt } \frac{I_x}{I_0} = 2 \text{ lgt } \frac{p_x}{p_0} - \text{lgt } \frac{\rho_x c_x}{\rho_0 c_0}$$
$$+ \text{ lgt } \frac{k}{k_0} \qquad \text{Il} // (I_0 \text{ watts/cm}^2) \quad (2\text{B-}6)$$

The most convenient magnitude for each reference quantity is clearly unity.

From this it is seen that an absolute magnitude which is equal to the product of powers of other absolute magnitudes may be expressed in terms of a relative magnitude and the term thus expressing it equated to the sum of multiples of other terms similarly expressing other absolute magnitudes. In transforming an equation of one form into an equation of the other it is necessary that standard relative magnitudes of like ratio value be used for all quantities, and that the values of the several reference quantities satisfy the equation expressing the relation between the absolute magnitudes. When these conditions are met, the exponents indicating the powers of the absolute magnitudes appearing in the original equation become the coefficients indicating the multiples of the corresponding numbers of standard relative magnitudes which appear in the derived equation.

An expression such as $2 \text{ lgt } (p_x/p_0)$, which appears in Eq. (2B-6), is a number of logits. The ratio thus expressed is the square of a pressure ratio. The term may therefore be said to represent a number of pressure squared logits. In this case it must be recognized that the reference quantity is the square of a pressure.

When the magnitudes of several quantities of unlike kind are expressed in logits relative to appropriate reference quantities, and these logit values are added together, the information appearing on the right of the double solidus in the dimensional identification accompanying the resultant is derived from information similarly presented for the components. This is accomplished in the same manner as that used in the case of the familiar dimensional equations. The only difference is that in the present case the number of units, as well as their magnitude, must be considered.

2B-2 Transmission Loss—The Decibel

One of the important uses of relative magnitudes is in measuring the performance of energy transmission systems. It is desirable that we consider this application briefly at this point since any use which we make of these quantities for evaluating acoustic waves in water must be consistent with their subsequent use in evaluating the systems by which these waves, and others related to them, may be transmitted.

The performance of an electric transmission system may be studied in terms of relative electric power, relative electric voltage, or relative electric current. For acoustic transmission systems it is possible to use relative acoustic power, relative acoustic intensity, relative acoustic pressure, or relative magnitudes of several cognate quantities. Of these quantities relative rates of energy flow have the unique advantage that they may be used as measures of the transmission capabilities of portions of transmission systems in which the energy transmitted is changed in form. Because of this, and for other reasons which will appear later, the property of an energy transmission system which determines the rate at which it transmits energy has become one of particular significance in sonar, as well as in other branches of communication engineering.

Relative power has been used for many years for evaluating the performance of energy transmission systems. The **efficiency** of such a system, or of any portion of such a system, is measured by the ratio of the power of the energy delivered by that system, or portion of a system, to the power of the energy received. Other relative powers measure other significant characteristics, such as the effectiveness with which energy is transmitted across a junction, or with which the energy available at one junction is made available at another. Each of these relative power magnitudes, which may be called a **transmission factor,** measures a property of an energy transmission system. Transmission factors cannot, however, be expressed directly in terms of a dimensional unit; the transmission factor measuring the resultant efficiency of a sequence of system elements is the product of the factors measuring the individual efficiencies of the separate elements. Physical quantities which may be expressed in terms of dimensional units are those which combine by addition, not by multiplication.

The performance of an energy transmission system may also be expressed in terms of a quantity which is logarithmically related to a transmission factor and which may be evaluated in terms of a dimensional unit. This quantity is known as **trans-mission loss.** Transmission loss is that property of an energy transmission system to which is ascribed reduction in the rate at which energy is transmitted through that system. A given transmission loss may be associated with the junction between two portions of a system, or with the portion of a system between two junctions.

Reductions in rates of energy flow by which transmission losses are measured may be expressed in terms of relative power, of relative energy flux, of relative energy per unit band, of relative intensity, of relative energy flux per unit band, of relative power per unit band, or of relative intensity per unit band.

The portions of energy transmission systems to which transmission factors or transmission losses are assigned are designated as **transducers.** The fundamental properties of transducers will be discussed in some detail later. For the present it will be sufficient to note that transducers for converting acoustic energy received from water to electric energy are known as **hydrophones.** Transducers for converting electric energy to acoustic energy, and radiating this acoustic energy in water, are known as **sonar projectors.** Whenever the danger of confusing these with motion picture projectors is slight, they are usually spoken of simply as projectors. Hydrophones and projectors, together with microphones, telephone receivers, and loudspeakers, are known generically as **electroacoustic transducers.**

In general, the transmission loss of any extended portion of a transmission system may be computed as the sum of the losses associated with its component transducers plus the losses associated with the junctions between these transducers. These losses may be added together without regard to any conversions of energy from one form to another which may take place in any transducer. It is evident that the use of transmission loss is of great convenience in measuring the performance of the electroacoustic transducers used in sonar. The summation of contiguous losses will be discussed more fully in Sec. 4-G.

The **unit transmission loss**[10] used in the United States is the **decibel.** This unit was introduced[11] about 25 years ago, at which time it was known simply as "the transmission unit." The decibel, as originally defined, and as it will be used in this book, is that unit transmission loss for which the ratio of the reduced rate of energy flow to the unreduced rate of energy flow is $10^{-0.1}$. An equivalent definition of the decibel specifies it as that transmission loss which, when present in an energy transmission system, causes the rate at which energy is transmitted by that system to be reduced by 20.56682+ percent. The decibel has the fundamental dimension of transmission loss.

The relation between the transmission loss measuring some characteristic of an energy transmission system, in decibels, and the transmission factor measuring that same characteristic directly in terms of a relative rate of energy flow is given by the fundamental equation

$$N = \lg \frac{1}{\eta} \qquad (2B-7)$$

where

N = the transmission loss measuring some characteristic of an energy transmission system, or of a portion of such a system (db)

η = the transmission factor measuring the same characteristic (a numeric)

Whenever the transmission factor is a number greater than unity, as it is in the case of an amplifier, the transmission loss would have a negative sign. In such cases the logarithm of the reciprocal of the transmission factor is written with a positive sign and designated as a **transmission gain.**

When considering the ratio of the rates of energy flow which measures a transmission loss, it is necessary that the systems, or portions of systems, delivering and receiving energy be specified. The transmission losses of any portion of a system transmitting electric energy without change in form is thus measured by the ratio of the rate of flow of electric energy received from a specified junction to the rate of flow of electric energy delivered to a specified junction.

When considering the transmission losses of an electroacoustic transducer, the acoustic energy may be the total acoustic energy delivered to, or received from, the medium surrounding the transducer. It is often desirable, however, to consider the acoustic energy delivered to, or received from, a specified small area of the medium. In the latter case, it will be convenient to define a transmission loss measured by that ratio one factor of which is the rate of flow of the total electric energy delivered to, or available from, the transducer and one factor of which is the rate of flow of the

acoustic energy delivered to, or available from, a specified area of water surface.

When dealing with the transmission loss between two points both of which are in the acoustic medium, the ratio measuring the loss may be the ratio of two powers each of which is the rate at which acoustic energy flows through a specified small area of water surface. Each of these powers is the product of the area in question multiplied by the acoustic intensity throughout this area. Since the magnitude of the area is the same in both factors of the power ratio, this ratio is the ratio of the two intensities. Power ratios and intensity ratios are, in fact, both equivalent to energy ratios: in one case the two factors represent energies flowing in unit time; in the other they represent energies flowing in unit time and through unit area.

In the same manner, the ratio of two powers per unit band is equivalent to an energy ratio. In this case we are dealing with energies flowing in unit time and in unit frequency bands. Finally, the ratio of two intensities per unit band is equivalent to an energy ratio; here we are dealing with energies flowing in unit times, unit areas, and unit frequency bands. The ratio of two powers per unit band is also equal to the ratio of two powers, and the ratio of two intensities per unit band to the ratio of two intensities. These facts add to the utility of the concept of transmission loss. In dealing with waves having a continuous spectrum it is often necessary to be able to determine as a function of frequency the reduction in power per unit band taking place in a given system. At any frequency, the transmission loss of the system may usually be found with little difficulty by measuring the reduction, resulting from that loss, in the power of sinusoidal waves having that frequency. The transmission loss thus measured is the loss which reduces the power per unit band, at this same frequency, of any wave having a continuous spectrum, which may be transmitted through the system.

The magnitude of a transmission loss, measured in terms of an intensity ratio, is expressed in decibels by the relation

$$N_{b/a} = - \lg \frac{I_b}{I_a} \qquad (2B-8)$$

where

$N_{b/a}$ = the transmission loss measured by a given

reduction in relative acoustic intensity (db)

I_b = the reduced acoustic intensity (watt/cm²)

I_a = the unreduced acoustic intensity (watt/cm²)

On the basis of the relation $I = p^2/\rho c$, given in Art. 2A-5, it is possible to write

$$\lgt \frac{I_b}{I_a} = 2 \lgt \frac{p_b}{p_a} - \lgt \frac{\rho_b c_b}{\rho_a c_a} \qquad (2B\text{-}9)$$

It must not be inferred from this equation that the quantities on the right are expressed in decibels because their sum is a measure of transmission loss. Neither are these terms in intensity logits because their sum is in intensity logits. Relative magnitudes of unlike kind, when expressed as equivalent numbers of standard ratios, combine by addition to give a resultant which is a relative magnitude, similarly expressed, of a kind different from any of them. This follows from the fact that absolute magnitudes of unlike kind combine by multiplication to give a resultant which is an absolute magnitude of a kind different from any of them. In this equation the quantity $2 \lgt(p_b/p_a)$ is the number of pressure squared logits equivalent to the ratio of the squares of two pressures. The quantity $\lgt(\rho_b c_b/\rho_a c_a)$ is the number of conductance logits equivalent to the ratio of two acoustic conductances. The algebraic sum of these two quantities is the number of intensity logits equivalent to the corresponding ratio of two acoustic intensities.

In the special case where $\rho_b c_b = \rho_a c_a$, $\lgt(\rho_b c_b/\rho_a c_a) = 0$, and $\lgt(I_b/I_a) = 2 \lgt(p_b/p_a)$. Under this restricted condition the magnitude of a transmission loss, in decibels, may be established by measuring a change in acoustic pressure, as well as by measuring a change in acoustic intensity. Conversely, under this same condition, if the transmission loss is known the change in intensity and the change in pressure are both known.

In a similar manner the transmission losses of electric transmission systems may be written in terms of voltage or current ratios, as well as in terms of power ratios, provided the voltages and currents are taken at a single pair of terminals at which the impedance is constant, or at terminals at which the impedances are identical. Tables of transmission losses and their corre-

sponding power ratios are available in many handbooks. These tables also show voltage and current ratios which, under conditions of constant electric impedance, may be measured in terms of these losses. The ratio values appearing in such tables may be used with ratios of acoustic intensity and, if the specific acoustic conductance is constant, with ratios of acoustic pressures.

Any discussion of the decibel would be incomplete without brief mention of its physiological significance. It is a well established characteristic of our ears and eyes that, over a considerable range of intensity, they normally interpret equal percentage changes in stimulating energy as equal increments of sensation. For normal sounds, such as noise or music, the ear can just about detect a change in power ratio corresponding to a loss of two decibels. The threshold of hearing is generally accepted as being at 10^{-16} watts/cm² for air-borne sounds. A sound having an intensity 90 db greater than this is painfully loud. The great convenience of the decibel in physiological studies of vision and hearing is one of the several reasons for its extensive use.

It is interesting to note that a scale of decibels has a close counterpart in another and perhaps more familiar number scale. It will be recalled that the Brown and Sharpe scale of wire sizes associates a change of two to one in circular area with a change of three numbers on the gauge scale. A change of four to one in area, or of two to one in diameter is, then, indicated by a change of six gauge numbers. Compare this with the decibel scale, substituting power for area, and pressure— or voltage—for diameter.

2B-3 Transmission Level

The transmission losses of an energy transmission system are, by definition, measured by changes in the rate at which energy is transmitted by that system. The change required to reduce a given rate to a specified reference rate may, therefore, be uniquely identified with a transmission loss. This permits us to define the **transmission level** of the energy at any point in an energy transmission system as the rate of flow of that energy as expressed in terms of (1) a specified reference rate of flow and of (2) the transmission loss by which the actual rate of flow must be reduced to equal the reference rate.

When evaluating a rate of energy flow as a transmission level it is as necessary that the reference rate be specified as when expressing an absolute magnitude in terms of the number of logits by which it differs from a reference magnitude. The same form of notation may be used in the two cases. We may, in fact, write the transmission level measuring an intensity magnitude as

$$L_x = \text{lgt} \frac{I_x}{I_0} \text{ db} // I_0 \text{ watts/cm}^2$$

$$= \text{lgt} \frac{I_x}{I_0} \text{ Il} // I_0 \text{ watts/cm}^2 \qquad (2B\text{-}10)$$

It is evident from the foregoing that the transmission losses of an energy transmission system may be measured as the differences between transmission levels. This may be seen at once by the equation

$$L_a - L_b = \text{lgt} \frac{I_a}{I_0} - \text{lgt} \frac{I_b}{I_0}$$

$$= \text{lgt} \frac{I_a}{I_b} = N_{b/a} \qquad (2B\text{-}11)$$

The absolute value of the reference quantity vanishes from the ratio measuring the difference between the two levels. This is accompanied by the disappearance of the specification for the reference quantity from the dimensional identification. This conforms to the conventions recommended for expressing absolute magnitudes in terms of logits and reference magnitudes.

If, in Eq. (2B-6), $\rho_x c_x = \rho_0 c_0$, and $k = k_0$, $\text{lgt}(I_x/I_0) = 2 \text{ lgt}(p_x/p_0)$. The situation here is analogous to that in which it was shown that transmission losses might, in some cases, be measured in terms of pressure ratios. Here the transmission level of the intensity I_x, referred to the intensity I_0, is also a measure of the magnitude of the pressure p_x, referred to the pressure p_0. For this reason the quantity $2 \text{ lgt}(p_x/p_0)$ is commonly spoken of as the **pressure level** of the pressure p_x relative to the pressure p_0. This is permissible only when the acoustic conductance per unit area of the medium in which the pressures are measured is constant. When this method of expression is used it is as necessary to indicate the nature and magnitude of the reference quantity as when expressing relative magnitudes in a manner which is applicable under all conditions. The method illustrated by Eq. (2B-4) may be used for this purpose. Whenever the symbol "db//1 μb" appears it is understood that the acoustic conductance per unit area is constant. The transmission loss in decibels corresponding to the ratio p_x/p_0 is twice the number of pressure logits by which this ratio may be expressed. Where it is necessary to avoid ambiguity, the quantity $\text{lgt}(I_x/I_0)$ may be described as an **intensity level.**

A transmission loss measures a property of a system transmitting energy. A transmission level measures a property of the energy being transmitted. The transmission level of the energy being transmitted by a given system may be varied by any amount which is not sufficient to cause a change in the physical constants of that system without affecting its transmission losses. As in Eq. (2B-11), the symbol N will be used for transmission loss and the symbol L for transmission level. Throughout this book the magnitudes of transmission losses will be expressed in decibels; the magnitudes of transmission levels will be expressed in decibels relative to a specified reference rate of energy flow.

It is sometimes desirable to evaluate the difference between two transmission levels which are not associated with a single energy transmission. Such differences do not fall within the definition of a transmission loss. The difference between two transmission levels which, although related by a common transmission system and by a common reference quantity, are associated with two separate energy transmissions will be designated as a **level differential.** It will be represented by the symbol ΔL. A level differential does not measure a property of an energy transmission system; it is, instead, a measure of the dimensionless ratio of the rates at which two energies are being transmitted, often simultaneously, past a specified point in such a system. A level differential is dimensionally similar to a transmission loss, even though it is not a system characteristic; no reference quantity appears in the dimensional identification of the resultant differential, which is here required to indicate only the nature and magnitude of the standard change in relative magnitude by which the dimensionless ratio of rates in question is evaluated. The term "level differential" is in fact no more than an alternative designation for the ratio of two rates of energy flow when expressed in appropriate logits. Its use is justified because of its relation to transmission losses and transmission levels.

The acoustic intensity generally accepted by those concerned with air-borne acoustic waves, as a reference quantity for transmission levels measured in terms of acoustic intensity, is

10^{-16} watts/cm². This is very nearly the minimum intensity which may be detected by the human ear. Assuming an acoustic conductance per unit area of 0.025 spec. acous. mhos, the acoustic pressure corresponding to this reference intensity is 0.0002 μb for an acoustic wave in air. It must be emphasized, however, that this is not independent of temperature and pressure.

As the interests of acoustical engineers have been extended to media other than air, there has been much discussion regarding reference quantities. There can be no question that the decibel is uniquely identified with ratios of rates of energy flow, and that it may be used with a ratio of acoustic pressures only when the specific acoustic conductance of the medium is constant. It has, nevertheless, been proposed that a single reference acoustic pressure be adopted for all media. It is, as we have seen, possible to express acoustic pressures in terms of transmission level, in decibels relative to a reference acoustic pressure, provided the acoustic conductance per unit area of the medium is constant. There are problems, however, such as those dealing with the propagation of acoustic energy across an air-water boundary surface, (Art. 3C-2), in which this necessary condition is not fulfilled. If, in such problems, transmission levels were expressed in terms of a common reference pressure, the difference between the transmission level reported for a point in one medium and that reported for a point in the other would be far from the true transmission loss between the two points. The possibility of error in expressing pressure in terms of transmission level is by no means confined to situations in which acoustic energy passes from one medium to another.

Consider the case of a sound source the acoustic output of which is measured in fresh water in terms of the transmission level, at a specified point, relative to a specified acoustic pressure. Assume that this source is now moved to sea water and the output again measured by the same method, relative to the same reference pressure. If the acoustic power output is exactly the same in the two cases the levels measured in this manner may differ by as much as 0.5 db. Such an error, although negligible in many practical problems, is not to be tolerated in the fundamental relations between standards of measurement.

The use of a reference acoustic pressure in connection with transmission levels demands close adherence to the restricted conditions under which such use is permissible. It has been repeatedly demonstrated that the dangers which may arise through the careless use of transmission levels for the evaluation of acoustic pressure are by no means imaginary; nor do the advantages claimed for such use appear sufficient to justify the risk. By restricting the use of transmission levels to the measurement of rates of energy flow, on the other hand, full utilization of the fundamental concept of transmission loss is possible. It may be employed with confidence, both in crossing a boundary between media having different specific acoustic impedances, and in traversing a section of an energy transmission system in which the energy is changed from one form to another. Throughout this book, therefore, transmission levels will be used only for expressing rates of energy flow. In view of the fact that the general use of relative magnitudes is greatly simplified if all reference quantities are unit absolute magnitudes, unit rates of flow, such as the watt per square centimeter, will be taken as the reference rates.

During the early part of World War II a pressure of 0.0002 μb was tentatively adopted as a standard reference quantity for underwater sounds. The results of many surveys of the magnitudes of ship sounds and of natural water noises have been reported as pressure levels in terms of this reference pressure. It has since been proposed that an acoustic pressure of 1 μb might be a more appropriate reference quantity for general use. A considerable amount of published data has been referred to this quantity.

The diagram of Fig. 2B-2 shows the relations between transmission levels of acoustic energy in decibels relative to a reference acoustic intensity of 1 watt/cm², and pressure levels expressed in decibels relative to a reference pressure, on the assumption that the acoustic conductance per unit area is constant. The relations between these levels have been derived by means of Eqs. (2B-6), and (2B-10), using the following reference magnitudes: $I_0 = 1$ watt/cm², $p_0 = 1$ μb, $1/\rho_0 c_0 = 1$ spec. acous. mho, and $k_0 = 1$ watt·sec/erg. When the pressure level is 2 lgt $(p/1)$ db//1μb, and the constant acoustic conductance per unit area is $6.5 \cdot 10^{-6}$ spec. acous. mhos, the intensity level is

$$L = 2 \text{ lgt } (p/1) + \text{lgt } 6.5 \cdot 10^{-6} + \text{lgt } 10^{-7}$$
$$= 2 \text{ lgt } (p/1) - 51.87 - 70.00 \qquad (2B\text{-}12)$$
$$= 2 \text{ lgt } (p/1) - 121.87 \text{ db//1 watt/cm}^2$$

When the pressure level is 2 lgt$(p/0.0002)$ db$//0.0002\mu$b, and the constant acoustic con-

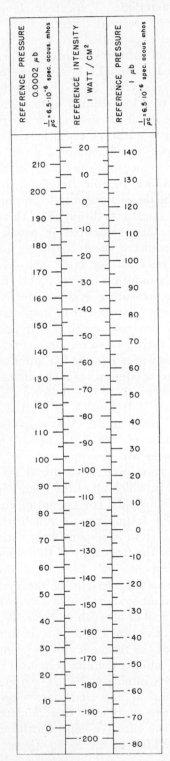

FIG. 2B-2. TRANSMISSION LEVELS. The relations between acoustic intensity levels and acoustic pressure levels in sea water, in decibels relative to specified reference quantities.

ductance per unit area is $6.5 \cdot 10^{-6}$ spec. acous. mhos, the intensity level is

$$L = 2 \text{ lgt } (p/0.0002) + 2 \text{ lgt } 0.0002$$
$$+ \text{lgt } 6.5 \cdot 10^{-6} + \text{lgt } 10^{-7}$$
$$= 2 \text{ lgt } (p/0.0002) - 73.98 - 51.87 - 70.00$$
$$= 2 \text{ lgt } (p/0.0002) - 195.85 \text{ db}//1 \text{ watt/cm}^2 \quad (2B-13)$$

The magnitude of the change which would result in the diagram of Fig. 2B-2 from a change in the value assumed for the constant acoustic conductance per unit area is determined by computing the change in intensity level resulting from a change in acoustic conductance per unit area when all other factors are held constant. In this case

$$L_b - L_a = - \text{ lgt } \frac{\rho_b c_b}{\rho_a c_a} \quad (2B-14)$$

On solving this equation in terms of numerical values it is found that the position of either of the pressure level scales would be moved upward, relative to the scale of intensity levels, by 0.1 db for an increase of 2.3 percent in the value assigned to the constant acoustic conductance per unit area. To alter this diagram to apply to air, instead of to sea water, it would be necessary to move the pressure level scales upward by approximately 36 db.

It is frequently desirable to determine the transmission level of some sound the intensity of which is known to be the sum of the intensities of two or more component sounds. The level differential between two sounds having intensities of I_1 and I_2 is

$$\Delta L = L_2 - L_1 = \text{lgt} \left[\frac{I_2}{I_0} \times \frac{I_0}{I_1} \right] = \text{lgt } \frac{I_2}{I_1} \quad (2B-15)$$

The difference between the levels of sounds having the intensities $I_1 + I_2$ and I_1 is

$$L_\Sigma - L_1 = \text{lgt } \frac{I_1 + I_2}{I_1} = \text{lgt} \left[1 + \frac{I_2}{I_1} \right] \quad (2B-16)$$

Since these two quantities are both unique functions of the ratio I_2/I_1 they are unique functions of each other. The graph of Fig. 2B-3 shows values of $L_2 - L_1$ plotted against corresponding values of $L_\Sigma - L_1$. This chart permits the evaluation of the level of one sound which occurs only in the presence of another, and which is manifest only by an increase in level above that observed

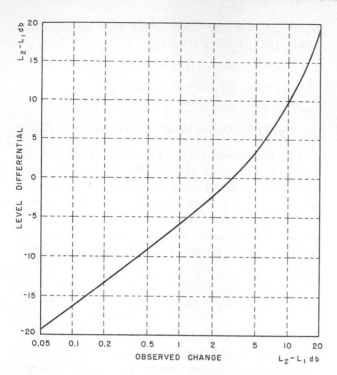

FIG. 2B-3. THE ADDITION OF TRANSMISSION LEVELS. A graph showing the level differential, $L_2 - L_1$, measuring the ratio of two acoustic intensities, as a function of the differential, $L_\Sigma - L_1$, measuring the ratio between the sum of these intensities and one of them.

for the constantly present sound. Against the observed change in level, $L_\Sigma - L_1$, the difference, $L_2 - L_1$, between the levels of the individual sounds, is read directly. The level, L_2, of the second sound is then obtained by adding this difference algebraically to the known level, L_1, of the first.

2B-4 Spectrum Level and Band Level

The rate of energy flow serving as a reference rate for evaluating the transmission level of the energy in a given energy transmission system may be a power per unit band, or an intensity per unit band, as well as a power or an intensity. A transmission level measuring a power per unit band, or an intensity per unit band, is usually spoken of as a **spectrum level.** A given spectrum level is usually associated with a specific frequency. To identify a transmission level measuring the power in a specified frequency band, or the acoustic intensity in a specified frequency band, it may be designated as a **band level.** The reference power per unit band to be used throughout this book will be $U_0 = 1$ joule/cyc. The reference intensity per unit band will be $J_0 = 1$ joule/cm² · cyc.

The graph obtained by plotting spectrum level as a function of frequency is known as a **spectrum level characteristic.** A spectrum level characteristic may be derived directly from a spectrum characteristic expressed in terms of power per unit band, or in terms of intensity per unit band, as described in Art. 2A-11. It is customary, when drawing a spectrum level characteristic, to plot frequency to a logarithmic scale. It is convenient if this scale is laid off in frequency logits.

To determine the power per unit band, or the intensity per unit band, of a given energy it is customary to measure the power, or the intensity, in some known narrow frequency band and to compute the desired magnitude on the assumption that it is constant throughout this band. The magnitude thus computed is usually identified with the geometric mean frequency of the known band. As we shall see later, the error resulting from this assumption is small. The **effective band width** of a measuring system selectively responsive to energy distributed in a spectrum is given in terms of the band width of a hypothetical system which satisfies two requirements: (1) over its assigned frequency band it has a uniform response equal to the maximum response of the actual system; (2) the width of this uniform response band is such that, if frequency is plotted to a linear scale, the areas under the response-frequency characteristics of the hypothetical and of the actual systems will be equal.

This situation may be analyzed by assuming a special case in which all of the energy is developed by a single sinusoidal component of known power, P_{act}. As the frequency to which the selective measuring system is responsive is varied, so as to sweep across the frequency of this component, the indicated response will vary in accordance with the response characteristic of the system. For a simple resonant system it will vary in the familiar manner typical of all such systems. When the frequency of maximum response is at frequencies on either side of the frequency of the component the system will show a definite response, indicating a definite power intensity, P_{ind}. The apparent power per unit band at any frequency showing such a response is the quotient of this indicated intensity divided by the effective band width, which as yet is unknown. That is,

$$U = \frac{P_{ind}}{\Delta f} \qquad (2B\text{-}17)$$

where

U = the apparent power per unit band, at some specified frequency (joule/cyc)

P_{ind} = the indicated power for a narrow frequency band the geometric mean frequency of which is at the specified frequency and over which the power per unit band may be assumed to be constant (watt)

Δf = the width of the narrow frequency band (cyc/sec)

If the indicated power is determined as a function of frequency the total power would be given by the integral of the power per unit band with respect to frequency, taken between limits including the entire response. This power would thus be written as

$$P_\Sigma = \int_0^\infty U\, df = \frac{1}{\Delta f} \int_0^\infty P_{ind}\, df \text{ watts} \quad (2B\text{-}18)$$

This total power must equal the actual power known to be associated with the given sinusoidal component. That is, $P_\Sigma = P_{act}$. It is thus evident that the effective band width must be

$$\Delta f = \frac{1}{P_{act}} \int_0^\infty P_{ind}\, df \text{ cyc/sec} \quad (2B\text{-}19)$$

Having established the value of the effective band width in this manner, the value of the apparent power per unit band at any frequency may now be determined by Eq. (2B-17).

The solid curve of Fig. 2B-4 shows the indicated relative power per unit band obtained by a simple resonant system, plotted as a function of frequency. The dotted curve shows the relative power per unit band which would be indicated by a system having a uniform response, throughout its response band, equal to the maximum response of the actual system and having a band width giving the same total power as the actual system. If f_1 and f_2 are the frequencies at which the indicated responses of the actual system are equal to one half the indicated response at the frequency, f_0, for which the response is a maximum, the effective band width of the actual system, and the equivalent width of the hypothetical system, can be shown to be

$$\Delta f = \frac{\pi}{2}(f_2 - f_1) \quad (2B\text{-}20)$$

where

Δf = the effective band width of a simple resonant system, selectively responsive to complex waves of energy (cyc/sec)

f_1 and f_2 = the frequencies at which the response, expressed in terms of power per unit band, or of intensity per unit band, is one half the response at the frequency of maximum response (cyc/sec)

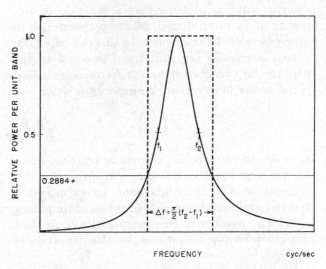

FIG. 2B-4. EFFECTIVE BAND WIDTH. The relative apparent power per unit band due to a single sinusoidal wave, as indicated by a simple resonant system, and the equivalent indication of a uniformly responsive system.

The two frequencies specified in this equation are known as the **quadrantal frequencies;** they will be discussed further in Art. 4C-2. The points on any response characteristic corresponding to these frequencies are often spoken of as the "half-power points," or as the "3-db down points."

If the limits of the hypothetical uniform response band which is equivalent to the actual response band of a simple resonant system is drawn on the diagram of relative power per unit band representing the actual response of that system in such manner that their geometric mean falls on the frequency of maximum response of the actual system, it will be found that they pass through points for which the relative response is $U/U_0 = 0.28840$. At these points the transmission loss through the system is 5.4 db greater than the minimum transmission loss.

From the foregoing it is seen that a spectrum characteristic showing measured power per unit band as a function of frequency may indicate a power per unit band as being associated with a given frequency when there is no actual energy component within several cycles per second of that frequency. On the basis of the method described for measuring power per unit band, however, any computation of power made by integrating the power per unit band shown by the spectrum characteristic thus derived will give the correct value for any band likely to be encountered in practice.

When the intensity per unit band of some given acoustic wave is measured as a function of frequency it is often found to be proportional to some power of the frequency. In this case the ratio of two intensities per unit band is equal to the ratio of the two corresponding frequencies raised to the power in question. We may thus write

$$\frac{J_b}{J_a} = \left(\frac{f_b}{f_a}\right)^n \qquad (2B-21)$$

If we are to express this change in relative intensity per unit band in terms of a transmission differential it will be convenient to express the change in relative frequency in terms of frequency logits. The number of frequency logits equivalent to a given frequency ratio is, by the definition of the logit,

$$M = \text{lgt} \ (f_b/f_a) \qquad (2B-22)$$

where

M = the number of frequency logits equivalent to some given frequency ratio, or to some given change in relative frequency (fl)

f_b/f_a = the given change in relative frequency (a numeric)

If, for the condition specified by Eq. (2B-21), the spectrum level, in decibels relative to a reference intensity per unit band, is plotted against frequency, in frequency logits relative to a reference frequency, the resulting characteristic will be a straight line. Its slope will be

$$\frac{N}{M} = \frac{\text{lgt} \ (J_b/J_a)}{\text{lgt} \ (f_b/f_a)} = n \quad \text{db/fl} \qquad (2B-23)$$

This graphical method is probably the simplest method of determining the power of the frequency to which the intensity per unit band is proportional.

It is common practice to give the slope of a spectrum level characteristic as the change in level, or change in relative intensity, in decibels, accompanying a change in relative frequency of one octave. The number of octaves equivalent to some given band ratio, f_b/f_a, is

$$M_{oct} = \log_2 \frac{f_b}{f_a} = \frac{\log_{10} (f_b/f_a)}{\log_{10} 2}$$

$$= \frac{\log_{10} (f_b/f_a)}{0.301+}$$

$$= \frac{\text{lgt} \ (f_b/f_a)}{3.01+} \quad \text{oct} \quad (2B-24)$$

The relation between frequency logits and octaves is established at once by comparing Eqs. (2B-22) and (2B-24). This shows that

$$\text{lgt} \ (f_b/f_a) = M = 3.01 M_{oct} \quad \text{fl} \quad (2B-25)$$

One octave, in other words, is equal to 3.01+ frequency logits. By substituting Eq. (2B-25) into Eq. (2B-23) it is found that the slope of a spectrum level characteristic in decibels per octave is

$$\frac{N}{M_{oct}} = 3.01 \ \frac{N}{M} = 3.01n \quad \text{db/oct} \quad (2B-26)$$

For the special case where intensity per unit band is proportional to some power of the frequency the intensity for some specified frequency band may be computed from the intensity per unit band at a single frequency and the slope of the spectrum level characteristic. Since, in this case, the intensity per unit band at any frequency, f_x, may be written in terms of a known intensity per unit band, J_k, at some other frequency, f_k, as $J_x = J_k(f_x/f_k)^n$ the intensity for a given band may be written as

$$I = \int_{f_a}^{f_b} J_x \, df = \frac{J_k}{f_k{}^n} \int_{f_a}^{f_b} (f_x)^n \, df$$

$$= \frac{J_k}{(f_k)^n} \frac{(f_b)^{n+1} - (f_a)^{n+1}}{n+1} \quad (\text{when } n \neq -1)$$

$$= J_k f_k \log_e (f_b/f_a) \quad (\text{when } n = -1) \quad (2B-27)$$

where

I = the intensity of the acoustic energy in a given frequency band (watt/cm²)

J_k = the known intensity per unit band of this energy at some specified frequency (joule/cm²·cyc)

$f_k =$ the specified frequency at which the intensity per unit band is known (cyc/sec)

$f_a =$ the lower frequency limit of the given band (cyc/sec)

$f_b =$ the upper frequency limit of the given band (cyc/sec)

$n =$ the exponent indicating the power of the frequency to which the intensity per unit band is proportional throughout the entire region under consideration, or the constant slope of the spectrum level characteristic (db/fl)

In the above equation the frequency of known intensity per unit band, f_k, may be any frequency within the portion of the spectrum for which the slope of the spectrum level characteristic is n decibels per frequency logit. It may, therefore, be the geometric mean frequency of the band in question. By means of Eq. (2B-21) we may write $J_k/(f_k)^n = J_{gm}/(f_{gm})^n$ where J_{gm} is the intensity per unit band for the geometric mean frequency, f_{gm}. Since the intensity per unit band J_k and both frequencies are known, the intensity per unit band J_{gm} is also known. We may also let $f_b = Kf_{gm}$ and $f_a = (1/K)f_{gm}$, where K is the square root of the band ratio, f_b/f_a. If these substitutions are made in Eq. (2B-27) there results

$$I = J_{gm}f_{gm}\left[\frac{K^{2(n+1)} - 1}{(n+1)K^{n+1}}\right] \quad \text{(when } n \neq -1\text{)}$$

$$= J_{gm}f_{gm}[2 \log_e K] \quad \text{(when } n = -1\text{)} \quad \text{(2B-28)}$$

The width of the frequency band for which the intensity is to be determined may be written as

$$\Delta f = f_b - f_a = \left[\frac{K^2 - 1}{K}\right]f_{gm} \quad \text{(2B-29)}$$

Substituting the value of f_{gm} derived from this last equation into Eq. (2B-28), we obtain

when $n \neq -1$

$$I = J_{gm}(\Delta f)\left[\frac{K}{K^2 - 1}\frac{K^{2(n+1)} - 1}{(n+1)K^{n+1}}\right]$$

and when $n = -1$

$$I = J_{gm}(\Delta f)\left[\frac{K}{K^2 - 1}2 \log_e K\right] \quad \text{(2B-30)}$$

These equations show that, in the special case where the intensity per unit band is proportional to some power of the frequency, the intensity for a given band is obtained as the product of (1) the intensity per unit band at the geometric mean frequency of the band, (2) the width of the band, and (3) a dimensionless correction factor. When the slope of the spectrum level characteristic, in decibels per frequency logit, is $n = 0$ or $n = -2$ the correction factor reduces to unity. In these two particular examples of the special case here under consideration, then, the intensity is given directly as the product of the intensity per unit band at the geometric mean frequency of the band in question and the width of this band.

Since the correction factor appearing in Eq. (2B-30) is dimensionless the product of this factor and the actual band width has the dimensions of a band width. This product is, in fact, the width of a frequency band of such magnitude that if it were occupied by energy having a constant intensity per unit band equal, at any frequency, to the actual intensity per unit band at the geometric mean frequency of the band in question, the intensity of this uniformly distributed energy would be the same as the intensity of the energy actually occupying the given frequency band. The product of the width of the actual frequency band and the dimensionless **band correction factor** may be described as the **equivalent band width** of energy having a specified distribution throughout a specified frequency band. This equivalent band width is not to be confused with the effective band width defined earlier in this article. Effective band width is a property of an energy transmission system; equivalent band width is a property of the energy being transmitted.

The concept of equivalent band width is, of course, applicable to electric waves as well as to acoustic waves. In the case of electric waves the power of the energy in a given frequency band would be given as the product of the power per unit band at the geometric mean frequency of that band and the equivalent band width computed from the actual band width and the band correction factor.

The level of the intensity given by Eq. (2B-30) may be written in terms of the spectrum level at the geometric mean frequency of the frequency band in question and the equivalent band width as

$$L_{\Delta f} = L_{gm} + \text{lgt}\frac{\Delta f}{(\Delta f)_0} + \text{lgt}\,\mathcal{F}(K, n) \quad \text{(2B-31)}$$

53

where

$L_{\Delta f}$= the band level of the energy in a specified frequency band throughout which the spectrum level characteristic has a constant slope (db//1 watt/cm^2)

L_{gm}= the spectrum level of the energy at the geometric mean frequency of the specified frequency band (db//1 joule/cm$^2 \cdot$ cyc)

$\Delta f = f_b - f_a$
= the width of the specified frequency band, for which f_a and f_b are the limiting frequencies (cyc/sec)

$(\Delta f)_0 = 1$ cyc/sec
= the reference band width

$\mathfrak{F}(K, n)$= the band correction factor, applicable to the given spectrum level characteristic and band ratio, appearing in Eq. (2B-30) (a numeric)

n= the constant slope of the spectrum level characteristic (db/fl)

$K = \sqrt{f_b/f_a}$
= a constant
(a numeric)

It is evident from this equation that the quantity lgt $\mathfrak{F}(K, n)$ is the level differential measuring the amount by which the actual band level exceeds tne band level which would be computed on the assumption of a constant spectrum level equal to the spectrum level at the geometric mean frequency of the given band. Values of this level differential, in decibels, are shown in Fig. 2B-5. This differential is plotted as a function of the slope, n, of the spectrum level characteristic with band ratio, $f_b/f_a = K^2$, as a parameter.

The following important conclusion may be drawn from Eq. (2B-31). If the intensity per unit band of some complex wave increases in such manner that the slope of its spectrum level characteristic remains unchanged the increase in spectrum level at any frequency, within the limits for which this condition is satisfied, is numerically the same as the increase in band level for any assigned band within these same limits.

Whenever the members of a series of frequency bands have equal band ratios the bands are said to be **proportional bands**. A **proportional band level characteristic** is one in which the band levels

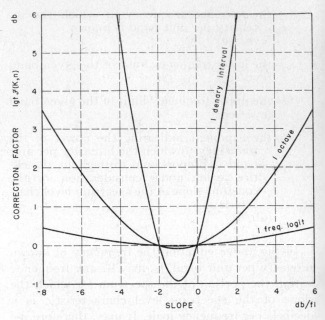

Fig. 2B-5. Band Level Correction. The level differential to be added to the band level corresponding to the intensity, computed for a given frequency band on the assumption that the intensity throughout the band is the same as that at its geometric mean frequency, to obtain the true band level. Values of this correction are plotted as a function of the slope of the spectrum level characteristics, with band ratio as a parameter.

of a series of proportional bands are plotted against their geometric mean frequencies, or against their upper or lower boundary frequencies.

When energy having a spectrum level characteristic of constant slope is subdivided into proportional bands the term appearing in brackets in Eq. (2B-28) will be constant. The intensity in any of the proportional bands is therefore

$$I = k_1 J_{\text{gm}} f_{\text{gm}} \qquad (2B-32)$$

But under these restricted conditions $J_{\text{gm}} = k_2(f_{\text{gm}})^n$. Consequently, the band intensity is

$$I = k_1 k_2 (f_{\text{gm}})^{n+1} \qquad (2B-33)$$

This demonstrates that if the spectrum level characteristic applying to a given energy transmission has a constant slope any proportional band level characteristic applying to the same transmission will also have a constant slope and that this constant slope will be 1 db/fl greater than the slope of the spectrum level characteristic. If slopes are given in decibels per octave, the slope of the proportional band level characteristic will be approximately 3 db/oct greater than the slope of the spectrum level characteristic.

2B-5 Equivalent Spectrum Level Characteristic

The assumption of a spectrum level characteristic of constant slope is convenient and proper when dealing with nominal outputs of representative types of sound sources. For any given sound source the spectrum may often vary with frequency in such manner that this assumption is unwarranted. It is then evident that the information obtained by measurements of the energy in bands having band ratios of the order of one frequency logit or more will be inadequate for plotting a true spectrum level characteristic. An **equivalent spectrum level characteristic** may, however, be used to represent this information.

An example of acoustic energy having a distribution with respect to frequency of the character in question is described graphically in Fig. 2B-6. Here the intensity per unit band of the acoustic energy is plotted as a function of frequency. If the spectrum is divided into a number of bands, as shown by the vertical lines, it is obvious that throughout any one band the intensity per unit band is rarely proportional to a constant

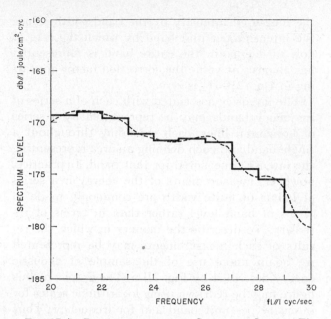

FIG. 2B-7. REPRESENTATION OF SPECTRUM LEVEL. The equivalent spectrum level characteristic giving the same band levels, in the bands defined by the line segments, as those corresponding to the intensities per unit band shown in Fig. 2B-6.

power of the frequency. It is certainly true that a constant power of the frequency cannot be assigned to the rate of flow of energy in any one band on the basis of measurements of the rates of flow in adjoining bands. We may not, therefore, compute the true intensity per unit band at any one frequency without more information than is provided by measurements of the intensity associated with bands of the width indicated.

The intensity associated with any one band is represented graphically by the area bounded by the curve showing intensity per unit band, the verticals through the limiting frequencies, and the frequency axis. There are an infinite number of curves for which this area would have the same value as for the true, but unknown, curve. Any one of these curves represents the limited information obtained by a single intensity measurement as correctly as any other. We may, therefore, represent this information by any of these curves which we find convenient. For many purposes a straight horizontal line, corresponding to a constant intensity per unit band throughout the band in question, is a logical choice. This line is drawn between the limiting frequencies of the band at such an intensity per unit band that the area under it is the same as the area under the true characteristic between the same limits. This intensity per unit band is computed by dividing

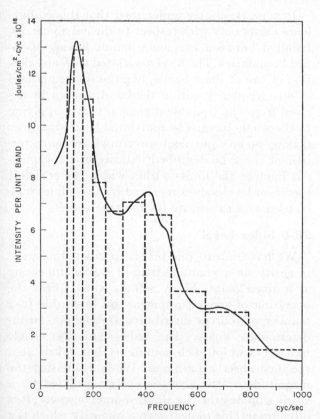

FIG. 2B-6. REPRESENTATION OF INTENSITY PER UNIT BAND. A characteristic showing intensity per unit band as a function of frequency for a sound source having a continuous spectrum.

the measured intensity by the band width. Since the intensity per unit band by which the rate of flow of energy in the entire band is represented has a constant value the correction factor appearing in Eq. (2B-31) is zero.

The intensity associated with each of a series of frequency bands may be represented by a series of horizontal lines, each extending throughout a single band and each defining an area representing the intensity measured for that band. In practice, however, measurements of the energy in a series of bands of finite width are commonly made in terms of band level rather than in terms of intensity. To describe the manner in which the results of such measurements may be represented we again make use of the sample of acoustic energy described by Fig. 2B-6. The graphs of this figure may be redrawn using logarithmic scales for intensity per unit band and for frequency. Thus drawn, proportional bands are represented by scale increments of equal length. The frequency scale may, in other words, be laid off in frequency logits. The characteristic derived from the true, but unknown, values of intensity per unit band is the true, but also unknown, spectrum level characteristic. This characteristic is shown in Fig. 2B-7 as a dotted line. For each band a constant value of spectrum level is shown by a solid horizontal line. These constant spectrum levels are obtained from the corresponding constant intensities per unit band previously plotted on Fig. 2B-6. Any of these constant intensities per unit band is the quotient obtained by dividing a measured intensity by a band width. When logarithmic values are used, therefore, the corresponding value of spectrum level may be obtained directly from the corresponding measured value of band level by subtracting the number of frequency logits giving the width of the band relative to a band of unit width.

When the frequency spectrum is divided into logit bands, as in Fig. 2B-7, in such manner that the lower limiting frequency of the first band is 1 cyc/sec the seventh band has a width of approximately 1 cyc/sec. The conversion factor for this seventh band is lgt(5.0119 − 3.9811) = 0.1317 fl. This factor increases by exactly one frequency logit for each interval above this seventh interval and decreases by exactly one frequency logit for each interval below it. The value of the factor for any interval is, therefore, computed by subtracting the number 6.8683 from the logarithm to the

base $10^{0.1}$ of the upper limiting frequency of the interval. For calculations where it is permissible to assume that the limiting frequencies are given by the American Standard Preferred Numbers of the 10-series the conversion factor for the seventh interval may be assumed to be zero. All other factors are then derived by subtracting the number seven from the logarithms to the base $10^{0.1}$ of the upper limiting frequencies. These logarithms will always be integers, by virtue of the manner in which the interval boundaries are defined.

When logarithmic scales are used, as in Fig. 2B-7, the areas under the constant spectrum level line and under the true spectrum level line, for any band, are not necessarily equal. The value of constant spectrum level does, nevertheless, lead to the true value of band level as accurately as would the value given by the true spectrum level characteristic. Insofar as the energy associated with each of the specified bands is concerned, therefore, the series of horizontal lines representing the constant spectrum levels associated with these bands may be described as an equivalent spectrum level characteristic.

It must be clearly understood that this equivalence exists only with respect to the energy as distributed between frequency bands having specified boundaries. The level associated with any portion of one of these bands, like the spectrum level at any frequency within the band, cannot be derived from the equivalent constant level applying to the whole band. The individual horizontal lines making up an equivalent spectrum level characteristic of the type described indicate in a conspicuous manner the limits within which the constant spectrum level values reported by these lines may be used as a substitute for the true values.

2B-6 Index Level

We have, up to this point, considered acoustic intensity as a characteristic of waves appearing at a given point. Many sounds which affect the operation of sonar equipment are often due to a number of sources distributed throughout an indeterminate space. The only significant single measurement of such sounds is that taken at a specified observation point. When evaluating the magnitude of the acoustic energy radiated by a single ship or other localized source, however, it is often preferable to deal with a quantity which is a unique measure of the magnitude of that energy, and from which its effect at many specified points may be determined. For this purpose the **index level** of a sound is defined as the level which that sound would have at a point one yard from the point of its apparent origin, assuming such a point to exist, if it were generated at this apparent source point but produced the same effects at distant points as the effects it actually does produce. This index level is readily deduced from measurements made at a distance from an actual source, using known or assumed relations between intensity and distance to compute what the intensity would be at a point nearer the source. The method for making this computation will be discussed in Art. 3A-1. If the source is of considerable extent, as in the case of a battleship, it may well be that there is no single point at which the actual acoustic intensity reaches the magnitude corresponding to this computed index level. This in no way lessens the utility of the concept of index level. It suggests, however, that the data on which its computation is based should be obtained at a sufficient distance from the source to justify the assumption that it behaves as a point source.

2-C SOUND WAVES FOUND IN THE SEA
2C-1 Noise

Traditionally the vast region beneath the surface of the ocean is understood to offer the ultimate in quiet. Actually this legend is not supported by fact; sound levels found even in the most secluded parts of the ocean are comparable to those existing in a quiet garden.

Many of the sounds present in the waters of the ocean are produced without relevant purpose. They may result from natural phenomena, or from the activities of marine creatures. They may also result from operations of men which are undertaken for reasons other than their generation. In this latter case they may be produced unintentionally or unavoidably. Sounds of these various types are often made up of many components the magnitudes of which vary, with time, in a random manner independently of each other. They sometimes exhibit more or less regularly recurrent variations which may be identified with some repetitive process. Although it is possible to obtain information from many of these sounds, intelligible characteristics are not voluntarily imparted to them for the purpose of establishing communication. Such sounds are generally referred to as **noise.**

Many formal definitions for noise have been proposed by acoustical engineers. It is, for example, often described as an "undesired sound." To determine whether or not a sound is desired, however, the interests and intentions of the listener must first be established. The word "noise," like many others in our daily speech, has a number of well understood meanings. Several of these have acquired technical status as well. No attempt will be made here to restrict, by a precisely formulated definition, the significance to be attached to this word.

2C-2 Signals and Interference—Signal Differential

Every application of sonar involves making some kind of an observation on a sound wave. In some cases it is sufficient merely to detect the presence of a sound wave identified with a given source. In others it is desired to determine the magnitude of a given wave, or to establish the nature of its time variation. Any sound wave upon which it is required to make an observation of any kind is known as a **signal wave,** or more often, simply as a **signal.** This designation applies to that portion of the response of any component of a sonar system resulting directly from an acoustic signal wave as well as to the acoustic wave itself. We may thus speak of the electric signal wave generated in the driving circuits of echo-ranging equipment, or of the electric signals in the various components of a receiving system.

In every application of sonar, also, there will be found waves which, occurring simultaneously with the signal, impair the accuracy or the reliability of the desired observation. Sometimes the damage is so slight as to be negligible; sometimes it may be disastrous. It is always troublesome to those attempting to observe a signal wave and, conversely, advantageous to those who deplore the observation. Any wave which would interfere with an attempted observation of a signal is known as **interference.** As before, this designation applies to the response of any component of the system as well as to the acoustic energy in the water. It may thus be understood to include electrical disturbances in receiving circuits and airborne sounds heard simultaneously with the signal as delivered by a loud-speaker or by headphones.

Many of the sounds present in the sea may be considered either as interference or as signals, depending on the interests of a possible observer. The noise made by a vessel, for example, constitutes a **noise signal** when sonar equipment is used for its detection by direct listening; it immediately becomes interference when an attempt is made to determine the range of the vessel by timing an echo-signal transmission. We shall, for this reason, classify underwater sounds on the basis of both source and significance.

Signal energy usually arrives at a given receiving point in the form of plane waves. The intensity deduced from the response of a hydrophone of known sensitivity is, therefore, the true intensity of these waves. Interference, on the other hand, usually arrives from many sources and over many paths. Some of these sources are often so near the receiving point that the assumption of plane waves is not permissible. The intensity of interfering acoustic energy deduced from the response of a given hydrophone is, consequently, the equivalent plane wave intensity defined in Art. 2A-9. This method of expressing the magnitude of interfering acoustic energy has the advantage that it permits a direct and significant comparison with the magnitude of signal energy. The intensity of acoustic interference is thus understood to be the equivalent plane wave intensity as measured by a pressure-sensitive hydrophone having a response which is independent of the direction of the path along which acoustic energy arrives at the hydrophone. The transmission level of interference computed from its equivalent plane wave intensity is usually spoken of as the **noise level.**

The magnitude of a signal wave relative to the magnitude of a wave which interferes with its reception may properly be described as the **signal-to-interference ratio.** It has long been the custom in communication engineering, however, to speak of this quantity as the **signal-to-noise ratio.** This term has been retained by sonar engineers, even though the signal, as well as the interference, often falls within the class of sounds which are commonly regarded as noise. In this book, signal-to-noise ratio will be expressed quantitatively in terms of acoustic intensities, or intensities per unit band, when dealing with acoustic waves in water and in terms of electric powers, or powers per unit band, when dealing with electric waves in some component of a sonar system. The level differential expressing the value of a signal-to-noise ratio will be designated as a **signal differential.**

In every application of sonar the signal-to-noise ratio of the ultimate response of the system has some critical value below which observations of

the signal are unsatisfactory. This ratio is a significant constant, to be taken carefully into account in the design and operation of all sonar equipment. Its value is not fixed but depends upon many factors which cannot profitably be discussed apart from the detailed consideration of specific applications. In general, it depends upon the nature of the observation to be made. It is common experience during direct-listening operations, for example, to find that a signal of pronounced rhythmic character may be detected at a much lower signal-to-noise ratio than can a signal more nearly approaching random noise in character. This is analogous to the experience, familiar to everyone, of being able to hear and to understand speech in a location, such as a factory or subway train, where the intensity of interfering noise is high compared to the intensity of the speech sounds. When indicating or recording instruments are used their characteristics frequently determine the minimum tolerable value of signal-to-noise ratio.

In discussing signal-to-interference ratios we do not necessarily include under interference all energy, in the form of acoustic or electric waves other than the signal, which may be present at any given point in the water or in the sonar equipment. Rather, the concept of interference is here limited to those waves which would, if of sufficient intensity, interfere with the observation of the signal. As with the minimum tolerable value of signal-to-interference ratio, the interference effective at any point depends upon the nature of the signal and upon the characteristics of the equipment. If, for example, the components of some signal fall within a narrow band of frequencies the response of the receiving circuits, or of the final indicating instrument, may be restricted to this same narrow band. Waves having other frequencies would, under these conditions, cause no confusing response and hence would not be considered as interference. Similarly, the use of a directional hydrophone limits the response of the system to waves arriving along bearings close to that of the signal source; waves from other directions are then prevented from contributing to the interference. It may thus be said that selective circuits or directional hydrophones have the effect of improving the signal-to-noise ratio. Other artifices, which will be considered later, may be used for this purpose in special circumstances.

In a system containing an electroacoustic transducer for receiving acoustic signals interference may enter at any point. Given such a system, let us assume that the transmission level of the interference entering at some point following the transducer greatly exceeds the transmission level of the interference at that point due to energy entering at some other point. The signal differential at this point is then the difference between the level of the signal and the level of this entering interference. This signal differential may be increased by amplification. Since this requires that the level of the signal be increased without increasing the level of the interference by an equal amount, this amplification must be introduced between the point at which the interference enters and the transducer in which the signal assumes its electric form. Any increase in signal level obtained by amplification thus introduced is accompanied by an equal increase in the level of any interference due to energy present at the amplifier input. If this amplification is increased sufficiently this amplified interference, having been transmitted to the point in question, will reach a level equal to the level of the interference entering at that point. Further increase in amplification will raise the levels of both signal and interference, and will be accompanied by no further increase in signal differential. The maximum value to which signal differential may be raised by amplification is thus seen to be the value existing at the input terminals of the amplifier.

Since it is possible to connect an amplifier directly to the electric terminals of a hydrophone it is evident that amplification may be used to improve signal differential with respect to any interference entering a signal receiving system after the hydrophone. Amplification cannot increase the value of signal differential above that existing in the hydrophone. Interference in the hydrophone may be due either to electrical disturbances in the hydrophone or to its response to acoustic interference entering from the water. When the interference in a hydrophone is due to self-generated electric noise an improvement in signal differential may be effected only by increasing the hydrophone response to acoustic waves or by reducing internal disturbances. Signal differential may be improved by improved hydrophone design until, as in the case of increasing amplification, a limiting value is reached at which the signal differential within the transducer is equal to the signal differential of the energy received from the preceding portion of the transmission system.

We thus see that the signal-to-noise ratio in the water is a limiting value which cannot be raised either by improving the hydrophone sensitivity or by increasing the amount of amplification. It is not infrequently depreciated by equipment which is improperly built or inadequately maintained. It is gratifying to note that the sensitivities of modern hydrophones are so high that voltages generated in response to the minimum acoustic interference likely to be encountered exceed those due to internal electrical disturbances. The performance of sonar systems, therefore, as measured by the minimum signal level in the water at which reliable observations are possible is, in the final analysis, fixed by the magnitudes of other waves in the water. For this reason it is important that we examine with some care all sound waves likely to be found in the water.

2C-3 Thermal Noise

There is no such thing as absolutely quiet water. Even if it were possible to isolate a sample of water completely from all external influences there would still be minute movements of the molecules, due to thermal agitation, accompanied by the release of acoustic energy. This molecular agitation, which is proportional to the absolute temperature of the water, is spoken of as **thermal noise.** It is not propagated from a definite source but comes into existence throughout the entire body of the medium. It does not, in consequence, affect a hydrophone in the same manner as does the energy of acoustic waves which are propagated along definite paths. The apparent intensity of thermal noise, as it affects the performance of sonar equipment, is a function of the constants of the specific hydrophone used; it cannot be reported as existing at some definite level in the water independently of these constants. For this reason, it will be more appropriate to discuss the quantitative effects of thermal noise in the water when we come to consider the characteristic properties of hydrophones. For the present it will be sufficient to note that the apparent spectrum level of thermal noise is so low, as compared with noises due to other causes, that it may generally be disregarded. It is, in fact, significant at this point because it establishes a lower limit to noise in water below which it is impossible to pass.

2C-4 Cavitation Noise

The upper limit to the normal behavior of water as an acoustic medium is determined by the fact that when the instantaneous value of acoustic pressure exceeds the static pressure the resultant pressure becomes negative for a portion of each cycle and the integrity of the water is destroyed. The production of small voids, or cavities, in the water which occurs under this condition is known as **cavitation.** At the surface the acoustic intensity corresponding to the equality between static and acoustic pressures is approximately $\frac{1}{3}$ watt/cm². Although this intensity is far above the range of signal and noise levels usually found throughout a body of water, it is less than the apparent intensity near the surface of a transducer driven at high power. Actually it has been found possible, under certain conditions, to radiate more acoustic power from a vibrating surface than the amount corresponding to the cavitation pressure. In general, however, cavitation may be looked upon as establishing an upper limit of acoustic pressure beyond which the water departs from the normal behavior thus far considered.

Cavitation is of importance in the practical application of sonar quite apart from any limitations which it may impose on the intensity of transmitted signals. The tiny cavities formed in water during cavitation are initially evacuated. They occur, moreover, in water which usually contains more or less dissolved air, the solubility of which depends upon the pressure. The suddenly reduced pressure accompanying the formation of these cavities is so low that it is certain to be less than the pressure for which the water is saturated by the air already in solution. Air must, therefore, immediately escape into each cavity. A certain amount of water vapor also enters at the same time. When the total pressure in the neighborhood of a cavity resumes a positive value the cavity collapses to the point where the pressure of the acquired air is the same as the hydrostatic pressure. The result is an air bubble which may remain in the water for some time. The partial collapse is accompanied by the release of acoustic energy. In other words, cavitation is a noisy process. It is, in fact, one of the prominent components of ship sounds and of the disturbing noise developed by the motion of hydrophones through the water. We shall meet it frequently, both as interference and as signal.

2C-5 General Water Noise

When noise in the sea is due to a number of sources, or when the sources are not easily identified, it is sometimes spoken of as **ambient noise.** This broad classification often includes noises due to movement of the water, to marine life, or to human enterprise. Ambient noise is generally characterized by the fact that it does not appear to have any clearly defined directional distribution with respect to the listening point, nor does it show any marked change in intensity with change in the position of the listening point.

The minimum ambient noise of practical significance is that due to movement of the water itself. The term **water noise** will hereafter be used to designate acoustic energy resulting primarily from this cause. General water noise may be generated in a number of ways. The breaking of surf on a shore may produce sufficient noise to be heard for several miles. In shallow water tidal currents may cause small stones or pebbles on the bottom to move sufficiently to create appreciable sound. The disturbance of sand on a beach, even when the waves do not break, produces a sound in the water which may be detectable for several hundred yards. When direct-listening operations are conducted on a vessel lying to at a distance from shore the predominant noise is generally that due to waves breaking against the hull. Action with or against foreign bodies is, however, not necessary for the development of water noise. The impact of masses of water with each other, occurring whenever there is a breaking of wave crests, and the escape of air bubbles, trapped as a result of wave action, are sufficient to produce water noise.

In many cases it is as difficult to identify the source of noise found in the water beneath the surface of the sea as it sometimes is in the air above. Moreover, it is not surprising to find that general water noise varies considerably in character and in magnitude, both from place to place, and from time to time. In the deep water of the open sea, however, the effect of indeterminate factors is reduced to a minimum and it is reasonable to assume that the sounds there observed are due solely to disturbed water. Noise levels measured in deep water remote from the shore may, in fact, be considered as representing the lower limit likely to be found in practice.

Measurements of this basic water noise in a wide variety of locations, and under varying conditions, have yielded statistical information as to its magnitude. The resulting averages, as might be expected, have been found to vary with the state of the sea. Values for the spectrum level of water noise as a function of frequency and sea state are shown in Fig. 2C-1. These values are those generally accepted as nominal values; they represent a compact statistical summary of the results of many measurements.

It is, of course, true that sea state is not a quantity which may be measured with either precision or accuracy. Each value of sea state represents a range of conditions. The boundaries between these conditions are usually defined in terms of wave height. The spectrum levels for any sea state, therefore, may lie anywhere between values

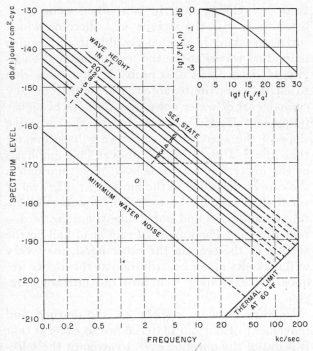

FIG. 2C-1. SPECTRUM LEVELS OF WATER NOISE. The spectrum levels of water noise giving the intensity per unit band as a function of frequency, with sea state and wave height as parameters.

shown on the diagram by the lines identified by the limiting wave heights for that sea state. In any single situation the spectrum level actually encountered may fall outside these limiting values by as much as five decibels, or even more.

Values of spectrum level lower than those shown by the lowest curve are rarely encountered. This curve, then, may be considered as representing **minimum water noise** conditions. As such, it gives significant reference levels against which to compare other noise levels.

It is evident from these curves, since they are parallel, that the slope of the spectrum level characteristic of water noise, considered as a function of frequency, is independent of sea state. This slope does, in fact, appear to be more nearly constant than would be expected from the variations

in spectrum level observed under conditions which would otherwise be described as similar. The phrase generally used in stating the value of this slope is "minus five decibels per octave." Translating from octaves to frequency logits, in order that a single logarithmic base may be used for all quantities, this becomes "minus five thirds decibel per frequency logit." From this it is at once evident that the spectrum intensity of water noise decreases as the 5/3 power of the frequency.

This constancy of the slope of the spectrum level characteristic of water noise simplifies the computation of water noise band levels. When Eq. (2B-31) is used for this purpose it is evident that the quantity n appearing in the band correction factor is constant. This factor then becomes a unique function of the relative width of the frequency band. The supplementary curve on the diagram of Fig. 2C-1 gives values of this correction factor, in decibels, as a function of relative band width. These values, it must be remembered, apply only to energy having a spectrum level characteristic the slope of which is $-5/3$ db/fl.

The curve marked "Thermal Limit" on the diagram of Fig. 2C-1 represents the limit beyond which it is impossible to measure acoustic energy in water. The significance of this curve may be explained, for our present purposes, in terms of an ideal hydrophone having a response independent of the direction of propagation of the acoustic energy reaching it, and having an electric system generating no electric voltage due to internal thermal effects. For such an ideal hydrophone the power per unit band, at any frequency, generated by thermal agitation of the water at the temperature indicated would be the same as that generated by plane waves of acoustic energy having, at the same frequency, the intensity per unit band shown by the curve. The method used in computing the values given by this curve will be discussed in Chapter 4.

From the data given by Fig. 2C-1 the spectrum level of water noise at a given frequency, or the band level of water noise for a given frequency band, may be obtained as a function of wave height. A curve showing the band level of water noise for the frequency band between 100 cyc/sec and 10 kc/sec, plotted as a function of wave height, is given in Fig. 2C-2. It has been found possible to deduce the sea state, and hence, to a rough approximation, the wave height, from observed values of wind velocity. It is therefore possible to relate the magnitude of water noise

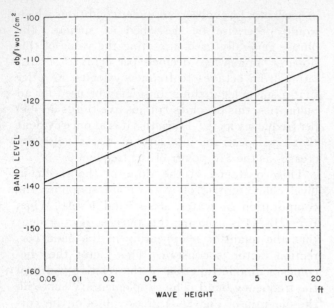

FIG. 2C-2. EFFECT OF WAVE HEIGHT ON WATER NOISE. The statistical average of the band level of noise due to wave action, in the 0.1 to 10 kc/sec band, as a function of the height of the waves, as measured from trough to crest.

with wind velocity. A curve showing this relation, for the band between 100 cyc/sec and 10 kc/sec, is given in Fig. 2C-3.

On the basis of information thus far obtained, it appears that both the magnitude and the frequency characteristic of water noise is independent of the depth at which the observation is made. This applies to depths up to about 300 ft. The

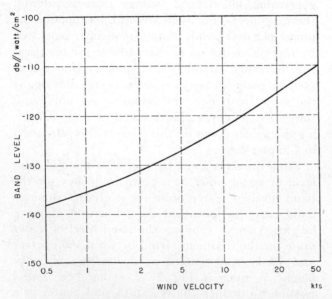

FIG. 2C-3. EFFECT OF WIND VELOCITY ON WATER NOISE. The statistical average of the band level of noise due to wave action, in the 0.1 to 10 kc/sec band, as a function of wind velocity.

quality of the noise does, however, vary somewhat with depth. As the hydrophone is lowered the sounds of individual waves, which can be separately identified near the surface, merge into a more nearly continuous sound. At the same time there is a noticeable decrease in short time variations from the average noise level.

In shallow water, or near shore, noise due to movement of the water will probably exceed the levels just indicated. This will certainly be true if there is breaking surf. In fact, when using sonic listening gear in the vicinity of a shore on which surf is breaking it is often possible to distinguish individual waves above the level of general background noise. It is also probable that noise due to surf will contribute more to the lower frequency components of water noise than to those of higher frequency. Under such conditions the negative slope of the spectrum level curve will be greater than the 5/3 db/fl quoted above. This emphasis of the lower frequencies is even more marked in the case of noise due to the movement of gravel or small stones on the bottom. This produces a distinct rumbling sound not unlike the noise of distant thunder. The impact of rain or of hail on the surface of the sea, on the other hand, may very well make its major contribution at the higher frequencies, extending well into the ultrasonic region.

Conditions with respect to the nature and movement of bottom material are so diverse that it is out of the question even to attempt the selection of a statistical average for the magnitude of the resultant water noise. The situation with respect to rain is somewhat more susceptible to quantitative evaluation although, unfortunately, little statistical data is yet available. In one case reported, a moderately heavy rainfall appears to have raised the level, in the band between 0.1 and 10 kc/sec, some 20 db above the value given in Fig. 2C-2.

In the case of the impact of waves against the hull of a vessel attempting to operate listening gear, or against a buoy or other rigging from which a hydrophone may be suspended, the major contributions to water noise generally appear at the lower end of the frequency spectrum. In many cases, however, particularly where a hollow metal buoy is involved, there may be a pronounced emphasis on frequencies in a restricted band. In such cases the signal-to-noise ratio may be markedly improved by the use of circuits which suppress these predominating components.

2C-6 Noise Due to Marine Life

Fish and other forms of marine life share with birds, beasts, and insects the aptitude to create sonic disturbances in the medium wherein they dwell. Curiously, although this fact had long been common knowledge to fishermen and to biologists, its announcement to workers in the field of acoustics was greeted with some astonishment. It is now known that **fish noise** is the limiting interference to the operation of sonar equipment in many locations.

Small fish known as croakers are prolific contributors to this form of subaqueous noise. These fish are representatives of a variety classified as drumfish. Each is equipped with a gas-filled bladder on which it beats with a vibrating muscle. The technique consists in striking a series of ten to fifteen blows at a rate of six or eight blows per second. This sequence, during normal operation, is repeated at intervals of five to ten seconds. Whenever an individual performer approaches close to a hydrophone the sounds, as reproduced in the air-borne form by a loud-speaker, are suggestive of a persistent woodpecker.

The sonic output of a single croaker is not large. However, in locations which appeal to them they congregate in large numbers. In Chesapeake Bay, for example, it has been estimated that during the summer months there may be as many as 300 million at one time. When the members of a group such as this join their efforts, the utility of neighboring sonar equipment is seriously impaired. The sounds then coming from a loud-speaker resemble in character those from a swarm of locusts. They might be described as a throbbing roar through which individual drum rolls are occasionally detected.

An interesting feature of this percussion concert is its time schedule. It customarily begins, at a low level, shortly before dusk and becomes progressively stronger as darkness approaches. It reaches its maximum level generally within an hour or so after sunset, remains at this level for another hour or so, and then declines at about the same rate as that at which it formerly increased. By midnight, or shortly thereafter, it has either dropped below the level of general water noise or has ceased entirely. At its peak the level for the 0.1 to 10 kc/sec band, has frequently been measured as −74 db//1 watt/cm². Normal water noise in the same locations would be expected to have a level approximately 65 db less than this.

A reduction in signal-to-noise ratio of as much as 65 db is a serious handicap to the protection of harbor entrances by sonar equipment. The situation is somewhat relieved, however, when we come to consider the frequency characteristic of the disturbance. The curves of Fig. 2C-4 show the spectrum level characteristics of noise due to croakers, at the peak of their daily activity, as observed in Chesapeake Bay during May and July 1942. The reasons for the differences between these two observations may be left to the biologists; our interest lies in the fact that on the basis of this data a method by which signal differential may be improved

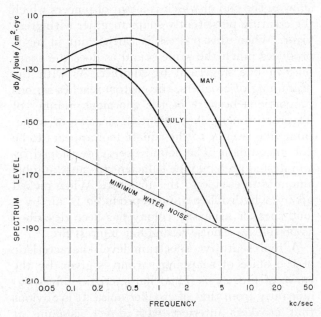

FIG. 2C-4. CROAKER NOISE. Spectrum level characteristic of noise due to croakers, as found in Chesapeake Bay.

is at once apparent. Although we have not yet examined the spectra of ship sounds we may anticipate a later article to the extent of noting that the slope of the spectrum level characteristics, at the higher frequencies, although negative, like croaker noise, has a much lower numerical value. Because of this it was found possible to effect a most worthwhile improvement in signal differential by the use of electric circuits discriminating against the lower frequencies. This was strikingly demonstrated by one test in which a phonograph recording was made of the sounds received during the passage of a freighter over the known position of a bottom-mounted hydrophone. This record was taken at a period of considerable croaker activity. During the making of the record, and on subsequent normal reproductions, it was impossible to detect any acoustic signal from the ship through the disturbing noise. However, on playing the record through an electric system suppressing all components below 2000 cyc/sec the rhythm of the propellers could be easily distinguished. By including such discrimination in the equipment as installed it was found possible to use recording instruments quite successfully under conditions where the noise would otherwise have obscured the indication completely.

Another noisy tenant of the ocean is the snapping shrimp. This is a relatively small creature, about an inch long or less. It has one prominent claw on the end of which is a pair of pincers which the creature persistently snaps together with great vigor. When this process is carried out in air it produces much the same sound as does the snapping of one fingernail by another. As with the drumming of croakers, the custom reaches serious proportions because of the enormous number of its practitioners. A population density of something like twenty to the square foot appears to be not uncommon. The sound energy developed by an infested area may be sufficient to cause audible amounts to escape to the air above. When picked up by a hydrophone and reproduced in air by a loud-speaker a nearby colony has been described as producing a noise resembling a forest fire.

A representative spectrum level characteristic of the noise of snapping shrimp is given by the curve of Fig. 2C-5. This characteristic differs significantly from that of croaker noise. It is obvious that croakers interfere with direct listening at sonic frequencies whereas shrimp interfere with echo ranging or with ultrasonic listening. As with all data on noises in the sea, this curve represents a summary statement based on data having considerable variability. In any given location observed levels may be expected to vary as much as 20 decibels from those shown.

Shrimp noise shows little seasonal or daily variation but maintains a fairly uniform level over long periods. The daily variation in band level for a given location may show a change of 3 to 5 db, the peak, if any, appearing during the hours of darkness.

Locations in which the ambient noise may be expected to contain a considerable amount of shrimp noise are numerous and spread over a large portion of the globe. They do not occur in regions where the surface temperature drops below 52 °F during the winter nor where it does not

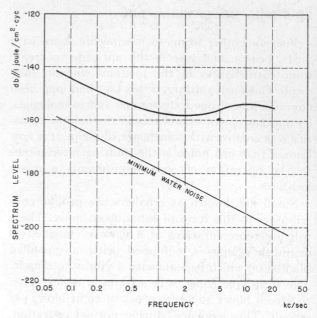

FIG. 2C-5. SNAPPING SHRIMP NOISE. Spectrum level characteristic of noise due to snapping shrimp, representative of several locations.

reach 60 °F during some part of the year. The greatest population densities are generally found in water the depth of which is between 30 and 150 ft. Whenever shrimp noise is found in water of greater depth it is likely to be at a lower acoustic intensity. It is not to be expected in significant amounts in water over 180 ft deep. The character of the bottom appears to be a factor of considerable importance. Rock, coral, shell, or other material offering means of concealment appears to be a prerequisite. Since this variety of shrimp is not edible it seems unlikely that its sonic activities will ever be classed as signals; its position as a source of interference, however, seems well assured.

Of the various forms of marine life which contribute to ambient noise croakers and snapping shrimp are, perhaps, the most important thus far encountered. There are many others. Several relatives of the croaker produce sounds which may occasionally reach disturbing levels. These do not, however, appear to form such large colonies as do the croaker and hence are not responsible for such high sound levels. Mention must be made of one individual who demonstrates remarkable powers as a soloist. This is the toad fish. It is said that the male is, on occasion, charged with guarding the eggs and that his chief means of offense during this period is a most effective noise-making equipment. This consists of a bladder which, when distended, is stroked by a muscular member, much as a violin string is stroked by a bow. The resulting noise is of such high level that it has been suggested it may actually do physical injury to approaching marauders.

During the last war many reports were received of weird noises heard over sonic listening equipment or even over ultrasonic equipment the input to which had been heterodyned to the sonic portion of the spectrum. It is quite certain that some of these are due to porpoises and some to whales. The descriptions of the noises made by porpoises are so varied as to be useless for purposes of identification. They have been said to bark like a dog, gobble like a turkey, or to make a distinctive bubbling whistle like nothing but a porpoise. They are often heard during echo-ranging operations over equipment responsive to a narrow band of ultrasonic frequencies only. They seem, at such times, to be commenting on the echo-ranging transmissions.

2C-7 Man Made Noise

Many of the sounds existing in the waters of the ocean originate in consequence of human activity. The most common of these sounds are, of course, those due to ships. Ship noises in the water, as might be expected, somewhat resemble the noise of general traffic on shore. In neither case can the level or character of the noise be defined with any rigor since it is subject to so many indeterminate variables. In the next article we shall endeavor to examine ship sounds which may be encountered as signals and to assign them quantitative values. First, however, we shall examine briefly the more general noise due to a number of vessels, of different kinds, at different speeds, and at different distances, which may be considered as a component of ambient noise. Many surveys have been made of the noise levels present in various harbors. From these it is possible to derive nominal values, on a statistical basis, for what may be called **traffic noise**. By traffic noise is meant the general disturbance due to ships which is not associated with a specific vessel or, what is more significant, which has no definite directional distribution relative to a given observation point and which shows little change in intensity with change in position.

During these surveys situations were encountered in which ship sounds, which might be classified as ambient noise, reached a level, for the 0.1 to 10 kc/sec band, of as much as -90 db//1 watt/cm². Obviously, then, ship noise may be

expected at any level between this value and the value for minimum water noise. Any average value of ship noise level which may be established for any location, or for any type of situation, will certainly represent the mean of a wide range of values. It has, in fact, been found that the statistical variation observed in a single location, under presumably fixed conditions, is something like 8 db.

The spectrum level characteristic of ship traffic noise does not differ greatly from that for general water noise. It may, perhaps, have a somewhat greater tendency to distinct peaks. The negative slope of traffic noise will, on the average, be somewhat greater than for water noise. The curve of Fig. 2C-6 shows a typical spectrum level characteristic for ship traffic noise.

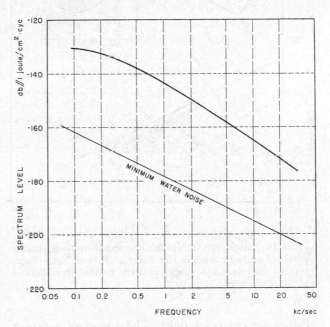

FIG. 2C-6. TRAFFIC NOISE. A typical spectrum level characteristic of ship traffic as taken in the waters of New York Harbor.

In harbors contiguous to busy industrial areas there is always a certain amount of noise which gets into the water from machinery operating on barges, on piers, or even on shore at some distance from the water's edge. When dredging operations are carried on near underwater listening stations noises such as the creaking of sheaves, when picked up by the hydrophone and reproduced on a loudspeaker, are almost indistinguishable from sounds from the same source heard directly through the air. A pile driver is almost certain to send out water-borne acoustic waves which can be detected for several miles. Noises found in the water have frequently been identified as coming from a railway train. Such noise is, in fact, quite usual when a train passes over a bridge having one or more piers with submerged foundations.

Extensive industrial establishments near harbors or channels invariably make contributions to the ambient noise found in those locations. General industrial noise, like ship traffic noise, is sometimes almost indistinguishable from general water noise. At other times the nature of the activ-

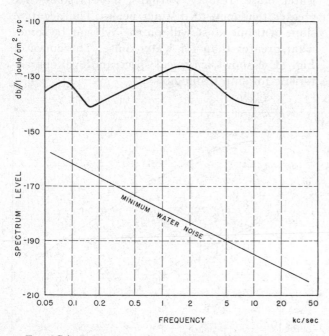

FIG. 2C-7. INDUSTRIAL NOISE. The spectrum level characteristic of ambient noise in the water at Boston Navy Yard, reported as being due almost entirely to the operations of machines on shore.

ities is strikingly evident. The sound of a power riveter, for example, or of a punch press, is about the same when heard over a sonar listening system as when heard in the factory.

A spectrum level characteristic of noise found in the vicinity of the Boston Navy Yard is given in Fig. 2C-7. The sources here may be assumed to include both water-borne equipment and machinery having fixed foundations ashore. The equivalent plane wave level of this noise, for the 0.1 to 10 kc/sec band, is approximately -80 db//1 watt/cm^2. The report on this measurement states that the observed band level was subject to variations of as much as 15 db.

In most cases, sounds reaching the water from machinery afloat or ashore have only broadly de-

fined directional distribution with respect to bearing about a listening point. This lack of directional variation may be due to reverberation or to transmission through the bottom rather than through the water.

2C-8 Ship Sounds as Signals

In the majority of all applications of sonar equipment involving direct listening the signal of interest is made up of acoustic waves radiated by some ship or submarine. The compilation of statistical data relative to these ship sounds, which was begun on a small scale during World War I, was carried forward as a project of major importance during World War II.

A common technique for obtaining quantitative data concerning the sounds of ships is to mount a carefully calibrated hydrophone on the bottom of some channel where ships of any size may be sent over it, following some prescribed course accurately, and maintaining any desired speed. The bottom in the vicinity of such a testing range should be of soft mud or other material which is a poor acoustic reflector. The hydrophone is usually supported on a tripod which holds it a few feet above the bottom. It is connected by electrically conducting cable to a shore station where recording instruments are maintained. Acoustic level is usually measured as a function of frequency. During any measuring run both the distance and the bearing of the hydrophone relative to the vessel under test will vary continuously. These quantities, then, must be observed accurately in relation to the measured acoustic levels and their effects included in the data as ultimately compiled.

Measurements may be grouped into two general classifications. In one, the distance between ship and hydrophone is sufficient to justify considering the dimensions of the ship as negligible. In this case the observed intensities may be reported in terms of index level (Art. 2B-6). They will usually be found to be a function of the bearing of the observation point relative to the ship or, what is equivalent, of the angle made by the ship with the line joining it to the observation point. This angle is known as the **aspect** of the ship.

In the second class of measurements the hydrophone is brought close to the ship in an effort to obtain data pertaining to the point of origin of such components as may be separately identified. Early measurements of this class were made by locating the hydrophone in relatively shallow water and observing level as a function of position during the passage of the vessel. In subsequent studies, particularly of submarines, the hydrophone has been suspended near the hull while the craft was tied up in a dock. The purpose here was to study the sounds put into the water by various auxiliaries.

It is hardly necessary to say that the sounds sent out by a given ship depend upon its type, size, method of operation, and other variables. Ship sounds in water are quite as characteristic of their source as are the sounds of vehicles on land. There is as little chance of mistaking a PT-boat for a submarine as there is of confusing an airplane with a horse and buggy. Those who have spent long hours listening to ship sounds in some neighborhood are able to identify individual ships frequenting that neighborhood by the character of their signals just as readily as they can identify acquaintances by their voices.

Qualitative familiarity with the infinite variety of ship sounds can be acquired only by listening to them. Many excellent phonograph recordings have been made which are quite as good, in many cases, as signals received directly from the water for developing an acquaintance with the sounds of ships as heard over sonar listening gear. For interpreting the significance of these sounds as they affect either the design of sonar equipment for detecting enemy vessels, or the construction of our own vessels so as to improve their likelihood of escaping detection, we require data expressing their characteristics in quantitative terms. The obvious fact that the magnitudes reported in any brief survey may represent no more than statistical averages from which specific values deviate greatly does not seriously impair their utility. They serve the necessary purpose of indicating general trends and thus form an indispensable common basis for the discussion of the relative performance possibilities of apparatus under practical working conditions.

We shall first review the findings of the various statistical surveys as to the spectrum level characteristic of surface ships. The value which has been assigned to the slope of this curve, for vessels at normal operating speed, is -2 db/fl. This quantity is suitable for general considerations of the requirements of listening equipment almost without regard to the type of vessel. One reason for the repeated appearance of slopes having this magnitude is undoubtedly due to the fact that much of the acoustic energy, particularly at frequencies above 1 kc/sec, results from cavitation.

This is caused by vortices at the propeller blade tips and, in some cases, by negative pressures at portions of the blade surface. It may also be produced by motion through the water of structural members, such as rudder posts or projecting struts, attached to the ship's hull.

At frequencies below 1 kc/sec cavitation may release considerable amounts of energy in relatively narrow frequency bands. With large high-speed propellers this band usually appears below 200 cyc/sec. It has been found as low as 20 cyc/sec. It is characterized by a tendency to move downward in frequency as propeller speed increases.

Although, except for the low-frequency peak, the spectrum of cavitation is essentially continuous with frequency it is by no means constant with time. Throughout the sonic and ultrasonic regions the acoustic energy resulting from cavitation is strongly modulated in synchronism with the rotation of the propellers. Because of this it is almost always possible to count both the rhythm of individual blades and the fundamental shaft rhythm. The oscillogram of Fig. 2C-8 shows the time variation in amplitude—or pressure—of the signal developed by a large freighter.

It is part of the basic training of sonar operators to learn to count propeller revolutions and to deduce the number of blades. This is relatively easy with single screw vessels but may be quite difficult with multiple screw ships.

Propeller blades develop acoustic energy in water by vibrating mechanically as well as by cavitation. This motion may be set up in consequence of hydrodynamic forces between the blades and the water. For a given ship the acoustic energy resulting from vibration will generally be concentrated in a restricted frequency band and will generally show a pronounced maximum at some characteristic critical speed. The blades may also be set into vibration by periodic forces transmitted along the shaft. In the case of vessels using gear drive the gear tooth frequency is sometimes approximately the same as the resonance frequency of the blades. When this happens the propeller becomes a powerful sound transmitter. The total acoustic energy, in addition to being high in absolute amount, is usually concentrated in a narrow frequency band and also in a clearly defined directional beam. Propeller singing, unlike cavitation noise, is rarely modulated at blade or shaft speed but exists as a more or less steady tone.

At normal operating speeds and above, the

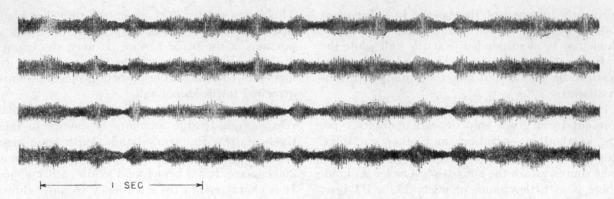

FIG. 2C-8. SHIP SOUNDS. An oscillogram showing the time variation in acoustic pressure constituting the acoustic signal radiated into the water by a large freighter.

curve of the spectrum level characteristic has been found, in general, to be relatively smooth. It is, indeed, quite often a comparatively straight line for all frequencies above 1 kc/sec. The slope of this straight portion decreases with increasing speed becoming, on the average, something like −1.8 db/fl at top speed. Below 1 kc/sec the spectrum level characteristic begins, in most cases, to curve downward with decreasing frequency in such a way that it passes through a maximum at some frequency between 100 and 500 cyc/sec. The low-frequency peaks due to cavitation not infrequently fall in the vicinity of this same frequency.

As speed is reduced below the normal cruising speed the effects of cavitation become less pronounced. Below 1 kc/sec this is evidenced by the disappearance of the low-frequency cavitation peak; at higher frequencies the result is an increase in the negative slope of the spectrum level characteristic. At very low speeds the slope of the characteristic may become as much as −3.2 db/fl for the region above 1 kc/sec. Now, however, the curve is less likely than at higher speeds to be either straight or smooth throughout this region. Spectrum levels at the upper sonic frequencies and above drop more or less continuously with decreasing speed and vanish almost completely when the ship has lost all way. There may come a point however, where the low-frequency components reach a minimum level at which they remain even when the ship is motionless in the water. These components are due to auxiliaries and to other ship activities the sounds of which escape to the water through the hull.

Some of the characteristics of ship sounds mentioned above are illustrated by the curves of Fig.

2C-9. These give the results of measurements on a single vessel. This particular specimen was selected because it contains, in a single example, many of the effects of change in speed which have been described.

Changes in the slope and in the shape of the spectrum level characteristic are, of course, accompanied by changes in the absolute value of index level. As a result of a statistical analysis of

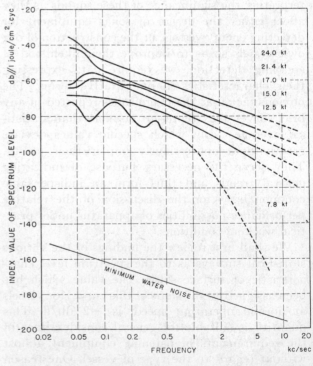

FIG. 2C-9. SPECTRUM LEVELS OF SURFACE VESSEL NOISE. The spectrum level characteristics, plotted as index values with ship's speed as a parameter, obtained by measurements on a large cruiser. The supplementary reference shows the probable minimum spectrum level of water noise.

many reports it has been found possible to obtain a surprisingly close correlation between these absolute values and the speed and tonnage of the vessels to which they apply. Because of the fact that irregularities in the spectrum level characteristic are more or less confined to the lower portion of the sonic spectrum, data concerning index level as a function of speed and size has been compiled in terms of the index value of spectrum level at 5 kc/sec. Not only is this data far less erratic than that for spectrum levels at lower frequencies, it is more consistent than data as to band level. These statements are, of course, not unrelated since, in view of the magnitudes and signs of the slopes of the spectrum level characteristics, the band level is determined almost entirely by energy at low frequencies.

The index value of spectrum level at 5 kc/sec, as a function of speed, representative of vessels having a displacement of 400 tons is given by the curve of Fig. 2C-10. This shows the index value of spectrum level to increase at the rate of 6 decibels per velocity logit. This rate is, for many practical purposes, independent of displacement for all ships of more than 400 tons. For such ships the index value of the spectrum level will, on the average, exceed the value given by the curve of Fig. 2C-10 by the amount shown, as a function of displacement, in Fig. 2C-11. The index value of

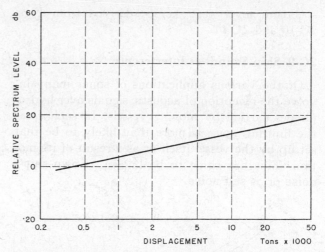

FIG. 2C-11. EFFECT OF SIZE ON SHIP SOUNDS. The incremental amount, as a function of displacement, by which the index value of spectrum level at 5 kc/sec for a given ship is likely to exceed the value given by Fig. 2C-10.

spectrum level at 5 kc/sec of the acoustic signal which a ship of given size and speed puts into the water is obtained by adding the number of decibels corresponding to its displacement tonnage to the index value of spectrum level corresponding to its speed. In 68 percent of all cases where this is done the resulting estimate is likely to be within 5.5 db of the actual value. Signals from tankers and freighters may show greater deviations from values thus computed than those from passenger and naval vessels. The method cannot be used with any assurance for vessels of less than 400 tons.

From the known relation between the index value of spectrum level and speed, at 5 kc/sec, and the known effect of speed on the slope and shape of the spectrum level characteristic it is now possible to derive relative spectrum level characteristics which may be considered as typical of vessels of over 400 tons. Such characteristics are shown in Fig. 2C-12. The reference point of the scale of relative levels is taken as the index value of spectrum level at 5 kc/sec for normal operating speed. This is assumed to be about 80 percent of the maximum speed attainable. The curve for low-speed operation may be considered as applying at approximately 20 percent of normal operating speed.

The curves of Fig. 2C-12 are, as stated, drawn to a scale of relative levels. A close approximation to the probable average index values of spectrum level may be obtained, in any given case, by adding to the ordinates of Fig. 2C-12 the value of

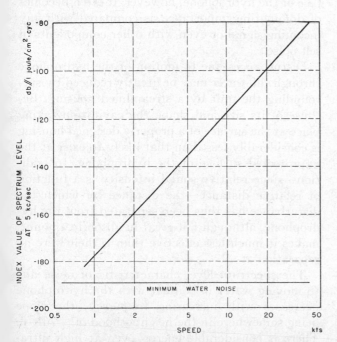

FIG. 2C-10. EFFECT OF SPEED ON SHIP SOUNDS. The index value of spectrum level at 5 kc/sec, as a function of speed, typical of ships of 400 tons displacement.

spectrum level at 5 kc/sec derived from Figs. 2C-10 and 2C-11.

2C-9 Ship Sounds as Interference

Of the various applications of sonar many involve the reception of acoustic signals over hydrophones carried by moving vessels. In such cases the limiting noise is more than likely to be that set up by the vessel itself or as a result of its motion. This has come to be known as **own-ship's noise** or as **self noise.**

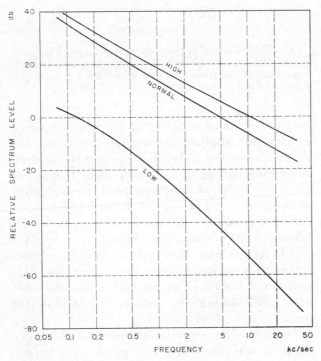

Fig. 2C-12. Spectrum Levels of Surface Vessel Noise. Relative spectrum level characteristics, typical of all large surface vessels, representing the statistical average of many observations. High speed is taken as 125 percent and low speed as 20 percent of the normal operating speed.

Many of the factors discussed in connection with ship traffic noise or with ship sounds considered as signals appear also in connection with own-ship's noise, although sometimes with a quite different quantitative effect; there are other factors which become important here which do not appear at all in these other classifications.

In connection with ship sounds it must be remembered that data presented in earlier articles apply to listening points at such distances from the ship that the latter may be thought of as a single point at which all components of the received sound originate. When the listening station is located within the volume occupied by a source as complex and as extensive as a ship this is no longer true. Components of the total sound now come from individual sources separated by distances comparable to that between the observation point and any one of them. This not only gives a directional distribution to the several noise components but may completely change their relative intensities from those observed at a remote point. Insofar as previous data may give information as to the change in relative level, accompanying a change in speed, to the frequency characteristic of some specific disturbance, or to some other general effect, they may be helpful in problems having to do with self noise. Restrictions which are inherent in the concept of index level must, however, not be ignored.

One of the most troublesome components of own-ship's noise is that originating in direct contact with the surface of the hydrophone. Some of this is due to the impact of air bubbles created at the air-water boundary by the motion of the ship's hull; some is developed as a result of cavitation in the immediate vicinity of the hydrophone. The absolute level of this type of noise is so low that it is insignificant as compared with other sounds of the ship when picked up jointly at a distance; because of its close proximity to the sensitive surface of the hydrophone, however, it often becomes of dominating importance as compared with any incoming signal or even with other components of self noise.

Disturbances due to motion of the hydrophone through the water may be greatly reduced by surrounding the unit by a streamlined housing. Because of its size and shape the cavitation taking place at the surface of a properly designed housing is considerably less than that likely to exist at the unprotected surface of the hydrophone. In addition—since relative sound intensity is a function of relative distance—the distance by which the disturbance has thus been separated from the hydrophone, although not great in absolute amount, makes it much less effective than if their were no separation at all.

The spectrum level characteristic of noise due to moving water in contact with the hydrophone decreases with increasing frequency, the slope being somewhere in the neighborhood of −2db/fl. There is considerable energy even at high ultrasonic frequencies. As is evident from the nature of the disturbance there is practically no apparent directional distribution to its effect on a directional hydrophone.

Noise may reach the hydrophone from the propulsion machinery or from auxiliaries by direct transmission through the frame of the ship and the hydrophone supports. This damage may be somewhat avoided by the use of suitable shock mountings in the hydrophone supports. However, any noise from these sources which actually reaches the water, and which is in the same frequency band as the desired signal, cannot thereafter be segregated from acoustic waves constituting the signal. Noise reaching the hydrophone by metallic conduction has no apparent directional distribution.

One type of own-ship's noise which is almost inescapable is that due to **wave slap** against the hull. This is generally the limiting factor when, in an effort to obtain the maximum possible detection range, the ship is laid to with auxiliaries quieted. Wave slap is sometimes worse when a ship is at anchor than when drifting because of the greater motion through the water. When under way, a prominent contribution to this noise is made by the bow wave. There is little qualitative difference between self noise due to the impact of water against the hull and general water noise. Individual waves are, naturally, more easily identified in the former case. Like water noise, wave slap is very troublesome at low sonic frequencies and extends well into the ultrasonic region, the slope of the spectrum level characteristic being approximately $-5/3$ db/fl.

In a self-propelled vessel noise created by the propellers is a major source of local disturbance as well as of the signal heard at a distance. Considered as self noise it may exceed in absolute effective magnitude noise created directly on the surface of the hydrophone; it often takes precedence over noise developed on the surface of a protective housing. Fortunately, this source of disturbance is sufficiently well localized and at a sufficient distance from the hydrophone so that significant discrimination may be obtained on a directional basis. The frequency characteristic of propeller noise, as well as its relation to the speed of the ship, has been discussed in articles dealing with the acoustic signals developed by ships. The difficulty of making useful generalizations regarding the absolute level of self noise applies here as well as elsewhere. It may be noted, however, that in the case of the narrow band of ultrasonic frequencies used in echo ranging the directional discrimination of the transducer may keep propeller noise below other local interference except for an arc of something like 60° centered directly astern. This value applies rather generally in the case of surface craft. For surface ships the increase in local interference picked up by a directional transducer trained dead astern may be as much as 40 db above the level of interference on other bearings or of interference having no directional distribution.

There are marked differences, both qualitative and quantitative, between the self noise of a submarine operating submerged and of a vessel operating on the surface. In the case of a submerged submarine there is no air-water boundary at which waves can break, either against the hull or against other water masses. The absence of this boundary also prevents the formation of air bubbles in the water which, if present, might strike directly against the moving hydrophone. In the aggregate these factors combine to make a submerged submarine of the type now in service, an exceptionally quiet platform on which to mount an underwater listening station. When attempting to listen from a self-propelled surface ship, on the other hand, the interfering noise exceeds that in almost any other application of sonar.

The magnitude of the interference due to own-ship's noise is, like all other interference, usually expressed in terms of the transmission level corresponding to its equivalent plane wave intensity. The contribution made by any given source, such as the ship's propellers, to the equivalent plane wave level of interference is usually much less than the contribution of this same source to the index level of the sound output of the vessel as determined by the signal level at some remote point. This is to be expected since any point suitable for a hydrophone is usually several yards distant from any of the actual sources contributing to the total ship noise. Because of this the actual equivalent plane wave level observed at the hydrophone is, in general, considerably lower than the index level, which is computed on the assumption that it exists at a distance of one yard from the source of all of the acoustic energy radiated. If this were not so it would, of course, be virtually impossible to make observations from one vessel of the sounds radiated by a distant vessel. Inasmuch as the two levels described above are referred to a common reference intensity, and apply to a single energy transmission, their difference may be expressed in terms of a transmission loss.

The magnitude of this loss depends on many factors and may be expected to vary between widely separated limits. It has been found that a figure of 35 db may be taken as the order of magnitude of this loss in a number of representative situations.

REFERENCES

1. Proposition XLVIII, Book II, of Newton's *Principia*, as translated by Andrew Motte in 1729.
2. J. D. COLLADON and J. K. F. STURM, *Annales de Chimie et de Physique* (2) 36, 236 (1827), and Poggendorff's *Annalen der Physik und Chemie 12*, 171 (1828).
3. AMAGAT, *Comptes Rendus*, 116, 41 (1893).
4. S. KUWAHARA, "Velocity of Sound in Sea Water and Calculation of Velocity for Use in Sonic Soundings," *Hydrographic Rev.*, Vol. 16, No. 2, pp. 123–140 (1939).
5. H. F. OLSON, *Elements of Acoustical Engineering* (D. Van Nostrand Company, Inc., New York, 1940), p. 81.
6. Committee Z24.1, *American Standard Acoustical Terminology* (American Standards Association, July 31, 1951), Definition No. 2.015 reads as follows: Specific Acoustic Impedance (Unit Area Acoustic Impedance). The specific acoustic impedance at a point in the medium is the complex ratio of sound pressure to particle velocity.
7. C. W. CLAPP and F. A. FIRESTONE, "An Acoustic Wattmeter, an Instrument for Measuring Sound Energy Flow," *JASA*, Vol. 13, No. 2, p. 124, Oct. 1941.
8. R. W. SAMSEL and G. E. HENRY, "An Underwater Acoustic Intensity Probe," Presented at a Meeting of the Acous. Soc. Amer., Philadelphia, Pa., May 7, 1953.
9. J. W. HORTON, "Fundamental Considerations Regarding the Use of Relative Magnitudes," *Proc. I.R.E.*, Vol. 40, No. 4, April 1952, p. 440.
   J. W. HORTON, "The Bewildering Decibel," *Elec. Eng.*, Vol. 73, No. 6, p. 550.
10. "The Bewildering Decibel," *loc. cit.* (This paper discusses the dimensional nature of transmission loss in some detail.)
11. R. V. L. HARTLEY, "The Transmission Unit," *Elec. Commun.*, Vol. 3, No. 1, July 1924. (This describes, in detail, the nature and properties of the quantity in question.)
    W. H. MARTIN, "Decibel—The Name for the Transmission Unit," *Bell System Tech. J.*, Vol. 8, No. 1, pp. 1–2, January 1929. (This announces the adoption, by the International Advisory Committee on Long Distance Telephony in Europe, of the designation "decibel" for the transmission unit specified by the preceding reference.)

CHAPTER 3

THE PROPAGATION OF UNDERWATER SOUND

Thus far we have confined our attention, in general, to acoustic waves as they exist at a fixed point some distance from their source. It is next in order to consider the changes in these waves as they travel from one point to another.

As we stood at a fixed point and watched the waves go by we saw that they moved with a certain velocity of propagation which was determined by the elasticity and the density of the water. This velocity is maintained as the waves travel through the water, changing only as these constants of the medium change. The rate at which these waves carry energy, on the other hand, is far from constant. It usually changes continuously as the waves move from place to place. It is with these changes in the rate of energy flow that we are now chiefly concerned.

3-A TRANSMISSION LOSSES IN WATER

3A-1 Propagation Loss

In studying the several manifestations of acoustic energy as they vary from point to point, rather than as they exist at a single point, terms descriptive of the spacial distribution of this energy are needed. To provide one of these, a **wave front** has been defined as any surface in the medium throughout which a single value of the phase term, $\omega S/c$, given in Eq. (2A-4) applies at any instant. As energy is propagated by radiation, wave fronts move outward from their source. The energy associated with a point on a wave front moves along an imaginary line known as a **ray path.** The ray paths encountered in acoustics, which are commonly called **sound rays,** are analogous to the light rays of optics. Ray paths and wave fronts are mutually perpendicular. The assumption of a plane wave is equivalent to assuming the ray paths to be parallel; the assumption of a spherical wave front is equivalent to assuming that the ray paths diverge radially from a common center.

In underwater sound, ray paths are the routes over which acoustic energy is propagated through the water. Points between which changes in acoustic intensity are to be studied will, in general, lie on some specified ray path. These changes in intensity may conveniently be expressed in terms of the transmission losses discussed in Art. 2B-2. The transmission loss associated with any given length of ray path in water will be specifically designated as a **propagation loss.** The propagation loss between two points is, in general, a function of frequency. It is measured, at any specified frequency, by the ratio of (1) the intensity of sinusoidal acoustic waves of that frequency at the point more distant from their source to (2) the intensity which these same waves had at the point nearer their source. The basic formula by which the magnitude of a given propagation loss is expressed in decibels, as given by Eq. (2B-8), may be written as

$$N_w = - \lgt \frac{I_2}{I_1} \qquad (3A-1)$$

where

$N_w =$ the propagation loss between two specified points on a ray path in water, at some specified frequency (db)

$I_1 =$ the intensity of sinusoidal acoustic waves of the specified frequency at the point nearer their source (watt/cm²)

$I_2 =$ the intensity of the same waves after having reached the more distant point (watt/cm²)

It is obvious that the propagation loss between two points is measured by the difference between the transmission levels of sinusoidal waves at those points. Having been thus measured, it indicates the difference between the spectrum levels, at the frequency to which it applies, of energy having a continuous spectrum which may be propagated along the same path. Propagation loss may also be used to express a change in the band level associated with the energy in a specified frequency band. The computation of this loss requires that due account be taken of the manner in which the propagation loss of the path and the spectrum level of the energy vary with frequency throughout the band in question.

3A-2 The General Propagation Loss Equation—Spreading and Attenuation

If sound energy is propagated from a single source point throughout an infinite homogeneous medium the energy reaching any point will do so by a ray path which is a straight line. Such ray paths are, as already noted, the radii of spherical wave fronts. The area of a spherical wave front increases as it is propagated away from its source, being proportional to the square of its distance from that source. The reduction in acoustic intensity due to an increase in the area over which a given acoustic energy is distributed is said to result from **spreading.** In the ideal situation here postulated spreading occurs in accordance with the familiar **inverse square law** applicable, in general, to all forms of radiant energy.

In actual situations, the acoustic medium with which we have to deal is the water forming the ocean. This is neither infinite in extent nor homogeneous in composition. We have already seen (Art. 2A-3) that the density of the ocean varies with depth, and that both its density and its elasticity vary with temperature. These changes in the physical constants of the medium are accompanied by changes in the velocity of propagation. These, in turn, result in a bending of the sound rays. This is known as **refraction.** Considered as an acoustic medium, the waters of the oceans form a thin layer on the earth's surface. Sound rays propagated within such a thin layer are likely, sooner or later, to reach one of its boundary surfaces. At either of these surfaces abrupt changes in specific acoustic impedance are to be expected. Because of these impedance discontinuities much of the energy propagated along a ray path intercepted by an ocean surface is turned back into the water by **reflection.** Refraction and reflection both require that amendments be made to the inverse square law. In many cases each of these effects tends to restrict spreading in the vertical direction. The intensity of acoustic energy the wave fronts of which expand cylindrically rather than spherically obeys a first power law rather than a second power law.

Reflections are not limited to points on the boundaries of the medium but may take place throughout its entire volume, due to the presence of innumerable foreign bodies. These, which may include microscopic air bubbles or whales, as well as submarines, vary widely as to size and acoustic impedance. The presence of such reflectors represents the normal state of affairs in the ocean; no sample of sea water may be considered as representative without them. Modifications of the direction in which acoustic energy is propagated caused by reflections from these foreign bodies are said to be due to **scattering.** In some situations practically all of the energy to reach certain regions of the sea does so because of scattering.

Since the propagation of a sound wave in water is attended by repeated compressions and expansions of the medium it is inevitable that there should be friction between the water molecules. This converts some of the acoustic energy into heat. While this conversion is insignificant as far as warming the ocean is concerned it is by no means negligible when viewed in terms of the energy remaining in a sound wave after it has passed through any appreciable amount of water. Energy losses associated with this phenomenon are said to be due to **absorption.**

The factors which have been described affect the propagation loss of sea water in two different ways. It is, for this reason, convenient to represent them by two component losses. These two losses are not contiguous, as is usually the case with component losses; they are, instead, to be considered as concurrent losses, neither of which is likely to exist without the other. It is, in fact, never possible to isolate one from the other for independent measurement. Each is, nevertheless, separately affected by oceanographic conditions, and each separately affects the design parameters and performance characteristics of sonar equipment. It is, consequently, necessary that they be studied individually.

The first of these losses is the **spreading loss.** This is directly associated with spreading, or with the increasing area over which energy, otherwise of constant intensity, is distributed. In the ocean, as we have seen, spreading does not always obey the inverse square law. We may, however, assume that as a result of spreading the acoustic intensity of waves from a given point source will vary as some power of their distance from that source. We may thus write

$$\frac{(I_2)_{\text{spr}}}{I_1} = \left(\frac{S_2}{S_1}\right)^n \qquad (3A-2)$$

where

$I_1 =$ the actual acoustic intensity at the beginning of a specified length of ray path due to sinusoidal acoustic waves having a specified frequency (watt/cm²)

$(I_2)_{spr} =$ the intensity which would exist at the distant end of the specified length of path due to these same acoustic waves if the only reduction in their intensity were that due to spreading (watt/cm²)

$S_1 =$ the distance of the beginning of the specified length of ray path from the source of the acoustic waves (kyd)

$S_2 =$ the distance of the distant end of the specified length of path from the same source (kyd)

$n =$ an exponent (Il/Sl)

The second basic component of propagation loss is **attenuation loss.** This is due to the combined effects of scattering and absorption. It is analogous to the loss suffered by electric energy transmitted over a wire line, where there is no spreading loss. If a given small volume of water, such as a centimeter cube, were to be traversed by plane waves of acoustic energy, moving along parallel paths without spreading loss, the intensity at the exit boundary would be less than that at the entrance boundary because of attenuation. Some portion of the entering acoustic energy would be diverted from its original path by scattering and some portion would be converted from its original form by absorption.

The **attenuation** of a medium through which radiant energy is propagated causes a reduction in the intensity of this energy which is characterized by the fact that, if the attenuation is constant, the fractional reduction per unit distance is also constant. Let the fractional reduction in intensity due to a single unit length of path be

$$\frac{(I_{S+1})_{attn}}{I_S} = k$$

where k is a constant less than unity. The quantity I_S is the intensity at the beginning of the unit length of path, and $(I_{S+1})_{attn}$ is the intensity which would exist at the end of this unit length if there were no spreading loss. The fractional reduc-

tion due to ΔS unit lengths of ray path is then

$$\frac{(I_{S+\Delta S})_{attn}}{I_S} = k^{\Delta S}$$

It will be found convenient to let $k = (10^{0.1})^{-a}$ be the fractional change in intensity due to the attenuation of a path having a unit length of one kiloyard. The fractional change due solely to the attenuation of a path $\Delta S = (S_2 - S_1)$ kyd in length is thus

$$\frac{(I_2)_{attn}}{I_1} = (10^{0.1})^{-a(S_2-S_1)} \qquad (3A-3)$$

where

$I_1 =$ the intensity of sinusoidal acoustic waves of specified frequency at the entrance end of the length of path in question (watt/cm²)

$(I_2)_{attn} =$ the intensity which would exist at the exit end of this length, due to these same waves, if the only reduction in intensity were that due to attenuation (watt/cm²)

$(S_2 - S_1) =$ the length of path (kyd)

$a =$ a coefficient (Il/kyd)

The intensity ratio given by this equation measures the reduction in acoustic intensity due solely to the attenuation offered by a specified length of water path. It is, therefore, the ratio of the intensity actually existing at the exit end of the path to the intensity which would have existed at this same point if there had been no attenuation. In other words,

$$\frac{(I_2)_{attn}}{I_1} = \frac{I_2}{(I_2)_{spr}} \qquad (3A-4)$$

where

$I_2 =$ the actual acoustic intensity at the exit end of the specified length of path, S_2 kyd from a point source of sinusoidal acoustic waves of specified frequency (watt/cm²)

The intensity $(I_2)_{spr}$ shown here is identical with the intensity shown by Eq. (3A-2) as existing at the exit end of the increment of path length as a result of spreading in the absence of attenuation.

We may, therefore, eliminate this hypothetical intensity from the preceding equations and arrive at an expression for the combined effect of spreading and attenuation. This expression is

$$\frac{I_2}{I_1} = \left(\frac{S_2}{S_1}\right)^n (10^{0.1})^{-a(S_2-S_1)} \qquad (3A-5)$$

When this ratio is substituted into Eq. (3A-1), the defining equation for propagation loss, there results the general equation for the propagation loss suffered by acoustic energy propagated, at some specified frequency, between two specified points. This propagation loss is

$$N_w = - \lg t \frac{I_2}{I_1} = - n \lg t \frac{S_2}{S_1} + a(S_2 - S_1) \quad (3A-6)$$

where

$N_w =$ the propagation loss of a specified length of ray path at a specified frequency (db)

$I_1 =$ the intensity at the entrance end of this length of path of acoustic energy propagated along the path as sinusoidal waves of the specified frequency (watt/cm²)

$I_2 =$ the intensity of these waves at the exit end of the length of path (watt/cm²)

$S_1 =$ the distance of the entrance end of the length of path as measured from the source of the sinusoidal waves (kyd)

$S_2 =$ the distance of the exit end of the length of path as measured from the same source (kyd)

$n =$ the exponent of the distance ratio identified with spreading (db/Sl)

$a =$ the coefficient of the distance identified with attenuation (db/kyd)

It is evident from this last expression that the coefficient, a, is equal to the **attenuation loss per unit distance.** It is, therefore, known as the **attenuation coefficient** and is expressed quantitatively in decibels per kiloyard.

That component of the propagation loss which represents the effect of spreading, or the spreading loss, is given by the term

$$-n \lg t \frac{S_2}{S_1} = N_{\text{spr}} \qquad (3A-7)$$

That component which represents the effect of attenuation, or the attenuation loss, is

$$a(S_2 - S_1) = N_{\text{attn}} \qquad (3A-8)$$

From the preceding discussion it is evident that spreading loss and attenuation loss are related to range in quite different ways. The spreading loss associated with a given increment of ray path depends on the distance of that increment from the sound source fully as much as on its length. Attenuation loss, on the other hand, is directly proportional to path length, regardless of the distance of this length from the source. A second important difference is that spreading loss is independent of frequency, whereas attenuation loss varies with frequency in a manner which is of profound significance in many applications of sonar. The relation between attenuation and frequency will be considered in Art. 3A-6.

For the concept of propagation loss to have real utility it should facilitate the computation of the magnitudes of acoustic waves at any point due to sound sources at known ranges. The formula of Eq. (3A-6) does not lend itself directly to this purpose. Because of the appearance of the ratio of two ranges in the expression for spreading loss it is necessary that two finite ranges be specified. To satisfy this condition it is customary, in reporting the propagation loss from some given source, such as a ship, to start from a point 1 yd closer to the observation point than the effective center of the source. This is the point for which the index level was defined in Art. 2B-6. It may, therefore, be designated as the **index point.** The selection of this point is equivalent to making $S_1 = 1$ yd $= 0.001$ kyd in the spreading loss term of Eq. (3A-6); it may be neglected in the attenuation loss term. The general propagation loss equation then reduces to

$$N_w = - n (\lg t S + 30) + aS \text{ db} \quad (3A-9)$$

This shows the difference, in decibels, between the index level of a source, as computed for a point 1 yd from its effective center, on a given ray path, and the level at a point S kyd from the same center on the same ray path. It is seen that the index level of some given source may be derived from the measured level at a known distance from that source by adding to the known level the value of the propagation loss computed by this equation.

When the location of the effective center of some sound source is unknown this method cannot, of course, be employed. If, however, the direction of the source is known both its distance and its index level may be determined by measurements made at two points on a line through it. Assume that the distances of these points from the source are such as to justify neglecting the attenuation loss, and that the spreading loss obeys the inverse square law. Under these conditions $n = -2$, and $a = 0$, in Eq. (3A-5). If, as we are assuming, the source is distributed in space it is probable that the energy which it delivers to the water is distributed in frequency as well. It may, in fact, have a continuous spectrum. We cannot, therefore, measure the intensities of sinusoidal waves having some given frequency. We therefore measure the acoustic pressures due to energy associated with some narrow spectrum interval. We also measure the distance between the two points at which these pressures exist. Let the distances, as yet unknown, of the two points from the source in question be S_1 and S_2, and let the acoustic pressures measured at these points in a narrow band, having a geometric mean frequency of some specified value, be p_1 and p_2. If the intensity of sinusoidal waves of this specified frequency varies as the inverse square of the distance from the source these measured pressures must vary as the inverse first power of this distance. The product of pressure and distance is, therefore, a constant and

$$p_1 S_1 = p_2 S_2 = p_0 S_0 \qquad (3A\text{-}10)$$

where p_0 is the pressure at the index point $S_0 = 1$ yd from the effective center of the source. From this it follows that

$$\frac{p_1}{p_2} = \frac{S_2}{S_1}, \qquad \frac{p_1 - p_2}{p_2} = \frac{S_2 - S_1}{S_1}$$

and

$$S_1 = \frac{S_2 - S_1}{p_1 - p_2} p_2 \qquad (3A\text{-}11)$$

Since the separation, $S_2 - S_1$, between the points, and the pressures, p_1 and p_2, at these points are known the distance S_1, between one point and the apparent center of the source may be computed. The pressure p_0 at the index point, for which the distance is $S_0 = 1$ yd, is also computed by substituting either of the distances thus established into Eq. (3A-10) together with the corresponding known pressure.

The index point has been located at a distance of one yard from the effective center of the source because of the standard Navy practice of measuring ranges in yards. Many transducer design

problems, on the other hand, are carried out in metric units. In such cases it is customary to report the performance of a projector in terms of the acoustic intensity at a point one meter from its center. To correlate this with the propagation loss equation we must, in Eq. (3A-6), make $S_1 = 0.0010936$ kyd. The constant term in Eq. (3A-9) then becomes $-29.6\ n$ db, instead of $-30\ n$ db.

3A-3 The Measurement of Propagation Loss

Practically all measurements of propagation loss are made with sinusoidal acoustic waves. There are two reasons for this. The first is that it is essential for the loss to be specified as a function of frequency. The second is that by using a single-frequency wave the receiving equipment may be made highly selective, thus excluding a considerable amount of ambient noise energy which might otherwise cause erroneous readings.

At the transmitting station a known amount of acoustic energy is radiated into the water by a suitable projector. The amount of energy thus transmitted, or, more specifically, its index level on the path in question, may be determined in either or both of two ways. The projector may be calibrated in advance and the acoustic output computed from the measured electric input. A calibrated hydrophone may also be used and the acoustic intensity at a known short distance from the projector measured in terms of the voltage developed therein. The hydrophone must, of course, be so located that it is on the path passing through the receiving station.

At the receiving station an accurately calibrated hydrophone is required. This may or may not be directive. Directional hydrophones have the advantage that they have low sensitivity to extraneous noise arriving along bearings other than that of the transmitted signal wave and hence tend to give a better differential between the signal level to be measured and the level of interference. In general the hydrophone is so designed as to be responsive over a wide frequency band, discrimination on a frequency basis being more readily adjusted if restricted to the electrical circuits.

In many measurements of propagation loss, particularly in those in which an effort is made to determine the value of the attenuation coefficient, the transmitted signals have been in the form of pulses of short duration. The object in such cases has been to complete the measurement of intensity due to transmission over the direct ray path before the arrival of energy which may have been reflected from the surface or from the bottom of the ocean.

The transmission of signals interrupted to form pulses also offers a convenient method for accurately determining the range between the source and observing stations. This is accomplished by transmitting an electromagnetic pulse over a radio link simultaneously with the acoustic pulse sent through the water. From the difference between the times of arrival of the two pulses at the receiving station, and the known velocities of propagation applying to each, the distance over which they have traveled may be computed.

3A-4 The Evaluation of Propagation Loss Components

Having obtained measured values of propagation loss at a number of points, at various distances from a sound source in a given location, the next problem is to determine the magnitudes of the spreading exponent and of the attenuation coefficient appearing in the general propagation loss equation. As already noted, it is impossible to measure the spreading loss and the attenuation loss separately. The magnitudes of the constants associated with these component losses may, however, be deduced from the manner in which the total loss varies with distance from the source.

For our present purposes the spreading exponent and the attenuation coefficient may be considered as the unknown variables in Eq. (3A-9). Since there are two of these unknowns their values may be computed from two known values of propagation loss corresponding to two known ranges. These data provide two equations which may be solved as a simultaneous pair. It has been found, however, that propagation loss measurements are subject to great variability. It is, therefore, desirable to base the constant values assigned to the two quantities in question on data obtained at a number of points.

If the value of spreading loss, as given by the relation

$$N_{spr} = - n (\lg t\, S + 30) \qquad (3A\text{-}12)$$

is plotted against the logarithm of the range the resulting curve will be a straight line. For the attenuation term this is not the case; the attenuation loss

$$N_{attn} = aS \qquad (3A\text{-}13)$$

is represented by a curved line when plotted on semi-log paper. Representative values of these

two losses and of their sum, forming the total propagation loss, are shown plotted in this manner in Fig. 3A-1. It is at once evident that if both terms contribute to the total loss a plot of their sum on semi-log paper will be curved.

In some cases a straight line is obtained if measured values of propagation loss are plotted against a logarithmic scale of range. This is prima facie evidence that the attenuation loss is so small as to

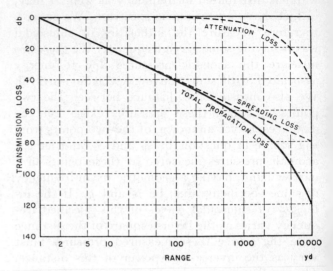

FIG. 3A-1. COMPONENTS OF PROPAGATION LOSS. Spreading loss, attenuation loss, and the propagation loss representing their sum, plotted against a logarithmic scale of range.

be negligible and that the entire loss obeys some power law.

The situation described above is reversed if the data are plotted to show the two component losses against a linear scale of range, as in Fig. 3A-2. Here the attenuation loss is represented by a straight line and the spreading loss by a curved line. As before, if both exist their sum must be a curved line.

Preliminary estimates of the values of the two constants appearing in Eq. (3A-9) may be made by solving a number of pairs of simultaneous equations, corresponding to different range values. On the basis of an average value for the attenuation coefficient, a, derived in this manner, values of spreading loss may be computed by the relation

$$N_{spr} = N_w - aS \qquad (3A\text{-}14)$$

If, when plotted against range to a logarithmic scale, this remainder appears as a straight line the correctness of the value selected for the attenuation constant is confirmed.

Having obtained a straight line characteristic for the spreading loss the value of the spreading exponent, n, associated with this loss may be derived at once from the slope of the characteristic. The slope of a spreading loss characteristic is given as the change in spreading loss per logit change in range. We may thus write for the slope of this characteristic

$$\frac{\lg t\,I_2 - \lg t\,I_1}{\lg t\,S_2 - \lg t\,S_1} = \frac{(N_{\text{spr}})_1 - (N_{\text{spr}})_2}{\lg t\,S_2 - \lg t\,S_1} = n \quad (3A\text{-}15)$$

The situation here is seen to be analogous to that occurring when acoustic intensities are proportional to some power of the frequency and which, consequently, results in a spectrum level characteristic which is a straight line when plotted against the logarithm of the frequency.

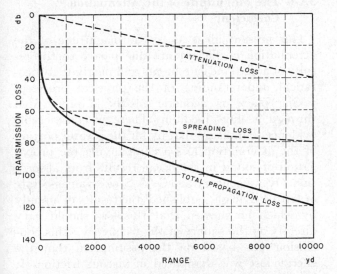

Fig. 3A-2. Components of Propagation Loss. The same values of propagation loss as shown in Fig. 3A-1, plotted against a linear scale of range.

A value for the attenuation coefficient, a, has already been obtained as a by-product during the evaluation of spreading loss. It is sometimes desirable, however, to determine a suitable single value for the attenuation coefficient by a process which is analogous to that described above for the spreading exponent. On the basis of an estimated, or derived, value for the spreading exponent the attenuation loss may be written as

$$V_{\text{attn}} = N_w - n(30 + \lg t\,S) \quad (3A\text{-}16)$$

This remainder may be plotted against a linear scale of range and the best straight line drawn through the resulting points. The average value of

the attenuation coefficient is then given by the slope of this characteristic, in decibels per unit change in range.

The processes which have been carried out in this article have been based on an intuitive recognition of certain phenomena which accompany the propagation of acoustic energy through water. Actually what has been accomplished is the empirical derivation of a simple formula which expresses the relation found, in a large number of situations, between propagation loss and range. The consideration of an ideal reference medium and of the phenomena occurring therein served primarily as a guide to the selection of the form of equation most likely to fit observed data. The verification of this form, which is effected by a series of successive approximations, and the values of the numerical constants involved, will be considered in the following articles.

3A-5 The Magnitude of the Spreading Exponent

Much data on propagation loss has been obtained in connection with acoustical surveys of harbors and similar locations. The water in these locations has, in general, been relatively shallow and the distances relatively short, as compared with conditions under which sonar equipment may be operated in the open sea. In consequence, the effect of attenuation has, in many of these cases, been negligible. A sample of propagation loss data taken under these conditions is given by the curve of Fig. 3A-3. From an examination of many

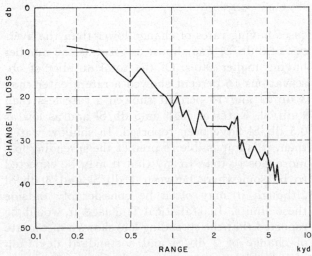

Fig. 3A-3. Observed Propagation Loss. Typical values of propagation loss, measured as a function of range, at a frequency of 600 cyc/sec.

such curves statistical data as to the value of the spreading exponent has been assembled.

For frequencies between 600 and 20,000 cyc/sec this statistical analysis shows the average rate of change of the spreading loss to be 2 db/Sl. It was, however, found to vary considerably in all locations studied, although the variations shown by one location did not differ greatly in kind or amount from those shown by others. The manner in which these variations are grouped statistically is shown in Fig. 3A-4. In general, the number of

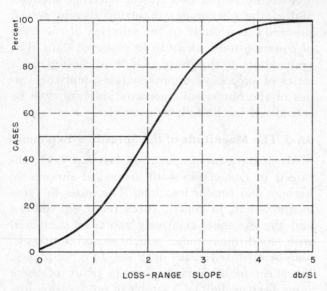

FIG. 3A-4. THE STATISTICAL VARIATION OF SPREADING LOSS. The statistical distribution of values of spreading exponent, measured for conditions such that spreading is the predominant factor. The number of cases is that percentage of the total for which the loss per distance logit is less than the indicated value.

cases having rates of change lower than the average of 2 db/Sl was almost as great as the number having higher rates. Of the total number of observations 16 percent showed a rate greater than 3 db/Sl and 16 percent showed a rate less than 1 db/Sl. Rates as high as 5 db/Sl and as low as 0.5 db/Sl have been reported. In shallow water, then, it is impossible to predict the spreading loss more closely than to say that it may be expected to be somewhere between 1 db/Sl and 3 db/Sl although it may often be considerably outside these limits. In statistical language it would be reported that the spreading loss shows a mean rate of change of 2 db/Sl and a standard deviation of 1 db/Sl.

From the relation, Eq. (3A-15), between spreading loss per distance logit and the exponent of the

spreading term it is seen that, in shallow water, the intensity of acoustic waves, on the average, falls off with distance in accordance with the inverse square law. It may, however, frequently obey the inverse first power law (1 db/Sl) or, with equal likelihood, the inverse cube law (3 db/Sl). The first is easily accounted for if the acoustic energy is confined to a horizontal medium of fixed thickness; the second is undoubtedly explained by interference between directly transmitted and reflected waves.

Spreading must, by definition, obey some power law. Situations will be found, however, where the relation between distance and intensity is not given directly in terms of distance from the actual source. Such situations will be considered in more detail in the following section.

3A-6 The Magnitude of the Attenuation Coefficient

Our present ideas as to the magnitude of the attenuation coefficient are due partly to the results of actual measurements and partly to a theoretical understanding of the physical processes taking place as acoustic energy is propagated through a fluid medium. There is considerable evidence to indicate that by far the greater portion of the attenuation loss accompanying the propagation of sound in the ocean results from absorption. Over a century ago G. G. Stokes, an associate of Lord Rayleigh, published[1] the results of a study by which he showed that this loss should vary directly as the square of the frequency. This conclusion was based on the assumption that the energy lost was dissipated in viscous friction. It has since been found[2] that for pure water values of the attenuation coefficient computed in accordance with this theory agree closely with the results obtained by measurement provided both shear and dilational viscosities are taken into account. Values of the attenuation coefficient measured for sea water are also in agreement with this theory for frequencies above about 1000 kc/sec. For lower frequencies, however, the attenuation coefficient for sea water is higher than for pure water and higher than can be accounted for by viscous absorption alone. This additional loss is now attributed to the heat of dissociation of the dissolved salts. At frequencies below about 5 kc/sec the value of the attenuation coefficient is due almost wholly to this dissociation. In this portion of the spectrum both theory and measurement show that this loss varies as the square of the frequency. At higher frequencies the loss due to dissociation becomes constant. Between 5 kc/sec and 1000 kc/sec a characteristic showing the magnitude of the resultant attenuation coefficient, in decibels per kiloyard, as a function of frequency passes through a gradual transition from one square law curve to the other. A characteristic covering these three regions is shown in Fig. 3A-5. The points shown on this graph represent the findings of many observers, in many locations, and over a number of years. The curve has been computed by means of the formula

$$a = \frac{40f^2}{4100 + f^2} + 0.000275f^2 \text{ db/kyd} \quad (3\text{A-17})$$

In this expression the frequency, f, is given in kilocycles per second. The first term corresponds to the dissociation loss; the second to the viscous losses. For low frequencies this expression reduces to $a = 0.01 f^2$ db/kyd; for high frequencies it becomes $a = 0.000275 f^2$ db/kyd. The constants of this expression have been selected empirically to obtain the best fit between a curve having the shape required by theory and the data obtained by actual measurement in the ocean. It has been found, in general, that if the attenuation loss, in decibels, computed for some given distance by the formula of Eq. (3A-17) is subtracted from the total propagation loss measured for that same distance the remainder is very nearly the loss which would be computed by the inverse square spreading law. This statement applies to measurements made in deep water far from shore.

In those portions of the frequency spectrum where either the dissociation loss or the viscous loss predominates, the magnitude of the attenuation coefficient decreases with increasing temperature. Below 5 kc/sec the magnitude of the coefficient, in decibels per kiloyard, is reduced by 50 percent as the temperature changes from 40 °F to 70 °F. The relative change, for the same change in temperature, is slightly less than this above 1000 kc/sec. In the region of transition the attenuation coefficient may, in some cases, increase slightly with increasing temperature. Measured attenuation coefficients used in arriving at the constants of Eq. (3A-17) are those observed at a temperature of 50 °F. This is, to a close approximation, the temperature of the water through which is propagated the greater portion of all sounds in the ocean which travel to any considerable distance. It is, in general, for such sounds that the effect of attenuation is of greatest significance.

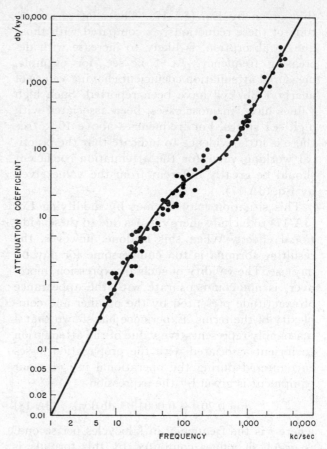

FIG. 3A-5. THE ATTENUATION COEFFICIENT. The results of individual measurements of the value of the attenuation coefficient for sound propagation through sea water. The curve corresponds to the quantity

$$a = \frac{40 f^2}{4100 + f^2} + 0.000275 f^2 \text{ db/kyd}$$

The physical chemistry which has been invoked in attempting to find a theoretical basis for the relation between the value of the attenuation coefficient and frequency applies only to the effects of absorption. It has already been noted that scattering, due to inhomogeneities in the water, may also contribute to that fractional reduction in acoustic intensity which is proportional to distance. As we shall see later, the acoustic energy propagated along many of the paths found in the ocean suffers repeated reflections, either from the surface, from the bottom, or from both. Energy losses due to these reflections may also be evaluated in terms of a constant fractional reduction in intensity per unit distance. Because of these effects the actual value of the attenuation coefficient is likely to be greater than that given by Eq. (3A-17). The relative magnitude of these reductions, as compared with those due to absorption, is likely to increase with decreasing frequency. At 1 kc/sec, for example, measured attenuation coefficients having values of nearly 1 db/kyd have been reported. Such high values have, in most cases, been associated with high sea states. For frequencies above 10 kc/sec there is little evidence to indicate that the practical working value for the attenuation coefficient should be greatly different from the value given by Eq. (3A-17).

This situation may be met by modifying Eq. (3A-17) to include energy losses due to these additional effects. When this is done, however, the resulting formula is too cumbersome for day by day use. The validity of such an expression, moreover, is not commensurate with the appearance of exactitude presented by the number and complexity of the terms. Experience has shown that a reasonably representative value of the attenuation coefficient associated with the propagation losses encountered during the operational use of sonar equipment is given by the expression

$$a = 0.20f + 0.00015f^2 \text{ db/kyd} \quad (3A-18)$$

where f is the frequency in kilocycles per second. A graph of values computed by this formula is shown in Fig. 3A-6. These values may be considered as nominal values of the attenuation coefficient.

There will be many occasions when the apparent propagation loss of some water path, of only moderate length, will be such as to indicate an attenuation much greater than would be predicted on the basis of Eq. (3A-18). Such abnormally high attenuations are attributed to what has come to be called **quenched water.** This is a condition often encountered in shallow water, or near shores where there are strong currents accompanied by considerable turbulence. It is believed that the excessive reductions in acoustic intensity are the result of occluded air. This effect is exemplified by the behavior of a water path between given transmitting and receiving points when crossed by a vessel leaving a strong wake. Signals which had previously been of reasonable intensity will, in many cases, immediately vanish completely; they will often remain below their original intensity for an hour or so. Similar conditions have been observed as the result of a storm. Measurements of propagation loss between two points which show reasonable consistency for several days may sud-

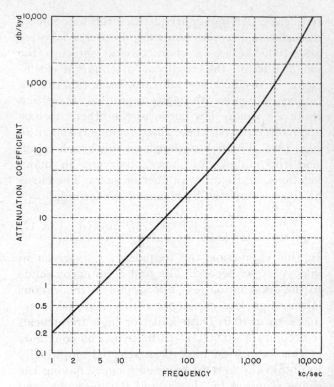

FIG. 3A-6. THE ATTENUATION COEFFICIENT. Representative values of attenuation coefficient plotted as a function of frequency, for use in computing nominal values of propagation loss.

denly show a marked increase after a period of rough weather, particularly if followed by a drop in temperature. It has also been noted that when the propagation loss for a given path is unusually high, as compared with its normal value, the effect of wakes is unusually strong.

Wakes are also characterized by the fact that they return definite echoes during echo-ranging operations. Indeed, one of the established techniques of evasion for a submarine is to increase speed momentarily, thus creating considerable turbulence, and at the same time to change course in such a way as to leave the disturbed water between itself and its pursuer. This wake not only increases the propagation loss to echo-ranging signals but introduces a false echo which may be confusing until recognized. These wakes which are deliberately formed as shields are known as **knuckles.**

3A-7 Nominal Values of Propagation Loss

In the preceding articles propagation loss has been discussed in terms of its variations with range or with location. Actually any value of propagation loss which has been identified with a given range or with a given location is itself the average of a succession of values which vary with time between widely separated limits. Some idea of the time variation in propagation loss may be obtained from the oscillograms which are reproduced in Fig. 3A-7. These are recordings of the deflection of a cathode-ray oscilloscope spot as focused on a continuously moving photographic film. Individual cycles of the 26-kilocycle wave are not shown separately but fill in an area between two enveloping curves the vertical distances

non is, in fact, similar to that which results in selective fading during radio transmission.

We have already seen that the propagation loss between two stations, such as were used for obtaining the oscillograms discussed above, may differ widely from day to day, or even from minute to minute, because of changes in the condition of the sea. It will be seen presently that effects due to refraction and to reflection cause major departures from the relation between acoustic intensity and distance as given by the propagation

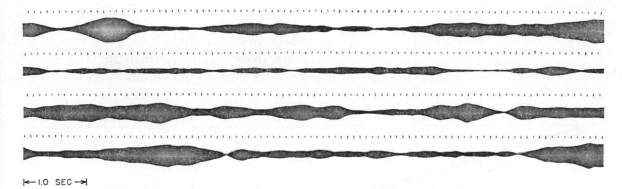

|←— 1.0 SEC —→|

FIG. 3A-7. THE TIME VARIATION OF PROPAGATION LOSS. Oscillograms showing variation in the acoustic pressure of a 26 kc/sec sound wave in water after propagation over a fixed path 1800 yd in length.

of which from the central axis are proportional to the acoustic pressure of the wave. During the recording of these oscillograms both the transmitting and the receiving vessels were at anchor and nominally fixed in position. The wave sent out by the transmitting vessel was of fixed frequency and was maintained at constant amplitude. It is evident from these oscillograms that the intensity of the received wave, which is proportional to the square of the deflection, changed from fairly definite maxima, which persisted for only brief intervals, to complete extinction in times measured in seconds. It will be observed that at several points the envelope of the wave passes through the zero axis without changing slope; it is not tangent to the axis but actually crosses from one side to the other. This indicates a complete reversal in phase of the received wave at this instant and supports the belief that short-time changes in intensity are the result of interference effects between waves reaching the receiving station over a number of different paths. This supposition is further strengthened by the fact that simultaneous observations of two received waves having slightly different frequencies show that their variations are not concurrent. The phenome-

loss formula. Incidental random variations, then, may also be assumed to result from these effects and to cause short-time deviations from the nominal value of propagation loss. The basis on which the constants of the propagation loss formulae have been derived, however, is such that the final result, as computed, represents the statistical average of all of these short-time variations. Apparently, then, the effects of refraction and of reflection have not been entirely excluded from the quantity which has been defined as nominal propagation loss. There are, however, gross effects due to these phenomena which cause large and, in many cases, predictable deviations from this estimated quantity. The propagation loss formula may, therefore, be understood to apply to effects present in an ideal medium plus minor, and unpredictable, deviations due to departures from the assumed ideal. As such it represents real conditions of practical significance.

From the foregoing it is evident that propagation loss, although nominally a function of range and frequency, is actually a function of time and place as well. Any values for the spreading exponent, n, or of the attenuation coefficient, a, which may be substituted into an expression such as Eq. (3A-9) can therefore be no more than statistical averages. The information given by such an equation may, nevertheless, be very helpful in a number of important problems. Its utility may be shown if the functional relationship of the propagation loss to range and frequency is presented graphically. For this purpose we shall let $n = -2$ and $a = (0.20f + 0.00015\ f^2)$ in the expression given by Eq. (3A-9). This gives as the practical working equation for nominal propagation loss, to be used whenever specific values of the range exponent and of the range coefficient are not available,

$$(N_w)_0 = 2 \lg S + (0.20f + 0.00015f^2)S + 60 \text{ db}$$

$$(3A-19)$$

where

$(N_w)_0 =$ the nominal value of the propagation loss of sea water, based on statistical averages, likely to be found at any time or place between a given index point and a given observation point (db)

$S =$ the range from the effective center of the source (kyd)

$f =$ the frequency of the wave (kc/sec)

Curves computed from this equation are shown in Fig. 3A-8 where the propagation loss is plotted against a logarithmic scale of range with frequency as a parameter. It is clear, from what has been said about variability, that the propagation loss actually associated with any range and frequency

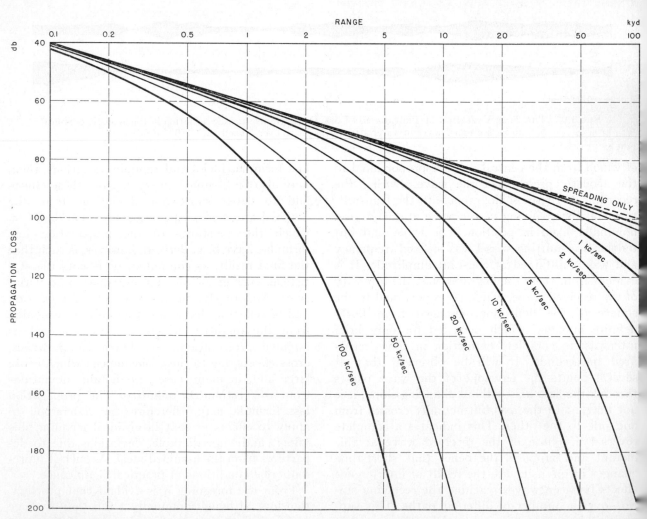

FIG. 3A-8. WORKING VALUES OF PROPAGATION LOSS. Propagation loss as a function of range, with frequency as a parameter, computed from the equation

$$N_w = 2 \lg S + (0.20f + 0.00015f^2)\ S + 60 \text{ db}$$

may differ from the value shown by this chart by several times the interval between two successive curves. The chart does, however, serve to indicate general trends. It shows, for example, that for ranges under 1000 yards little variation in the average value of propagation loss is to be expected as the frequency of the wave is changed. It also indicates that acoustic signals in water can be transmitted over longer distances at frequencies in the neighborhood of 10 kc/sec than at frequencies in the neighborhood of 100 kc/sec.

Perhaps the most important use of this formula, or of these curves, is as a common basis for the computation of changes in acoustic intensity as a function of range and frequency in analytical studies of the relation between the design constants and the operational behavior of equipment. Unless there is a generally accepted common basis it is inevitable that conclusions reached through such analyses will show little agreement. This use of nominal values of propagation loss will be discussed in some detail in Chapters 7 and 8.

3A-8 Propagation Anomalies

In many practical problems, including those relating to the utilization of propagation loss data as well as those relating to the statistical evaluation of such data, it is convenient to consider any deviation from the nominal value of propagation loss as a specific variable. To this end the difference between the actual propagation loss for a given length of water path and the nominal value of propagation loss identified with the distance covered by that path is known as the **propagation anomaly.** During the early study of the propagation of acoustic energy through the sea the term "anomaly" was applied to the difference between a measured propagation loss and ideal inverse square spreading loss. Attenuation is, however, as normal a property of the sonar medium as is spreading. With the accumulation of sufficient information to permit the statistical evaluation of a nominal value for the attenuation coefficient over a substantial portion of the frequency range of interest, it is now possible to include both attenuation and spreading losses in the total loss normally to be associated with a given range. It is, moreover, becoming possible to subdivide the remaining propagation anomaly into two components: one, designated as the **spreading anomaly,** may be identified with the geometry of the ray paths; the other, designated as the **at-**tenuation anomaly, may be identified with that portion of the total loss which appears as a constant fractional change per unit length of path.

As with total spreading loss and total attenuation loss it is never possible to isolate these two deviations from nominal loss for independent measurement. An estimate of the magnitude of each may, however, be obtained by the same method as that used for the separation of spreading and attenuation losses. The propagation anomaly is first determined, for a given range and frequency, by subtracting the nominal propagation loss from the measured loss. This is represented by

$$(N_w)_\Delta = N_w - (N_w)_0 = (N_{\text{spr}})_\Delta + (N_{\text{attn}})_\Delta \qquad (3A\text{-}20)$$

where

$\quad (N_w)_\Delta =$ the propagation anomaly (db)

$\quad N_w =$ the measured propagation loss (db)

$\quad (N_w)_0 =$ the nominal value of propagation loss (db)

$\quad (N_{\text{spr}})_\Delta =$ the spreading anomaly (db)

$\quad (N_{\text{attn}})_\Delta =$ the attenuation anomaly (db)

The total anomaly is resolved into its two components by a series of successive approximations. The conditions to be satisfied are that the spreading anomaly shall be represented by a straight line, or by a series of straight lines, when plotted against a logarithmic scale of frequency and that the attenuation anomaly shall be represented by a straight line when plotted against a linear scale of frequency.

3-B THE EFFECTS OF REFRACTION

The reduction in acoustic intensity described by the nominal propagation loss equation of the preceding section is based on the fundamental assumption that the sound rays involved lie along straight lines. Sound rays in the sea are almost always bent. This bending may result merely in diverting the beam of a directional transducer from the path normally associated with some given orientation. It may, in other instances, result in greatly modifying the manner in which geometrical spreading takes place and thus alter the spreading loss occurring along the beam. Not infrequently the bending of sound rays may be of such nature as virtually to destroy any sound transmission between two points separated by only a short distance. It is therefore essential to consider carefully the causes and consequences of the bending of sound waves in water.

3B-1 Relation to Velocity of Propagation

Those changes in the direction of a sound ray which are known as refractions are quantitatively related to changes in the velocity of propagation of the sound wave, either on passing from place to place in a single medium or on passing from one medium to another of quite different characteristics. Both of these situations are encountered in sonar. The relation between refraction and velocity in the case of sound waves in water is similar to that found in the case of light waves. Both obey **Snell's Law.** This law is expressed in terms of a ray path crossing the boundary between two regions having different velocities of propagation, as shown by the diagram of Fig. 3B-1. The two

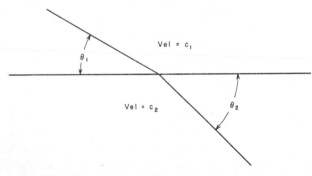

FIG. 3B-1. SNELL'S LAW. The change in the direction of a sound ray at a boundary where the velocity of propagation changes.

velocities may be indicated as c_1 and c_2 and the angles which the ray makes with the boundary surface as θ_1 and θ_2, respectively. Snell's Law then states that

$$\frac{c_1}{c_2} = \frac{\cos \theta_1}{\cos \theta_2} \qquad (3B\text{-}1)$$

This relation is independent of the direction along the ray in which the sound wave is traveling.

Those familiar with Snell's Law as applied in optics are accustomed to seeing this law expressed in terms of the sines of angles rather than in terms of the cosines. In underwater acoustics, however, it is the common practice to express the direction of a ray path in terms of the angle which it makes

with the surface of the water. Angles are, in other words, measured from the boundary plane rather than from the normal to that plane. Since the boundary planes of interest in underwater acoustics are usually horizontal the angle measuring the direction of a ray path is customarily designated as the **angle of inclination.**

3B-2 Refraction Between Two Media

Snell's Law, in the form given above, may be applied at once to the case of two homogeneous media, separated by a plane surface, having two different constant velocities. An examination of the diagram of Fig. 3B-1 and of the relations given by Eq. (3B-1) indicates that, if the ray is passing from a medium of given velocity to a medium of higher velocity, there will be some value of the angle, θ_1, in the first medium for which the angle, θ_2, in the second medium will be 0°. The refracted ray will, in other words, be parallel to the boundary plane. Energy cannot be transmitted across the boundary surface by a wave arriving along a path making an angle with the surface less than that for which the transmitted ray is parallel to the boundary. This limiting incident angle is known as the **critical angle.** Its value is obtained by placing $\cos \theta_2 = 1$ in Eq. (3B-1), whence

$$\cos \theta_1 = \cos \theta_{crit} = \frac{c_1}{c_2} \qquad (3B\text{-}2)$$

The velocity of propagation of acoustic energy may be given the nominal values of $c_1 = 330$ m/sec for air and of $c_2 = 1500$ m/sec for water. At an air-water boundary, then, the critical angle for an incident ray originating in air is

$$\theta_{crit} = \text{arc cos} \frac{330}{1500} = \text{arc cos } 0.220 = 77.3° \qquad (3B\text{-}3)$$

Any sound ray reaching the water at an angle less than 77.3° will be totally reflected, due to refraction, and none of its energy will enter the water. Any ray originating in water and reaching an air-water boundary will pass into the air, regardless of its incident angle. Having reached the air the path along which it continues will make an angle with the boundary surface which will not be less than the critical angle.

The effect on sound rays of passing through a plane surface bounding two media in which acoustic energy is propagated with different velocities may be examined in greater detail by means of the diagram of Fig. 3B-2. This diagram is drawn, as a matter of interest, to the correct scale for a sound ray which originates at a source in air and which passes through an air-water boundary to continue along a path in water. The general conclusions reached on the basis of this diagram

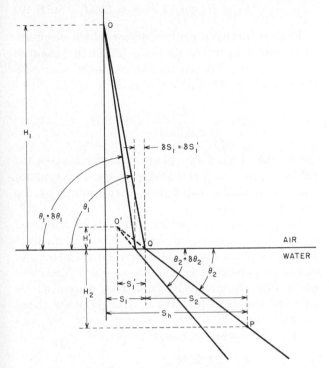

Fig. 3B-2. Refraction at an Air-Water Surface. The paths of neighboring sound rays in a vertical plane which enter a body of water from a point source in air.

apply, however, to any two homogeneous media separated by a plane boundary surface. For convenience we shall speak of this boundary plane as being horizontal.

In this diagram the line OQP represents a sound ray originating at the point source O in a homogeneous medium for which the velocity of propagation is c_1. The portion, OQ, of this ray which is in the medium containing its source is a straight line and defines a plane perpendicular to the medium boundary plane. Let this portion of the ray path make the angle θ_1 with the boundary plane. After crossing the boundary plane the ray continues in the same vertical plane as before but in a medium for which the velocity of propagation is c_2. The portion, QP, of this ray which is in the medium adjoining that containing its source is also a straight line. Let this line make the angle θ_2 with the boundary plane. The relation between these

two angles is determined by the velocities of propagation in the two media, in accordance with Eq. (3B-1). Now let a second ray leave the source, O, so that it lies in the same vertical plane as the first ray and makes the incremental angle $\delta\theta_1$ with the first ray. The portion of this second ray which is in the medium containing the source makes the angle $\theta_1 + \delta\theta_1$ with the medium boundary plane; the portion which is in the medium adjoining that containing the source makes the angle $\theta_2 + \delta\theta_2$ with this plane.

If the straight lines on the diagram representing the portions of the two ray paths which are in the second medium are extended back into the area representing the portion of the plane of the rays which is in the first medium they will intersect at some point, O'. With respect to this pair of neighboring rays in a vertical plane, then, the portions which are in a medium adjoining that containing their source diverge, with distance, as though they originated at the point O' and remained in a medium of constant velocity of propagation thereafter. This point, therefore, has the properties of a **virtual source** for the pair of rays in question.

Other pairs of neighboring ray paths from this same true source point and lying in this same vertical plane will appear to have other virtual source points. The positions of these virtual sources may be determined by further consideration of Fig. 3B-2. On this diagram the distance S_1 represents the length of the projection on the boundary plane of the portion, OQ, of a given ray path which is in the medium containing its source. The distance S_1' represents the length of the projection on the boundary plane of the extension, $O'Q$, into this medium, of the portion in the adjoining medium. The distances H_1 and H_1' represent, in a similar manner, the perpendicular distances of the true and virtual sources of this ray from the medium boundary plane. It is evident that

$$S_1 = H_1 \cot \theta_1 \quad \text{and} \quad S_1' = H_1' \cot \theta_2 \quad (3B-4)$$

By differentiating these two equations we have

$$\frac{dS_1}{d\theta_1} = \frac{-H_1}{\sin^2 \theta_1} \quad \text{and} \quad \frac{dS_1'}{d\theta_2} = \frac{-H_1'}{\sin^2 \theta_2} \quad (3B-5)$$

Also, by differentiating Eq. (3B-1),

$$\frac{d\theta_2}{d\theta_1} = \frac{c_2}{c_1} \frac{\sin \theta_1}{\sin \theta_2} \quad (3B-6)$$

Now it is evident that for any incremental change

in θ_1 the change in S_1' will be equal to the change in S_1. Consequently

$$\frac{dS_1}{d\theta_1} = \frac{dS_1'}{d\theta_2} \frac{d\theta_2}{d\theta_1} \qquad (3B\text{-}7)$$

By substituting the equalities of Eqs. (3B-5) and (3B-6) into Eqs. (3B-4) and (3B-7) it appears that

$$H_1' = H_1 \frac{c_1}{c_2} \frac{\sin^3 \theta_2}{\sin^3 \theta_1}, \text{ and } S_1' = S_1 \frac{\sin^2 \theta_2}{\sin^2 \theta_1}. \quad (3B\text{-}8)$$

It is possible in this manner to compute the locus of virtual source points for all rays leaving a common source in one medium in a plane perpendicular to a plane bounding that medium and entering a second medium. The locus of virtual sources for sound rays in water which have thus

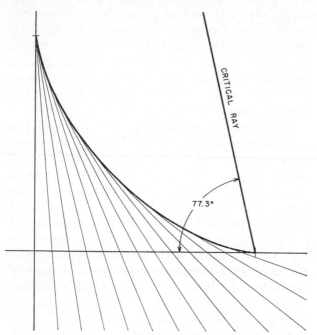

Fig. 3B-3. The Locus of Virtual Source Points. The locus of virtual source points for sound rays in a vertical plane which have entered a body of water from a true source in the air above.

originated at a true source point in air is shown in Fig. 3B-3. This locus has been computed by assuming nominal values for the velocities of propagation of acoustic energy in air and in water. For a ray perpendicular to the medium boundary plane $\theta_1 = \theta_2 = 90°$ and $\sin \theta_1 = \sin \theta_2 = 1$. The perpendicular distance from the boundary plane of the virtual source for this ray is thus

$$H_1' = \frac{c_1}{c_2} H_1 = H_1 \cos 77.3° = 0.220 H_1 \quad (3B\text{-}9)$$

The locus must, therefore, intersect the vertical through the source at this point. This locus reaches the horizontal boundary plane at the point of intersection of this plane and the ray making the critical angle with it. The distance of this intersection from the projection of the true source is

$$S_1 = H_1 \cot 77.3° = 0.224 H_1 \quad (3B\text{-}10)$$

For ray paths in a plane in air which originate at a source in water the locus of virtual sources starts on the perpendicular through the source to the boundary plane at a distance

$$H_1' = \frac{H_1}{\cos 77.3°} = 4.545 H_1 \quad (3B\text{-}11)$$

from the boundary plane. It terminates at $(H_1' = \infty, S_1' = \infty)$, remaining on the same side of the perpendicular through the true source as the actual ray paths.

Neighboring rays which leave their common source point at equal angles with a medium boundary plane but in different vertical planes do not have a common virtual source point. The complete locus is, in fact, the surface generated by rotating the locus for rays in a single plane about an axis through the true source point and perpendicular to the boundary plane.

3B-3 Velocity Gradients

Within a single medium the velocity of propagation may vary from place to place. Continuous changes in velocity within a single medium cause refractions which may have as great an effect upon acoustic intensity as those accompanying the passage of a wave from one medium to another. One of the more important effects influencing the transmission of sound waves through large bodies of water is that due to refractions caused by variations in velocity with temperature. The prediction and interpretation of these refractions is an essential technique of sonar. The limitations which they impose on the reliable reception of echo-ranging signals determine the most effective routines for the operation of its sound gear by any craft engaged in searching for a submarine. A knowledge of the probable disposition of the sound rays sent out by echo-ranging equipment also permits a submarine commander so to maneuver as to reduce considerably the likelihood of his detection by the enemy. These examples make it clear that the refraction of sound rays within the water of the ocean is of more than academic interest.

Every boy who has been in swimming knows that the water of the ocean changes in temperature from place to place. It is generally warmer near the mouth of a river than at some other location along the coast. It is also likely to vary with the depth below the surface. On warm, sunny afternoons in spring, for example, it is almost certain to be warmer at the surface than near the bottom.

The relation between the velocity of propagation and temperature has been given by Eq. (2A-21). In Article 2A-3 are also stated the corrections to be made for the effect of salinity on velocity and for the effect of pressure, which varies with depth, on velocity. Gradual changes in the velocity of propagation with distance within a single medium are known as **velocity gradients.** They are expressed quantitatively as the change in velocity per unit distance. The rate of change of temperature with distance is known as the **temperature gradient.** The rate of change of salinity is, similarly, known as the **salinity gradient** and the rate of change of density as the **density gradient.** Changes in velocity which are due solely to increases in pressure are sometimes spoken of, incorrectly, as pressure, or even as density, gradients. Actually pressure gradients and density gradients are not used as such in sonar although they are very important in other phases of subsurface navigation. Any change in velocity with depth not accounted for by a change in temperature or in salinity may best be described as the **pressure component** of the velocity gradient.

When changes in velocity within a medium are such that the velocity in any horizontal plane is constant it is said that the velocity gradient has no horizontal component or that there is a vertical velocity gradient. From the coefficients given in Eq. (2A-21) it is possible to write a general expression for the **vertical velocity gradient.** Thus

$$g = 0.0182 + (11.25 - 0.090T)(\text{temp grad})$$

$$+ (4.3)(\text{sal grad}) \qquad (3B\text{-}12)$$

where

$g =$ the vertical velocity gradient
   (1 ft/sec·ft = 1/sec)

$T =$ the temperature of the water
   (°F)

(temp grad) = the change in temperature with depth
   (°F/ft)

(sal grad) = the change in salinity with depth
   (parts per thousand/ft)

In the above expression a positive gradient indicates that the quantity to which it applies increases with increasing depth below the surface. It will be noted that the pressure component of the vertical velocity gradient appears as a constant term, 0.0182 1/sec. The effect of temperature gradient on velocity gradient is seen to be, itself, a function of temperature. A constant temperature gradient, then, is not accompanied by a constant velocity gradient. In practice this effect may frequently be neglected and velocity gradients are commonly computed for the average temperature throughout the layer under consideration. The chart of Fig. 3B-4 gives values for the coefficient of the term which expresses the value of the tem-

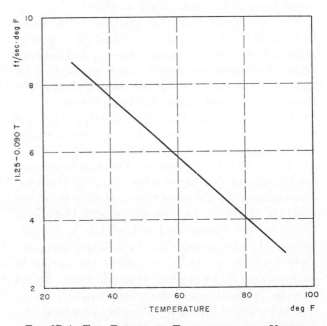

FIG. 3B-4. THE EFFECT OF TEMPERATURE ON VELOCITY GRADIENT. Values of the coefficient by which to multiply the temperature gradient to obtain the temperature component of velocity gradient, plotted as a function of the average temperature.

perature component of velocity gradient. This coefficient is given as a function of temperature and is useful in computing the velocity gradient for a known temperature gradient.

Where there are appreciable temperature gradients their effects, as given by the above equation, are generally so large that density and salinity gradients may frequently be neglected. It is certainly true that temperature gradients cause the greatest concern in subsurface warfare. When there is no temperature gradient, however, changes in pressure with depth invariably introduce refractions which greatly affect the paths taken by sound rays in the sea. Salinity gradients are generally the least significant although they may introduce serious velocity gradients, both vertical and horizontal, in the vicinity of river mouths where large quantities of fresh water are emptied into the ocean.

3B-4 The Bathythermograph

The temperature of the water of the ocean, as a function of depth, may be determined by an instrument known as the **bathythermograph.** This device was developed by the Wood's Hole Oceanographic Institution shortly before World War II and has since become standard equipment on vessels engaged in subsurface warfare.

The arrangement of this instrument is shown in Fig. 3B-5. The record is inscribed on a smoked glass slide held on a moving carrier in a cylindrical body. A temperature-depth graph is recorded by the instrument as it is lowered to, and then raised from, the required depth. This graph is traced by a stylus moved along the arc of a circle by a radial arm. This arm, in turn, is driven by a Bourdon tube connected to a long capillary, both of which are filled with liquid xylene. The expansion and contraction of this liquid with changing temperature deforms the Bourdon tube and thus alters the position of the stylus. Depth is indicated by a spring-loaded piston enclosed within a metallic bellows. Water pressure on the bellows and outer surface of the piston acts against the spring in such manner as to displace the slide holder by an amount proportional to the water depth.

The record obtained by a single immersion of a bathythermograph is known as a **bathythermogram.** The values of temperature and of depth given by such a record are reached by viewing it through a special grid, calibrated for the particular instrument used. The form of this grid is shown in Fig. 3B-6. An actual trace appears as a clear line

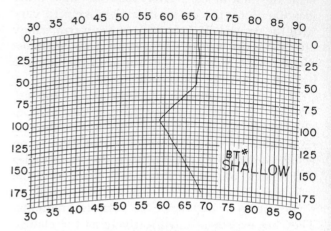

FIG. 3B-6. THE BATHYTHERMOGRAM. The form of a record obtained by the bathythermograph, as viewed through superimposed coordinate scales of temperature and depth.

on the smoked glass, rather than as the heavy black line representing this trace in the illustration.

3B-5 Refraction in a Continuous Medium

Consider a thin layer of constant velocity of propagation separated from adjoining regions by horizontal boundary planes at which occur changes in velocity. Any ray crossing the region between these two planes is a straight line and hence—unless perpendicular—defines a vertical plane. As this ray enters an adjacent region its angle with the horizontal boundary plane is altered in accordance with Snell's Law. It is not, however, deflected from the vertical plane already defined. From this it follows that any ray in a medium

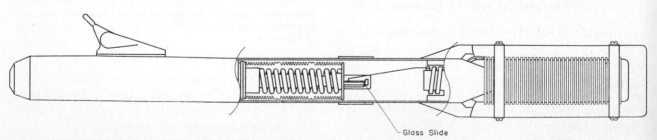

FIG. 3B-5. THE BATHYTHERMOGRAPH. An apparatus for automatically recording the temperature of the ocean as a function of depth.

having a velocity gradient lies wholly within a single vertical plane.

When the velocity of propagation varies continuously with depth the medium may be considered as being made up of horizontal layers of infinitesimal thickness in each of which the velocity is constant. Snell's Law applies at each boundary between two such layers. Within one layer the ray is, for the infinitesimal increment of its length thus specified, a straight line making an angle θ with each boundary. Snell's Law requires that, for any given ray, the cosine of this angle of inclination, $\cos\theta$, within any layer of infinitesimal thickness shall be proportional to the velocity of propagation, c, within the same layer. This applies to all layers through which the ray may pass. When the velocity varies continuously with depth the angle of inclination must also vary continuously with depth and the path of the ray will be represented by a curved line lying in a vertical plane.

The Snell's Law relation may be expressed in terms of a convenient constant

$$c_V = \frac{c}{\cos\theta} \qquad (3\text{B-}13)$$

where

$c_V =$ the Snell's Law constant for a given ray (ft/sec)

$c =$ the velocity of propagation characteristic of the medium at some point on the ray (ft/sec)

$\theta =$ the angle of inclination of the ray at the same point (deg)

The constant defined above, which will be designated as the **Snell's Law constant,** holds for every point on the ray to which it applies, regardless of the manner in which the velocity of propagation may vary, provided the inclination of the ray is not altered by reflection at a surface which is not horizontal. It is a characteristic of the ray.

By placing $\theta = 0$ in the above equation it is seen that the Snell's Law constant for a given sound ray is equal to the velocity which would be found at any level at which the ray path becomes horizontal. For this reason, it is sometimes called the **vertex velocity.** Conversely, the path must always become horizontal on reaching any level at which the velocity has this value. It may never cross such a level into a region of higher velocity. The

Snell's Law constant, then, may be looked upon as the maximum velocity which may be reached by the ray to which it applies. Since Snell's Law is independent of the nature of the velocity gradients these statements are not restricted to the case of a single medium.

3B-6 Refraction when the Velocity Gradient is Constant

The path of a sound ray in a medium of varying velocity of propagation is most simply described for the case in which the velocity gradient is constant. In any actual situation the entire region likely to be of interest may be treated as though it were made up of subdivisions throughout each of which the gradient remains constant. It is, moreover, generally possible to define the boundaries of such subdivisions with satisfactory reliability.

In the diagram of Fig. 3B-7 the curved line

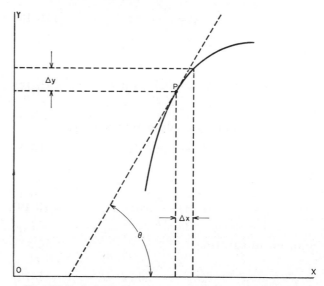

FIG. 3B-7. SNELL'S LAW IN A CONTINUOUS MEDIUM. The fundamental geometry of the path of a sound ray in a continuous medium of varying velocity of propagation.

represents a portion of the path of a sound ray in a medium where the velocity gradient is vertical. The directions in which horizontal and vertical distances are measured are indicated as the x and y directions, respectively. The gradient at the point P, is, by definition,

$$\frac{dc}{dy} = g \qquad (3\text{B-}14)$$

It is, in other words, the derivative of velocity with respect to depth.

When we impose the condition that the vertical

velocity gradient be constant throughout any region the above quantity immediately becomes a constant characteristic of the entire region. We may examine the path of a sound ray through such a region in terms of this constant, characteristic of the medium, and of Snell's Law constant, characteristic of the ray, as given by Eq. (3B-13).

By integrating Eq. (3B-14) there is obtained

$$y = \frac{c}{g} \qquad (3B\text{-}15)$$

Since the origin of the coordinate axes has not yet been fixed we are free to specify that vertical distances, y, shall be measured from that horizontal level at which $c=0$. This avoids the introduction of a constant of integration into Eq. (3B-15).

By combining Eqs. (3B-13) and (3B-15) we obtain

$$y = \frac{c_V}{g} \cos \theta \qquad (3B\text{-}16)$$

whence

$$dy = - \frac{c_V}{g} \sin \theta \; d\theta \qquad (3B\text{-}17)$$

But, by elementary analytical geometry,

$$dy = \tan \theta \; dx \qquad (3B\text{-}18)$$

hence

$$dx = - \frac{c_V}{g} \cos \theta \; d\theta \qquad (3B\text{-}19)$$

and, on integrating,

$$x = - \frac{c_V}{g} \sin \theta \qquad (3B\text{-}20)$$

Again a constant of integration may be avoided by now specifying that horizontal distances, x, are to be measured from the vertical through the point at which $\theta = 0$.

By squaring Eqs. (3B-16) and (3B-20) and adding, there results

$$x^2 + y^2 = \left(\frac{c_V}{g} \right)^2 \qquad (3B\text{-}21)$$

This is the equation of a circle having the radius c_V/g. The center of this circle is at the origin of the system of coordinate axes the location of which has just been selected. The horizontal axis of this coordinate system is, then, by Eq.

(3B-15), at the vertical level where the velocity of propagation would be zero, provided the region of constant gradient were sufficiently extensive. This level is determined entirely by the constants of the region. The horizontal position of the center is determined by the location of any one point on the path and by the angle of incidence at that point. When considering the paths of rays in a vertical plane crossing a region of constant vertical velocity gradient the intersection of the vertical plane with the horizontal level of zero velocity is known as the **line of centers.**

The constants defining any ray path and its position with respect to the system of rectangular coordinates may be derived in terms of conditions known or postulated for some given point P. From the known velocity, c_P, and the known angle of inclination, θ_P, at this one point it is possible to obtain at once the Snell's Law constant, $c_V = c_P / \cos \theta_P$, characteristic of the specified ray. These same constants and the gradient, g, give the radius of the ray path.

$$r = \frac{c_V}{g} = \frac{c_P}{g \cos \theta_P} \qquad (3B\text{-}22)$$

This is obviously a constant characteristic of the specified ray in the specified medium.

The vertical distance between the given point and the horizontal axis of the coordinate system for which the relation given by Eq. (3B-21) is valid, as given by Eq. (3B-15), is $y_P = c_P/g$. When the velocity gradient is positive this quantity is also positive. Since positive vertical distance is measured downward this means that the line of centers is above the region of constant gradient and hence that all rays in that region tend to curve upward. When the gradient is negative the line of centers is below the region and all rays bend downward.

One of the most important constant gradient layers is that known as the **isothermal layer.** This is frequently encountered in practice and results from the thorough mixing of the upper portion of the ocean by wave motion. When the temperature and salinity are constant throughout any layer the velocity gradient is due entirely to changes in pressure with depth. The gradient of an isothermal layer, then, has the constant value $g = 0.0182$ 1/sec. This gradient is positive.

As shown by the preceding analysis the paths of all rays in an isothermal layer must, because of the positive gradient, be concave upward. On the basis of a nominal velocity of $c = 4800$ ft/sec at the surface and a gradient of $g = 0.0182$ 1/sec it is seen that the line of centers for this region is approximately 50 miles above the surface. Since this is the shortest radius which any ray path in this region may have it is obvious that the curvature is not great. It is, however, sufficient to have a most important effect on the performance of sonar equipment.

With information as to the quantitative relation between velocity and depth derived from the bathythermogram we may apply the relations just developed to the computation of sound ray paths in the medium as a whole. Since we shall consider only vertical velocity gradients these paths will be confined to vertical planes. They may, therefore, be represented graphically by two-dimensional plots, known as **ray diagrams,** in which the range of points on a given ray is shown as a function of depth.

In ray diagrams the coordinates of positive vertical distance, which represents depth, are laid off below the origin rather than above, as in the more conventional manner; positive angles, therefore, are measured clockwise from the horizontal. It is also customary to consider a distance measured to the right of a specified point on the ray path as a positive distance. The diagram of Fig. 3B-8 shows the paths of sound rays in regions of constant vertical velocity gradient with angles and distances laid off on a system of coordinates in accordance with the above conventions.

3B-7 Limiting Rays and Shadow Zones

Before undertaking an examination of the quantitative methods for developing the paths of sound rays we shall consider qualitatively the behavior of certain typical ray paths of special significance. This will aid in making a suitable selection of paths to be computed for a given ray diagram.

A situation of considerable importance occurs when, in a given layer of water, the velocity of propagation increases with distance measured inward from either boundary until reaching a level at which its value passes through a maximum. No ray for which the value of the Snell's Law constant, c_v, characteristic of the ray path is less than this maximum velocity can cross the level at which this occurs. A ray for which the value of the characteristic constant is the same as the maximum velocity will become tangent to this level. Any ray which is tangent to a plane at which the velocity of propagation has a maximum value, either

at a boundary of the medium or at a level where the velocity gradient changes sign, is known as a **limiting ray.** It is not necessary for the gradient on either side of such a plane to be constant in order to satisfy this definition.

At a maximum velocity plane, where there is a change in the sign of the gradient, there will be a

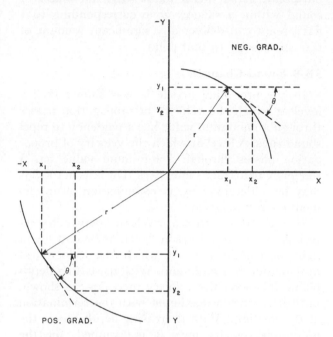

FIG. 3B-8. THE GEOMETRY OF SOUND RAY PATHS. The analytical parameters associated with the paths of sound rays in media having constant vertical velocity gradients.

change in direction of curvature of the path of any ray which crosses. This applies to a path for which the characteristic constant exceeds the maximum velocity of the region by an infinitesimally small increment. In fact, the limiting ray may be considered as splitting at the point of tangency with the maximum velocity level and continuing as two diverging branches. The region between these two branches, or between the branch which remains on one side of the maximum velocity level and a layer other than water, is known as a **shadow zone.** The diagram of Fig. 3B-11 shows a limiting ray having diverging branches and the shadow zone included between them.

It is clear that in a shadow zone defined by the position of some given source the intensity of sound is much less than would be computed by the propagation loss equation, if, indeed, there is any sound at all. In the ideal case the only sound which can reach a shadow zone from the position defining its boundaries must do so by reflection.

In this case sound rays which enter the shadow zone will appear to originate at some point other than the true source.

It can be shown that sound rays through any point in the shadow zone defined by the position of some given point themselves form a shadow zone and that this shadow zone includes the original point. From this it follows that no source of sound within a shadow zone corresponding to a fixed point can deliver any significant amount of acoustic energy to that point.

3B-8 Sound Channels

In the preceding article it was shown that a level at which the velocity of propagation passes through a maximum value has a tendency to repel sound rays. A level at which the velocity of propagation passes through a minimum value has a tendency to attract sound rays. The reason for this may be understood by an examination of an elementary ray diagram.

In Fig. 3B-9 is shown a velocity-depth characteristic which discloses a level, indicated by a light horizontal line, at which the velocity of propagation is a minimum. With increasing depth below this level the velocity increases, as shown, until it reaches a maximum with the termination of the medium. With decreasing depth above the minimum velocity level it is assumed, for the moment, that the velocity may increase indefinitely. The lower level of maximum velocity and a level above, indicated on the diagram by a horizontal dotted line, at which the same velocity is again found, define a unique layer.

The Snell's Law constant discussed in Art. 3B-5 is, by definition, the velocity of propagation at a level where the ray path, for which it is a characteristic, becomes horizontal. It was pointed out in that article that this characteristic may be interpreted as the maximum velocity attainable by an element of wave front traveling along this ray path, and that the ray may never cross such a level to enter a region of higher velocity. If, therefore, the characteristic constant of any ray originating within a layer such as that indicated on the diagram has the same value as the maximum velocity to be found in the layer the ray must follow a path which takes it to one of the two boundary levels and must, on arrival, be tangent to that level. Thereafter the ray must return to the layer along a path which crosses the minimum velocity level and, again encountering a level where the velocity of propagation has its characteristic limiting value, must become tangent to the other boundary level. The ray path must, in other words, remain within the given layer, crossing and recrossing the level of minimum velocity, and becoming tangent first to one and then to the other of the two boundary levels. The courses of two tangent rays satisfying these conditions are shown by the heavy curved lines marked $(c_V)_{tan}$ in the ray diagram.

Any ray which originates within the given layer and which has a characteristic constant of greater value than that of a tangent ray will arrive at one boundary level or the other with a finite angle of inclination. If the first boundary reached terminates the medium, and if it is an effective sound absorber, the energy associated with the ray will leave the layer permanently. Should the ray first

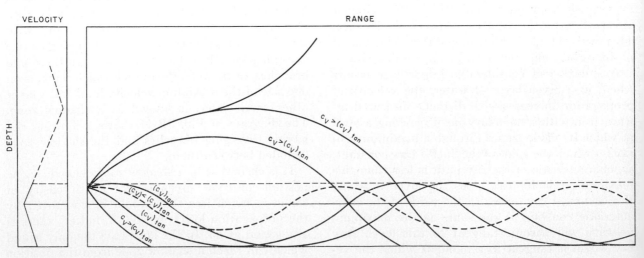

FIG. 3B-9. SOUND CHANNEL. A ray diagram showing the effect of a minimum velocity level.

reach a boundary beyond which its wave element may continue with increasing velocity its path may ultimately become horizontal and finally return to the layer. It will then cross the minimum velocity level and pass out of the layer at the opposite boundary where, as before, it may be absorbed. These two conditions are illustrated in the diagram by ray paths marked $c_V > (c_V)_{\text{tan}}$. Not all rays which leave the layer at a level beyond which the velocity of propagation continues to increase return to the layer. They may reach a boundary of the medium and be absorbed or, under other conditions, encounter a level at which the velocity gradient changes sign whereupon they will pass into a region separated from the given layer by a shadow zone. In any case there will be some critical value of the characteristic ray constant which will establish the maximum range at which acoustic energy may leave the layer permanently. Beyond this range all energy within the layer must remain until dissipated by attenuation. This energy is associated with ray paths having values of characteristic constant, c_V, equal to or less than the critical value, $(c_V)_{\text{tan}}$, for a limiting tangent ray. Because of this tendency to prevent the escape of acoustic energy a horizontal layer which is bounded by levels at which the velocity of propagation is greater than at any depth within the layer is known as a **sound channel.**

As shown by the diagram the maximum thickness of a sound channel layer may be considered as being fixed by the lowest value at which the velocity of propagation ceases to increase with increasing distance from the level of minimum velocity. This value may be found at a boundary of the medium or at a level where the velocity gradient changes sign. On the opposite side of the minimum velocity level there will be a complimentary level at which the velocity of propagation has this same value. These two levels are fixed solely by the relations between the velocity of propagation and depth and are entirely independent of the location of the sound source. The portion of the total output of any source which may be concentrated within the sound channel layer is, however, dependent on the vertical position of the source.

If, in the ray diagram of Fig. 3B-9, a horizontal line is drawn within the sound channel layer it will intersect a limiting tangent ray at two points. At these points the angles of inclination will be equal in magnitude but of opposite sign. These two

angles have the critical values for tangent rays in the given layer associated with the indicated horizontal level. For a sound source located at this vertical height there will be, therefore, in the vertical plane corresponding to the ray diagram, two limiting tangent rays, one inclined downward and one inclined upward, making equal angles with the horizontal. Such tangent rays are indicated on the ray diagram by the two heavy curved lines marked $(c_V)_{\text{tan}}$. That portion of the total output of a sound source which is included between limiting tangent rays, having angles of inclination equal to the value established by the vertical position of the source, must remain within the sound channel. Ray paths having angles of inclination less than that of a tangent ray do not remain constantly between a pair of such rays but follow their own paths, as shown by the dotted line marked $c_V < (c_V)_{\text{tan}}$. Sound energy emitted from a source between tangent rays, and thus retained by a sound channel, is, in general, propagated in accordance with the inverse first power law.

In order to concentrate the greatest possible portion of the total output of a source in a sound channel it is evident that the critical angle of inclination at the source must have the greatest possible absolute value in order that the separation between the two tangent rays shall be as large as possible. This value is, as shown by Eq. (3B-13), given by the relation $\cos \theta = c/(c_V)_{\text{tan}}$. The value of the constant, $(c_V)_{\text{tan}}$, is fixed by the conditions defining the sound channel. In order to make θ large we must make $\cos \theta$ small and hence must locate the source at the level where c has its minimum value, that is, at the minimum velocity level.

The isothermal surface layer usually results in a sound channel. Here the minimum velocity level occurs at the sea surface. Sound rays reaching this surface are repeatedly returned to the medium by reflection and repeatedly brought back to the surface by refraction. Sound channels also exist far below the surface of the ocean. Here there will be a region above which the temperature decreases with increasing depth, but below which it is essentially constant. Above this region the velocity gradient, being controlled by the temperature, will be negative. Below this region, being controlled by the pressure, it has a positive value which varies but little from that to be found in the isothermal surface layer. Within this characteristic region the velocity of propagation passes gradually through a minimum as the gradient changes from negative to positive with increasing depth. The region thus attracts sound energy, in the manner already described, to form a deep sound channel. This is utilized in a method of signaling, known as **Sofar**, whereby small explosive charges are dropped from aircraft or vessels in distress and fired by pressure-actuated fuses upon reaching the critical temperature, or minimum velocity level. Sound energy released by the explosion is, therefore, concentrated in the sound channel. It may be picked up by hydrophones located in the same channel at distances of as much as 2000 miles.

3B-9 The Computation of Ray Diagrams

In ray diagrams depth is usually drawn to a larger scale than is range. Were this not done any diagram of practical length would be unreadably small in the vertical direction. Because of this distortion, however, ray paths do not appear on ray diagrams as arcs of circles but as portions of ellipses. They may not, for this reason, be drawn with compasses. Such a procedure would hardly be feasible in any case because of the fact that for many gradients the line of centers would be far outside the limits of the drawing board. The method actually used is to compute the horizontal components of increments of path length associated with assigned increments of depth.

An examination of many bathythermograms indicates that in a large number of cases the entire body of water of interest may be considered as made up of a relatively few layers in each of which the velocity gradient may be assumed constant. It will be advantageous to select increments of depth for which to carry out the computation so as to subdivide these constant gradient layers into an appropriate number of thinner layers. This is necessary in order to obtain a sufficient number of points for the reliable establishment of the curve representing the ray path. Increments of vertical distance, ΔD, are obtained directly from the selected depth levels, D; values of the horizontal range, S, corresponding to these depths, are obtained by properly combining computed values for horizontal components, ΔS, of increments of path length.

To compute these required horizontal components of portions of a ray path it is necessary to know the angle of inclination, θ_P, of the ray and the velocity of propagation, c_P, of the medium at some given point, P. It is also necessary to know the depths of the levels bounding layers of constant vertical velocity gradient and the value of the gradient, g, within each such layer. With these data it is possible to compute the value of the Snell's Law constant, $c_V = c_P/\cos \theta_P$, characteristic of the ray in all layers, and the value of the radius, $r_N = c_P/(g_N \cos \theta_P)$, characteristic of the ray in a specified layer, N. Since the velocity of propagation, c_D, may, with the data available, be derived for any given depth, D, the angle of inclination at that depth may be determined at once from the relation $\cos \theta_D = c_D/c_V$. Knowing the angle of inclination at each level the horizontal component of the increment of path length included between any two successive levels, m and n, may be computed by the relation given in Eq. (3B-20), from which may be written

$$\Delta S = x_n - x_m = r(\sin \theta_m - \sin \theta_n) \quad (3B\text{-}23)$$

To carry out the computation exactly as indicated requires that values of the velocity, of the angle of inclination, and of the cosine of this angle be known with considerable precision. For an isothermal layer, for example, the velocity at a given level may be about 5000 ft/sec. The velocity 50 ft below this level will then be $(0.0182)(50) = 0.910$ ft/sec greater. Consequently

$$\cos \theta_n = \frac{c_n}{c_m} \cos \theta_m = (1.000182)(\cos \theta_m)$$

The computation of the angle of inclination may be greatly simplified by taking advantage of the relation of Eq. (3B-16), by which may be written

$$\Delta D = y_n - y_m = r(\cos \theta_n - \cos \theta_m) \quad (3B\text{-}24)$$

whence

$$\cos \theta_n = \cos \theta_m + \frac{\Delta D}{r} \quad (3B\text{-}25)$$

In this equation the term $\Delta D/r$, being an incremental difference, need not be computed with any great precision in order to obtain values of $\cos \theta_D$ to the required accuracy. It should be noted, however, that in this term $r = c_V/g$ and must retain the sign of the gradient. In some cases it may be found advantageous to determine this incremental difference between values of the cosine of the angle of inclination by means of any one of the equivalent expressions.

$$\frac{\Delta D}{r} = \frac{g(\Delta D)}{c_V} = \frac{\Delta c}{c_V} \quad (3B\text{-}26)$$

In routine computations it is advisable to use seven-place trigonometric tables when converting from $\cos \theta_D$ to $\sin \theta_D$.

Another expression which is frequently used in the computation of ray diagrams is obtained by dividing Eq. (3B-23) by Eq. (3B-24), which gives

$$\frac{\Delta S}{\Delta D} = \frac{\sin \theta_m - \sin \theta_n}{\cos \theta_n - \cos \theta_m} \qquad (3B\text{-}27)$$

On simplifying this by trigonometric identities there is obtained

$$\Delta S = \Delta D \cot \frac{\theta_m + \theta_n}{2} \qquad (3B\text{-}28)$$

Many questions having to do with the refraction of sound rays in the sea involve limiting rays or other rays which are horizontal at some known level. For such paths it is often convenient to make use of two additional constants. The vertical distance between a given point, P, and the line of centers will be designated as H. This height is fixed by constants of the medium at the given point and is

$$H = \frac{c_P}{g} \qquad (3B\text{-}29)$$

Here, as before, c_P is the velocity of propagation at the point P and g is the gradient of the layer in which this point is located. The vertical distance between the point P and the level at which the ray is horizontal will be designated as $D_{\max}$. The value of this constant, which depends on both the ray and the medium, is

$$D_{\max} = r - H = \frac{c_V - c_P}{g} = r(1 - \cos \theta_P). \quad (3B\text{-}30)$$

The relations between these various quantities, in terms of the analytical geometry of a circular ray path, are shown diagrammatically in Fig. 3B-10. From these relations the horizontal component of the distance between a given point and the point at which the ray is horizontal may be expressed in any of the following ways:

$$S = \sqrt{2HD_{\max} + D^2_{\max}} \qquad (3B\text{-}31)$$

$$= \sqrt{2rD_{\max} - D^2_{\max}} \qquad (3B\text{-}32)$$

$$= \frac{1}{g}\sqrt{c_V{}^2 - c_P{}^2} \qquad (3B\text{-}33)$$

$$= r \sin \theta_P \qquad (3B\text{-}34)$$

$$= H \tan \theta_P \qquad (3B\text{-}35)$$

$$= D_{\max} \cot (\theta_P/2) \qquad (3B\text{-}36)$$

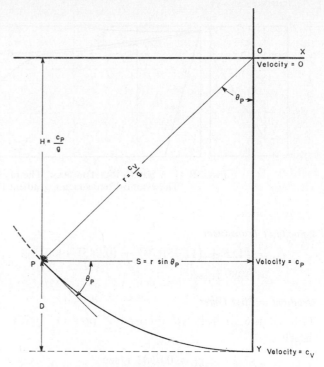

Fig. 3B-10. The Geometry of a Sound Ray. The analytical parameters associated with a sound ray in terms of its point of tangency with a given horizontal plane.

A frequently occurring case in which these simplified formulas are convenient is in the determination of the shortest distance to a shadow zone. Assume the depth of an isothermal layer below the sound source to be $D_{\max} = 80$ ft and the gradient to be $g = 0.0182$ 1/sec. It is not necessary to know the velocity of propagation with any great exactness and we shall assume that $c_P = 4900$ ft/sec. In Eq. (3B-31) the term $2HD_{\max} = 2c_P D_{\max}/g = 4.3 \cdot 10^7$ ft². The term $D^2_{\max}$ is, therefore, entirely negligible and the distance required is

$$S = \frac{1}{3}\sqrt{2HD_{\max}} = 2200 \text{ yd}$$

The details involved in constructing ray diagrams, using the principles which have just been set forth, may, perhaps, be described most clearly by solving an actual quantitative problem. The several ray paths considered in this example are shown in Fig. 3B-11.

PROBLEM:

Assume a bathythermogram which shows a constant temperature of 70 °F to a depth of 65 ft and a linear decrease thereafter to 56 °F at 265 ft. It is required to determine certain significant ray paths for a transducer located at a depth of 15 ft.

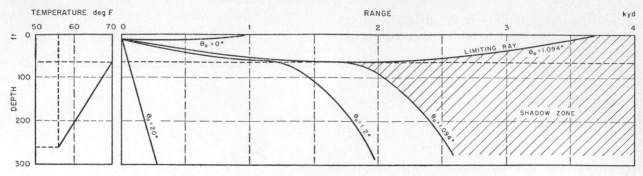

FIG. 3B-11. A SOUND RAY DIAGRAM. The ray paths of the illustrative problem of Art. 3B-9. The assumed temperature gradient is shown in the conventional manner.

Velocity at Transducer

$$c_{15} = 4422 + (11.25)(70) - (0.045)(4900)$$
$$= 4989 \text{ ft/sec}$$

Gradient in First Layer

This is due entirely to increasing pressure with depth.

$$g_{\mathrm{I}} = 0.0182 \ 1/\text{sec}$$

Gradient in Second Layer

$$\text{Average temperature} = 63 \text{ °F}$$

$$\text{Temperature gradient} = \frac{-14}{200} = -0.070 \text{ °F/ft}$$

$$g_{\mathrm{II}} = 0.0182 - [(11.25) - (0.090)(63)](0.070)$$
$$= -0.376 \ 1/\text{sec}$$

Path of a Ray Initially Horizontal

Since the ray is horizontal at a known point, and since it is wholly within a layer for which the vertical velocity gradient has a single value, it will be convenient to measure horizontal and vertical components of all increments of path length from the known point. Thus

$$\Delta D = D - 15 \text{ ft}$$

$$r = H = \frac{4989}{(0.0182)(1)} = 274{,}100 \text{ ft}$$

$$\cos \theta = 1 + \frac{\Delta D}{r}$$

$$S = \Delta S = \frac{r \sin \theta}{3} \text{ yd}$$

D ft	ΔD ft	ΔD/r	cos θ	θ deg	sin θ	S yd
15	0	0	1.0000000	0	0	0
10	− 5	−0.0000182	0.9999818	0.346	0.00604	552
5	−10	−0.0000365	0.9999635	0.490	0.00855	782
0	−15	−0.0000547	0.9999452	0.600	0.01047	957

Path of Limiting Ray in First Layer

All components of incremental distances will here be measured from the point of tangency at $D = 65$ ft.

$$\Delta D = D - 65 \text{ ft}$$

$$r = H + D - 15 = 274{,}100 + 50 = 274{,}200 \text{ ft}$$

$$\cos \theta = 1 + \frac{\Delta D}{r}$$

$$\Delta S = \frac{r \sin \theta}{3} \text{ yd}$$

$$S = S_{65} \pm \Delta S \text{ yd}$$

D ft	ΔD ft	ΔD/r	cos θ	θ deg	sin θ	ΔS yd	S yd
65	0	0	1.0000000	0	0	0	1746
40	−25	−0.0000912	0.9999188	0.730	0.01274	1165	581 or 2911
15	−50	−0.0001823	0.9998177	1.094	0.01909	1746	0 or 3492
0	−65	−0.0002371	0.9997619	1.247	0.02176	1990	3736

Path of Limiting Ray in Second Layer

Here, also, all components of incremental distances will be measured from the point of tangency.

$$\Delta D = D - 65 \text{ ft}$$

$$c_{65} = c_{15} + 50\, g_{\mathrm{I}}$$

$$= 4989 + (50)(0.0182) = 4990 \text{ ft/sec}$$

$$r = \frac{4990}{(-0.376)(1)} = -13{,}410 \text{ ft}$$

$$\cos \theta = 1 + \frac{\Delta D}{r}$$

$$\Delta S = \frac{r \sin \theta}{3} \text{ yd}$$

$$S = S_{65} + \Delta S = 1746 + \Delta S \text{ yd}$$

D ft	ΔD ft	$\Delta D/r$	$\cos \theta$	θ deg	$\sin \theta$	ΔS yd	S yd
65	0	0	1.000000	0	0	0	1746
115	50	−0.003729	0.996271	4.950	0.08629	386	2132
165	100	−0.007457	0.992543	7.002	0.12190	545	2291
215	150	−0.011185	0.988815	8.578	0.1492	667	2413
265	200	−0.01491	0.98509	9.906	0.1720	769	2516

Path Starting in Proximity to Limiting Ray

From the previous computation it was found that the angle of inclination of the limiting ray at $D=15$ ft was 1.094°. For the present case we shall assume a ray having an initial angle of inclination of 1.2°. Since the ray will pass through layers having different velocity gradients, and since it is not horizontal at any point now known, increments of path length will be taken between successive levels in accordance with the general method.

$$\theta = 1.2°, \quad \cos \theta_{15} = 0.9997807$$

$$c_V = \frac{4989}{0.9998} = 4990 \text{ ft/sec}$$

$$\Delta S = \frac{r_N \Delta \sin \theta}{3} \text{ yd}$$

Layer	g 1/sec	ΔD ft	$r = c_V/g$ ft	$\Delta D/r$
I	0.0182	25	274,100	0.0000912
II	−0.376	50	−13,410	−0.003727

D ft	$\cos \theta$	θ deg	$\sin \theta$	$\Delta \sin \theta$	ΔS yd	S yd
15	0.9997807	1.200	0.0209424			0
				0.004938	451	
40	0.9998719	0.917	0.0160040			451
				0.007417	678	
65	0.9999631	0.492	0.0085869			1129
				−0.078100	349	
115	0.996236	4.973	0.0866863			1478
				−0.03548	159	
165	0.992509	7.017	0.1221638			1637
				−0.02720	122	
215	0.988782	8.590	0.1493628			1759
				−0.02288	102	
265	0.985055	9.918	0.1722386			1861

Path Remote from Limiting Ray

$$\theta_{15} = 20°, \quad \cos \theta_{15} = 0.9396926$$

$$c_V = \frac{4989}{0.9397} = 5309 \text{ ft/sec}$$

Layer	g 1/sec	ΔD ft	$r = c_V/g$ ft	$\Delta D/r$
I	0.0182	25	291,700	0.0000857
II	−0.376	50	−14,120	−0.003541

D ft	$\cos \theta$	θ deg	$\sin \theta$	$\Delta \sin \theta$	ΔS yd	S yd
15	0.9396926	20.000	0.3420201			0
				0.0002296	22	
40	0.9397783	19.986	0.3417905			22
				0.0002460	24	
65	0.9398640	19.971	0.3415445			46
				−0.009497	45	
115	0.936323	20.551	0.351041			91
				−0.009200	43	
165	0.932782	21.115	0.360241			134
				−0.008954	42	
215	0.929241	21.666	0.369195			176
				−0.008694	41	
265	0.925700	22.203	0.377889			217

The horizontal lines in the columns for $\cos \theta$ and for $\Delta \sin \theta$ are warnings that the constant increment, $\Delta D/r$, or the constant multiplier, $r/3$, change values.

3B-10 The Computation of Spreading Loss

Even though a ray diagram locates the paths of sound rays quantitatively the information thus obtained remains qualitative as far as indicating the actual propagation loss between two given points is concerned. The ray path may define the location and extent of a shadow zone with all the accuracy which the available data justify; and it may be assumed that the spreading loss from the point of origin of a family of ray paths to the region from which they are all excluded is, if not actually infinite, at least high enough to reduce acoustic signals below useful intensities. It is, however, equally important to know the actual magnitudes of the spreading losses to points not in the shadow zone. For example, how does the spreading loss depart from the inverse square law in a region of constant gradient, where the ray paths are curved instead of straight? It is apparent from Fig. 3B-11 that the rate of separation between the limiting ray and a ray having a slightly greater angle of inclination at the origin increases abruptly on passing a layer boundary where the gradient changes sign. How great is the spreading loss represented by this increased rate of separation?

In an acoustic medium where the velocity of propagation varies in such manner that its gradients are everywhere vertical each ray path lies in a vertical plane. In such a plane let a sound ray originating at the source point O pass through another point P, as shown in Fig. 3B-12. Let the

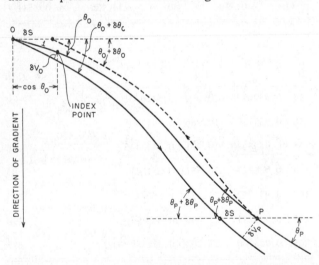

Fig. 3B-12. Divergence Along a Sound Ray. The geometric relations by which to compute the change in cross-sectional area of an incremental bundle of sound rays.

horizontal component of the distance between these two points be S. Let the velocity of propagation be c_0 at the level of the source and c_P at the level of the point P. Let the angles of inclination of the ray path joining these two points be θ_0 at the source and θ_P at the point P. Now let a second ray path leave the same source so that it lies in this same vertical plane and makes the incremental angle $\delta\theta_0$ with the first ray. This second

ray will cross the horizontal plane through the point P at the distance δS from this point.

The separation between these neighboring ray paths as measured at the point on the first which is at unit distance from the source is

$$\delta V_0 = \delta\theta_0 \qquad (3\text{B-}37)$$

The separation as measured from the point P is

$$\delta V_P = -\sin\theta_P\,\delta S \qquad (3\text{B-}38)$$

The negative sign is used here to agree with the diagram; any increase in θ causes a decrease in δS but an increase in δV_P.

Now rotate the two ray paths through the incremental angle $\delta\phi$ about a vertical axis through the source point, O. The perpendicular distance from this axis of the point on the original ray at unit distance from the source is $\cos\theta_0$. The horizontal distance through which this point is thus moved is consequently

$$\delta X_0 = \cos\theta_0\,\delta\phi \qquad (3\text{B-}39)$$

The horizontal distance through which the point originally at P is moved is

$$\delta X_P = S\,\delta\phi \qquad (3\text{B-}40)$$

The four ray paths just described define a volume in the acoustic medium known as a **ray bundle**. Since we are here concerned only with spreading losses it is assumed that all acoustic energy entering this volume at the source remains within its boundaries as it is propagated along the paths making up this bundle. On this assumption the acoustic intensity at any point on the original ray path must be inversely proportional to the cross-sectional area of this bundle. The ratio of the acoustic intensity at the index point, at unit distance from the source, to the acoustic intensity at the point P is therefore

$$\frac{I_0}{I_P} = \frac{\delta V_P}{\delta V_0}\frac{\delta X_P}{\delta X_0} = -S\frac{\sin\theta_P}{\cos\theta_0}\frac{\delta S}{\delta\theta_0} \qquad (3\text{B-}41)$$

As the incremental angle $\delta\theta$ approaches zero the incremental distance δS approaches zero and the ratio $\delta S/\delta\theta_0$ approaches the derivative $dS/d\theta_0$. The following equation then results

$$\frac{I_0}{I_P} = -S\frac{\sin\theta_P}{\cos\theta_0}\frac{dS}{d\theta_0} \qquad (3\text{B-}42)$$

This equation is valid regardless of the path followed by the ray between the points O and P provided only that this path remains in a single vertical plane, as required by the condition that the velocity gradients are everywhere vertical. As long as this condition is satisfied this formula is independent of the manner in which these vertical gradients vary in magnitude. A number of important facts pertaining to spreading losses in a medium having vertical velocity gradients may be deduced by the aid of this equation.

If we assume the ocean to be made up of a number of horizontal layers each of finite thickness and each of constant vertical velocity gradient, as was done in the computation of ray paths, it is usually possible to obtain a numerical solution for this equation. The horizontal component of that increment of path length which is included between two levels, m and n, in a constant gradient layer, N, is given by Eq. (3B-23). This expression may be differentiated with respect to θ_0, the angle of inclination at the source, remembering that r_N, $\sin \theta_m$, and $\sin \theta_n$ are all functions of this angle. When this operation is carried out there is obtained

$$\left[\frac{d}{d\theta_0} (\Delta S) \right]_m^n = \left[\Delta \left(\frac{dS}{d\theta_0} \right) \right]_m^n$$

$$= r_N \tan \theta_0 \left(\frac{1}{\sin \theta_m} - \frac{1}{\sin \theta_n} \right) \quad (3B-43)$$

This is the amount by which the derivative $dS/d\theta_0$ changes in passing from a point on the ray path at the level m to a point at the level n. The value of $dS/d\theta_0$ sought is obtained by computing the derivatives for all increments of path length, by this equation, and taking their sum.

Special attention must be given to cases in which the sound ray becomes horizontal.

When $\theta_n = 0$, $r_{N+1} = r_N$, and $\theta_{n+1} = - \theta_m$,

$$\left[\Delta \left(\frac{dS}{d\theta_0} \right) \right]_m^{n+1} = 2r_N \frac{\tan \theta_0}{\sin \theta_m} \quad (3B-44)$$

When $\theta_P = 0$,

$$\left[\Delta \left(\frac{dS}{d\theta_0} \right) \right]_m^P = - \infty$$

But

$$\sin \theta_P \left[\Delta \left(\frac{dS}{d\theta_0} \right) \right]_m^P = - r_N \tan \theta_0 \quad (3B-45)$$

When $\theta_0 = 0$,

$$\left[\Delta \left(\frac{dS}{d\theta_0} \right) \right]_0^1 = r_I \quad (3B-46)$$

When $\theta_0 = 0$, and $\theta_P = 0$,

$$\left[\Delta \left(\frac{dS}{d\theta_0} \right) \right]_m^P = - r_N$$

But

$$\sin \theta_P \frac{dS}{d\theta_0} = 0 \quad (3B-47)$$

The significance of this last relation will be considered later. When the sound ray in question is a limiting ray no solution is possible by this method for points beyond a point of horizontal tangency with a layer boundary; at such a point the range is a discontinuous function of the source inclination and has no derivative.

It is thus apparent that the change in acoustic intensity with distance along a sound ray may be computed, in most cases, by using data obtained during the computation of the path of that ray. The accompanying example illustrates the method of carrying out such a computation. With the correctly computed values are included values of the quantity $2 \lg t \, S$; this is the spreading loss which would be expected for the same distances, if there were a constant velocity of propagation or a constant velocity gradient.

PROBLEM:

Assume the same situation as that of the problem of Art. 3B-9. It is required to determine the spreading loss along a specified ray path.

Spreading Loss for Path Starting in Proximity to Limiting Ray

$$\theta_0 = 1.2°,$$

$$\cos \theta_0 = 0.9997807$$

$$\sin \theta_0 = \sin \theta_{15} = 0.0209424$$

$$\tan \theta_0 = 0.0209470$$

$$\Delta \left(\frac{dS}{d\theta_0} \right) = (r_N \tan \theta_0)(\Delta \csc \theta)$$

$$\frac{I_0}{I} = -S \frac{\sin \theta}{\cos \theta_0} \frac{dS}{d\theta_0}$$

$$N_{spr} = \lg t \frac{I_0}{I}$$

Layer	r_N yd	$r_N \tan \theta_0$ yd
I	91,370	1914.2
II	−4,470	−93.66

D ft	S yd	$\sin \theta$	$\csc \theta$	$\Delta \csc \theta$	$-\Delta(dS/d\theta_0)$ yd/rad	$-dS/d\theta_0$ yd/rad	I_0/I	N_{spr} db	$2 \lg t\, S$ db
15	0	0.0209424	47.750			0			
				−14.734	28,204				
40	451	0.0160040	62.484			28,204	$2.04 \cdot 10^5$	53.10	53.08
				−53.972	103,313				
65	1129	0.0085869	116.456			131,517	$1.27 \cdot 10^6$	61.04	61.06
				104.920	9,827				
115	1478	0.0866863	11.536			141,344	$1.82 \cdot 10^7$	72.60	63.41
				3.350	314				
165	1637	0.1221638	8.186			141,658	$2.85 \cdot 10^7$	74.55	64.30
				1.491	140				
215	1759	0.1493628	6.695			141,798	$3.77 \cdot 10^7$	75.76	64.91
				0.889	83				
265	1861	0.1722386	5.806			141,881	$4.61 \cdot 10^7$	76.64	65.39

When a ray path remains wholly within a layer in which the vertical velocity gradient is of constant magnitude

$$\frac{dS}{d\theta_0} = r_{\mathrm{I}} \tan \theta_0 \left[\frac{1}{\sin \theta_0} - \frac{1}{\sin \theta_P} \right]$$

$$= \frac{r_{\mathrm{I}}(\sin \theta_P - \sin \theta_0)}{\cos \theta_0 \sin \theta_P}$$

$$= \frac{-S}{\cos \theta_0 \sin \theta_P} \qquad (3B\text{-}48)$$

Whence

$$\frac{I_0}{I_P} = - \left[\frac{S \sin \theta_P}{\cos \theta_0} \right] \left[\frac{-S}{\cos \theta_0 \sin \theta_P} \right]$$

$$= \frac{S^2}{\cos^2 \theta_0} \qquad (3B\text{-}49)$$

If we consider two points, A and B, on such a ray path, we have

$$\frac{I_0}{I_A} = \frac{S_A{}^2}{\cos^2 \theta_0}, \quad \text{and} \quad \frac{I_0}{I_B} = \frac{S_B{}^2}{\cos^2 \theta_0} \qquad (3B\text{-}50)$$

Whence

$$\frac{I_A}{I_B} = \left(\frac{S_B}{S_A} \right)^2 \qquad (3B\text{-}51)$$

This demonstrates that for the portion of a sound ray which remains in the layer of constant vertical velocity gradient containing its source the acoustic intensity varies inversely as the square of the horizontal component of the distance from that source. It may be seen that Eq. (3B-49) conforms to this theorem since $\cos \theta_0$ is the horizontal component of the unit distance between the index point and the source.

In order to compute the spreading loss along a ray path by means of Eq. (3B-42) it is not always necessary to compute the numerical value of the derivative $dS/d\theta_0$ by Eq. (3B-43). It has been suggested by scientists of the Woods Hole Oceanographic Institution that, having determined a number of paths for a ray diagram by any convenient method, the spreading loss between the origin and any point on the diagram may be determined graphically. All that is required is that a plot be made of horizontal range as a function of source inclination for several rays which cross the horizontal level of the desired point. A smooth curve is then drawn through these points. At the ordinate corresponding to the range of the desired point the value of $dS/d\theta_0$ is read as the slope of the tangent to this curve. In deriving the value of this tangent the source inclination must be expressed in radians. The abscissa of this same point gives the value, θ_0, of the source inclination of the ray path through the desired point. A curve of range as a function of inclination at the level of the point in question permits the value of θ_P to be determined for this same point. A curve showing the relation between range and source angle, for a specified depth, obtained from the data for the ray diagram of Fig. 3B-11 is given in Fig. 3B-13.

Should it be more convenient the intensity ratio sought may be computed by the relation

$$\frac{I_0}{I_P} = S \frac{\cos \theta_P}{\cos \theta_0} \frac{dD}{d\theta_0} \qquad (3B\text{-}52)$$

Here the derivative $dD/d\theta_0$ gives the rate of change of depth with change in angle of inclination at the source for a constant range. This equation is derived by placing $\delta V_P = \cos \theta_P\, \delta D$ in Eq. (B-41).

This graphical method of computing spreading

loss is well suited for use with ray diagrams which are constructed by ray plotting machines. These machines operate under the control of a template cut to correspond to the relation between depth and velocity of propagation. They permit the plotting of ray paths under conditions where the assumption of constant gradient layers is not justified.

It is easily shown, by the methods of Art.

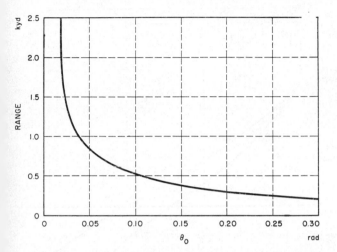

FIG. 3B-13. THE COMPUTATION OF SPREADING LOSS. The horizontal component of the length of a sound ray between its source and a specified level, plotted as a function of its source inclination. Computed from the same data as that of Fig. 3B-11 for a level of 215 ft.

3B-9, that the ray path followed by sound energy in going from a source at the point A to the point B is the same as the path followed, in the other direction, by sound energy in going from a source at the point B to the point A. It must not be concluded from this that the spreading loss between these two points is independent of the direction of energy flow. When the source is at A the ratio of the acoustic intensity at unit distance from A to the acoustic intensity at B may be written, in accordance with Eq. (3B-41), as

$$\frac{I_{A+1}}{I_B} = S \frac{\sin \theta_B}{\cos \theta_A} \frac{\delta S_B}{\delta \theta_A} \qquad (3B\text{-}53)$$

Similarly, when the source is at B the ratio of the acoustic intensity at unit distance from B to the acoustic intensity at A is

$$\frac{I_{B+1}}{I_A} = S \frac{\sin \theta_A}{\cos \theta_B} \frac{\delta S_A}{\delta \theta_B} \qquad (3B\text{-}54)$$

Returning now to Fig. 3B-12 it is seen that the sound ray which leaves the source O at the in-

clination $\theta_0 + \delta\theta_0$ crosses the level of the point P with the inclination $\theta_P + \delta\theta_P$ and at the distance δS_P from P. If, then, a sound ray leaves a source at this point of intersection at the inclination $\theta_P + \delta\theta_P$ in the direction of O it will pass through O with the inclination $\theta_0 + \delta\theta_0$. If this source is now moved the distance δS_P to the point P points on this ray at all levels will be moved by the same horizontal distance, as shown by the dotted line. The ray will then intersect the horizontal plane through O at the distance $\delta S_0 = \delta S_P$ from O. In the equations given above, then, $\delta S_B = \delta S_A$. From this it follows that, by combining Eqs. (3B-53) and (3B-54) and allowing $\delta\theta_A$ to approach zero,

$$\frac{I_A}{I_{B+1}} \frac{I_{A+1}}{I_B} = \frac{\cos \theta_B}{\cos \theta_A} \frac{\sin \theta_B}{\sin \theta_A} \frac{d\theta_B}{d\theta_A} \qquad (3B\text{-}55)$$

But by differentiating Eq. (3B-1)

$$\frac{d\theta_B}{d\theta_A} = \frac{c_B}{c_A} \frac{\sin \theta_A}{\sin \theta_B} = \frac{\cos \theta_B}{\cos \theta_A} \frac{\sin \theta_A}{\sin \theta_B} \qquad (3B\text{-}56)$$

Whence

$$\frac{I_A}{I_{B+1}} \frac{I_{A+1}}{I_B} = \frac{\cos^2 \theta_B}{\cos^2 \theta_A} = \left(\frac{c_B}{c_A}\right)^2 \qquad (3B\text{-}57)$$

From this the following theorem may be formulated. If two sources of acoustic energy having equal index intensities are located at two points in an acoustic medium which is nonhomogeneous, but in which the acoustic impedance varies continuously, each source will develop an acoustic intensity at the point occupied by the other of such magnitude that the ratio of the two intensities will be the square of the ratio of the velocities of propagation at the corresponding source points.

Certain of the relations which have been developed in the preceding paragraphs lead to an alternative method for computing the spreading loss through a series of layers each of constant vertical velocity gradient. To examine this method the ratio of the two cross-sectional areas of the ray bundle given by Eq. (3B-41) is separated into two factors. The first is the ratio of the horizontal dimensions of these areas. This may be written as

$$\frac{\delta X_P}{\delta X_0} = \frac{S_h}{\cos \theta_0} \qquad (3B\text{-}58)$$

where S_h is the horizontal component of the distance between the source and given points.

This measures the increasing separation between the two vertical planes defined by the two ray paths before and after they have been rotated by the incremental angle $\delta\phi$. The relations thus expressed are valid regardless of any change in the magnitude of the vertical velocity gradient. The second factor is the ratio of the dimensions measured in a single vertical plane. This factor is

$$\frac{\delta V_P}{\delta V_0} = \sin\theta_P \frac{\delta S}{\delta\theta_0} \qquad (3B\text{-}59)$$

It has already been shown that when the points O and P are in the same constant gradient layer this expression reduces to

$$\frac{\delta V_P}{\delta V_0} = \frac{S_h}{\cos\theta_0} \qquad (3B\text{-}60)$$

From this it follows, as already noted, that if two neighboring ray paths lying in a vertical plane remain in the constant gradient layer containing their source the ratio of their separations, measured from two points on one of them, is the ratio of the horizontal distances of these points from the source point.

A similar convenient relation between distance and separation can be established for the paths of these rays in layers not containing their source. The diagram of Fig. 3B-14 shows the paths of two such rays as they exist in the layer containing their source and in an adjoining layer. In the second layer, as in any other constant gradient layer, each of these paths is an arc of a circle. If these paths are extended they will intersect at some point. In some cases this point of intersection lies on the same side of the layer boundary as does the true source point. When this occurs the rays in the adjoining layer follow paths which are the same as though they originated at this point of intersection and remained thereafter in a single layer having a constant vertical velocity gradient equal to that of the second layer. This point, in other words, has the properties of a virtual source, similar to that described in Art. 3B-2, for neighboring rays in a single vertical plane. Within this second layer, then, as well as in the first, we may compute changes in separation in the vertical plane by the inverse first power law established by Eq. (3B-60). To do this it is necessary to determine the horizontal distance between the virtual source point and the point at which the original ray enters the second layer.

In order that the necessary conditions may be satisfied the rate of change of horizontal range with change in angle of inclination at the layer boundary must be the same for the ray from the virtual source as for the ray from the true source. On the diagram of Fig. 3B-14 the length S_1 is the horizontal component of the portion of the ray which is in the first layer, containing the source. The length S_1' is the horizontal com-

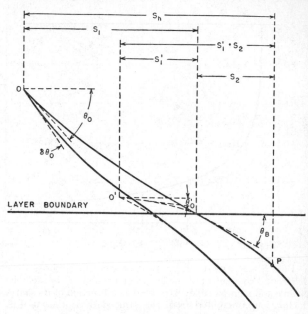

FIG. 3B-14. THE DIVERGENCE OF CURVED RAY PATHS. The relations between the paths of neighboring rays in a layer of constant vertical velocity gradient and a virtual source so positioned that, had the preceding layer been of the same gradient as the layer in question, the paths in the latter would have been the same as the actual paths.

ponent of the portion of ray path which would be added to the portion in the second layer if its entrance boundary were moved back to the virtual source for the pair of rays in this layer. The angle θ_0 is the inclination at the true source. This source point may be considered as lying in the horizontal plane which is the entrance boundary for the first layer. The angle θ_B is the inclination at the exit boundary of the first layer. The angle θ_0' is the inclination at the intersection of the circular arcs defined by the ray path as they exist in the second layer. The required condition may thus be expressed as

$$\frac{dS_1}{d\theta_B} = \frac{dS_1'}{d\theta_B} \qquad (3B\text{-}61)$$

But

$$S_1 = r_1(\sin\theta_0 - \sin\theta_B) \qquad (3B\text{-}62)$$

and

$$S_1' = r_{II}(\sin \theta_0' - \sin \theta_B) \qquad (3B\text{-}63)$$

These expressions may be differentiated with respect to the angle of inclination at the layer boundary in the same manner that Eq. (3B-23) was differentiated with respect to angle of inclination at the source to give Eq. (3B-43). By this operation there is obtained

$$\frac{dS_1}{d\theta_B} = r_I \tan \theta_B(\csc \theta_0 - \csc \theta_B) \qquad (3B\text{-}64)$$

$$\frac{dS_1'}{d\theta_B} = r_{II} \tan \theta_B(\csc \theta_0' - \csc \theta_B) \qquad (3B\text{-}65)$$

and

$$g_{II}(\csc \theta_0 - \csc \theta_B) = g_I(\csc \theta_0' - \csc \theta_B) \qquad (3B\text{-}66)$$

All quantities in this last equation except θ_0' will have been evaluated during the solution for the path of the ray in question. When the value of this quantity has been determined by solving this equation all quantities in Eq. (3B-63) except S_1' are known. The desired increment of path length may thus be determined.

It is evident that when the ray in question is horizontal at its source $\theta_0 = 0$ and a solution of Eq. (3B-66) is not possible. For this condition, however, Eq. (3B-56) shows that $d\theta_B/d\theta_0 = 0$. In other words, the angle of inclination, θ_B, at the layer boundary goes through a minimum value, given by the equation $\cos \theta_B = c_B/c_0$, when the ray is horizontal at its source. If the ray is not horizontal at the point in question, however, $dS/d\theta_0$ is finite, as shown by Eq. (3B-46). For this condition, then, the rate of change of inclination at the layer boundary with range must be $d\theta_B/dS_1 = 0$. For the hypothetical ray from the virtual source it is necessary that $d\theta_B/dS_1' = d\theta_B/dS_1 = 0$ and hence that $d\theta_B/d\theta_0' = 0$. From this it is evident that when a sound ray is horizontal at its true source the corresponding equivalent ray must also be horizontal at its virtual source. In this case, therefore, $\sin \theta_0' = 0$ and Eq. (3B-63) reduces to

$$S_1' = - r_{II} \sin \theta_B, \quad (\theta_0 = 0) \qquad (3B\text{-}67)$$

But for this same condition

$$S_1 = - r_I \sin \theta_B, \quad (\theta_0 = 0) \qquad (3B\text{-}68)$$

Hence

$$S_1' = \frac{r_{II}}{r_I} S_1 = \frac{g_I}{g_{II}} S_1, \quad (\theta_0 = 0) \qquad (3B\text{-}69)$$

For a constant gradient layer adjoining that containing the source of a sound ray, then, the change in separation between this ray and a near neighbor in the same vertical plane in going from the layer boundary to any given point, P, in the second layer is expressed by the ratio

$$\frac{\delta V_P}{\delta V_B} = \frac{S_2 + S_1'}{S_1'} \qquad (3B\text{-}70)$$

Here S_2 is the horizontal component of the distance between the entrance point to the second layer and the point, P, to which the change in acoustic intensity is to be measured.

We now have solutions for the changes in separation between the source and the boundary, and between the boundary and a point in the layer adjoining that containing the source. The ratio of the acoustic intensity at the index point to that at the final point, as determined solely by spreading, is obtained by combining the ratios measuring these changes in separation. By thus combining Eqs. (3B-58), (3B-60), and (3B-70), there results

$$\frac{I_0}{I_P} = \frac{\delta X_P}{\delta X_0} \frac{\delta V_B}{\delta V_0} \frac{\delta V_P}{\delta V_B}$$

$$= \frac{S_h}{\cos \theta_0} \frac{S_1}{\cos \theta_0} \frac{S_1' + S_2}{S_1'} \qquad (3B\text{-}71)$$

This may be expressed in terms of spreading loss as

$$N_{\text{spr}} = \text{lgt} \frac{S_1}{S_1' \cos^2 \theta_0}$$

$$+ \text{lgt } S_h + \text{lgt }(S_1' + S_2) \qquad (3B\text{-}72)$$

The first term in this equation is a constant for a given ray which originates in a layer of constant gradient but which has passed to a second constant gradient layer. This equation applies only in the second layer.

In the source layer the spreading loss is given directly by Eq. (3B-49), which here becomes

$$N_{\text{spr}} = 2 \text{ lgt } S_h - 2 \text{ lgt }(\cos \theta_0) \qquad (3B\text{-}73)$$

If the value of the quantity S_1' given by Eq. (3B-69) is negative it is an indication that the point of intersection sought and the true source are on opposite sides of the entrance boundary of the layer in question. In this case the rays converge, instead of continuing to diverge, after leaving this boundary. If the layer is sufficiently extensive the rays will actually intersect. Since this is a real intersection the point at which it occurs is a real **focus point** instead of a virtual source point. When the point to which spreading loss is to be computed falls on a focus point $S_2 = -S_1'$ and Eq. (3B-71) is indeterminate. For larger values of S_2, however, the equation is again valid. For an acoustic medium in which the velocity gradients are everywhere vertical the derivative of range with respect to source inclination appearing in Eq. (3B-42) has the value $dS/d\theta_0 = 0$ at a focus point provided the ray in question is not horizontal at this point. Any ray which is horizontal at its source will, however, have a focus at every other point at which it may become horizontal.

The accompanying example illustrates the application of this alternative method for computing spreading loss in a medium of varying vertical velocity gradient. It makes use of the same data as does the solution based on Eq. (3B-42) given earlier in this article. An examination of these two typical solutions should make it possible to decide which method is preferable in any given situation.

It is possible to repeat the process of this alternative method and to find the horizontal distance of the virtual source for a ray in a vertical plane as it exists in any one of a series of known constant gradient layers. Having determined this distance for each layer the change in separation between the ray in question and a neighboring ray in the same vertical plane may then be computed at once by the first power law expressed by Eq. (3B-60). Since the separation between the given ray and a neighboring ray having the same angle of inclination at the source may be computed in terms of the inverse first power of the distance from the true source all information for computing the change in acoustic intensity with distance, and hence for computing the spreading loss along the ray path, is available.

PROBLEM:

This is the same problem as that solved earlier in this article. The only difference is in the method of solution.

$$g_I = 0.0182 \ 1/sec \qquad \sin\theta_0 = 0.02094$$
$$g_{II} = -0.376 \ 1/sec \qquad \cos\theta_0 = 0.9998$$
$$r_{II} = -4770 \ yd \qquad \sin\theta_B = 0.008587$$

$$\csc\theta'_0 = -\left(\frac{0.376}{0.0182}\right)\left(\frac{1}{0.02094} - \frac{1}{0.008587}\right)$$

$$+ \frac{1}{0.008587} = 1491$$

$$\sin\theta'_0 = 0.0006706$$

$$S'_1 = -(4470)(0.00067 - 0.008587) = 35.3 \ yd$$
$$S'_1 + S_2 = S_h - (S_1 - S'_1)$$
$$= S_h - (1129 - 35) = S_h - 1094 \ yd$$

$$\frac{S_1}{S'_1 \cos^2\theta_0} = \frac{1129}{(35.3)(0.9998)^2} = 31.98$$

Layer	I	I	II	II	II	II	
D	40	65	115	165	215	265	ft
S_h	451	1129	1478	1637	1759	1861	yd
$S_1 - S'_1$			1094	1094	1094	1094	yd
$S'_1 + S_2$			384	543	665	767	yd
lgt S_h	26.64	30.53	31.70	32.14	32.45	32.70	
lgt S_h	26.64	30.53					
lgt $(\cos^2\theta_0)$	0.00	0.00					
lgt $(S'_1 + S_2)$			25.84	27.37	28.23	28.85	
lgt $\dfrac{S_1}{S'_1 \cos^2\theta_0}$			15.05	15.05	15.05	15.05	
N_w	53.28	61.06	72.59	74.54	75.73	76.00	db

3B-11 Focusing Effects in a Sound Channel

Having developed a technique for computing the spreading loss along ray paths in certain types of refractive media it is now possible to examine in more detail some of the effects appearing in sound channels. In the upper diagram, (A), of Fig. 3B-15 are shown the paths of sound rays which repeatedly cross a level at which the velocity of propagation passes through a minimum value. The conditions to which this diagram applies are as follows: the minimum velocity is $c_B = 4850 \ ft/sec$; the gradient above the level at which this velocity is found is $g_I = -0.5 \ 1/sec$ and the gradient below this level is $g_{II} = +0.5 \ 1/sec$; the source is assumed to be 30 ft above the minimum velocity level. Under these conditions rays which leave the source at inclination of $\theta_0 = \pm 6.35°$ become horizontal 90 ft above or below the minimum velocity level. These two rays, which are the rays shown in the diagram, are assumed to be the limiting rays for the layers on either side of the minimum velocity level. The dotted line in the diagram shows the path of a ray leaving the same source in the same vertical plane as the limiting rays but at an inclination differing from that of one of them by a small incremental angle.

As long as this limiting ray and its neighbor remain in the layer above the minimum velocity level the separation between them increases directly with horizontal distance from their source.

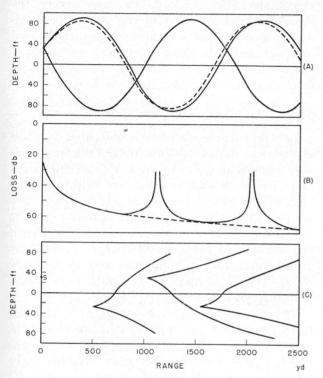

FIG. 3B-15. THE FOCUSING EFFECT IN A SOUND CHANNEL. The effects of refraction in proximity to a level at which the velocity of propagation is a minimum
(A) Ray paths in the sound channel
(B) Spreading loss along a ray leaving its source with an upward inclination
(C) Loci of focus points for rays leaving the source between the limiting rays shown in (A)

For the layer below the minimum velocity level their behavior may be examined by means of Eqs. (3B-66) and (3B-63). The radius of the ray in the first layer is

$$r_I = \frac{c_0}{g_I \cos \theta_0} = -\frac{4850 + (30)(0.5)}{(0.5)(0.99387)} = -9730 \text{ ft}$$

The radius for the same ray in the second layer differs only in sign and is

$$r_{II} = 9730 \text{ ft}$$

The inclination at the layer boundary is found by the usual methods.

$$\cos \theta_B = \cos \theta_0 + \frac{\Delta D}{r_I} = 0.99387 - \frac{30}{9730}$$

$$= 0.99081$$

Whence

$$\theta_B = 7.78°$$

The solution of Eq. (3B-66) gives

$$\csc \theta'_0 = \frac{g_{II}}{g_I} (\csc \theta_0 - \csc \theta_B) + \csc \theta_B$$

$$= -(-9.0457 - 7.3919) + 7.3919$$

$$= 24.8295$$

Whence

$$\theta'_0 = 2.31°, \quad \text{and} \quad \sin \theta'_0 = 0.04028$$

Consequently, by Eq. (3B-63),

$$S'_1 = r_{II}(\sin \theta'_0 - \sin \theta_0) = 9730(0.04028 - 0.13528)$$

$$= -930 \text{ ft} = -310 \text{ yd}$$

The value of this quantity indicates that after crossing the layer boundary the rays converge until they come to a focus at a horizontal distance of 310 yd beyond the point at which they enter the second layer.

Below the ray diagram of Fig. 3B-15 are plotted, in diagram (B), values of the spreading loss along the limiting ray leaving the source with a negative inclination. Each value of this loss corresponds to the point on the ray path directly above it. The spreading loss which would be computed for each point in the ray by means of the inverse square law is shown by the dotted line. It will be seen that as long as the ray remains in the same layer as the source the spreading loss cannot be distinguished from the loss computed for the same points by the inverse square law. Once the ray passes across the minimum velocity level, however, the actual spreading loss departs noticeably from the conventional inverse square law. At the focus point the intensity theoretically becomes infinite. However, this applies to an infinitesimally small area and hence requires no compromise with the principle of the conservation of energy. Nevertheless, there is a concentration of energy at this point which represents a **focusing effect** by the sound channel. Ideally the spreading loss between a source and a focus point is zero. Beyond a focus point the rays again diverge and the transmission loss once more increases until the rays again cross the minimum velocity level. As before, the reversal in sign of the gradient causes the rays again to converge until they are once more brought to a focus.

The convergence between rays in a single vertical plane for which the source inclinations differ by an infinitesimally small angle affects only that dimension of an elementary area of wave front, moving along the ray, which lies in the vertical plane. As this element moves away from the source it continues to expand in the horizontal direction at a constant rate regardless of the variations appearing in the ray diagram. For some portion of the ray the rate of contraction in the plane of the diagram is greater than the rate of expansion in the horizontal direction and the area of the element decreases. Whenever this occurs the spreading loss between the source and the position occupied by the elementary area also decreases as the area moves along the ray path. When the dimension in the vertical plane is zero the elementary area becomes zero, regardless of its horizontal dimension.

It would be predicted on the basis of ray diagrams alone that the energy in a sound channel is not distributed uniformly throughout a vertical plane crossing the channel. There are, in fact, regions which appear to be avoided by all rays retained by the channel and which therefore constitute shadow zones. From the foregoing it is also evident that there are points at which the acoustic intensity is greater than would be estimated on the basis of the inverse first power law. This law does, however, apply to the average intensity throughout any vertical plane crossing a sound channel. The curves, (C), in the lower diagram of Fig. 3B-15 represent the loci of the focus points of rays leaving the source between the two limiting rays shown in the upper diagram. These loci are seen to have a crude sort of symmetry with respect to the level of the transducer or to its mirror image. If the transducer were located at the minimum velocity level all loci would be symmetrical with respect to that level.

It is evident from this lower diagram that a vertical through a sound channel is likely to contain at least one focus point. The depth at which this appears will depend upon the distance from the source, upon the depth of the source, and upon the gradients on either side of the minimum velocity level. While it is possible in an ideal case to compute the depth at which to look for this focus point it would be quite unreasonable to expect to locate it with any certainty in an actual situation. For one thing the range would rarely be known, at least prior to the reception of a signal, with the required accuracy. In practice a focus point may be located by raising and lowering a hydrophone until the position of optimum signal strength is found. In cases where the signal is of short duration it would appear advantageous to use several hydrophones spaced at short intervals along a vertical line crossing the sound channel; at least one of these is likely to be near the most advantageous depth.

3B-12 The Effect on Transmission Time

In echo ranging, distance is measured in terms of the time during which a pulse of acoustic energy travels along a ray path to an echo target and returns. Wherever there are velocity gradients in the ocean the sound ray between two points will, in general, be longer than the straight line distance. Moreover, throughout this length the velocity of propagation changes constantly. It is natural, then, to inquire as to the magnitude of any error in range determination associated with these two factors.

This question may be answered through further analysis of the relations developed in Arts. 3B-6 and 3B-9. Since, however, the derivation of the required formulas involves only routine analytical geometry and would contribute little to an understanding of their significance the results will be given here without proof. The assumption of a constant vertical velocity gradient, which underlies all ray diagram relations thus far developed, will be continued. For this condition it may be shown that the time required for a wave element to travel between two points in a given horizontal plane, along a path which is the arc of a circle lying in a vertical plane, is

$$t = \frac{2}{g}\left(\sin\theta + \frac{\sin^3\theta}{3} + \frac{\sin^5\theta}{5} + \cdots\right) \quad (3B-74)$$

In this expression θ is the angle of inclination at which a ray path must pass through one of the given points in order to return to the horizontal plane at the other. The value of this angle may be determined by Eq. (3B-35) given the distance S, between the two points, the velocity, c, characteristic of the horizontal level, and the gradient, g, characteristic of the layer. By this equation

$$\tan \theta = \frac{gS}{2c} \qquad (3\text{B-}75)$$

The time which would be required to travel this same distance along a straight path lying in the horizontal plane at the velocity characteristic of the plane is also derived from Eq. (3B-35) as

$$t_d = \frac{S}{c} = \frac{2}{g} \tan \theta \qquad (3\text{B-}76)$$

The ratio of these two times is

$$\frac{t}{t_d} = \frac{1}{\tan \theta}\left(\sin \theta + \frac{\sin^3 \theta}{3} + \frac{\sin^5 \theta}{5} + \cdots \right) \quad (3\text{B-}77)$$

From the definitions given it is seen that t is the actual time occupied by an echo-ranging transmission and that t_d is the time which would normally be used in the range computation. It is evident, on the basis of Eq. (3B-77), that no deviation from a straight ray path likely to be encountered in practice will result in a large range error. Consider, for example, the case of a layer 100 ft deep throughout which there is a positive temperature gradient of 0.05 °F/ft. This represents a situation in which the range error due to refraction would be unusually large. Here the constant vertical velocity gradient has the value 0.268 1/sec. The limiting ray would leave the transducer at an angle of inclination of nearly 6° and would return to the level of the transducer at a range of approximately 1250 yd. The ratio of the travel times given by Eq. (3B-77) is calculated to be 0.99808. The travel time for the curved path, then, is less than for the straight path at constant velocity. The range error is seen to be of the order of 0.2 percent or, at the limiting range of 1250 yd to be about 2.5 yd. It will later be evident that other errors affecting the measurement of range will have values considerably in excess of this. Errors due to the curvature of ray paths by refraction, then, may generally be considered as negligible.

3-C THE EFFECTS OF REFLECTION

Reflections, as well as refractions, have an effect on the total transmission loss between a sound source and a receiving station. In general, however, these effects are not so readily calculated from known or measurable constants of the region nor may they be so reliably predicted in advance. An examination of the fundamental relations between the intensity of reflected energy and the constants of the medium is, nevertheless, of value in suggesting the order of magnitude of the loss to be expected under various conditions.

In echo ranging the laws governing acoustic reflections determine the intensity and other characteristics of the acoustic waves returned to the observation point in response to the original stimulating signal. In this case the echo from the target of interest may be considered as the signal to be received and echoes from all other reflectors as interference. Acoustic reflectors are thus secondary sources of underwater sound waves. In this chapter we are primarily concerned with the transmission of sound waves through bodies of water and shall, in consequence, limit our attention to those effects of reflection which influence the total transmission loss between two points.

3C-1 Relation to Specific Acoustic Impedance

In the same manner that the quantitative relations between refraction and the density and elasticity of the medium are conveniently expressed in terms of velocity of propagation so the quantitative relations between reflection and these same properties of the medium are conveniently expressed in terms of specific acoustic impedance. It is, in fact, because of this that acoustic impedance is of such great practical significance.

To investigate these relations let us consider an ideal plane surface separating two fluid media. The specific acoustic impedance on the side of the plane containing the sound source may be designated as $(\rho c)_1$; the specific acoustic impedance on the other side of the plane may be designated as $(\rho c)_2$.

In the boundary plane between these media two important conditions must be satisfied at all times. These are known as the **continuity of pressure** and as the **continuity of normal volume velocity.** The first of these requires that the acoustic pressure of the wave in the second medium equal the acoustic pressure of the wave in the first medium, both pressures being taken immediately adjacent to the boundary plane. The second condition requires that the component of volume velocity normal to the plane with which fluid from one side approaches it must, for an infinitesimally short distance, equal the component of volume velocity normal to the plane with which fluid on the other side moves away. This condition applies only to the normal component because we are here dealing with ideal fluids which are incapable of exerting shear stresses.

Before stating these conditions in mathematical notation we must define exactly what is meant by the phase relation between the motions of the incident and the reflected waves. The situation at the boundary plane is shown diagrammatically in Fig. 3C-1. The positive direction of particle velocity is understood to be the same as the direction of propagation of the wave front.

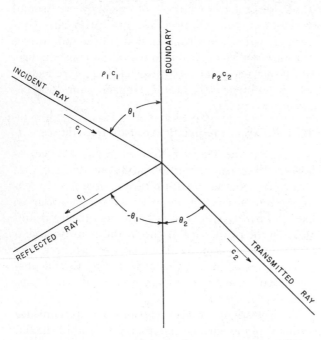

FIG. 3C-1. REFLECTION AT THE BOUNDARY BETWEEN TWO MEDIA. The geometrical relations between incident, reflected, and transmitted sound rays at a boundary where the specific acoustic impedance changes value.

It is also understood that the angle of reflection is equal in magnitude but opposite in sign to the angle of incidence. The normal components of the volume velocities of the incident, the reflected, and the transmitted waves are, therefore, respectively $u_1 \sin \theta_1$, $-u_r \sin \theta_1$, and $u_t \sin \theta_2$.

The condition of continuity of normal volume velocity therefore requires that

$$(u_i - u_r) \sin \theta_1 = u_t \sin \theta_2 \qquad (3C\text{-}1)$$

The condition of continuity of pressure requires that

$$p_i + p_r = p_t \qquad (3C\text{-}2)$$

From Eq. (2A-33) we have $u = p/\rho c$ for plane waves. For this condition, then,

$$(p_i - p_r) \frac{\sin \theta_1}{(\rho c)_1} = (p_i + p_r) \frac{\sin \theta_2}{(\rho c)_2} \qquad (3C\text{-}3)$$

From this the ratio of the acoustic pressures of the reflected and incident waves is found to be

$$\frac{p_r}{p_i} = \frac{(\rho c)_2 \sin \theta_1 - (\rho c)_1 \sin \theta_2}{(\rho c)_2 \sin \theta_1 + (\rho c)_1 \sin \theta_2} \qquad (3C\text{-}4)$$

When the quantity $(\rho c)_2 \sin \theta_1$ is less than the quantity $(\rho c)_1 \sin \theta_2$ it is evident that the sign of this ratio is negative. This indicates that the phase of the reflected wave differs by 180° from that assumed in writing Eqs. (3C-1) and (3C-2).

From Eqs. (3C-2) and (3C-4) the ratio of the acoustic pressures of the transmitted and incident waves is found to be

$$\frac{p_t}{p_i} = \frac{2(\rho c)_2 \sin \theta_1}{(\rho c)_2 \sin \theta_1 + (\rho c)_1 \sin \theta_2} \qquad (3C\text{-}5)$$

These pressure ratios may be transformed into ratios of acoustic intensity by means of the relation $I = p^2/\rho c$, given by Eq. (2A-33). In the case of incident and reflected waves both waves are in the same medium and the specific acoustic conductance is the same for both. The ratio of the intensities is then simply

$$\frac{I_r}{I_i} = \frac{p_r^2}{p_i^2} = \frac{[(\rho c)_2 \sin \theta_1 - (\rho c)_1 \sin \theta_2]^2}{[(\rho c)_2 \sin \theta_1 + (\rho c)_1 \sin \theta_2]^2} \qquad (3C\text{-}6)$$

For the ratio of the intensities of the transmitted and incident waves we have

$$\frac{I_t}{I_i} = \frac{p_t^2}{p_i^2} \frac{(\rho c)_1}{(\rho c)_2} = \frac{4(\rho c)_1 (\rho c)_2 \sin^2 \theta_1}{[(\rho c)_2 \sin \theta_1 + (\rho c)_1 \sin \theta_2]^2} \qquad (3C\text{-}7)$$

This is the ratio which measures the transmission loss suffered by acoustic energy, following a given ray path, on crossing the boundary between two media having different specific acoustic impedances. It is evident that this transmission loss is not independent of the direction of energy flow.

In the case of normal incidence $\theta_1 = \theta_2 = \pi/2$ and $\sin \theta_1 = \sin \theta_2 = 1$. The relation given by Eq. (3C-6) then reduces to

$$\frac{I_r}{I_i} = \frac{[(\rho c)_2 - (\rho c)_1]^2}{[(\rho c)_2 + (\rho c)_1]^2} \qquad (3C\text{-}8)$$

and Eq. (3C-7) reduces to

$$\frac{I_t}{I_i} = \frac{4(\rho c)_1 (\rho c)_2}{[(\rho c)_1 + (\rho c)_2]^2} \qquad (3C\text{-}9)$$

3C-2 Reflections from the Surface

On the basis of the magnitude of the ratio of the specific acoustic impedances of the media which meet at the surface of the sea this surface should be an effective reflector. On the average it is, moreover, ideally flat. It is only the presence of water waves, large compared to the lengths of acoustic waves, which prevents this surface from being an almost perfect reflecting plane. As it is, surface reflections play an important part in the transmission of underwater sound.

Whenever the surface layer of the ocean shows a positive temperature gradient surface reflections act to produce a sound channel. When the gradient of the surface layer is positive the level of minimum velocity occurs at the surface. An acoustic wave approaching the surface has a vertical component in the direction of decreasing velocity of propagation. On being reflected it returns to the layer with a vertical component in the direction of increasing velocity. The effect is the same as though the ray crossed a minimum velocity level and entered a layer having a gradient of opposite sign from that of the layer from which it emerged. In either case the sign of the gradient in the layer in which the ray path takes a new course is such as to refract the wave back toward the minimum velocity level.

While the appearance of sound channels due to surface layers of positive gradient are by no means rare, and often show signal transmissions of exceptionally long range, it should be noted that they are inherently unstable. Whenever the temperature gradient is positive the density decreases with depth, surface water tends to sink and water from lower levels to rise, thus establishing an isothermal layer. Any sudden drop in air temperature, however, is likely to set up a positive gradient, at least for a short time, particularly if the sea is calm.

The depth of a sound channel of this type is determined by the depth of the positive gradient. Any ray which reaches a level of maximum velocity with a finite angle of inclination will, on crossing this level, promptly be refracted away from the level. As always, the level of maximum velocity will be associated with a shadow zone. As indicated by the ray diagram of Fig. 3C-2, there will be regions where the shadow zone penetrates within the nominal boundaries of the sound channel. This diagram has been drawn for

a sound channel due to a gradient of $+0.5$ 1/sec below a reflecting plane surface. The data for these curves are, in fact, the same as for those of Fig. 3B-15; they are here plotted on one side of the minimum velocity layer instead of on both sides as in the previous case. The ray diagram, (A), of Fig. 3C-2 shows a sufficient number of rays, leaving the source between the two limiting rays, to indicate the envelope of the group of rays which constitute the sound channel. This

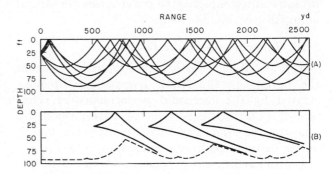

FIG. 3C-2. SOUND CHANNEL DUE TO SURFACE REFLECTION. The effects due to a positive velocity gradient below a reflecting surface
(A) Ray paths forming the sound channel
(B) Loci of focus points of rays in the sound channel

envelope may be considered as the actual lower boundary of the sound channel. This true boundary is shown by the dotted line in the diagram, (B), of loci of focus points. It is evident that points of maximum intensity, due to ray focusing, are in close proximity to the shadow zone.

At any point on the envelope of the channel the actual position of the ray which there establishes the boundary depends upon the angle with the horizontal of the air-water surface at the point where it is reflected. A slight change in this surface angle, due to wave motion or other surface disturbance, may cause the channel boundary to cross and recross a given receiving point. At one instant such a point may be on a maximum intensity curve, at other times it may be in the shadow zone. The variations to be expected in the total transmission loss, under such conditions, are quite adequate to account for many of the rapid changes in signal intensity so frequently encountered in sonar.

Although it is true that the loci of focus points represent lines of maximum intensity it must be remembered that the indicated zero transmission loss applies only to the loss due to divergence. Since these maximum intensity loci extend to

considerable ranges it is clear that the effect of
attenuation may become considerable. To this
must be added a substantial transmission loss due
to dispersion of energy on reflection from the
surface. While this surface may return to the
water a large portion of the acoustic energy falling on it, much of this energy may be reflected in
directions other than that corresponding to the
angle between the incident ray and the horizontal. When the sea is rough this dispersion may
be sufficient completely to prevent the formation
of an effective sound channel.

3C-3 Reflections from the Bottom

The fact that acoustic waves are reflected from
the bottom of the sea is convincingly demonstrated by the successful performance of echo-
sounding apparatus; it is also confirmed by
quantitative studies of intensity patterns found,
under certain conditions, in shallow water.

Bottom reflections depend to a marked degree
upon the nature and topography of this boundary. The bottom rarely comes as close to being
an ideal plane as, on occasion, does the surface
of the ocean. In some locations it is, however,
both flat and smooth for large distances. The
nearest approach to an ideal plane reflector is
found in the case of a flat bottom of hard sand.
This has a high coefficient of reflectivity and is
often free from irregularities which are large compared to the lengths of acoustic waves until the
higher ultrasonic frequencies are reached. A rocky
bottom has a high coefficient of reflectivity but
is, in general, neither flat nor smooth; although
it returns to the water a large portion of the
acoustic energy reaching it this energy is scattered in a random manner in all directions.

Mud bottoms are often good absorbers of
acoustic energy although in some cases sound
waves may penetrate a layer of mud and be reflected by a lower layer of hard material. There
are instances where echo-sounding gear has
shown two readings; one corresponding to the
top and one to the bottom of a layer of mud. A
mud bottom is considered as a prerequisite in
any body of water to be used for the calibration
of transducers.

Many of the phenomena characteristic of
surface reflection are found also to result from
bottom reflection. A negative gradient in the
water above a hard, smooth bottom may form
a sound channel in the same manner as does a
positive gradient in a surface layer. In shallow

water this sound channel may extend all the
way to the surface.

In considering the effect of bottom reflections
on the total propagation loss between two points
in the water it is necessary, as in the case of
surface reflections, to take account of several
concurrent effects. In fact, bottom reflections
generally appear as an additional factor in situations already complicated by several other effects.
Surface reflections can and do exist when there
are no bottom reflections; bottom reflections,
which are generally significant only in the case
of shallow water, rarely appear when there are
no surface reflections. The combination of surface and bottom reflections may, in shallow
water, act to produce a sound channel by confining acoustic energy to the thin layer of water.
Such a sound channel may occur even though
there is no appreciable amount of refraction. In
such cases the transmission loss would be expected
to vary, on the average, in accordance with an
inverse first power law. Due to the interference
between rays reaching given points by paths of
different lengths deviations from this average
are often of considerable magnitude.

The curve of Fig. 3C-3 shows values of transmission loss, as a function of range, taken in

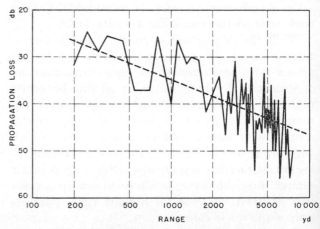

FIG. 3C-3. THE EFFECT OF BOTTOM REFLECTIONS. Propagation loss, as a function of range, observed over a bottom of
hard sand. Soundings showed little variation over the ranges
indicated.

Block Island Sound. The data from which this
curve is plotted were taken at 600 cycles and
consequently show little effect of attenuation.
It will be noted that, in this case, the slope of the
dotted line, which represents the statistical
average of these transmission loss values, is considerably less than the -2 db/Sl corresponding
to the inverse square law.

3C-4 Multiple Path Transmission

Reflections from the surface or from the bottom of the ocean may affect the transmission of acoustic energy through the water because of interference between directly transmitted waves and reflected waves. Reflections from the surface often exhibit a phenomenon similar to that known in optics as the **Lloyd mirror effect.** It is also frequently spoken of as the **image effect.**

In the diagram of Fig. 3C-4 let D_0 be the depth

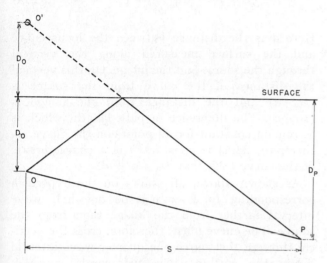

FIG. 3C-4. THE LLOYD MIRROR EFFECT. The geometric relations between intersecting directly transmitted and reflected sound rays.

of a sound source, O, and let D_P be the depth of any receiving point, P. Let S be the horizontal component of the distance between these points. The velocity of propagation will be assumed constant throughout the entire region with which we are here concerned. In the case of an ideal plane surface the angles which the incident and reflected rays make with the horizontal are equal. The reflected wave then appears to come from an image, O', of the true source. This is located above the surface on a vertical through the true source, source and image being at equal distances from the surface. In accordance with Eq. (3C-4) the reflected wave suffers a reversal in phase at the surface since the specific acoustic impedance of the reflecting medium is less than that of the transmitting medium. The pressure of the reflected wave at the point P will, in general, be less than the pressure of the direct wave because some of its acoustic energy escapes to the air and some is scattered by surface irregularities.

At the receiving point let p_d be the rms value of

the pressure due solely to the directly transmitted wave. Let p_r be the rms pressure due to the reflected wave. Let ψ be the phase delay corresponding to the difference between the lengths of the paths connecting the point P with the source and with the image. Since the reflection of an acoustic wave in water by an air-water boundary is accompanied by a reversal in phase the phase difference between the direct and reflected waves will be $-\psi$. Let $K = p_r/p_d$ be the ratio, characteristic of the surface and of the angle of incidence, between the pressures of the two waves. These pressures may be represented as phasors, as in Art. 2A-9. The rms value of the resultant pressure may then be written, as in Eq. (2A-83), as

$$p_\Sigma = p_d\sqrt{1 + K^2 - 2K\cos\psi} \qquad (3\text{C-}10)$$

The intensity which would be computed by substituting this resultant pressure into Eq. (2A-87) is the equivalent plane wave intensity, as defined in Art. 2A-9. This equivalent plane wave intensity may, in this case, be written as

$$I_{\text{equi}} = \frac{p_\Sigma^2}{\rho c} = I_d(1 + K^2 - 2K\cos\psi) \qquad (3\text{C-}11)$$

where I_d is the component of the resultant intensity due to energy arriving over the direct ray path. The situation here under consideration has some resemblance to those, discussed earlier, in which energy is received from a number of independent sources. A major difference is that in the present case energy may reach the receiving point by only two paths, instead of by a large number, and, under ideal conditions, the phase angle between the corresponding pressures will have a fixed value, determined by the locations of source and receiver, instead of a random value. Under these conditions the equivalent plane wave intensity will, in general, differ from the resultant intensity.

The propagation loss between a given source and a given receiver, under these circumstances, would be evaluated in terms of the apparent energy rather than of the actual resultant energy reaching the receiving point. The nominal value of propagation loss, applying to the direct ray path, would give the level of the energy received over that path as measured by the intensity I_d. To obtain the resultant propagation loss it is necessary to include an additional transmission loss identified with the ratio between this intensity and the equivalent plane wave intensity, I_{equi}. This is one form of spreading anomaly. Its value is derived at once from Eq. (3C-11) as

$$(N_{spr})_\Delta = \lg t \frac{I_d}{I_{equi}}$$

$$= -\lg t\,(1 + K^2 - 2K \cos \psi) \quad (3\text{C-}12)$$

For all values of phase angle the resultant energy, defined as the sum of the energies arriving over the two transmission paths, has an intensity

$$I_\Sigma = I_d + I_r = \frac{p_d{}^2 + p_r{}^2}{\rho c} = I_d(1 + K^2) \quad (3\text{C-}13)$$

When the ratio K is unity, a value which it may frequently approach in practice, $(1+K^2)=2$ and the resultant intensity is twice the intensity associated with the direct ray path. When K is unity the quantity $(1+K^2 - 2K \cos \psi)$, appearing in Eq. (3C-12), varies between 0 and 4 as the phase angle varies between 0 and π. The spreading anomaly, therefore, varies between infinity and -6 db. These values indicate that the equivalent plane wave intensity may be zero or that it may be four times the intensity associated with the direct ray path. In the latter case it is equal to twice the resultant intensity. For values of the constant K which are less than unity the Lloyd anomaly passes through a maximum negative value, corresponding to a transmission gain, whenever $\psi=(2n-1)\pi$, n being any positive integer. At such times $\cos \psi = -1$ and the quantity $(1+K^2 - 2K \cos \psi)$ has a positive maximum which is greater than unity. When $\psi = 2n\pi$, $\cos \psi = +1$, the quantity in brackets has a positive minimum value less than unity, and the transmission loss due to the Lloyd effect has a maximum value.

When $n=1$, $\psi=(2n-1)\pi=\pi$, and the reflected wave has been delayed in phase by one half cycle. The path length from the image must therefore be exactly one half cycle longer than the path from the source. The phase reversal at the surface contributes a second half cycle to the phase shift and the reflected wave lags the direct wave by a full cycle, thereby causing the acoustic pressures to add in phase for any sustained wave. Any position for which $\psi=\pi$ will show this maximum value for the transmission gain due to the Lloyd effect. Since this requires that the difference between the distances of the point in question from

the source and from the image shall be constant the locus of such points must, by analytical geometry, be a hyperbola. The loci of maximum gain points are thus seen to be a family of hyperbolas, each member of which corresponds to a single value of n.

From analytical geometry the equation of a hyperbola may be written, using our present notation, as

$$\frac{D_p{}^2}{a^2} - \frac{S^2}{b^2} = 1 \quad (3\text{C-}14)$$

Here a is the distance between the locus curve and the surface measured along the vertical through the source and the image. On this vertical the distance of the curve from the source is $(D_0 - a)$ and the distance from the image is $(D_0 + a)$. The difference in path length, which is to remain constant for all points on the curve, is, therefore, $2a$. The constant b is a characteristic of the curve such that $D_0{}^2 = a^2 + b^2$.

As shown above, all points on the hyperbola corresponding to $\psi = \pi$ will be one half wave interval farther from the image than from the source. The curve must, therefore, cross the vertical through the source one quarter wave interval below the surface. In other words, $a_1 = \lambda/4$. Curves corresponding to successive values of $\psi = n\pi$ will cross this vertical at points which are spaced by quarter cycle intervals, or at distances $a = n(\lambda/4)$ below the surface. These curves will be minimum pressure loci when n is even and maximum pressure loci when n is odd. Given these points, the depth of the source, and the relation of Eq. (3C-14) it is possible to plot the loci of all points for which the transmission loss or the transmission gain due to the Lloyd effect is a maximum. The curves of Fig. 3C-5 show these loci for a source at a depth of $D_0 = 9(\lambda/4)$. The solid lines indicate maximum negative anomaly and the dotted lines maximum positive anomaly. This diagram represents the situation which would exist when transmitting a signal having a frequency of 1000 cyc/sec from a projector located approximately 11 ft below the surface. The loci of maximum and minimum pressures, resulting from **multiple path transmissions,** as represented by this diagram, form a standing-wave pattern as defined in Art. 2A-8.

Regardless of the depth of the source the family of maximum pressure loci includes, as one limiting

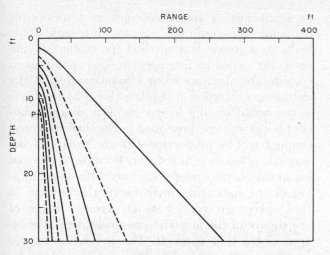

FIG. 3C-5. THE LLOYD MIRROR EFFECT. The loci of maximum values of transmission gain (solid lines) and of transmission loss (dotted lines) due solely to the image interference effect. The source is at a depth of $9(\lambda/4)$.

hyperbola, a straight line lying in the plane of the reflecting surface. This is a maximum loss locus. Whenever the source is at a depth which is exactly a whole number of quarter cycle intervals the other limiting hyperbola is a straight line starting at the source and extending vertically downward. As the depth of the source increases this line appears alternately as a maximum gain and as a maximum loss locus. As the depth of the source increases, also, the separation between the locus lines decreases.

Since the angle ψ is the phase delay corresponding to $2a$, the difference in path length, is

$$\psi = \frac{2\pi}{\lambda}(2a) = \frac{4\pi a}{\lambda} \text{ radians} \qquad (3C-15)$$

The Lloyd anomaly between the source and any given point may be computed by substituting the equality $b^2 = (D_0{}^2 - a^2)$ into Eq. (3C-14) and solving for a in terms of the depths of the source and of the specified point and of the horizontal distance between them. The value of ψ, obtained by substituting this value of a into the above equation, is then used in Eq. (3C-12) to compute the Lloyd anomaly. In plotting Lloyd anomaly along any given line, such as a constant depth line, it will be found more convenient to assign a series of values to a and to compute S from Eq. (3C-14). The loss will be computed in the same manner as before. In applying this method it should be noted that the maximum value which may be assigned to the independent variable is $a_{\max} = D_0$. The re-

sults obtained on computing the Lloyd anomaly by this method for a horizontal through the source specified in connection with the maximum locus lines of Fig. 3C-5 are shown in Fig. 3C-6.

The resultant effect of multiple path transmissions must be taken carefully into account in any attempt to evaluate the sound output of a given source through the measurements of acoustic energy made at some distance. Suppose, for example, that the relation between acoustic output and frequency is to be determined for a sonar projector. We have just seen that there may be a standing-wave pattern in the water due to the Lloyd effect and that the positions of the loci of maximum and minimum pressures forming this pattern vary with varying frequency. If the output of the projector were to be measured with a hydrophone in a fixed position it is evident that

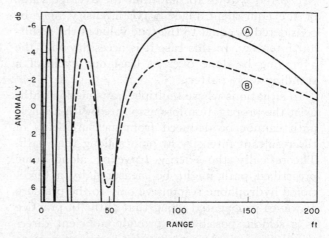

FIG. 3C-6. THE LLOYD MIRROR EFFECT. The transmission loss along a horizontal through the source specified for Fig. 3C-5. The reflection coefficient is $K=1$ for Curve (A), and $K=0.5$ for Curve (B).

changes in indicated intensity might be due to motion of this pattern quite as much as to changes in projector output. Suppose, however, that measurements of resultant pressure are made at a distance from the source sufficient to justify the assumption that the pressures of the direct and reflected waves are constant over a region of such extent that the phase angle between these pressures may vary between 0 and 2π radians. Under these conditions the sum of the squares of the values of resultant pressure obtained from n independent measurements, taken at random throughout this region, will have the value

$$n p_\Sigma{}^2 = p_d{}^2 [n(1 + K^2) - 2K \Sigma_n(\cos \psi)] \qquad (3C-16)$$

Since the phase angle, ψ, will, under these conditions, exhibit random variations the average value of its cosine will be zero. The average value of the square of the resultant rms pressure is consequently

$$(p_\Sigma{}^2)_{\text{aver}} = \frac{\Sigma_n(p_\Sigma{}^2)}{n} = p_d{}^2(1 + K^2) \quad (3\text{C-}17)$$

On substituting this quantity into Eq. (3C-13) the resultant intensity is found to be

$$I_\Sigma = \frac{(p_\Sigma{}^2)_{\text{aver}}}{\rho c} \quad (3\text{C-}18)$$

The quantity on the right of this equation is, by definition, the average value of the equivalent plane wave intensity. Under the conditions here postulated, as well as under those described in Art. 2A-9, it thus appears that the average value of the equivalent plane wave intensity may be considered as equal to the true value of the resultant intensity. In this case it is necessary that the averaging be done over at least one cycle of a standing-wave pattern.

In situations where multiple transmission paths exist the propagation loss associated with a single path cannot be deduced from measurements of the resultant intensity at points along that path. Theoretically the energy traveling along some prescribed path might be measured by a directional hydrophone responsive only to the pressure of waves propagated along that path. In practice it is seldom possible to provide sufficient directional discrimination to prevent some response to waves passing the same point along other paths. An expedient which is commonly adopted in attempts to evaluate the propagation loss along a direct ray is to transmit a signal of known index intensity from a controlled source for a very short interval of time. The intensity of this signal as received over the direct ray path is then determined before energy traveling along other paths reaches the receiving point.

It is often unnecessary to move a measuring hydrophone in order to obtain a series of pressure readings from which to compute the resultant intensity in the manner described above. As we have seen (Art. 3A-7) the resultant propagation loss between two points is almost certain to show rapid variations of considerable magnitude. This is generally indicative of the presence of a standing-wave pattern and of the fact that this pattern is moving relative to any fixed point. Time averages of pressure squared are, in such cases, quite

as significant as space averages as a means for deducing the resultant acoustic intensity. This leads to a convenient method for evaluating the resultant acoustic intensity at any point at a considerable distance from a sound source. If the voltage generated in a nondirectional hydrophone is impressed on the heater element of a thermocouple the voltage developed in the thermoelectric element will be proportional to the square of the acoustic pressure in the water. Because of thermal lag in the thermocouple, together with any damping of the indicating instrument, the reading of this instrument represents an average value of the square of the acoustic pressure taken over an appreciable time interval. The indicating instrument, may, therefore, be calibrated to read resultant acoustic intensity directly. It is rare that the indication of such an instrument is actually constant. It does, however, show much less variation than is observed on a device responsive to the instantaneous value of acoustic pressure. The manner in which this pressure varies with time, as shown by a cathode ray oscilloscope, is illustrated in Fig. 3A-7. A thermocouple and meter connected to the same hydrophone would show variations of something like two or three decibels. The rate of variation would also be much slower than those indicated by the oscilloscope. These variations suggest that the averaging period of the thermocouple is not sufficient completely to average out the effects of multiple transmission paths. Additional averaging may easily be supplied by the observer.

The relation between the acoustic energy measured in accordance with the method described above and the acoustic energy sent into the water by the sound source must be understood in any attempt to evaluate the index level of sound at the source by measurements at a distance. Normally the index level would be assumed to be given as the sum of the nominal propagation loss along a direct ray between source and measuring point and the level measured at the latter. This is true only when all of the energy to reach the measuring point is propagated along the direct ray. In shallow water, or where both source and receiver are near the surface, the amount of energy reaching the measuring point by reflection may approach or even exceed, the amount reaching it along the direct ray. The level at the measuring point would then exceed that due to directly transmitted energy by something like 3 db. Increases of as much as 6 db have been measured. Index levels computed on the basis of such measurements are thus likely to exceed the actual index level on a line between source and measuring point by an equal amount.

In the measurement of the sound output of ships or similar sources this discrepancy need not be considered as an error. The value assigned as the index level represents the apparent index level under conditions closely approximating those existing in practice. It is, then, the proper value to use in any estimates of the strengths of the signals likely to be received from the source in question over distances to which predicted values of propagation loss may be assigned.

When measuring the output of projectors, however, conclusions as to the total amount of acoustic energy delivered to the water may depart considerably from the true value if it is assumed that index levels computed in this manner correctly represent the amount of energy transmitted in the direction of the direct ray.

The Lloyd effect has been discussed for the ideal case of a plane reflector bounding a medium throughout which the velocity of propagation is constant. This ideal is often approached in practice, particularly at transducer calibrating stations, where the effect is of major significance. The effect also occurs under conditions where there are definite velocity gradients. When these appear concurrently with reflections, interference phenomena differ in two qualitative respects from those found in the ideal case. One of these is a distortion of the standing-wave pattern. For example, in the case of a negative gradient the limiting hyperbola which normally lies in the reflecting surface leaves this surface at the point of tangency with the limiting ray and thereafter follows the limiting ray. Other locus lines are similarly deflected downward. Another qualitative change is the appearance of additional locus lines, due to repeated reflections, whenever the surface layer shows a positive gradient. To indicate the major effects disturbing normal propagation in this case, then, it would be necessary to add to the loci of focus points due to refraction, as shown by diagram (B) of Fig. 3C-2, the maximum gain and maximum loss loci due to the Lloyd effect, as distorted by refraction.

3-D THE COMBINED EFFECTS OF REFRACTION AND REFLECTION

We have, in the preceding section, given qualitative consideration to situations in which both refraction and reflection influence the manner in which acoustic energy may be propagated through

the ocean. It remains to consider quantitatively the resultant effect of these two phenomena on the acoustic energy crossing the boundary between two acoustic media.

3D-1 Transmission Between Two Media

To examine the spreading loss suffered by acoustic energy propagated from a source in a medium having a constant velocity of propagation and a constant specific acoustic impedance to a receiving point in an adjoining medium having a different constant velocity of propagation and a different constant specific acoustic impedance we may return to the diagram of Fig. 3B-2. This diagram shows two neighboring ray paths in a plane perpendicular to the plane bounding two such media. By means of the formulas given in Art. 3B-2 it would be possible to compute the cross-sectional area of a ray bundle originating at a source in one medium and crossing this boundary to continue in the adjoining medium. This computation may be carried out more simply, however, by making use of the relation stated in Eq. (3B-41). This shows the ratio of the cross-sectional area of a ray bundle at any point therein to its area at the index point, unit distance from its origin. This equation applies to a ray bundle, having a rectangular cross section, one side of which lies in a plane parallel to the direction of variations in the velocity of propagation. It is valid regardless of the manner in which the velocity of propagation varies with distance, provided these variations have no component perpendicular to the plane. In applying Eq. (3B-41) to the diagram of Fig. 3B-2 it is to be noted that $S = S_h$, $\theta_0 = \theta_1$, and $\theta_p = \theta_2$. The ratio of the incremental area, δA_P, of the ray bundle at the receiving point to its incremental area, δA_0, at the index point is, then,

$$\frac{\delta A_P}{\delta A_0} = - S_h \frac{\sin \theta_2}{\cos \theta_1} \frac{\delta S_h}{\delta \theta_1} \qquad (3D\text{-}1)$$

The horizontal component of the distance between the source point, O, and the receiving point, P, in the medium adjoining that containing this source point, is

$$S_h = H_1 \cot \theta_1 + H_2 \cot \theta_2 \qquad (3D\text{-}2)$$

Here, as before, H_1 is the perpendicular distance of the source point from the medium boundary plane and H_2 is the perpendicular distance of the receiving point from this plane. The angle θ_1 is the inclination of the ray in the first medium, containing the source, and the angle θ_2 is the inclination of the same ray in the adjoining medium. By differentiating the above equation there is obtained

$$-\frac{dS_h}{d\theta_1} = \frac{H_1}{\sin^2\theta_1} + \frac{c_2}{c_1}\frac{H_2\sin\theta_1}{\sin^3\theta_2} \qquad (3D\text{-}3)$$

Since $\delta S_h = \delta\theta_1(dS_h/d\theta_1)$ this derivative may be substituted into Eq. (3D-1) for the ratio $\delta S_h/\delta\theta_1$. We thus obtain

$$\frac{\delta A_P}{\delta A_0} = \frac{S_h}{\cos\theta_1}\left[\frac{H_1\sin\theta_2}{\sin^2\theta_1} + \frac{c_2}{c_1}\frac{H_2\sin\theta_1}{\sin^2\theta_2}\right] \qquad (3D\text{-}4)$$

If the energy entering the ray bundle in question remained in that bundle the power of the energy passing through any cross-sectional area would be constant and the ratio of the acoustic intensities at the index and receiving points would be the reciprocal of the ratio of the cross-sectional areas at these points. Energy does, however, leave the ray bundle at the medium boundary and the rate at which energy flows along the bundle is reduced abruptly at this point. The change in intensity accompanying this reduction in power is given by Eq. (3C-7). At the same point there is also a change in the cross-sectional area of the bundle. Let the area of the boundary plane occupied by this bundle be δA. The area of the incident bundle is then $\delta A_i = \delta A \sin\theta_1$ and of the transmitted bundle $\delta A_t = \delta A \sin\theta_2$. The ratio of the powers of the incident and transmitted acoustic energy is given by the product of the ratio of the incident and transmitted intensities and the ratio of these areas. It is, in other words, using for the ratio of intensities the value given by Eq. (3C-7),

$$\frac{P_i}{P_t} = \frac{I_i(\delta A_i)}{I_t(\delta A_t)} = \frac{I_i\sin\theta_1}{I_t\sin\theta_2}$$

$$= \frac{[(\rho c)_2\sin\theta_1 + (\rho c)_1\sin\theta_2]^2}{4(\rho c)_1(\rho c)_2\sin\theta_1\sin\theta_2} \qquad (3D\text{-}5)$$

Now the power of the energy at the index point is the same as the power of the incident energy and the power of the energy at the receiving point is the same as the power of the transmitted energy. The ratio of the intensities measuring the transmission loss from a source in a medium having a constant velocity of propagation and a constant specific acoustic impedance to a receiving point in an adjoining medium having a different constant velocity of propagation and a different

constant specific acoustic impedance is, consequently,

$$\frac{I_0}{I_p} = \frac{P_i(\delta A_P)}{P_t(\delta A_0)} \qquad (3D\text{-}6)$$

It is, in other words, the product obtained by multiplying Eqs. (3D-4) and (3D-5).

The propagation loss due to the combined effects of refraction and reflection for sound energy entering a body of water from a source in air 100 yd above the water surface has been computed by this relation. The results are shown in graph (A) of Fig. 3D-1. These computations are made for rays separated by equal angular increments at the source; they occupy the angle between the normal to the air-water surface and the ray meeting this surface at the critical angle. The propagation losses computed for the paths of these rays after they have entered the water are shown by constant loss contours separated by 5-db intervals. Similar contours are shown for points in the air above the water as computed directly by the inverse square law. By means of the same equation the propagation loss due to spreading and reflection has been computed for the case of a sound source in water 100 yd below an air-water surface. The results are shown by graph (B) of Fig. 3D-1. In this case the sound rays considered leave the source in water at angular intervals of 10°.

It will be noted that the value of the power ratio given by Eq. (3D-5) is unchanged by interchanging the subscripts used therein. This indicates that the fractional reduction in the acoustic energy propagated within a given ray bundle which crosses the boundary between two homogeneous acoustic media is independent of the direction in which this energy is propagated. By applying the same test to Eq. (3D-4) it is evident that the change in the area of the bundle does depend on the direction of energy flow. The fractional reduction in the intensity, as given by Eq. (3D-6), must, therefore, depend on direction. The fact that the intensity ratio of Eq. (3C-7) depends on direction whereas the power ratio of Eq. (3D-5) does not is accounted for by the fact that the effect of direction on intensity is due wholly to the relation between the change in the separation between ray paths and direction.

When acoustic energy is propagated from a source at a point where the velocity of propagation and the specific acoustic impedance have

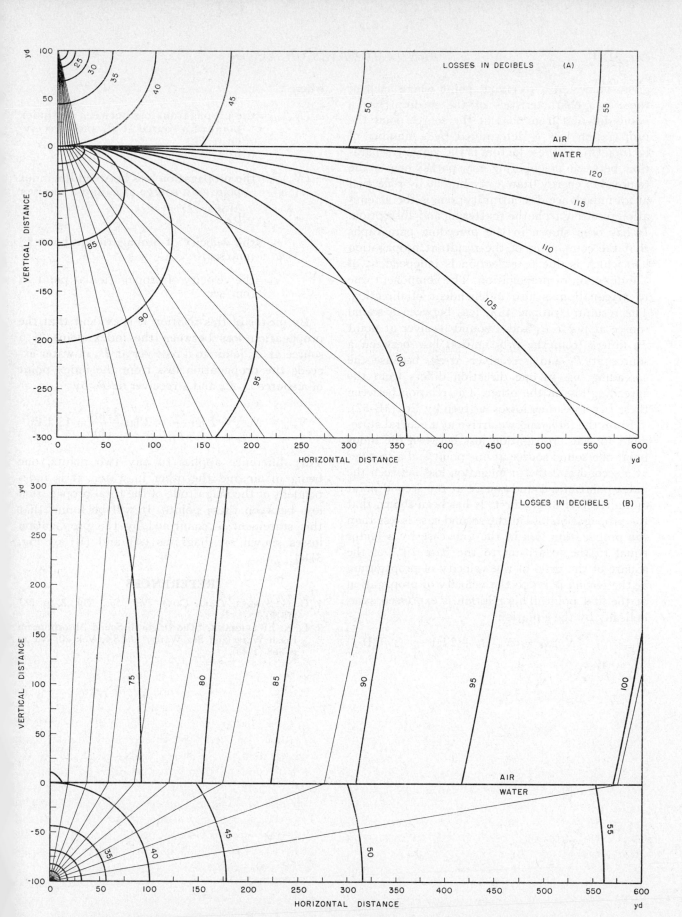

Fig. 3D-1. Propagation Loss Contours. Constant propagation loss contours for sound from a source at a perpendicular distance of 100 yd from an air-water boundary surface.

119

given values to a receiving point where each of these two characteristics of the medium has a value different from that at the source point the propagation loss is determined by a number of factors. One of these factors is the varying separation between neighboring ray paths; one is the removal of energy from a ray bundle by reflection at an impedance discontinuity; one is the attenuation resulting from the scattering and absorption. It has been shown in the preceding paragraphs that the component of the resultant propagation loss which is due to reflection is independent of the direction of propagation. The component due to attenuation is also independent of direction. The resultant propagation loss between a sound source at point P_a and a sound receiver at point P_b differs from the propagation loss between a source at P_b and a receiver at P_a because the spreading loss in one direction differs from the spreading loss in the other. The relation between these two spreading losses is given by Eq. (3B-57).

From the foregoing we arrive at a general statement for the propagation loss between the index point of a sound source at one point and a receiver at a second and the propagation loss between the index point of a sound source at the second point and a receiver at the first. It has been shown that the propagation loss in the second case is less than the propagation loss in the first case by a factor equal to the logarithm to the base $10^{0.1}$ of the square of the ratio of the velocity of propagation at the second point to the velocity of propagation at the first point. This relation is expressed symbolically by the equation

$$(N_w)_{a/b} = (N_w)_{b/a} + 2 \lgt \frac{c_b}{c_a} \qquad (3D\text{-}7)$$

where

$(N_w)_{a/b} =$ the propagation loss between the index point of a source at P_a and a receiver at P_b
(db)

$(N_w)_{b/a} =$ the propagation loss between the index point of a source at P_b and a receiver at P_a
(db)

$c_a =$ the velocity of propagation at point P_a
(cm/sec)

$c_b =$ the velocity of propagation at point P_b
(cm/sec)

By means of this relation it is evident that the propagation loss between the index point of a source at P_a in air to a receiver at P_w in water exceeds the propagation loss from the index point of a source at P_w and a receiver at P_a by

$$V_{a/w} - N_{w/a} = 2 \lgt \frac{c_w}{c_a} = 2 \lgt \frac{1500}{330} = 13.2 \text{ db}$$

This difference applies to any two points, one being in air and the other in water; it is independent of the magnitude of the total propagation loss between these points. It will be found that this statement is confirmed by the propagation losses shown on diagrams (A) and (B) of Fig. 3D-1.

REFERENCES

1. G. G. STOKES, *Trans. Camb. Phil. Soc.*, Vol. 8, p. 287 (1845).
2. L. N. LIEBERMANN, "The Origin of Sound Absorption in Fresh Water and Sea Water," *JASA*, Vol. 20, No. 6, p. 868 (1948).

CHAPTER 4

TRANSDUCERS

The advantages to be gained by converting acoustic signals to electric signals for observation, or by developing a signal in the electric form and then converting to the acoustic form for transmission, have already been mentioned. Quite apart from the facility with which signals may be handled when in the form of electric waves these conversions between acoustic and electric energy make it possible to design sonar systems which are, in general, more efficient than systems in which the energy is in the acoustic form throughout. To make acoustic signals perceptible to the human ear it is necessary that they be in the form of air-borne waves. The losses encountered when acoustic energy is transmitted, in either direction, between air and water have been discussed in detail in Art. 3D-1. It is, in fact, possible to convert acoustic energy in water to electric energy in a circuit, and then to convert this electric energy to acoustic energy in air, with less loss than is suffered by transmitting acoustic waves directly from one medium to the other. In addition, conversion to electric waves makes it possible to amplify the signals thus transmitted by means of conventional electronic amplifiers. For these reasons practically every modern sonar system includes one or more elements the function of which is to couple electric circuits to the water.

Any portion of an energy transmission system which, for convenience, may be considered as a subdivision having distinctive properties, is known as a **transducer.** A transducer has been formally defined as an element of an energy transmission system connecting one specified portion of that system, known as a **source,** to a second specified portion, known as a **load.** This is a general definition; it applies to system elements in which the energy transmitted from source to load is unchanged in form and also to elements in which it is translated from one form to another. At the moment we are particularly interested in transducers which, in addition to transmitting energy from one portion of some given system to another, also convert that energy from the electric to the acoustic form, or from the acoustic to the electric. Regardless of the direction in which this conver-

sion is effected the transducer by which it is accomplished is known as an **electroacoustic transducer.** An electroacoustic transducer which is used to initiate, or to transmit, acoustic waves in water is specifically designated as a **sonar projector.** An electroacoustic transducer used for receiving acoustic waves from water is known as a **hydrophone.** Many of the electroacoustic transducers used in sonar, which will hereafter be spoken of| as **sonar transducers,** are suitable for both purposes. In the daily language of sonar engineers projectors and hydrophones are spoken of collectively as transducers; it would be redundant, as well as cumbersome, to refer to them always as electroacoustic transducers. It must be remembered, however, that the term "transducer" does not, of necessity, imply a conversion from one form of energy to another.

4-A TRANSDUCERS, TRANSMISSION LOSSES, AND IMPEDANCES

Before undertaking an examination of specific methods for evaluating the performance of projectors and hydrophones it would be well to review those methods which are applicable to all transducers. These general methods are the result of many years of experience by many scientists and engineers. They have been carefully integrated to form a unified engineering technique. Any extensions which are needed to permit this technique to be applied to new problems must be made in such manner as to preserve its present coherence.

In the evaluation of transducer performance we shall make much use of the concept of **transmission loss.** Transmission loss has already been discussed briefly in Art. 2B-2. It was there defined as that property of an energy transmission system to which is ascribed reduction in the rate at which energy is transmitted through that system. The unit transmission loss, which has already been used extensively in earlier sections of this book, is the **decibel.** This same unit will be used for the evaluation of transducer performance.

Transmission losses are significant because they are related to changes in the rate at which energy is transmitted through some given system. It is frequently difficult to measure absolute values of these rates directly. By applying the concept of transmission loss to transducers, however, changes in these rates may be evaluated in terms of easily measured impedances. Transmission loss, like impedance, is a property of energy transmission systems. The transmission losses of a system, like its impedances, determine certain relations which must be satisfied by quantities associated directly with any energy which that system may transmit. Since transmission loss and impedance are both related to the energy transmitted by systems of which they are properties it is not surprising that they are related to each other. It is, in fact, this relation which gives transmission loss much of its utility. Information as to the transmission loss associated with any given transducer is conveniently obtained in terms of known or measurable impedances. The information thus obtained leads at once to information as to the effectiveness with which the transducer will perform a given function in a given system. The relations between the transmission losses and the impedances of transducers will be examined in detail in the following articles of this section.

Any energy transmission system may be considered as made up of a series of transducers connected sequentially and providing a continuous path between an energy source and an energy load. In general, transmission losses occur within every transducer in such a system and at every junction point between these transducers, or between transducers and the source and load. Whenever the greater of the two powers appearing in the power ratio measured by some given transmission loss is the same as the lesser of the two appearing in the ratio measured by some other loss the two ratios are said to be measured by **contiguous transmission losses.** The resultant ratio obtained by multiplying together two such ratios is measured by a transmission loss which is the sum of the two contiguous losses measuring the individual ratios. The overall transmission loss of any energy transmission system is thus seen to be computable as the sum of the contiguous losses appearing at its several junctions and within its several transducers.

It is our present purpose to study these contiguous losses, their interrelations, and their relations to the impedances characteristic of the transducers, the sources, and the loads with which they are associated.

The discussion will be in terms of a system transmitting electric energy. Many of the conclusions reached, however, will be equally applicable to systems transmitting other forms of energy, or to systems in which energy is converted from one form to another. In general, statements made for an electric system in terms of voltage, current, power, and impedance will be true for mechanical systems if made in terms of forces, velocities, powers, and impedances. Similar statements in terms of acoustic pressures, volume velocities per unit area, acoustic intensities, and unit area acoustic impedances may be made for acoustic systems. The possibility of using transmission losses for evaluating the performance of transducers in which energy transformations take place, as well as of those which transmit a single form of energy, is another of the advantages of this method of studying energy transmission systems.

4A-1 The Equivalent Circuit of a Junction

The essential elements of an energy transmission system which determine the transmission phenomena taking place at a **junction** point in such a system may be represented by the simple electric network shown in Fig. 4A-1. The point in

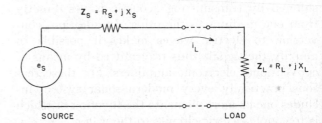

FIG. 4A-1. TRANSITION LOSS. The significant impedances at a junction in an energy transmission system.

question is represented by a two-terminal junction. The portion of the system supplying energy to this junction is represented, at a single frequency, by a single complex impedance in series with a single sinusoidal electromotive force. It has been well established in the theory of electric networks, as stated by Thevenin's theorem, that no matter how complex an energy source may be its behavior with respect to the voltage, power, and current delivered to any system to which it may be connected, may be completely represented, at a single frequency, by this single impedance and this single voltage. This simple source thus represents the actual source and all transducers between it and the junction in question.

Thevenin's Theorem: If an impedance be connected between any two points of a circuit the resulting steady-state current through that impedance will be such that its phasor is the quotient obtained by dividing (1) the phasor of the potential difference between the two points prior to the connection by (2) the sum of the phasors of the connected impedance and the impedance of the circuit measured between the two points prior to the connection.

This theorem also shows that the portion of the system to which energy is delivered may be represented, at a single frequency, by a single complex impedance. This simple load represents the actual load and all transducers between it and the junction in question.

There are a number of significant quantities associated with the transmission of energy across a junction in an energy transmission system. Each of these will be found in the simple source and the simple load just described. These quantities will be defined as follows.

e_S The **source voltage** of an energy source is the rms voltage which would be measured at the terminals of that source if they were open-circuited.

i_S The **source current** of an energy source is the rms current which would be measured at the terminals of that source if they were short-circuited.

e_L The **load voltage** of an energy load is the rms voltage between the terminals of that load when connected to a specified source.

i_L The **load current** of an energy load is the rms current through the terminals of that load when connected to a specified source.

Z_S The **source impedance** of an energy source is the impedance which would be measured at the terminals of that source if they were not connected to a load and if the source voltage were zero.

Z_L The **load impedance** of an energy load is the impedance which would be measured at the terminals of that load if they were not connected to a source.

P_L The **load power** of an energy load is the average rate of flow of energy through the terminals of that load when connected to a specified source.

It may be shown, by a method analogous to that by which Eq. (2A-51) was derived, that the

absolute value of a complex impedance is equal to the ratio of the rms value of the voltage across it to the rms value of the current through it. The relation between source current, source voltage, and source impedance may thus be written as

$$i_S = \frac{e_S}{|Z_S|} \qquad (4A\text{-}1)$$

The load current may be written, in a similar manner, as

$$i_L = \frac{e_S}{|Z_S + Z_L|} = i_S \frac{|Z_S|}{|Z_S + Z_L|} \qquad (4A\text{-}2)$$

The load voltage is then given as

$$e_L = i_L |Z_L| = e_S \frac{|Z_L|}{|Z_S + Z_L|} \qquad (4A\text{-}3)$$

By means of Eq. (2A-43) it was shown that the average rate of flow of acoustic energy through unit area of surface in a medium transmitting acoustic energy is obtained by multiplying the product of the rms values of acoustic pressure and particle velocity at that surface by the cosine of the phase angle between them. In a similar manner it may be shown that the average value of electric power at a junction point in a system transmitting electric energy is obtained by multiplying the product of the rms values of electric current and voltage at that junction by the cosine of the phase angle between them. Also, by a method similar to that used in deriving Eq. (2A-49), it may be shown that the cosine of the phase angle, ψ, between the voltage and the current at the terminals of a given impedance is equal to the ratio of the resistive component of that impedance to its absolute magnitude. Symbolically, then,

$$\cos \psi_L = \frac{R_L}{|Z_L|} \qquad (4A\text{-}4)$$

The load power is consequently

$$P_L = e_L i_L \cos \psi_L = e_L i_L \frac{R_L}{|Z_L|} \qquad (4A\text{-}5)$$

By substituting values of load current and load voltage obtained from Eq. (4A-3) this power becomes

$$P_L = i_L^2 R_L = e_L^2 G_L \qquad (4A\text{-}6)$$

Here R_L is the resistive component of the load

impedance and $G_L = R_L / |Z_L|^2$ is the conductive component of the load admittance. The derivation of this last equality is given in Eq. (2A-38). By means of Eq. (4A-2) the load power may also be written as

$$P_L = e_S^2 \frac{R_L}{|Z_S + Z_L|^2}$$

$$= e_S^2 \frac{R_L}{(R_S + R_L)^2 + (X_S + X_L)^2} \quad (4A-7)$$

This last expression is derived from that immediately preceding by the general laws governing the manipulation of phasors.

4A-2 Available Power—Conjugate Impedances

By differentiating Eq. (4A-7) with respect to R_L and X_L it will be found that the load power obtainable from a given source has its maximum value for a load of such impedance that $R_L = R_S$ and $X_L = -X_S$. Two impedances having resistive components which are equal and reactive components which are equal in magnitude but opposite in sign are known as **conjugate impedances.**

The rate at which a given source would deliver energy to a load having an impedance which is the conjugate of the source impedance is designated as the **available power** of that source. The available power characteristic of an energy source is one of the significant quantities associated with the transfer of energy from that source to any load. In addition to the quantities already defined, therefore, we have

P_S The **source power** of an energy source is the available power of that source. This is the rate at which that source would deliver energy to a load having an impedance which is the conjugate of the source impedance of that source.

It will be noted that while the source power is the maximum power which may be obtained from a given source the source current is not the maximum current nor is the source voltage the maximum voltage.

An expression for the available power of an energy source may be derived from Eq. (4A-7) by substituting the relations, $|Z_S + Z_L| = 2R_S$ and $R_L = R_S$, which exist in the case of conjugate impedances. On making these substitutions, and also that showing the relation between open-circuit source voltage and short-circuit source current, as given by Eq. (4A-1), this available source power is found to be

$$P_S = \frac{e_S^2}{4R_S} = \frac{i_S^2}{4G_S} \quad (4A-8)$$

Here R_S is the resistive component of the source impedance and $G_S = R_S / |Z_S|^2$ is the conductive component of the source admittance.

4A-3 Transition Loss

The transmission loss associated with any junction in an energy transmission system is a measure of the rate at which energy is actually transferred across that junction relative to the rate at which it would be transferred if the load were of such characteristics as to permit the source to develop all of its available power. We thus have

N_{tsn} The **transition loss** at the junction between an energy source and an energy load is the transmission loss measured by the ratio of the source power of that source to the load power of that load.

This loss may be expressed in terms of the source and load impedances by taking the ratio of the source and load powers as given by Eqs. (4A-8) and (4A-7). When this loss is expressed in decibels it may be written as

$$N_{tsn} = \lg \frac{P_S}{P_L} = \lg \frac{|Z_S + Z_L|^2}{4R_S R_L} \text{ db} \quad (4A-9)$$

This is one of the most important transmission losses, from both the theoretical and the practical points of view, which we are likely to encounter in dealing with energy transmission systems.

The value of the transition loss at any junction appears to be a function of four independent variables. It may, however, be written as a function of two variables related, respectively, to the magnitudes and to the phases of the source and load impedances. This facilitates an examination of the effect of departures from the condition of ideal conjugacy. One of these variables is the ratio between the resistive components of the source and of the load; the other is the tangent of the phase angle of the combined source and load impedances. For the transition loss given by Eq. (4A-9) these two quantities are $r = R_S / R_L$ and $\tan \psi = (X_S + X_L)/(R_S + R_L)$. On substituting these quantities into this equation there is obtained

$$N_{tsn} = \lg \frac{(1 + r)^2}{4r} + \lg (1 + \tan^2 \psi) \text{ db} \quad (4A-10)$$

Any transition loss may thus be considered as the

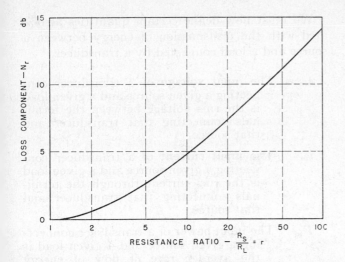

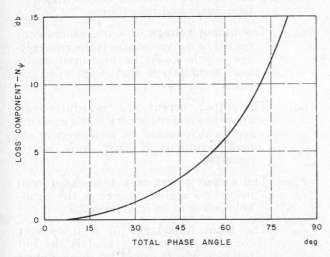

FIG. 4A-2. TRANSITION LOSS. Values of components of the transition loss, as functions of the deviation of either the magnitude or the phase of the load impedance from the conjugate value of the source impedance. The total transition loss is

$$N_{tan} = N_r + N_\psi$$

4A-4 The Equivalent Circuit of a Transducer

The essential elements of that portion of an energy transmission system which connects two junction points in that system may be represented by a simple network connecting a simple source and a simple load. It has been established, in a manner analogous to that used in establishing Thevenin's theorem, that at a single frequency the portion of an energy transmission system included between two points may be represented by a simple four-terminal network. This network must satisfy three requirements: (1) When its load terminals are connected to an impedance equal to the load impedance of the actual load, the impedance measured between its source terminals must be the same as the impedance to which the actual source is connected; (2) when its source terminals are connected to an impedance equal to the source impedance of the actual source, the impedance measured between its load terminals must be the same as the impedance to which the actual load is connected; (3) the rate at which it would transfer energy from the actual source to the actual load must be the same as the rate at which energy is actually transferred. These three conditions may be met by a simple network having three branches, each containing a single complex impedance. Such a network is shown in Fig. 4A-3, together with the circuits representing the source and the load which it connects.

Since the network assumed in this case contains no source of energy any energy delivered to the load must first be received from the source. A transducer connecting a given source and a given load, and developing a load power which is independent of sources of energy controlled by the given source, is known as a **passive transducer.**

The impedance branches making up the simple network are also assumed to be independent of the magnitudes and directions of any currents which may flow through them. In this case the complete network, including source, transducer, and load, will be found to satisfy the reciprocity theorem.

Reciprocity Theorem: If, in any electric network composed of linear elements, a given electromotive force applied between two given terminals produces a current at a point in some branch of the network then the same voltage acting at this second point in the network will produce the same current between the two original terminals if they are short-circuited.

sum of two components, one of which is a unique function of the ratio of the source and load resistances and the other a unique function of the phase angle of the total circuit. Values of these component losses are shown graphically in Fig. 4A-2.

An examination of Eq. (4A-9) shows that if the values of R_L and R_S are interchanged, and if the values of Z_L and Z_S are interchanged, the value of the power ratio is unchanged. This demonstrates that the transition loss between two energy transmission systems is independent of the direction of energy flow. This is shown also by Eq. (4A-10); here the value of the transmission loss is unchanged if r is replaced by $1/r$.

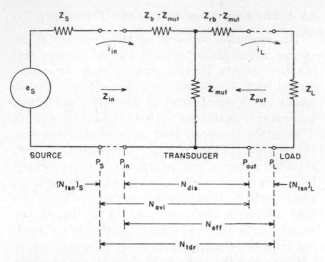

FIG. 4A-3. TRANSDUCER LOSSES. The several transmission losses by which the performance of a transducer is evaluated, shown in relation to the power magnitudes with which they are identified.

P_S = the source power of the energy *available* from the source
P_{in} = the input power of the energy *delivered* to the transducer
P_{out} = the output power of the energy *available* from the transducer
P_L = the load power of the energy *delivered* to the load
$(N_{tsn})_S$ = the source transition loss
$(N_{tsn})_L$ = the load transition loss
N_{dis} = the dissipation loss
N_{avl} = the available power loss
N_{eff} = the efficiency loss
N_{tdr} = the transducer loss

A transducer which, when connecting an energy source and an energy load, completes a system which satisfies the principle of reciprocity is known as a **reversible transducer.** The transducers which we shall consider in this section are both passive and reversible.

In the diagram of Fig. 4A-3 the four-terminal network represents all transducers between two specified junctions in an energy transmission system. The simple source represents the actual source and all transducers between it and one junction; the simple load represents the actual load and all transducers between it and the other junction. For our present purposes we shall consider the network as a single transducer.

From the foregoing it is evident that at the junction between an energy source and a transducer connecting this source to an energy load the transducer and the load have, jointly, the properties of an energy load. Similarly, at the junction between an energy load and a transducer connecting this load to an energy source the transducer and the source have the properties of an energy source.

We must now define certain quantities associated with the transmission of energy between a source and a load connected by a transducer.

e_{in} — The **input voltage** of a transducer connecting a given source and a given load is the rms voltage between the terminals connecting that transducer and that source.

i_{in} — The **input current** of a transducer connecting a given source and a given load is the rms current through the terminals connecting that transducer and that source.

P_{in} — The **input power** of a transducer connecting a given source and a given load is the average rate of flow of energy through the terminals connecting that transducer and that source.

e_{out} — The **output voltage** of a transducer connected to a given source is the rms voltage which would be measured at its load terminals if they were open-circuited.

i_{out} — The **output current** of a transducer connected to a given source is the rms current which would be measured at its load terminals if they were short-circuited.

P_{out} — The **output power** of a transducer connected to a given source is the available power at its load terminals.

Z_{in} — The **input impedance** of a transducer connected to a given load is the impedance which would be measured at its source terminals if they were not connected to a source.

Z_{out} — The **output impedance** of a transducer connected to a given source is the impedance which would be measured at its load terminals if they were not connected to a load and if the source voltage of the source were zero.

Z_b — The **blocked impedance** of a transducer is its input impedance when its load terminals are open-circuited.

Z_f — The **free impedance** of a transducer is its input impedance when its load terminals are short-circuited.

Z_{rb} — The **reverse blocked impedance** of a transducer is its output impedance when its source terminals are open-circuited.

Z_{rf} — The **reverse free impedance** of a transducer is its output impedance when its source terminals are short-circuited.

Z_{mut} The **mutual impedance** of a transducer is the quotient obtained by dividing the phasor representing the open-circuit voltage between one pair of its terminals by the phasor representing the current through the other pair.

Z_{tfr} The **transfer impedance** of a network made up of a given source and a given load connected by a given transducer is the quotient obtained by dividing the phasor representing the source voltage of the source by the phasor representing the load current of the load.

In an actual transducer there may be no real point corresponding to the single junction point of the three branches of the network representing this transducer. Even if it existed such a point would, in all probability, be inaccessible. The values of the three impedances representing a real transducer must, therefore, be derived from measurements made at its terminals. It is for this purpose that the blocked and free impedances defined above are required.

4A-5 Relations Between Transducer Impedances

From an inspection of Fig. 4A-3 it will be seen that the open-circuit voltage mentioned in the definition of mutual impedance is, in the network representing the transducer, the same as the voltage drop across the shunt branch of this network. This shunt branch must, therefore, represent the mutual impedance as defined. The impedances of the two series arms may thus be expressed in terms of the blocked impedances of the transducer and this mutual impedance as $Z_b - Z_{mut}$ and $Z_{rb} - Z_{mut}$.

By inspection of the diagram of Fig. 4A-3 it is evident that we may write

$$Z_f = (Z_b - Z_{mut}) + \frac{Z_{mut}(Z_{rb} - Z_{mut})}{Z_{rb}} \quad (4A-11)$$

and

$$Z_{rf} = (Z_{rb} - Z_{mut}) + \frac{Z_{mut}(Z_b - Z_{mut})}{Z_b} \quad (4A-12)$$

These two equations show that the value of the mutual impedance may be derived from measurable terminal impedances by either of two relations. These are

$$Z_{mut} = \sqrt{Z_{rb}(Z_b - Z_f)}$$
$$= \sqrt{Z_b(Z_{rb} - Z_{rf})} \quad (4A-13)$$

On squaring both sides of the last equality written above it is found that

$$\frac{Z_b}{Z_f} = \frac{Z_{rb}}{Z_{rf}} \quad (4A-14)$$

We may thus state as a theorem that the ratio of the blocked to the free impedances measured at one pair of terminals of a passive reversible transducer is equal to the ratio of the blocked to the free impedances measured at the other pair.

Also, again by inspection of the circuit diagram, we may write

$$Z_{in} = (Z_b - Z_{mut}) + \frac{Z_{mut}(Z_{rb} - Z_{mut} + Z_L)}{Z_{rb} + Z_L} \quad (4A-15)$$

and

$$Z_{out} = (Z_{rb} - Z_{mut}) + \frac{Z_{mut}(Z_b - Z_{mut} + Z_S)}{Z_S + Z_b} \quad (4A-16)$$

Whence

$$Z_{mut} = \sqrt{(Z_b - Z_{in})(Z_{rb} + Z_L)}$$
$$= \sqrt{(Z_{rb} - Z_{out})(Z_S + Z_b)} \quad (4A-17)$$

It may be shown from these equations, by simple algebraic manipulation, that

$$\frac{Z_S + Z_{in}}{Z_{out} + Z_L} = \frac{Z_S + Z_b}{Z_{rb} + Z_L} = \frac{Z_b - Z_{in}}{Z_{rb} - Z_{out}} \quad (4A-18)$$

In the foregoing paragraphs it has been shown how the mutual impedance of a transducer may be expressed in terms of measurable terminal impedances. The transfer impedance may, in a similar manner, be expressed in terms of these same terminal impedances and the source and load impedances. It may be desirable, in some cases, to substitute the mutual impedance for those terminal impedances to which it is related. Expressions including the mutual impedance are usually less cumbersome than those given in terms of directly measurable impedances only. Such expressions for the transfer impedance are derived in the following paragraphs.

The input current of a transducer may be written in terms of related quantities as

$$i_{in} = \frac{e_{in}}{|Z_{in}|} = \frac{e_S}{|Z_S + Z_{in}|} \quad (4A-19)$$

The load current developed by a transducer in its load is the fraction of its input current which is not shunted by the mutual impedance. That is,

$$i_L = i_{in} \frac{|Z_{mut}|}{|Z_{rb} + Z_L|}$$

$$= e_S \frac{|Z_{mut}|}{|Z_S + Z_{in}| \, |Z_{rb} + Z_L|}$$

$$= e_S \frac{|Z_{mut}|}{|Z_{out} + Z_L| \, |Z_S + Z_b|} \qquad (4A\text{-}20)$$

Similarly, the open-circuit output voltage of a transducer is the fraction of the source voltage of its source which appears across the mutual impedance when the load is removed.

$$e_{out} = e_S \frac{|Z_{mut}|}{|Z_S + Z_b|} \qquad (4A\text{-}21)$$

Also, by Thevenin's theorem,

$$i_L = \frac{e_{out}}{|Z_{out} + Z_L|} \qquad (4A\text{-}22)$$

We may now write an expression for the transfer impedance, based on its definition. This is

$$|Z_{tfr}| = \frac{e_S}{i_L} = \frac{|Z_{out} + Z_L| \, |Z_S + Z_b|}{|Z_{mut}|}$$

$$= \frac{|Z_S + Z_{in}| \, |Z_{rb} + Z_L|}{|Z_{mut}|} \qquad (4A\text{-}23)$$

By substituting expressions for the mutual impedance given by Eq. (4A-17) the transfer impedance may be expressed in terms of directly measurable quantities.

$$|Z_{tfr}| = |Z_{out} + Z_L| \sqrt{\frac{|Z_S + Z_b|}{|Z_{rb} - Z_{out}|}}$$

$$= |Z_S + Z_{in}| \sqrt{\frac{|Z_{rb} + Z_L|}{|Z_b - Z_{in}|}} \qquad (4A\text{-}24)$$

It is evident that if, in one of these expressions, Z_{out} is replaced by Z_{in}, Z_L by Z_S, Z_S by Z_L, Z_b by Z_{rb}, and Z_{rb} by Z_b the other expression will be derived. This verifies the theorem that the transfer impedance of a network made up of an energy source and an energy load connected by a reversible transducer is independent of the direction of energy flow. This theorem is, of course, simply a statement of the reciprocity theorem in terms of the quantities defined for use in our present problem.

In many problems having to do with transducers the blocked and mutual impedances will

be among the first characteristic constants to be determined. It is, therefore, convenient to have formulas by which to compute the input impedance resulting when the load has a given impedance, or the output impedance resulting when the source has a given impedance. These formulas may be derived from those already established by simple algebra. They are

$$Z_{in} = Z_b - \frac{Z_{mut}^2}{Z_{rb} + Z_L} \qquad (4A\text{-}25)$$

and

$$Z_{out} = Z_{rb} - \frac{Z_{mut}^2}{Z_b + Z_S} \qquad (4A\text{-}26)$$

Knowing the mutual impedance of a transducer it is possible to deduce the impedance of a source from impedances measured at the output terminals, or to deduce the impedance of a load from impedances measured at the input terminals. Formulas for this purpose are obtained by solving those given above for the quantities in question. These formulas are

$$Z_S = \frac{Z_{mut}^2}{Z_{rb} - Z_{out}} - Z_b \qquad (4A\text{-}27)$$

and

$$Z_L = \frac{Z_{mut}^2}{Z_b - Z_{in}} - Z_{rb} \qquad (4A\text{-}28)$$

4A-6 The Transmission Losses of a Transducer

By the same methods as those used to derive expressions for the source and load powers at a single junction we may derive expressions for the input and output powers of a transducer between two junctions. The input power of such a transducer is

$$P_{in} = (i_{in})^2 R_{in} = e_S^2 \frac{R_{in}}{|Z_S + Z_{in}|^2} \qquad (4A\text{-}29)$$

The output power of such a transducer is

$$P_{out} = \frac{(e_{out})^2}{4R_{out}} = i_L^2 \frac{|Z_{out} + Z_L|^2}{4R_{out}} \qquad (4A\text{-}30)$$

We may now define six transmission losses associated with a transducer, or with the portion of an energy transmission system included between two specified points in that system. Each of these losses is defined in terms of a power ratio. In each case, however, it is possible to express the loss in terms of absolute values of impedance. The definitions of these transmission losses and the expressions by which they may be evaluated are as follows.

$(N_{tsn})_S$ The **source transition loss** at the junction between an energy source and a transducer connecting that source to an energy load is the transmission loss measured by the ratio of the source power of the source to the input power of the transducer.

$$(N_{tsn})_S = \lg t \frac{P_S}{P_{in}}$$

$$= \lg t \frac{|Z_S + Z_{in}|^2}{4R_S R_{in}} \ db \quad (4A\text{-}31)$$

$(N_{tsn})_L$ The **load transition loss** at the junction between an energy load and a transducer connecting that load to an energy source is the transmission loss measured by the ratio of the output power of the transducer to the load power of the load.

$$(N_{tsn})_L = \lg t \frac{P_{out}}{P_L}$$

$$= \lg t \frac{|Z_{out} + Z_L|^2}{4R_{out} R_L} \ db \quad (4A\text{-}32)$$

N_{dis} The **dissipation loss** of a transducer connecting an energy source and an energy load is the transmission loss measured by the ratio of the input power of the transducer to its output power.

$$N_{dis} = \lg t \frac{P_{in}}{P_{out}}$$

$$= \lg t \frac{4R_{in} R_{out} |Z_{tfr}|^2}{|Z_S + Z_{in}|^2 |Z_{out} + Z_L|^2}$$

$$= \lg t \frac{4R_{in} R_{out} |Z_S + Z_b|^2}{|Z_{mut}|^2 |Z_S + Z_{in}|^2} \ db \quad (4A\text{-}33)$$

N_{avl} The **available power loss** of a transducer connecting an energy source and an energy load is the transmission loss measured by the ratio of the source power of the source to the output power of the transducer.

$$N_{avl} = \lg t \frac{P_S}{P_{out}}$$

$$= \lg t \frac{R_{out}}{R_S} \frac{|Z_{tfr}|^2}{|Z_{out} + Z_L|^2}$$

$$= \lg t \frac{R_{out}}{R_S} \frac{|Z_S + Z_b|^2}{|Z_{mut}|^2} \ db \quad (4A\text{-}34)$$

N_{eff} The **efficiency loss** of a transducer connecting an energy source and an energy load is the transmission loss measured by the ratio of the input power of the transducer to the load power of the load.

$$N_{eff} = \lg t \frac{P_{in}}{P_L}$$

$$= \lg t \frac{R_{in}}{R_L} \frac{|Z_{tfr}|^2}{|Z_S + Z_{in}|^2}$$

$$= \lg t \frac{R_{in}}{R_L} \frac{|Z_{rb} + Z_L|^2}{|Z_{mut}|^2} \ db \quad (4A\text{-}35)$$

N_{tdr} The **transducer loss** of a transducer connecting an energy source and an energy load is the transmission loss measured by the ratio of the source power of the source to the load power of the load.

$$N_{tdr} = \lg t \frac{P_S}{P_L}$$

$$= \lg t \frac{|Z_{tfr}|^2}{4R_S R_L} \quad (4A\text{-}36)$$

$$= \lg t \frac{|Z_{out} + Z_L|^2 |Z_S + Z_b|^2}{4R_S R_L |Z_{mut}|^2} \ db$$

On examining the impedance values appearing in these formulas for the transmission losses which may be associated with a transducer it is found that not one of the six is a unique characteristic of the transducer. The available power loss is independent of the load but dependent on the source; the efficiency loss is independent of the source but dependent on the load; the other four losses are dependent on both source and load.

To specify the unique properties of a transducer completely, at a single frequency, it is necessary to specify three impedances. These may, of course, be the impedances of the three branches of the equivalent network. They may also be any three of the two blocked and the two free impedances measured at the transducer terminals. They may, and perhaps more conveniently, be any two of these four terminal impedances and the mutual impedance.

There are two additional transmission losses which are frequently encountered in the theory of electrical transmission systems. These may be expressed in terms of losses already defined. Like these previously defined losses they may also be expressed in terms of measurable impedances.

N_{rfl} The **reflection loss** at the junction between an energy source and an energy load is the transmission loss measured by the ratio of (1) the load power which would be measured if source and load were connected by a hypothetical transducer having an input impedance equal to the source impedance of the source, an output impedance equal to the load impedance of the load, and developing the same volt-amperes at its load terminals as are developed at its source terminals, to (2) the actual load power when source and load are connected directly to each other.

N_{insn} The **insertion loss** of a transducer connecting an energy source and an energy load is the transmission loss measured by the ratio of (1) the load power which would be measured if the load were connected directly to the source, to (2) the actual load power when source and load are connected by the transducer in question.

In the case of each of these losses both the reference load power and the actual load power specified by the definition may be expressed in terms of the source power of the given source and the transmission losses measuring the ratio of this source power to the load powers in question.

In the case of reflection loss the transmission loss measured by the ratio of the source power, P_S, of the given source to the reference load power, P_{ref}, of the given load when the two are connected by the hypothetical transducer is the transducer loss of this transducer in this connection. For this transducer $Z_{in} = Z_S$, $Z_{out} = Z_L$, and $e_L i_L = e_{in} i_{in}$, or $i_L{}^2 |Z_L| = i_{in}{}^2 |Z_{in}|$. From this it follows that $i_{in} = i_L \sqrt{|Z_L/Z_S|} = e_S / |2Z_S|$ and $Z_{tfr} = 2\sqrt{|Z_S Z_L|}$. When these substitutions are made in Eq. (4A-36) the reference transducer loss, associated with the reference load power, is found to be

$$(N_{tdr})_{ref} = \lg \frac{P_S}{P_{ref}} = \lg \frac{|Z_{tfr}|^2}{4R_S R_L}$$

$$= \lg \frac{|Z_S Z_L|}{R_S R_L} \quad \text{db} \qquad (4A\text{-}37)$$

The transmission loss measured by the ratio of the same source power, P_S, to the actual load power, P_{act}, is the normal transition loss for the junction in question. This transition loss may be written as

$$(N_{tsn})_{act} = \lg \frac{P_S}{P_{act}} = \lg \frac{|Z_S + Z_L|^2}{4R_S R_L} \quad \text{db} \quad (4A\text{-}38)$$

The ratio of the reference power to the actual power is measured by the loss obtained by subtracting the reference transducer loss from the actual transition loss. The reflection loss, which also measures this ratio, is thus found to be

$$N_{rfl} = \lg \frac{P_{ref}}{P_{act}} = (N_{tsn})_{act} - (N_{tdr})_{ref}$$

$$= \lg \frac{|Z_S + Z_L|^2}{4 |Z_S Z_L|} \quad \text{db} \qquad (4A\text{-}39)$$

It may be shown, on the basis of the relations assumed above, that the ratio of the reference load power to the actual load power described in the definition of reflection loss is equal to the ratio of (1) the volt-amperes which would be developed at the terminals of the given source if it were connected to a load having an impedance equal to the source impedance to (2) the volt-amperes developed at the terminals of the same source when connected to the specified load. Reflection loss is sometimes defined in terms of the ratio of these two volt-ampere values.

In the case of insertion loss the ratio of the source power of the given source to the reference load power specified by the definition is measured by the normal transition loss between that source and that load. The ratio of this same source power to the actual load power developed by the transducer in question is measured by the transducer loss of that transducer in the given connection. The ratio of the reference load power to the actual load power is thus measured by the transmission loss obtained by subtracting a reference transition loss from an actual transducer loss. This ratio is, by definition, the ratio measured by the insertion loss of the transducer. This insertion loss is thus seen to be

$$N_{insn} = \lg \frac{P_{ref}}{P_{act}} = (N_{tdr})_{act} - (N_{tsn})_{ref}$$

$$= \lg \frac{|Z_{tfr}|^2}{4R_S R_L} - \lg \frac{|Z_S + Z_L|^2}{4R_S R_L}$$

$$= \lg \frac{|Z_{tfr}|^2}{|Z_S + Z_L|^2} \quad \text{db} \qquad (4A\text{-}40)$$

The specific transmission loss defined as insertion loss cannot be used in connection with a transducer in which energy is converted from one form to another. This is an obvious consequence of the fact that the two power magnitudes in question are those which would be developed at a load capable of receiving energy directly from a given source. No such restriction is imposed on dissipation loss, available power loss, efficiency loss, or transducer loss.

4A-7 Resultant Transmission Losses

The manner in which the dissipation loss of a transducer combines with one or the other of the transition losses to form either the available power loss or the efficiency loss is evident from the relations between the power ratios measured by these losses. The fact that the transducer loss is the sum of the dissipation loss and both of the transition losses is similarly evident. These relations are shown graphically, in the manner usually employed for dimensioning a mechanical drawing, in Fig. 4A-3.

Any transducer connecting an energy source with an energy load for which the transition and dissipation losses are zero is said to be an **ideal transducer**. Such a transducer must have an input impedance which is the conjugate of the source impedance, an output impedance which is the conjugate of the load impedance, and must develop at the load all of the available power of the source. Since the transition and dissipation losses are zero the available power loss, the efficiency loss, and the transducer loss must also be zero. Transducer loss is sometimes defined as the loss measuring the ratio of the power developed at a given load by a given source when connected by an ideal transducer to the power developed at the same load when connected to the same source by the transducer in question.

The formulas for dissipation loss in terms of impedance, given by Eq. (4A-33), contain two expressions in which all impedances are directly measurable. If the subscripts, indicating the network branches, appearing in one of these expressions are replaced by the subscripts which would be used for the same branches if energy were transmitted from the load to the source the expression is converted to the alternative equivalent expression. This demonstrates, as was demonstrated for transition loss, that the dissipation loss of a transducer connecting two energy trans-

mission systems is independent of the direction of energy flow.

Since dissipation losses and transition losses are both independent of the direction of energy flow transducer losses, which are equal to sums of these two types of loss, are also independent of direction. If the direction of energy flow is reversed through any transducer forming part of an energy transmission system the loss measured as an available power loss for one direction of flow becomes the efficiency loss for the other. Conversely, the loss measured as an efficiency loss for one direction becomes the available power loss for the other.

Considerations of the relations between the various losses associated with a transducer, and of the power ratios measured by these losses, show that transition losses and dissipation losses are contiguous to each other. Available power losses are contiguous to available power losses. Efficiency losses are contiguous to efficiency losses. Transducer losses are *not* contiguous to transducer losses; they are contiguous to dissipation losses, to available power losses preceding them, and to efficiency losses following them.

From this it appears that the resultant transducer loss of a series of transducers between two junctions in an energy transmission system is the sum of alternate transition and dissipation losses between these junctions. The resultant available power loss is the sum of the individual available power losses. The resultant efficiency loss is the sum of the individual efficiency losses.

Any transmission loss is, it will be recalled (Art. 2B-3), the difference between two transmission levels. By subtracting a resultant available power loss from the **available power level** at one junction we obtain the available power level at another junction, more distant from the source. By subtracting a resultant efficiency loss from the **actual power level** at one junction we obtain the actual power level at another. By subtracting a resultant transducer loss from the available power level at one junction we obtain the actual power level at another.

Whenever the output of a transducer, or series of transducers, connects a source of electric energy to a circuit, such as a vacuum-tube amplifier, which may be considered to have an infinitely high load impedance it is assumed that no power s developed at the load. Transition loss at such a junction is thus without significance. In such situations the open-circuit voltage appearing at the junction may be computed from the power available and from the output impedance at that point by means of Eq. (4A-8).

The properties of an energy transmission system which may be measured by a transmission loss, computed solely from data as to system parameters, are those which apply at a single frequency only. The power ratios measured by such losses are ratios of the powers of sinusoidal waves. If the transducer is transmitting energy having a continuous spectrum any one of the transmission losses defined in the preceding paragraphs gives the ratio of two powers per unit band at that frequency for which the impedances associated with that loss are valid.

Ratios of the powers corresponding to the energy of waves having a continuous spectrum which is contained in some specified frequency band may, of course, also be measured by transmission losses. The loss measuring such a ratio, however, is not a unique property of the transmission system; it cannot be derived from a transmission loss characteristic, computed as a function of frequency, nor from any other known constants of the system. Any transmission loss applying to a band of frequencies is a function of the transmission loss characteristic applying to the system and of the spectrum level characteristic applying to the energy being transmitted. The spectrum level characteristic of the final power is derived from the spectrum level of the initial power by subtracting the transmission loss characteristic, point by point. Initial and final band powers are obtained by converting spectrum levels to powers per unit band, again point by point, and integrating this power per unit band over the band. The resulting band powers are then expressed as band levels. The difference between these band levels is the band transmission loss applying to energy which varies with respect to frequency, as indicated by the initial spectrum level characteristic, when transmitted by a system having a transmission loss which has the magnitude, considered as a function of frequency, indicated by the transmission loss characteristic. It cannot be used to derive the final band level from the initial band level of energy which varies with frequency in any other manner.

Many measurements of transmission loss, particularly in laboratory studies of electric circuits, are made by a comparison method. There is required a suitable source of sinusoidal waves, usually containing a vacuum-tube oscillator, and a suitable load, containing some form of indicating or recording instrument. These are connected first by the circuit being studied and then by a calibrated adjustable resistance network known as an "attenuation box." By adjusting the known transmission loss of the attenuation box until it develops the same load power at the load as the circuit under investigation the transmission loss of the latter is determined.

The circuits used in attenuation boxes are four-terminal networks. They usually have three branches, each of which is a variable resistance. The values of these resistances are such that if a resistance having a particular value, known as the **characteristic impedance** of the box, is connected between one pair of terminals the impedance measured between the other pair will be a resistance having this same characteristic value, regardless of the adjustment of the box. Many of the commercially available attenuation boxes are designed to have a characteristic impedance of 500 ohms resistance.

A resistance network of this type may be considered as a reversible, passive transducer. When it is connected between a source and a load each of which has an impedance equal to the characteristic impedance of the network the transmission loss indicated by the dials connected to the adjusting mechanism is the transducer loss of the network, in decibels. In this case the source and input impedances form one conjugate pair and the load and output impedances another. The source and load transition losses are therefore zero. The dial reading thus indicates the dissipation loss, the available power loss, and the efficiency loss, as well as the transducer loss.

When an attenuation box is connected to a source having a source impedance equal to the characteristic impedance of the box the loss indicated by its dials is an available power loss, regardless of the load impedance. When connected to a load having a load impedance equal to the characteristic impedance the loss indicated is an efficiency loss, regardless of the source impedance. If an attenuation box is connected between a source and a load only one of which has an impedance equal to the characteristic impedance the total transducer loss is the sum of the indicated loss and the transition loss at the so-called mismatched junction, where the connected impedance is not the conjugate of the characteristic impedance. In this case the impedance of the network at this mismatched junction is its characteristic impedance, regardless of the setting, and the transition loss is constant provided the connected impedance is constant. If this connected impedance is known the constant transition loss may be computed. The transducer loss of the network is therefore known for all settings. When an attenuation box is connected between a source and a load neither of which has an impedance equal to the characteristic impedance of the box the input and output impedances of the network will both vary with its adjustment. None of the transmission losses actually associated with the network in such a situation are conveniently related to its dial settings.

4A-8 Duality Relations

The transmission losses of a transducer may be evaluated in terms of admittances as well as in terms of impedances. The formulas used in one case are identical in form with the corresponding formulas used in the other, as is required by the duality principle.[1]

In accordance with the duality principle the equivalent circuit of the transducer, its source, and its load becomes that shown in Fig. 4A-4. The

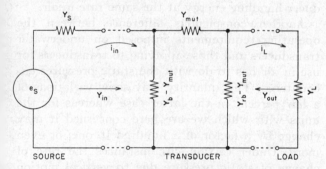

FIG. 4A-4. EQUIVALENT ADMITTANCE NETWORK. A network, having admittance branches, which is related by the duality principle to the network having impedance branches shown in Fig. 4A-3.

currents, voltages, and powers defined in connection with the equivalent impedance network are unchanged when we consider the equivalent admittance network. For the equivalent admittance network the **source admittance** is the reciprocal of the source impedance of the impedance network. It would be defined as the quotient obtained by dividing the phasor representing the short-circuited source current by the phasor representing the open-circuited source voltage. In a similar manner, the **load admittance** in one case is the reciprocal of the load impedance in the other. Such direct relationships between admittances and impedances do not exist for the portions of the two networks which represent the transducer. For example, for the impedance network the

blocked impedance was defined as the input impedance when the transducer was connected to a load of infinite impedance. By the duality principle, the **blocked admittance** of a transducer must be its input admittance when connected to a load having an infinite admittance. The blocked admittance of a transducer is, in other words, the input admittance when the output terminals are short-circuited. The free impedance of a transducer is its input impedance when its output terminals are short-circuited. The blocked admittance of a transducer is, therefore, the reciprocal of its free impedance. Similarly, the **reverse blocked admittance** is the reciprocal of the reverse free impedance. Conversely, the **free admittance** of a transducer is the reciprocal of its blocked impedance and the **reverse free admittance** is the reciprocal of its reverse blocked impedance.

If the definition for the **mutual admittance** of a transducer is derived from the definition for its mutual impedance in accordance with the duality principle the mutual admittance must be defined as the quotient obtained by dividing the phasor representing the short-circuited current at one pair of terminals by the phasor representing the voltage across the second pair of terminals when the first pair is short-circuited. Similarly, the **transfer admittance** of a network made up of an energy source and an energy load connected by a transducer is the quotient obtained by dividing the phasor representing the source current of the source by the phasor representing the load voltage of the load. On the basis of the foregoing, the formulas for converting transducer impedances to transducer admittances in accordance with the duality principle are as follows.

$$Y_S = \frac{1}{Z_S}, \qquad Y_L = \frac{1}{Z_L},$$

$$Y_{\text{in}} = \frac{1}{Z_{\text{in}}}, \quad Y_{\text{out}} = \frac{1}{Z_{\text{out}}} \qquad (4A\text{-}41)$$

$$Y_b = \frac{1}{Z_f}, \qquad Y_f = \frac{1}{Z_b},$$

$$Y_{rb} = \frac{1}{Z_{rf}}, \qquad Y_{rf} = \frac{1}{Z_{rb}} \qquad (4A\text{-}42)$$

$$|Y_{\text{mut}}| = \frac{|Z_{\text{mut}}|}{|Z_b \cdot Z_{rf}|} = \frac{|Z_{\text{mut}}|}{|Z_f \cdot Z_{rb}|},$$

$$|Z_{\text{mut}}| = \frac{|Y_{\text{mut}}|}{|Y_b \cdot Y_{rf}|} = \frac{|Y_{\text{mut}}|}{|Y_f \cdot Y_{rb}|} \qquad (4A\text{-}43)$$

$$| Y_{\text{tfr}} | = \frac{| Z_{\text{tfr}} |}{| Z_S \cdot Z_L |}, \quad | Z_{\text{tfr}} | = \frac{| Y_{\text{tfr}} |}{| Y_S \cdot Y_L |} \quad (4A\text{-}44)$$

It may be shown by simple algebraic substitution that the mutual admittance of a transducer may be expressed in terms of admittances measured at its terminals as

$$Y_{\text{mut}} = \sqrt{Y_{rb}(Y_b - Y_f)}$$

$$= \sqrt{Y_b(Y_{rb} - Y_{rf})}$$

$$= \sqrt{(Y_b - Y_{\text{in}})(Y_{rb} + Y_L)}$$

$$= \sqrt{(Y_{rb} - Y_{\text{out}})(Y_b + Y_S)} \quad (4A\text{-}45)$$

The identity in form existing between these equalities and those of Eqs. (4A-13) and (4A-17) is self-evident.

The transfer admittance of a transducer may be expressed in terms of network admittances as

$$| Y_{\text{tfr}} | = \frac{| Y_{\text{out}} + Y_L | \, | Y_S + Y_b |}{| Y_{\text{mut}} |}$$

$$= \frac{| Y_S + Y_{\text{in}} | \, | Y_{rb} + Y_L |}{| Y_{\text{mut}} |} \quad (4A\text{-}46)$$

These equations are identical in form with those of Eq. (4A-23).

By substituting appropriate equalities selected from the preceding group of equations into the equations for the six basic transmission losses associated with a transducer as given in terms of impedances the following expressions for these losses in terms of admittances are derived.

$$(N_{\text{tsn}})_S = \lgt \frac{| Y_S + Y_{\text{in}} |^2}{4 G_S G_{\text{in}}} \quad \text{db} \quad (4A\text{-}47)$$

$$(N_{\text{tsn}})_L = \lgt \frac{| Y_{\text{out}} + Y_L |^2}{4 G_{\text{out}} G_L} \quad \text{db} \quad (4A\text{-}48)$$

$$V_{\text{dis}} = \lgt \frac{4 G_{\text{in}} G_{\text{out}} | Y_S + Y_b |^2}{| Y_{\text{mut}} |^2 | Y_S + Y_{\text{in}} |^2} \quad \text{db} \quad (4A\text{-}49)$$

$$N_{\text{avl}} = \lgt \frac{G_{\text{out}}}{G_S} \frac{| Y_S + Y_b |^2}{| Y_{\text{mut}} |^2} \quad \text{db} \quad (4A\text{-}50)$$

$$N_{\text{eff}} = \lgt \frac{G_{\text{in}}}{G_L} \frac{| Y_{rb} + Y_L |^2}{| Y_{\text{mut}} |^2} \quad \text{db} \quad (4A\text{-}51)$$

$$N_{\text{tdr}} = \lgt \frac{| Y_{\text{out}} + Y_L |^2 | Y_S + Y_b |^2}{4 G_S G_L | Y_{\text{mut}} |^2} \quad \text{db} \quad (4A\text{-}52)$$

4-B THE DESIGN OF SONAR TRANSDUCERS

For the same reason that the human ear is poorly adapted, acoustically, to underwater listening, electroacoustic devices such as telephone transmitters, receivers, microphones, and loudspeakers need more than water-proofing to make them adequate for underwater signaling. It is true that during the First World War several fairly acceptable listening hydrophones were developed which differed from devices designed to operate with air-borne sounds only insofar as they were modified to permit immersion. In spite of the fact that submarines were detected by these hydrophones they were far from having the mechanical and acoustical characteristics dictated by the properties of the medium in which they were used. Their success was, in fact, due more to deficiencies in submarine design than to the excellence of their own construction. For any underwater transducer to conform properly to its environment it should operate with about sixty times the force and one sixtieth the displacement, or velocity, of a transducer handling energy at the same rate in air.

Another conspicuous difference between the operating requirements imposed on underwater transducers and those applying to transducers for use in air has to do with the static pressures encountered. This quantity may show variations of a few percent in the latter case whereas for the units with which we are here concerned it may change by a factor of a hundred to one, or even more. Under certain circumstances the rate of change of static pressure due to vertical motion of the hydrophone may be many times the rate of change of pressure due to an acoustic wave. These factors must be kept in mind during both the design and the operation of underwater electroacoustic transducers.

4B-1 Magnetostriction and Electrostriction

One of the most effective methods of meeting the requirements noted above is to utilize certain materials which have the property of developing strains when subjected to electric or magnetic fields, or, conversely, of developing such fields when subjected to mechanical stress. These properties are known as **magnetostriction,** in the case of magnetic fields, and as **electrostriction,** in the case of electric fields. When variations in the strength of a magnetic or an electric field take place at a frequency within the acoustic spectrum, acoustic waves will be generated in any material exhibiting the appropriate effect which may be present in that field. These waves may be propagated from the material to water. When acoustic waves are propagated from water to such a material the resulting mechanical stresses will be accompanied by variations in field strength. These, in turn, may be propagated as electric waves in a suitable circuit.

Materials in which these effects reach practical magnitudes have specific acoustic impedances which may be 10 to 30 times the specific acoustic impedance of water. Although these impedance ratios are by no means small they do, nevertheless, permit more effective acoustic coupling between electric circuits and water than can be realized with electroacoustic transducers intended for coupling circuits to air.

The magnetostrictive effect was first described by the British scientist James Prescott Joule in 1842.[2] The effect is, for this reason, frequently spoken of as the Joule effect. It originally referred to changes in the dimensions of certain magnetic materials under the influence of a magnetic field. The effect is now known to be reversible; any magnetostrictive material which has been magnetized, and which retains its magnetization, will show a change in its magnetizing force when stressed.

The first report of the electrostrictive effect was made by the Curie brothers, Jacques and Pierre, in France, in 1880.[3] Their work related to a form of electrostriction known as **piezoelectricity.** They had observed that when certain crystals, such as quartz, tourmaline, or Rochelle salt, were stressed electric charges of unlike potential appeared on non-adjacent surfaces. It was later shown that when potential differences were applied to these same surfaces strains were set up within the crystals.[4]

Certain materials which do not show a potential difference when stressed show strains when brought within an electric field. Many of these materials, however, once they have been subjected to electric forces behave thereafter as though they were piezoelectric and do then develop potential differences when stressed. Such materials are said to have been **polarized** and to have retained their polarization. The analogy between the polarization of these materials, which are electrostrictive, and the magnetization of magnetostrictive materials is self-evident.

4B-2 Electric Coupling to Magnetostrictive Material

The important magnetostrictive materials are nickel and nickel alloys such as permalloy, nichrome, and monel metal. All of these have been used in applications of the magnetostrictive effect. Nickel has a practical advantage over its alloys due to the fact that, in addition to showing an adequate magnetostrictive effect, it is stable and reproducible even at commercial purities.

The stresses developed in magnetostrictive materials may be measured most conveniently in terms of the strains which accompany them. In general discussions of the magnetostrictive effect it is customary to show the relation between the fractional change in length, $\Delta l/l$, and the flux density, B, measured in gausses. For many materials, in fact, the stress can be shown to be proportional to the square of the flux density. No such simple relation exists between the strength of the magnetizing field and the stress because of the fact that the permeability varies with flux density. In the practical application of magnetostriction as an electroacoustic coupling agent we are, nevertheless, concerned primarily with overall performance. We shall, therefore, consider these changes in permeability as part of the total effect with which we have to deal. This may be done conveniently by graphical methods. The curve of Fig. 4B-1 gives quantitative values, characteristic of nickel, for the fractional change in length, $\Delta l/l$, parallel to the direction of magnetic flux, as a function of the intensity of the magnetic field, H, in oersteds, causing this flux. The curve given by the dotted line shows, using the scale at the top of the diagram, the relation between strain and flux density. The permeability may be deduced at any point by computing the ratio $\mu = B/H$. The effect of saturation is evident at the higher values of field strength. It can be seen that the strain is closely proportional to the square of the flux density regardless of the extent to which the material is saturated.

In the case of nickel the application of a magnetic field results in a stress which causes the material to contract. Under the same conditions a sample of permalloy would increase in length. The direction of the stress, in either case, is independent of the direction of the magnetizing force.

The established relation between the magnetic field intensity set up by an electric current in a coil of wire and the magnitude of that current is

$$H = \frac{0.4\pi n i}{l} \qquad (4B\text{-}1)$$

where

H = the intensity of the magnetizing force (oersted)

i = the current in the coil (amp)

n = the number of turns in the coils (a numeric)

0.4π = a constant relating the systems of units (dimensionless)

l = the length of the coil (cm)

By means of this equation and of the data given by Fig. 4B-1, it is possible to draw, for any given case, a curve showing the relation between the strain due to the magnetostrictive effect and the magnitude of the electric current inducing the effect. Since the direction of the stress is independent of the direction of the magnetic flux, and hence of the current, this curve must be symmetrical about the zero-current axis as shown in Fig. 4B-2. The time variation of stress does not follow exactly the time variation of current because of lags in the change of flux due to hysteresis. Except for these the stress for a given

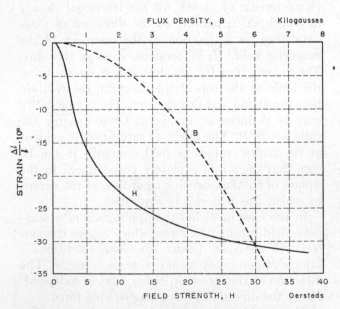

FIG. 4B-1. THE MAGNETOSTRICTIVE EFFECT. The strain appearing in nickel, as a consequence of the magnetostrictive effect, plotted as a function of field strength and also of flux density.

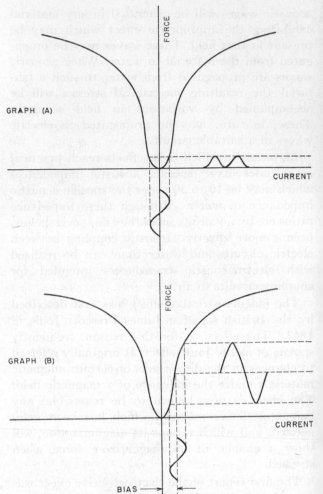

FIG. 4B-2. MAGNETOSTRICTIVE RESPONSE CHARACTERISTICS. Variations in stress appearing in nickel due to variations in magnetizing current (A) without polarizing bias and (B) with polarizing bias.

current may be determined graphically as shown at (A) in Fig. 4B-2. The instantaneous current assumed here is of the form $i_{inst} = i_{max} \cos \omega t$. If the magnitude of this current is small the force is, to a first approximation, proportional to the square of its instantaneous amplitude. We may, therefore, write for the force due to the magnetostrictive effect

$$F = k i_{inst}^2 = \frac{k i_{max}^2}{2} + \frac{k i_{max}^2}{2} \cos 2\omega t \qquad (4B\text{-}2)$$

The first term corresponds to a constant unidirectional force and may be considered as representing rectification; the second term corresponds to a force varying sinusoidally at twice the frequency of the current and may be considered as harmonic distortion. There is no force for which the time variations reproduce those of the impressed current, which represents the signal in its electrical form. Such a force may be developed by biasing the system so that variations of signal current cause the magnetic flux to vary about some constant value or some finite average value. In general, the optimum value of bias would be one which locates the zero value of signal current on the current-stress curve at a point where the rate of change of stress with current is a maximum. This condition is shown graphically in diagram (B) of Fig. 4B-2. It is evident that when driven in this manner the force variations in the magnetostrictive material are, except for any curvature of the characteristic, proportional to the current. The force then reproduces the signal with little distortion unless an attempt is made to cover too great a portion of the characteristic.

It is apparent from the linearity of the curve that the point where the rate of change of stress with current is a maximum not only produces the maximum force for a given current but also results in very nearly the minimum distortion. The upper limit beyond which the force-current ratio cannot be increased by increasing the bias is set by magnetic saturation of the nickel rather than by failure of the magnetostrictive effect. The optimum point occurs near the point of maximum magnetic permeability which, for nickel, is $\mu = (B/H) \approx 1200$.

When a constant biasing flux is provided independent of the signal the material is said to be polarized. Such a permanent flux may be maintained by a separate coil of wire carrying direct current, by a permanent magnet, or by a direct current superimposed, in a single coil, on the varying current. These last two methods of polarization are illustrated in Fig. 4B-3. The superimposed current method, shown at (B), involves the conventional composite connection. In this arrangement, inductance coils in the circuit supplying direct current prevent this circuit from absorbing energy from the signal current; similarly, blocking condensers exclude the direct current from the circuit supplying the electric signal.

Although the amount by which a sample of nickel changes in length when in a magnetic field is only a few parts per million the mechanical stress causing this change in length is considerable. For example, at the operating point shown

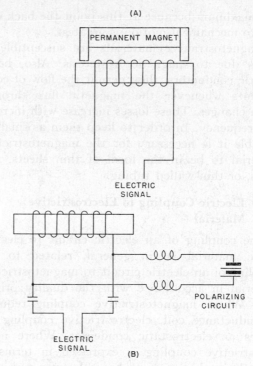

FIG. 4B-3. MAGNETOSTRICTIVE POLARIZING SYSTEMS. Methods of polarizing a magnetostrictive unit (A) by permanent magnet and (B) by direct current superimposed on signal through composite connection.

in (B) of Fig. 4B-2, which corresponds to a magnetic field strength of $H = 2.5$ gauss, the value of the strain is $\Delta l/l = 7.5 \cdot 10^{-6}$. The ratio of the stress to the strain is given quantitatively by the Young's modulus of elasticity which, for nickel, is approximately $2 \cdot 10^{12}$ dyne/cm². A magnetizing flux of 2.5 oersted, therefore, produces the same change in dimensions as would a longitudinal pressure of $6 \cdot 10^7$ dyne/cm², or of 1000 lb/in². At this point the percentage change in force with change in magnetic field strength is about twice the percentage change in field strength.

When used to convert acoustic energy into electric energy the strains set up in magnetostrictive material, under the influence of an acoustic wave, cause a change in the value of any magnetic flux which may be present in the material. For this use, also, it is necessary that the sample be magnetically polarized. In this case it is often possible, as noted in the preceding article, to magnetize the material by applying a strong field and thereafter to obtain the polarization from the remanent magnetism. When converting acoustic energy to electric energy, as well as when converting in the opposite direction, the optimum point occurs where the rate of change of flux with current is a maximum because at this point the back emf due to mechanical motion is greatest.

Magnetostrictive materials are susceptible to losses due to magnetic hysteresis. Also, being electric conductors, they permit the flow of eddy currents whenever the magnetic flux through them changes. These losses increase with increasing frequency. In order to keep them as small as possible it is necessary for the magnetostrictive material to be in the form of thin sheets, fine wires, or thin-walled tubing.

4B-3 Electric Coupling to Electrostrictive Material

The coupling of an electric circuit to electrostatic material is, in general, related to the coupling of an electric circuit to magnetostrictive material in accordance with the duality principle.[1] Where magnetostrictive coupling requires an inductance coil, electrostrictive coupling requires an electrostatic condenser. Where magnetostrictive coupling is expressed in terms of the relation between mechanical stress and electric current, electrostrictive coupling is expressed in terms of the relation between mechanical stress and electric voltage.

When tubes or sheets of magnetostrictive material are brought within a magnetic field stresses are developed which tend, in general, to cause a change in length in the direction of the magnetic lines of force. A single magnetostrictive coupling coefficient is usually sufficient. The situation when using electrostrictive coupling is more complex. When this material is obtained from piezoelectric crystals it is usually ground to the form of a block having rectangular surfaces. The behavior of such a block when in an electric field depends upon the nature of the crystal, the position which the block occupied in the crystal, and on the orientation of the block with respect to the electric field. It has, in fact, not one electrostrictive coupling coefficient but several. In general, there will be stresses tending to change each of the longitudinal dimensions of the block. There may also be torsional and flexural strains.

There are many materials from which electrostrictive elements may be obtained. There are also a large number of types of coupling block which may be produced from each of these materials. A detailed study of the many electrostrictive coupling arrangements thus made possible is beyond the scope of our present interest.

Several excellent texts are available to those who wish to examine these matters further.[5,6] In view of the complexity of the problems having to do with electrostrictive coupling it is encouraging to note that considerable progress has been made, particularly by a committee of the Institute of Radio Engineers, toward standardizing the terminology and symbols which may be employed.[7]

4B-4 Mechanical Coupling to Magnetostrictive Material

Our consideration of the factors pertinent to the mechanical coupling of magnetostrictive or electrostrictive material to an acoustic medium such as water will be limited to the case of magnetostriction. Although the detailed problems encountered in the two cases are by no means identical the principles employed are similar. It will be convenient to examine these principles in terms of a specific medium.

One method of coupling the force developed by magnetostriction to a fluid medium is to use a number of thin-walled magnetostrictive tubes to drive a solid metal block or plate. This block or plate, being in contact with the water, transmits mechanical energy derived from the magnetostrictive material to the fluid medium.

The mechanical features of this arrangement are shown in Fig. 4B-4. The thin-walled nickel

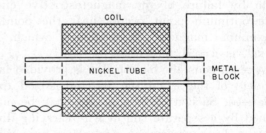

Fig. 4B-4. A Mechanically Coupled Magnetostrictive Radiator. An acoustic radiator driven by a magnetostrictive inertia element.

tube is generally fitted tightly into a hole in the block, which is usually of steel, and sweated securely by means of silver solder. The coil is supported by a cylindrical sleeve in such manner that it makes no mechanical contact with any moving part of the system. In practice the turns of the coil are concentrated, insofar as possible at the end of the tube in proximity to the plate. The diagram shows a single tube and a single steel block; actually the block may be a portion of a steel plate, other portions of which are simultaneously driven by other nickel tubes.

The behavior of this system when vibrating sinusoidally may be examined by the same method as that used in Chapter 2 for studying acoustic waves in water. The general equation of wave motion, Eq. (2A-15), derived in Art. 2A-3 is directly applicable to the case of longitudinal vibrations in solid rods or tubes. This equation is

$$\frac{d^2}{dt^2}\xi_{inst} = \frac{E}{\rho}\frac{d^2}{ds^2}\xi_{inst} \qquad (4\text{B-}3)$$

where

ξ_{inst} = the displacement of a cross-sectional area of the rod, perpendicular to the X-axis along which the longitudinal motion takes place (cm)

E = the modulus of elasticity of the material (dyne/cm)

ρ = the density of the material (gm/cm³)

t = time (sec)

s = distance along the axis of motion (cm)

It will be recalled that this equation was used to establish the relation $c^2 = E/\rho$ between the constants of the medium and the velocity of propagation and that it may be written as

$$\frac{d^2}{dt^2}\xi_{inst} = c^2\frac{d^2}{ds^2}\xi_{inst} \qquad (4\text{B-}4)$$

When the motion of the rod is sinusoidal, general solutions for this differential equation, in the form of Eq. (2A-4) or in the form of Eq. (2A-5), are

$$\xi_{inst} = k_1\cos\omega\left(t + \frac{s}{c}\right) + k_2\cos\omega\left(t - \frac{s}{c}\right)$$

$$= k_1\cos\frac{2\pi}{\lambda}(s + ct) + k_2\cos\frac{2\pi}{\lambda}(s - ct) \qquad (4\text{B-}5)$$

These equations describe two waves, which may be of different amplitudes, moving along the rod in opposite directions at the velocity c.

In the case of a rod of magnetostrictive material, in which the mechanical vibration is due solely to a force developed within the material, there will be no force tending to move the rod as a whole with respect to its surroundings. As the rod expands and contracts, therefore, the cross-sectional plane passing through its center of mass perpendicular to the direction of motion will remain at rest. Let us measure distance, s, along the rod from this zero-motion plane. Since $\xi_{inst} = 0$ when $s = 0$, we may write

$$\xi_{inst} = k_1\cos\omega t + k_2\cos\omega t = 0 \qquad (4\text{B-}6)$$

Consequently $k_2 = -k_1$ and the displacement at any point on the rod is

$$\xi_{inst} = k_1\cos\frac{2\pi}{\lambda}(s + ct) - k_1\cos\frac{2\pi}{\lambda}(s - ct) \qquad (4\text{B-}7)$$

or, by trigonometric identities,

$$\xi_{inst} = -2k_1\left(\sin\frac{2\pi s}{\lambda}\right)(\sin\omega t) \qquad (4\text{B-}8)$$

The negative sign may be neglected because it depends only on the initial assumptions as to the signs of k_1 and of k_2, which were arbitrary. This equation states that the longitudinal motion of any plane through the rod perpendicular to its axis is sinusoidal at the frequency $f = \omega/2\pi$, except where $s = 0$. It also states that the maximum value of displacement at any distance, s, from the center of mass is $2k_1\sin(2\pi s/\lambda)$. When the distance from the plane of zero motion to the end of the rod is such that $s = \lambda/4$ the maximum amplitude of vibration of the end plane is

$$2k_1\sin\frac{\pi}{2} = 2k_1 \qquad (4\text{B-}9)$$

If the total length of the rod is $\lambda/2$ the plane of zero motion will be at the center and the rod is known as a half-wave rod. If the rod is clamped at one end to a relatively heavy mass and the distance from this mass to the free end of the rod is $\lambda/4$ the rod is known as a quarter-wave rod.

The foregoing has given no clue as to the magnitude of k_1, the amplitude of vibration. This quantity is determined by the fact that, when the system is operating under steady-state conditions, a balance must exist between the energy delivered to the rod, through the agency of the magnetostrictive force, and the energy dissipated by its motion. The energy dissipated may be in the form of frictional losses or of radiation. It is this latter which is the useful output of the system. For a given electric input the amplitude of vibration will increase until the balance, characteristic of the steady state, is reached. This situation will be examined in more detail shortly.

The plate or block which, in a sonar transducer, is driven by a magnetostrictive tube may be considered as a lumped mass if its thickness is less than one-eighth the length of a wave. When such a load is fastened to one end of a nickel tube and the system set into longitudinal vibration magnetostrictively there must be, as before, one point on the axis at which there is no motion. In actual designs the relative masses of the load and of the driving tube are such that this zero-motion plane passes through the tube near its junction with the load, usually at a point 3 to 5 millimeters from the driven surface of the block. The tube then acts essentially as a quarter-wave rod with respect to the zero-motion plane.

To study the behavior of this system it will be convenient to replace the magnetostrictive driving rod, with its distributed mass and elasticity, by an equivalent lumped system. The equivalent mass, M_S, will be taken as that mass which, moving at the velocity characteristic of the free end of the rod, represents the same amount of kinetic energy as is associated with the actual rod. The equivalent elasticity will be taken as that of a weightless spring having a stiffness, K, such that, when connected between the moving equivalent mass and the moving load, its potential energy is the same as that associated with the actual rod. This equivalent mass and this equivalent stiffness may be computed by means of the integral calculus on the basis of the distributed constants of the actual rod. For the case of a rod which is exactly a quarter wave long, which is rigidly clamped at one end, and for which the amplitude of motion varies sinusoidally with length, it may be shown that the equivalent mass is $M = \frac{1}{2}(\rho A l)$, or one half the mass of the actual rod. The equivalent stiffness is

$$K = \frac{\pi^2 EA}{8l} \qquad (4B-10)$$

where EA/l is the stiffness of the actual rod in terms of its Young's modulus of elasticity, E.

For purposes of analysis, then, the system shown in Fig. 4B-4 may be replaced by the equivalent lumped system shown in Fig. 4B-5. The lumped mass, M_S, is that mass which is the equivalent of the actual tube. Its relation to the actual tube will differ somewhat from that stated above since it will, in general, not be

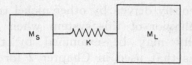

FIG. 4B-5. THE LUMPED EQUIVALENT OF A COUPLED RADIATOR. Lumped masses connected by weightless elastic member forming the equivalent of the unit shown in Fig. 4B-4. M_L is the radiating load and M_S is the mass equivalent to the driving tube.

exactly a quarter wave long. The equivalent stiffness, K, will also differ from the value given, for the same reason. The mass M_L is the lumped mass of the load representing the steel block, or the section of steel plate, which is driven by the magnetostrictive tube. This is equal to the mass of the actual block, or the actual mass of that portion of the plate associated with a given tube. The sinusoidally varying magnetostrictive effect may be thought of, in this equivalent system, as exerted between the two masses so that they alternately attract and repel each other.

The displacements of the two masses will be designated, respectively, as ξ_S and ξ_L where a positive sign indicates motion to the right. When the actual system is vibrating sinusoidally Eq. (4B-8) shows that all portions move in phase or in phase opposition. The two masses of the equivalent system, therefore, must move in true phase opposition and the extension of the elastic member, at any instant, must be $(\xi_L - \xi_S)$. The elastic force exerted on the mass M_L is therefore $K(\xi_S - \xi_L)$. Similarly, the elastic force acting on the equivalent driving mass, M_S, is $K(\xi_L - \xi_S)$. When this system is in steady-state vibration the forces developed by the magnetostrictive effect are exactly balanced by the losses due to friction and radiation. The elastic forces are then exactly equal to the forces required to accelerate the two masses. This condition may be represented by the two equations

$$M_S(a_{inst})_S = K(\xi_L - \xi_S) \qquad (4B-11)$$

and

$$M_L(a_{inst})_L = K(\xi_S - \xi_L) \qquad (4B-12)$$

whence

$$M_S(a_{inst})_S = - M_L(a_{inst})_L \qquad (4B-13)$$

In these equations $(a_{inst})_S$ and $(a_{inst})_L$ are, respectively, the accelerations of the equivalent driving mass and of the load mass. In general, if the displacement of a lumped mass is

$$\xi_{inst} = \xi_{max} \sin \omega t \qquad (4B-14)$$

the velocity with which it moves is

$$u_{inst} = \omega \xi_{max} \cos \omega t \qquad (4B-15)$$

and its acceleration is

$$a_{inst} = - \omega^2 \xi_{max} \sin \omega t \qquad (4B-16)$$

From Eq. (4B-13) and this general expression for acceleration there are obtained the relations

$$\frac{M_S}{M_L} = - \frac{(a_{inst})_L}{(a_{inst})_S} = - \frac{(\xi_{max})_L}{(\xi_{max})_S} \qquad (4B-17)$$

Here $(\xi_{max})_L$ and $(\xi_{max})_S$ are the maximum values of the displacements of the two lumped masses of the equivalent system as measured from their positions of rest.

Equations for the ratio of the kinetic energies associated with the two masses may also be written on the basis of the relations just derived. These are

$$\frac{M_S(u_{inst})^2_S}{M_L(u_{inst})^2_L} = \frac{M_S(\xi_{max})^2_S}{M_L(\xi_{max})^2_L} = \frac{M_L}{M_S} \qquad (4B-18)$$

whence

$$\frac{(u_{inst})_S}{(u_{inst})_L} = \frac{M_L}{M_S} \qquad (4B-19)$$

It is thus evident that, in the actual system shown in Fig. 4B-4, the amplitudes of vibration of the free end of the driving rod and of the driven plate are inversely proportional to their masses.

The relations just considered show that the effect of loading one end of a magnetostrictive driving tube has marked advantages with respect to the transfer of energy. At first sight it might appear absurd to attempt to develop the large force needed to radiate sound into water with no more substantial base than the small, thin-walled, nickel tube. This tube, however, is vibrating at resonance and hence with considerable amplitude. Were this tube to be coupled directly, and closely, to the water it would be unable to maintain this violent motion. The mass on the end of the tube causes the system to behave as a mechanical transformer, the velocity of motion on one side being much less than on the other. The low-velocity, high-force motion of the massive block is far more suitable for transferring energy to the water from the system than is the high-velocity, low-force motion of the nickel tube. Acoustic energy is, therefore, transferred from the system to the water with considerable efficiency. The impedance mismatch between the free end of the tube and the air with which it is in contact is, on the other hand, very great; hence energy is not lost at this point and the motion of the tube is not damped. The high velocity of the nickel tube may be looked upon as supplying the inertia force which its low mass is unable to furnish. If this method of loading were not used the high force developed in the nickel could be transferred to the water only by backing it up with a mass which was large as compared with the mass of the water. Such a mass would be heavy indeed. Because of its undamped motion, however, the nickel tube presents to the moving block a cross-sectional plane at which the motion is zero; an infinite mass could do no more . In view of the fact that this result is accomplished because of the negligible radiation from the free end of the tube it appears that there are two ideal bases from which to push against the water; one is of infinite mass and one is of zero mass. The one of zero mass is the more portable.

When a rod of uniform cross section is free to vibrate longitudinally without restraint at any point the sinusoidal distribution of amplitude indicated by Eq. (4B-8) must be symmetrical with respect to the center. If this condition were not satisfied the total displacement would not be zero at all times, as is necessary since the rod as a whole cannot move relative to its surroundings. To meet this requirement, and at the same time to cause the condition of maximum amplitude defined by Eq. (4B-9) to occur at the ends of the rod, the term $\sin(2\pi s/\lambda)$ must complete a whole number of half cycles during the length of the rod. In other words, the total length of the rod, l, must be such that, when substituted for s in Eq. (4B-8),

$$\sin \frac{2\pi s}{\lambda} = \sin \frac{2\pi l}{\lambda} = 0 \qquad (4B-20)$$

This will be true if

$$l = n \frac{\lambda}{2} \qquad (4B-21)$$

since then $2\pi l/\lambda = n\pi$. In these expressions n is any whole number.

The frequencies at which this condition exists

are found by substituting $\lambda = c/f$ into Eq. (4B-21) whereby there is obtained

$$f = \frac{n}{2} \frac{c}{l} \qquad (4B-22)$$

When $n = 1$ the rod is a half-wave rod vibrating at its fundamental frequency,

$$f_1 = \frac{c}{2l} \qquad (4B-23)$$

Other frequencies at which the maximum amplitude of motion occurs at the ends of the rod are obtained, in terms of this fundamental frequency, by substituting this equation into Eq. (4B-22) whereupon

$$f = nf_1 \qquad (4B-24)$$

In other words, this rod may vibrate with maximum amplitude at its ends for a fundamental frequency and for any whole number multiple of that frequency.

For a rod of uniform cross section rigidly clamped at one end the value of the term sin $(2\pi s/\lambda)$ must, for maximum amplitude at the end, complete a quarter cycle or a quarter cycle plus any whole number of half cycles during the length of the rod. In this case

$$\sin \frac{2\pi s}{\lambda} = \sin \frac{2\pi l}{\lambda} = 1 \qquad (4B-25)$$

which will be true if

$$l = (2n + 1) \frac{\lambda}{4} \qquad (4B-26)$$

since then $2\pi l/\lambda = (n + \frac{1}{2})\pi$. By substitution, as before,

$$f = \frac{2n + 1}{4} \frac{c}{l} \qquad (4B-27)$$

In this case, when $n = 0$ the rod is a quarter-wave rod vibrating at its fundamental frequency,

$$f_0 = \frac{c}{4l} \qquad (4B-28)$$

Frequencies of other maxima may be related to this fundamental frequency by substituting this equality into Eq. (4B-27) whereupon

$$f = (2n + 1)f_0 \qquad (4B-29)$$

It is thus seen that the amplitude has maxima at a fundamental frequency and at the odd-numbered multiples of that frequency.

4-C THE EQUIVALENT CIRCUIT OF AN ELECTROACOUSTIC TRANSDUCER

In the first section of this chapter it was shown how information as to the efficiency of a transducer might be deduced from information obtained through measurements of its terminal impedances, or how the magnitude of the impedance connected to one end might be deduced from impedances measured at the other. Similar deductions as to the behavior of an electroacoustic transducer may be made on the basis of measurements of electric impedances at the terminals provided for connection to the electric system which it is intended to couple to an acoustic medium. The fact that the impedances at the other junction differ in nature from those measured, being mechanical instead of electric, may alter the details of the processes employed; it has no effect on their principles.

Since all measured impedances are electric impedances it is convenient to treat all derived impedances as though they, too, were electric impedances. This requires, in effect, that computations be carried out in terms of an electric network which, insofar as the magnitudes of the transmitted energy are concerned, may be considered the electric equivalent of the actual electroacoustic transducer.

4C-1 Measurement of Electric Impedance of Sonar Transducers

The measurement of the electric impedance of a sonar transducer presents no unusual problems from the standpoint of conventional electrical engineering techniques. In general it is preferable, both for accuracy and for convenience, to use an alternating-current bridge. It is sometimes desirable to measure characteristic properties under normal operating conditions, hence the bridge circuits used with heavy-duty projectors may be called upon to handle currents comparable in magnitude to those for which the transducer was designed. There is, however, a substantial amount of evidence to indicate that measurements made at a level well within the capacity of commercial impedance bridges are adequate for most purposes.

Since many transducers are intended for operation at ultrasonic frequencies balanced detectors of the heterodyne type may be used. In some cases a visual indicator, such as a cathode-ray oscilloscope, may be more convenient. With echo-ranging transducers it is difficult to find equipment more suitable than the echo-ranging driver for supplying bridge current, or than the echo-ranging receiver for detecting the balance point. Whenever impedance measurements must be made where no bridge is available, current-voltage methods may be used provided they determine the phase relations accurately.

4C-2 Motional Impedance

The electric impedance at the electric terminals of an electroacoustic transducer depends, as does the impedance at one end of any transducer, on the impedance of the energy transmission system connected to the other end. Conversely, when a given system is connected to one end the impedance measured at the other depends on the characteristics of the transducer. It is, for this reason, often possible to devise a four-terminal—or two-junction—electric network which has the same impedances at one pair of terminals when various known electric impedances are connected to the other pair as the actual transducer has at its electric terminals when various known mechanical impedances are connected to the end normally presented to the acoustic medium. Such a network is said to be the **equivalent circuit** of the transducer. The electric impedances connected to its terminals are also said to be the electric equivalents of the mechanical impedances connected to the actual transducer.

Given such an equivalent circuit, and assuming such connected equivalent impedances to be load impedances, the ratio of the input power of the transducer to its load power can easily be computed. This ratio is, by definition, determined by the efficiency loss of the network which, as we have seen, may be computed in terms of its branch and terminating impedances. This ratio is the same as the ratio of the electric input power of the actual transducer to its acoustic load power. In fact, all of the transmission losses associated with the actual transducer, when connected between given source and load impedances, are the same as the corresponding losses of the equivalent network when connected between equivalent—or equal—electric source and load impedances. It is thus evident that whenever an equivalent circuit and an equivalent load can be established for a given electroacoustic

transducer by measurements of its electric impedances these measurements also yield sufficient information for the computation of its electroacoustic efficiency.

This method, originally devised by A. E. Kennelly,[8] is, in general, most successful with transducers having a single well defined mechanical resonance. We shall, therefore, examine such a transducer and attempt to establish its equivalent circuit and equivalent load from information obtained solely through measurements of its electric impedance. To be specific, a magnetostrictive electroacoustic transducer will be taken as an example.

The first step is to measure the electric impedance as a function of frequency with the transducer in water. The impedance thus measured will be represented as $Z_l = R_l + jX_l$ and designated as the **normally loaded impedance**. This is a specific designation for the impedance designated in Art. 4A-4 as the input impedance. These measurements must be taken over a portion of the spectrum which includes the frequency of mechanical resonance and which extends to frequencies well above and well below those at which the effects of this resonance are observable. These data may be presented graphically, as in Fig. 4C-1, by plotting resistance and reactance, separately, as functions of frequency.

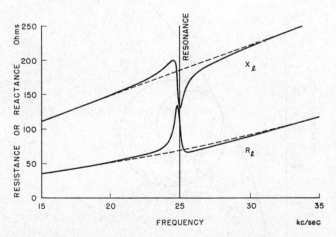

FIG. 4C-1. TRANSDUCER IMPEDANCE. The resistive and reactive components, R_l and X_l, of the electric impedance of a resonant magnetostrictive electroacoustic transducer, plotted as functions of frequency.

The manner in which these two impedance components vary with frequency at frequencies remote from the region of mechanical resonance suggests that the reactance is due to a simple inductance. The resistance appears to have a constant component, which may be called the direct-current resistance, and a component which varies as the square of the frequency. This variable component behaves in a manner known to be typical of the resistance due to eddy currents. If the mechanical system of the transducer were to be clamped so that no motion could occur it would be found that the resistance and reactance exhibit these same variations throughout the region of mechanical resonance. These variations may, therefore, be assumed to be characteristic of the electric elements of the transducer. The impedance having these variations is the blocked impedance, $Z_b = R_b + jX_b$, defined in Art. 4A-4. In practice it is virtually impossible to clamp the moving parts of a transducer intended for underwater service so that all motion is prevented. The blocked impedance for the region of mechanical resonance may, however, be determined graphically by interpolation, as shown by the dotted lines of Fig. 4C-1.

A second method of showing impedance data graphically is to plot reactance as a function of the corresponding resistance, as in Fig. 4C-2. A graph of this type is commonly spoken of as an **impedance diagram**. It is the locus of terminal points of phasors representing the impedance in question. Although this diagram has no frequency axis the frequencies at which specific pairs of resistance and reactance values are observed may be written against the corresponding points, as shown.

From the impedance diagram it appears that mechanical resonance is associated with a circular loop. Now it is known that the impedance diagram of a resonant circuit having a fixed resistance, a fixed inductance, and a fixed capacitance connected in parallel is a circle. This suggests that the circuit branch by which we hope to represent the mechanical system of the transducer in question may be such a shunt resonant circuit. The simplest electric network representing the actual transducer and its load might, then, consist of a shunt resonant circuit in series with branches showing the same impedance as the electric portion of the actual transducer. The electric impedance of the branch equivalent to the mechanical system, at any frequency, would, if this were the case, be obtained at once by subtracting the blocked impedance from the normally loaded impedance. The resistance and reactance thus computed constitute what is known as the **motional impedance** or, more specifically, the **normally loaded motional impedance** of the transducer. This impedance may be expressed as

$$Z_m = R_m + jX_m = Z_l - Z_b$$
$$= (R_l - R_b) + j(X_l - X_b) \quad \text{(4C-1)}$$

where

Z_m = the motional impedance of a normally loaded electroacoustic transducer (ohm)

Z_l = the measured normally loaded impedance of the same transducer (ohm)

Z_b = the blocked impedance of the same transducer (ohm)

R_m = the motional resistance, or the real part of the motional impedance (ohm)

X_m = the motional reactance, or the imaginary part of the motional impedance (ohm)

R_l = the normally loaded resistance, or the real part of the normally loaded impedance (ohm)

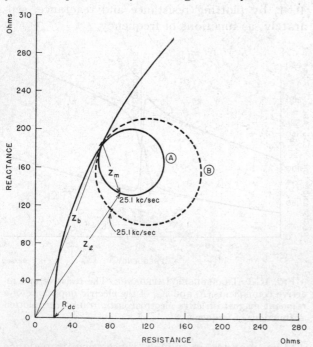

FIG. 4C-2. TRANSDUCER IMPEDANCE DIAGRAM. The impedance diagram obtained by plotting the reactance shown by Fig. 4C-1 as a function of the corresponding resistance.
A. Transducer in water
B. Transducer in air

X_l = the normally loaded reactance, or the imaginary part of the normally loaded impedance (ohm)

R_b = the blocked resistance, or the real part of the blocked impedance (ohm)

X_b = the blocked reactance, or the imaginary part of the blocked impedance (ohm)

When pairs of reactance-resistance values obtained in this manner are plotted as an impedance diagram it is found that they do, indeed, fall on a circle. This circle, moreover, passes through the origin of the coordinate system, as does the impedance diagram of a shunt resonant circuit. Unlike the impedance diagram of any known shunt resonant circuit, however, its center does not fall on the resistance axis. Much ingenuity has been expended in attempts to devise imaginary circuit elements which might so alter the phases of currents and voltages in a network similar to that here assumed as to tilt the motional impedance circle in the manner observed. It appears more logical, however, to accept the fact that a network in which a shunt resonant circuit is connected in series with elements corresponding to the electric system of an actual transducer does not show the same terminal impedance as the actual transducer.

Having failed to represent the given transducer by simple branch circuits connected in series, the next step is to try connecting branches in parallel. Experience has shown that this will succeed, for a magnetostrictive transducer, if the branch representing the mechanical system is connected across a branch representing all of the electric system except its direct-current resistance. When dealing with branches connected in parallel the relations between branch and resultant admittances are more convenient than those between branch and resultant impedances. The resultant admittance is, in fact, the sum of the branch admittances, just as in a series circuit the resultant impedance is the sum of the branch impedances. We shall, therefore, transform our impedance data into admittance data. This is done by means of the familiar formulas of electrical engineering given by Eq. (2A-38).

The direct-current resistance is not to be included in the network of parallel branches which we are now to consider. We shall, therefore, deal with impedances and admittances which are identified with a pair of imaginary terminals located between a series branch representing the direct-current resistance and the remainder of the network. The **modified normally loaded admittance**, $Y'_l = G'_l + jB'_l$, is computed, by means of formulas given above, from the modified normally loaded impedance. This, in turn, is computed as $Z'_l = Z_l - R_{dc}$, the difference between the measured normally loaded impedance, Z_l, and the direct-current resistance, R_{dc}, indicated by the impedance diagrams. In a similar manner the modified blocked admittance, $Y'_b = G'_b + jB'_b$, is computed from the modified blocked impedance, $Z'_b = Z_b - R_{dc}$.

An **admittance diagram** may be drawn for any varying admittance by plotting values of susceptance against corresponding values of conductance. A diagram thus drawn for the modified normally loaded admittance of our typical transducer is shown in Fig. 4C-3. As in the case of the original impedance diagram, resonance is seen to be associated with a circular loop.

The difference obtained by subtracting the modified blocked admittance from the modified normally loaded admittance is the **normally**

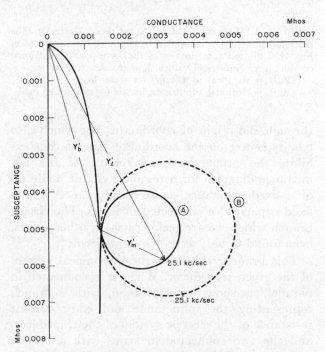

FIG. 4C-3. TRANSDUCER ADMITTANCE DIAGRAM. The susceptance computed from the impedance data of Fig. 4C-1 after subtracting the d-c resistance shown by Fig. 4C-2, plotted as a function of the corresponding conductance.
A. Transducer in water
B. Transducer in air

loaded motional admittance, $Y'_m = Y'_l - Y'_b$, of the transducer. This admittance cannot be computed directly from the original motional impedance; the original motional impedance applied to a series-connected branch, rather than to the shunt-connected branch now to be examined. An admittance diagram drawn for the motional admittance of our typical transducer, as in Fig. 4C-4, is seen to be a circle which not only passes

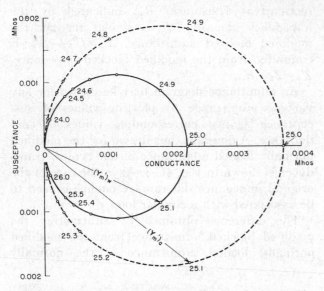

FIG. 4C-4. MOTIONAL ADMITTANCE CIRCLE DIAGRAM. The motional susceptance computed from the admittance data of Fig. 4C-3 plotted as a function of the corresponding motional conductance. Numerical values show frequency in kc/sec.
$(Y_m')_w$ = Motional admittance for water load
$(Y_m')_a$ = Motional admittance for air (or negligible) load

through the origin of coordinates but which also has its center on the coordinate axis. It thus exhibits the properties characteristic of the admittance diagram for a resonant circuit made up of a fixed resistance, a fixed inductance, and a fixed capacitance connected in series. The circuit branch which we are seeking has, in other words, been found to be a series resonant circuit.

This branch represents the mechanical system of the given transducer. When it is connected in parallel, as shown in Fig. 4C-6, with a branch representing the inductance and eddy current resistance of the electric system of the transducer, and the two connected in series with a branch representing the direct-current resistance, the resulting network has the same terminal impedance as the actual transducer. This condition is satisfied for any frequency covered by the original impedance measurements.

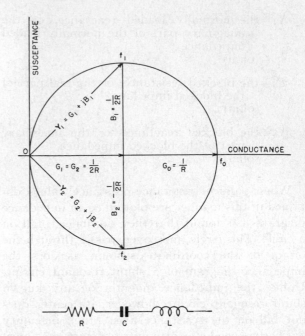

FIG. 4C-5. THE CIRCLE DIAGRAM OF A RESONANT CIRCUIT. The relations between the constants of a series resonant circuit and the dimensions of its motional admittance diagram.
f_0 = Phase resonance frequency
f_1 = Lower quadrantal frequency
f_2 = Upper quadrantal frequency

In the equivalent circuit shown in Fig. 4C-6 the admittance of the portion to the right of terminals T_2 is the modified normally loaded admittance. The admittance of the portion between terminals T_2 and T_3 is the modified blocked admittance. The admittance of the portion to the right of terminals T_3 is the normally loaded motional admittance.

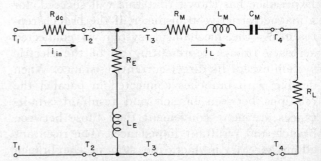

FIG. 4C-6. TRANSDUCER EQUIVALENT CIRCUIT. The equivalent circuit of a resonant magnetostrictive electroacoustic transducer and its load. Elements to the left of T_3 correspond to the electric system; elements to the right correspond to the mechanical system and its load.

Our present problem is greatly simplified by the fact that the constants of a series resonant circuit are directly related to the dimensions, in mhos, of its admittance diagram. Similar convenient relations exist between the constants of a shunt resonant circuit and the dimensions, in ohms, of its impedance diagram. Through their frequent use in the evaluation of resonant circuits these diagrams have come to be known as **circle diagrams**.

That the admittance diagram of a series resonant circuit is, indeed, a circle is demonstrated by deriving an expression for the distance of the admittance locus from the point ($G_0 = 1/2R$, $B_0 = 0$), where R is the fixed resistance of the circuit. The square of this distance is

$$\left(G - \frac{1}{2R}\right)^2 + B^2$$

$$= \left(\frac{R}{|Z|^2} - \frac{1}{2R}\right)^2 + \left(\frac{X}{|Z|^2}\right)^2 = \frac{1}{4R^2} \quad (4C\text{-}2)$$

The distance, in other words, has the constant value $1/2R$ mhos and the locus is a circle of this radius having the point ($G_0 = 1/2R$, $B_0 = 0$), on the conductance axis, as a center and passing through the origin of coordinates.

At the intersection of the admittance circle and the conductance axis $G = 1/R$, $B = 0$, and $Y = 1/R$

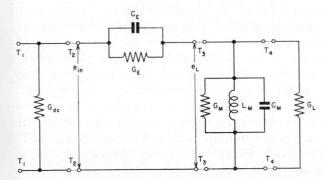

Fig. 4C-7. Transducer Equivalent Circuit. The equivalent circuit of a resonant piezoelectric electroacoustic transducer and its load. Elements to the left of T_3 correspond to the electric system; elements to the right correspond to the mechanical system and its load.

The value, in ohms, of the fixed resistance of a series resonant circuit is therefore equal to the reciprocal of the diameter, in mhos, of its admittance circle.

At this same intersection $X = 0$, since $B = 0$, and the point represents the condition of phase resonance. The frequency corresponding to this point is the frequency of mechanical resonance.

The value of the fixed inductance of a series resonant circuit may be determined in terms of the frequencies corresponding to the intersections of its circle diagram with the diameter perpen-

dicular to the conductance axis. These frequencies, and also those corresponding to the intersections of an impedance circle with its diameter perpendicular to the resistance axis, are the **quadrantal frequencies.** Significant relations between the constants of a series resonant circuit and its quadrantal frequencies are shown in the diagram of Fig. 4C-5.

At the lower quadrantal frequency, f_1, the susceptance and conductance of a series resonant circuit are numerically equal and of like sign. That is,

$$B_1 = G_1 = \frac{-X_1}{R^2 + X^2_1} = \frac{R}{R^2 + X^2_1} \quad (4C\text{-}3)$$

It is to be remembered that in the case of a series resonant circuit the resistance is constant, whereas the reactance, the conductance, and the susceptance all vary with frequency. The reactance of the series resonant circuit at this lower quadrantal frequency is thus

$$X_1 = \omega_1 L - \frac{1}{\omega_1 C} = -R \quad (4C\text{-}4)$$

where

$X_1 =$ the reactance, or the imaginary part of the impedance, of a series resonant circuit at its lower quadrantal frequency (ohm)

$\omega_1 = 2\pi f_1$, f_1 being the lower quadrantal frequency (rad/sec)

$L =$ the fixed inductance of the circuit (henry)

$C =$ the fixed capacitance of the circuit (farad)

$R =$ the fixed resistance of the circuit (ohm)

In a similar manner, at the higher quadrantal frequency, f_2, the susceptance and conductance are of equal magnitude but of opposite sign. The reactance is therefore

$$X_2 = \omega_2 L - \frac{1}{\omega_2 C} = R \quad (4C\text{-}5)$$

By subtracting the first of these equations from the second

$$(\omega_2{}^2 - \omega_1{}^2)L = (\omega_2 + \omega_1)R \quad (4C\text{-}6)$$

The value of the fixed inductance of the series

resonant circuit is thus given in terms of the known fixed resistance and the quadrantal frequencies as

$$L = \frac{R}{\omega_2 - \omega_1} \text{ henrys} \qquad (4C\text{-}7)$$

The value of the fixed capacitance may now be obtained in terms of the known inductance and the frequency of phase resonance, $f_0 = \omega_0/2\pi$, as

$$C = \frac{1}{\omega_0{}^2 L} \text{ farads} \qquad (4C\text{-}8)$$

The quadrantal frequencies of a resonant circuit are conveniently related to a figure of merit of the circuit known as its **Q factor**. For a series resonant circuit this factor is defined by the relations

$$Q = \frac{\omega_0 L}{R} = \frac{1}{\omega_0 C R} = \frac{1}{R}\sqrt{\frac{L}{C}} \qquad (4C\text{-}9)$$

On substituting the value of inductance given by Eq. (4C-7) into this equation it is found that

$$Q = \frac{\omega_0}{\omega_2 - \omega_1} = \frac{f_0}{f_2 - f_1} \qquad (4C\text{-}10)$$

It may also be shown, by Eqs. (4C-4) and (4C-5), that the frequency of phase resonance is the geometric mean of the quadrantal frequencies. That is,

$$f_0 = \sqrt{f_1 f_2} \qquad (4C\text{-}11)$$

and

$$Q = \frac{\sqrt{f_1 f_2}}{f_2 - f_1} \qquad (4C\text{-}12)$$

Similar relations exist for a circuit made up of a fixed conductance, G, a fixed inductance, L_P, and a fixed capacitance, C_P, connected in parallel. Here the conductance is constant and the susceptance, the resistance, and the reactance are all functions of frequency. The variable susceptance is $B = \omega C_P - (1/\omega L_P)$ mhos. The value of the fixed conductance is given as the reciprocal of the diameter of the impedance circle. By methods similar to those used with the series resonant circuit it may be shown that the remaining constants of this circuit are

$$C_P = \frac{G}{(\omega_2 - \omega_1)} \text{ farads}$$

$$L_P = \frac{1}{\omega_0{}^2 C_P} \text{ henrys}$$

and

$$Q = \frac{\omega_0 C_P}{G} = \frac{1}{\omega_0 L_P G} = \frac{1}{G}\sqrt{\frac{C_P}{L_P}} \qquad (4C\text{-}13)$$

The equivalent circuit and the equivalent load for a piezoelectric transducer are related to the equivalent circuits described above by the principle of duality.[1] The equivalent network for a piezoelectric transducer is shown in Fig. 4C-7. It will be noted that whereas in the case of the magnetostrictive transducer each equivalent branch is made up of series-connected elements, in the case of the piezoelectric transducer each equivalent branch is made up of shunt-connected elements. For the magnetostrictive transducer the branches representing the electric and mechanical systems are connected in parallel; for the piezoelectric transducer the branches representing these systems are connected in series. The series direct-current resistance in the magnetostrictive case becomes a shunt direct-current conductance in the piezoelectric case. The equivalent load of the magnetostrictive transducer is represented by a resistance in series with elements representing the remainder of the mechanical system; the equivalent load of the piezoelectric transducer is represented by a conductance in parallel with elements representing the remainder of the mechanical system. The blocked condition of the magnetostrictive transducer is represented by a load of infinite resistance, or an open circuit; the blocked condition of the piezoelectric transducer is represented by a load of infinite conductance, or a short circuit.

Impedance and admittance diagrams may be drawn for a piezoelectric transducer as well as for a magnetostrictive transducer. Where an impedance diagram would be used in one case, however, an admittance diagram would be used in the other. For a piezoelectric transducer, in other words, conductance and susceptance, rather than resistance and reactance, would be first plotted as functions of frequency. From these curves values of blocked admittance would be determined, in the same manner that values of blocked impedance were determined from the diagram of Fig. 4C-1. For a piezoelectric transducer an admittance diagram would next be drawn for the **normally loaded admittance.** This admittance diagram would have the same general form as the impedance diagram of Fig. 4C-2. Its intercept with the conductance axis would indicate the value of the direct-current conductance of the equivalent network of the piezoelectric transducer. This is analogous to the manner in which the direct-current resistance of the equivalent network of a magnetostrictive transducer is shown by its impedance diagram. This is possible because the admittance of the series branch representing the electric system of a piezoelectric transducer goes to zero at zero frequency, in the same manner that the impedance of the shunt branch representing the electric system of a magnetostrictive transducer goes to zero at zero frequency. A motional admittance diagram for a piezoelectric transducer, like the motional impedance diagram of a magnetostrictive transducer, will be found to be a circle passing through the origin of coordinates but having its center displaced from the real axis. If the direct-current conductance is subtracted from the total terminal admittance and a diagram of the modified normally loaded impedance constructed for the piezoelectric transducer it will be found to resemble the admittance diagram of Fig. 4C-3. Finally, a motional impedance circle diagram may be drawn for the difference between the modified normally loaded impedance and the modified blocked impedance. This will give a motional impedance circle diagram passing through the origin of coordinates and having its center on the resistance axis.

4C-3 The Computation of Efficiency

To examine the method by which the efficiency of an electroacoustic transducer is computed from the impedance data embodied in an equivalent electric network we shall return to the magnetostrictive transducer in terms of which the derivation of such a network has been described.

The branch circuit which is equivalent to the mechanical portion of an electroacoustic transducer produces an effect on the terminal impedance which represents the combined effects of the internal mechanical system and the external mechanical load offered by the acoustic medium. We have already seen that the blocked impedance of the transducer is the terminal impedance due to the electric system alone. We have also seen that for the magnetostrictive case the branch representing the mechanical system is in parallel with the branch representing this electric system.

The effect of preventing mechanical motion must, therefore, be represented, for such a transducer, by opening the branch representing the mechanical system. The portion of this branch which represents the external load thus appears to be in series with the portion which represents the internal mechanical system. This is in agreement with the conclusion that the elements of the resonant circuit representing the entire mechanical system are connected in series.

If the effect of preventing mechanical motion is represented by a circuit element of infinite impedance the effect of allowing unrestrained motion must be represented by a circuit element of zero impedance. If an equivalent circuit is found for the transducer when it has no mechanical load it is thus evident that the branch which then represents the mechanical system must be the same as the branch which represents the internal portion of the mechanical system when it is loaded.

The terminal impedance of a transducer when its load is removed has been defined in Art. 4A-4 as its free impedance, Z_f. For an electroacoustic transducer intended for underwater use this quantity may be measured directly. This is made possible because of the conditions which made it impossible to measure the blocked impedance. The difficulty of actually blocking such a transducer arose because its normal load has so high a mechanical impedance that it is not possible to find another which is enough higher to be considered an open circuit. It is by no means difficult to provide one which is enough lower to be considered a short circuit. All that is required is to remove the transducer from the water; the terminal impedance measured when it is in air may be considered as its free impedance. The situation is reversed for an electroacoustic transducer intended for use in air. Here the impedance of the normal mechanical load is so low that it is difficult to find one which is much lower. It is, on the other hand, not at all difficult to block such a transducer so that its mechanical motion is negligible by comparison with its normal motion.

The modified free admittance, $Y'_f = 1/(Z_f - R_{dc})$, at the imaginary terminals which do not include the element representing the direct-current resistance, is computed from the free impedance after subtracting the direct-current resistance. The difference obtained by subtracting the modified blocked admittance, as previously derived for these same imaginary terminals, from the modified free admittance is the **free motional admittance**, $(Y'_m)_a = Y'_f - Y'_b$, of the transducer as computed from measurements made when it is in air. The blocked impedance of a resonant magnetostrictive transducer, intended for underwater use, may, as we have seen, be deduced by graphical interpolation. The free impedance may be measured directly. All data for computing the free motional admittance is therefore available.

In the equivalent circuit shown in Fig. 4C-6 the admittance of the portion between terminals T_3 and T_4 is the free motional admittance. Removing the transducer from the water is represented, in this equivalent circuit, by shorting terminals T_4.

The free impedance measured at the terminals of the transducer which we have selected as an example is shown by the dotted line of Fig. 4C-2. The modified free admittance is shown by the dotted line of Fig. 4C-3. The free motional admittance computed from these data is, like the normally loaded motional impedance, a circle. As shown by the dotted line of Fig. 4C-4 this circle passes through the origin of the coordinate system and has its center on the conductance axis. In general, the free motional admittance of any resonant magnetostrictive transducer, intended for underwater use, will give such an admittance circle. For such transducers these circles usually show that the inductance and capacitance of the network branch which is equivalent to the internal portion of the mechanical system are the same as those of the network circuit which is equivalent to the total mechanical system. The resistance of the latter is usually considerably greater than the resistance of the former. Since the load resistance appearing in the former is assumed to be zero the difference between these two resistances is the impedance of the branch representing the mechanical load due to the acoustic medium. The fact that this equivalent load appears to be a pure resistance is in agreement with the fact that the mechanical impedance of the load offered by the medium is known to be a pure mechanical resistance, at any frequency for which the dimensions of the transducer are large as compared with the length of a wave. Our present data are restricted to such frequencies.

We now have all the specifications for an electric network the terminal impedance of which is the same, at any frequency, as the electric im-

pedance of the given transducer. This network is composed of branches which may be identified with the internal electric and mechanical systems of the transducer, and a branch which may be identified with the normal water load. We have, in other words, established the arrangement and constants of the equivalent circuits of the given transducer and its normal load. These equivalent circuits are shown in Fig. 4C-6. Given the network formed by these circuits it is a simple matter to determine the distribution of electric energy between its branches, and thus to determine the portions of the total energy delivered to the actual transducer which are dissipated in the form of electric energy in the internal electric system, dissipated in the form of mechanical energy in the internal mechanical system, and radiated in the form of acoustic energy in the water.

If i_{in} is the total terminal current, the total electric energy delivered to the network is, as shown by Eq. (4A-6),

$$P_E = i^2_{in} R_l \qquad (4C\text{-}14)$$

where R_l is the resistance component of the normally loaded impedance, measured at the transducer terminals T_1 when the transducer is in water. The voltage across the terminals T_2, and hence across the series circuit which has been found to be equivalent to the total mechanical system, is, by definition,

$$e_2 = i_{in} \left| Z'_l \right| \qquad (4C\text{-}15)$$

where Z'_l is the modified loaded impedance, computed for the circuits to the right of these terminals. The electric energy delivered to the series circuit representing the total mechanical system is then

$$P_M = e_2^2 (G_m)_w = i^2_{in} \left| Z'_l \right|^2 (G_m)_w \quad (4C\text{-}16)$$

where $(G_m)_w$ is the conductance component of the normally loaded motional admittance applying to the transducer in water. This is the conductance of the circuits to the right of terminals T_3. The electromechanical efficiency of the transducer is therefore

$$\eta_{EM} = \frac{P_M}{P_E} = \frac{\left| Z'_l \right|^2 (G_m)_w}{R_l} = \frac{(G_m)_w}{\left| Y'_l \right|^2 R_l} \qquad (4C\text{-}17)$$

The resistance of the equivalent circuit branch, representing the external mechanical load, or load due to the acoustic medium, is the difference, $R_L = (R_m)_w - (R_m)_a$, obtained by subtracting the resistance of the circuit giving the motional admittance circle for an air load from the resistance of the circuit giving the motional admittance circle for a water load. The resistance of the equivalent circuit branch representing the internal mechanical system is $R_M = (R_m)_a$, the resistance of the circuit giving the motional admittance circle for air. These resistances are shown in the equivalent circuit of Fig. 4C-6.

The power developed in the branch representing the mechanical system and its load may be written in terms of the current, i_M, flowing in that branch as

$$P_M = i^2{}_M(R_L + R_M) = i^2{}_M(R_m)_w \quad (4C\text{-}18)$$

This is the portion of the total electric energy delivered to the actual transducer which is converted to mechanical energy. The power developed in the branch representing the mechanical load due to the acoustic medium is

$$P_A = i^2{}_M R_L = i^2{}_M[(R_m)_w - (R_m)_a] \quad (4C\text{-}19)$$

This is equal to the energy radiated as acoustic energy. The mechanoacoustic efficiency is therefore

$$\eta_{MA} = \frac{P_A}{P_M} = \frac{(R_m)_w - (R_m)_a}{(R_m)_w}$$

$$= 1 - \frac{(R_m)_a}{(R_m)_w} \quad (4C\text{-}20)$$

It will be remembered that the resistance of a series resonant circuit is the reciprocal of the conductance of that circuit at resonance as given by the diameter of its admittance circle. The mechanoacoustic efficiency of our transducer, then, may be written in terms of the conductances corresponding to the diameters of the motional admittance circles obtained with the transducer in air and in water as

$$\eta_{MA} = 1 - \frac{(G_0)_w}{(G_0)_a} \quad (4C\text{-}21)$$

The overall electroacoustic efficiency of the transducer is consequently

$$\eta_{EA} = (\eta_{EM})(\eta_{MA}) = \frac{(G_m)_w}{|Y'_l|^2 R_l}\left[1 - \frac{(G_0)_w}{(G_0)_a}\right] \quad (4C\text{-}22)$$

where

η_{EA} = the electroacoustic efficiency of a resonant magnetostrictive transducer (dimensionless)

η_{EM} = the electromechanical efficiency of the same transducer (dimensionless)

η_{MA} = the mechanoacoustic efficiency of the same transducer (dimensionless)

$|Y'_l|$ = the absolute magnitude of the modified normally loaded admittance, as computed from the normally loaded impedance after subtracting the direct-current resistance (mho)

R_l = the resistance component of the normally loaded impedance, including the direct-current resistance (ohm)

$(G_m)_w$ = the conductance component of the normally loaded motional admittance (mho)

$(G_0)_w$ = the diameter of the normally loaded motional admittance circle, obtained with the transducer in water (mho)

$(G_0)_a$ = the diameter of the free motional admittance circle, obtained with the transducer in air (mho)

From data used in plotting the motional admittance circle of Fig. 4C-4 it is found that the frequency of mechanical resonance of the transducer in question, for both air and water loads, is

$$f_0 = 25.00 \text{ kc/sec}$$

This same diagram shows the quadrantal frequencies when the transducer has a water load to be

$$(f_1)_w = 24.794 \text{ kc/sec}$$

and

$$(f_2)_w = 25.211 \text{ kc/sec}$$

When normally loaded, then, the figure of merit of the resonant mechanical system is

$$Q_w = \frac{25.000}{25.211 - 24.794} = 60$$

The diameters of the motional admittance circles applying to the transducer in water and in air are

$$(G_0)_w = 0.002222 \text{ mhos}$$

and

$$(G_0)_a = 0.003704 \text{ mhos}$$

A t any frequency for which the transducer has useful response the mechanoacoustic efficiency is consequently

$$\eta_{MA} = 1 - \frac{2.222}{3.704} = 0.400$$

At the frequency of mechanical resonance, data taken from the motional admittance circle, the modified normally loaded admittance diagram, and the normally loaded impedance diagram indicate that

$$(G_m)_w = 0.002222 \text{ mhos}$$

$$Y'_l = 0.003572 - j0.005039 \text{ mhos}$$

$$|Y'_l|^2 = 3.815 \cdot 10^{-5} \text{ mhos}$$

$$R_l = 113.62 \text{ ohms}$$

At the frequency of mechanical resonance, then, the electromechanical efficiency is

$$\eta_{EM} = \frac{2.222 \cdot 10^{-3}}{(3.815 \cdot 10^{-5})(1.136 \cdot 10^2)} = 0.513$$

The overall electroacoustic efficiency at this frequency is thus

$$\eta_{EA} = (0.513)(0.400) = 0.2050$$

or, as usually expressed, 20.50 percent.

By reasoning similar to that used in the case of the magnetostrictive transducer it can be shown that the electroacoustic efficiency of a piezoelectric transducer is

$$\eta_{EA} = (\eta_{EM})(\eta_{MA})$$

$$= \frac{(R_m)_w}{|Z'_l|^2 G_l}\left[1 - \frac{(R_0)_w}{(R_0)_a}\right] \quad (4C\text{-}23)$$

where

η_{EA} = the electroacoustic efficiency of a resonant piezoelectric transducer (dimensionless)

η_{EM} = the electromechanical efficiency of the same transducer (dimensionless)

η_{MA} = the mechanoacoustic efficiency of the same transducer (dimensionless)

$(R_m)_w$ = the resistance component of the normally loaded motional impedance (ohm)

$|Z_l'|$ = the absolute magnitude of the modified normally loaded impedance, as computed from the normally loaded ad-

mittance after subtracting the direct-current conductance (ohm)

G_l = the conductance component of the normally loaded admittance, including the direct-current conductance (mho)

$(R_0)_w$ = the diameter of the normally loaded motional impedance circle, obtained with the transducer in water (ohm)

$(R_0)_a$ = the diameter of the free motional impedance circle, obtained with the transducer in air (ohm)

For this transducer the electromechanical efficiency is

$$\eta_{EM} = \frac{(R_m)_w}{|Z'_l|^2 G_l} \quad (4C\text{-}24)$$

and the mechanoacoustic efficiency is

$$\eta_{MA} = 1 - \frac{(R_0)_w}{(R_0)_a} \quad (4C\text{-}25)$$

If we examine each of the terms appearing in the formula for electromechanical efficiency of a magnetostrictive transducer, as given by Eq. (4C-17), we find that the normally loaded motional conductance, $(G_m)_w$, goes through a maximum at the frequency of mechanical resonance. The absolute value of the modified normally loaded admittance, Y_l', goes through a maximum for a somewhat higher frequency. The normally loaded resistance, R_l, goes through a maximum at a lower frequency. The net result of these variations is that the frequency of maximum efficiency is slightly lower, for a magnetostrictive transducer, than the frequency of mechanical resonance. This is shown by the curve of Fig. 4C-8, in which the electroacoustic efficiency of our typical transducer is given as a function of frequency.

A curve such as this indicates the manner in which a resonant system absorbs energy when a more extensive system, of which it forms a part, receives energy at a constant rate. The variation in efficiency is then the resultant effect of variations in the impedances of all elements of the complete system. It is sometimes desirable to know the manner in which a resonant system absorbs energy when responding to a driving force of constant magnitude but varying frequency. This

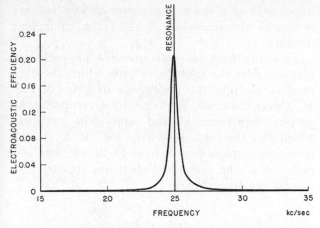

FIG. 4C-8. TRANSDUCER EFFICIENCY. The electroacoustic efficiency of a resonant magnetostrictive electroacoustic transducer, plotted as a function of frequency. Values shown are computed from the data of Figs. 4C-2, 4C-3, and 4C-4.

is a property of the resonant system only; it is not affected by associated systems.

In a series resonant electric circuit the power developed by a driving voltage of constant magnitude, e, is $P = e^2 G$, where $G = R/(R^2 + X^2)$ is the circuit conductance. For a series resonant circuit the resistance, R, is constant but the reactance, $X = \omega L - (1/\omega C)$, is a function of frequency. The conductance has a maximum, $G_0 = 1/R$, when $X = 0$. The frequency at which this occurs is, by definition, the frequency of phase resonance. At this frequency the power developed by the constant driving voltage is also a maximum. At either of its quadrantal frequencies the conductance of a series resonant circuit, as shown by Fig. 4C-5, is one half the conductance at its phase resonance frequency. The power developed at either quadrantal frequency is thus one half the power which would be developed at the phase resonance frequency by a driving voltage of the same magnitude. For this reason the quadrantal frequencies are often spoken of as the **half-power frequencies.**

A significant characteristic of a resonant system may be obtained by plotting, as a function of frequency, the ratio of the power developed at any frequency by a driving force of given magnitude to the power developed at the frequency of phase resonance by a driving force of the same magnitude. All that is required for the computation of such a characteristic is a knowledge of the figure of merit, Q, of the system and the frequency, f_0, of phase resonance. For a series resonant electric circuit the power at phase resonance may be written as $P_0 = e^2 G_0 = e^2(1/R)$. At any other frequency, f_x, the power is

$$P_x = e^2 G_x = \cfrac{e^2 R}{R^2 + \left(\omega_x L - \cfrac{1}{\omega_x C}\right)^2}$$

The ratio of the power at phase resonance to the power at any other frequency is thus

$$\frac{P_0}{P_x} = \cfrac{R^2 + \left(\omega_x L - \cfrac{1}{\omega_x C}\right)^2}{R^2}$$

$$= 1 + \left[\frac{Q(f_x - f_0)(f_x + f_0)}{f_x f_0}\right]^2 \quad (4C\text{-}26)$$

The characteristic sought is obtained by plotting the reciprocal of this ratio as a function of the varying frequency, f_x. The characteristic computed in this manner for our typical transducer is shown in Fig. 4C-9. When Q is large the change in

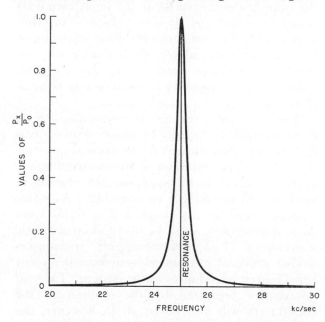

FIG. 4C-9. RELATIVE POWER RESPONSE. The ratio of the power developed by a resonant system at any frequency to the power developed at the frequency of phase resonance, for equal driving forces, plotted as a function of frequency.

frequency through the entire range of the characteristic is small and it is permissible to make the following approximations: $f_x - f_0 = \Delta f$, $f_x + f_0 = 2f_0$, and $f_x f_0 = f_0^2$. The equation then simplifies to

$$\frac{P_0}{P_x} = 1 + \left(2Q\frac{\Delta f}{f_0}\right)^2 \quad (4C\text{-}27)$$

4C-4 Impedance Conversion Factors

The equivalent network representing an actual electric transducer and an actual electric load may be established by the method described in Art. 4C-2. If this were done, however, there would be no assurance that the output and load impedances of this equivalent network would be of the same magnitude, or even of the same order of magnitude, as the actual output and load impedances. For example, an actual electric transducer and an actual electric load might be assembled of elements having resistances, inductances, and capacitances which were equal to those of some given network. An ideal lossless transformer might then be connected at the load junction of this system. This has the effect of altering the apparent magnitude of the load impedance without altering its phase angle. If, therefore, the actual load were to be replaced by another having an impedance differing from the original impedance by the square of the turns ratio of the transformer the impedances measured at the input terminals would be unchanged. It is not possible, in other words, solely by measurements made at the input terminals of a transducer, to determine whether the load impedance does, in fact, have a given value, or if it appears to have this value because of the presence of a transformer.

When we come to the representation of an electroacoustic transducer by means of an equivalent electric network we are, of course, representing mechanical impedances by electric impedances. We must, in this case, consider changes in kind as well as changes in magnitude. An effect analogous to that associated with a transformer does, nevertheless, exist in many electroacoustic transducers. Two electromagnetic transducers having identical mechanical systems will present equal output impedances to the medium. The load impedances presented by the medium to the transducers will also be equal. If, however, the coupling coil of one transducer were to have ten times as many turns as that of the other, the load impedance of the equivalent network representing this transducer would be approximately 100 times the corresponding impedance of the other.

Impedance measurements made at the electric input terminals of an electroacoustic transducer are not sufficient, in the absence of other information, to establish the actual values of the output and load impedances at the mechanical terminal of that transducer. If, however, either of these mechanical impedances can be evaluated by other means, the value of the other may be found through relations existing in the equivalent network. The evaluation of the mechanical output

impedance of a sonar transducer in this manner is one of the important uses of the equivalent network.

To study this use of equivalent networks we may consider the transducer from which the data used in plotting the impedance diagram of Fig. 4C-2 were obtained. We begin by determining the output impedance of the equivalent network, which has the form shown in Fig. 4C-6. At the resonant frequency, which is 25 kc/sec, the impedances of the individual elements appearing in this circuit diagram are

$$R_{dc} = \quad\quad 20 \quad \text{ohms}$$
$$R_E = \quad\quad 49.6 \quad \text{ohms}$$
$$\omega_0 L_E = \quad\quad 185.2 \quad \text{ohms}$$
$$R_M = \quad\quad 270 \quad \text{ohms}$$
$$\omega_0 L_M = \quad 27{,}000 \quad \text{ohms}$$
$$1/(\omega_0 C_M) = \quad -27{,}000 \quad \text{ohms}$$
$$(R_L)_w = \quad\quad 180 \quad \text{ohms}$$

To compute the output impedance it is necessary to know the electric impedance of the source to which the input terminals of the transducer are connected. It will here be assumed that this source impedance has been made the conjugate of the input impedance of the normally loaded transducer at its resonant frequency, or that its value is

$$\boldsymbol{Z}_S = 113.6 - j132.1 \text{ ohms}$$

The impedance of the portion of the system to the left of the terminals T_2, being made up of the source and the network element corresponding to the d-c resistance of the transducer connected in series, is obtained by adding the impedances of these elements. Its value may be written as

$$\boldsymbol{Z}_2 = (113.6 + 20.0) - j132.1$$
$$= 133.6 - j132.1 \text{ ohms}$$

The corresponding value of admittance, as computed by Eq. (2A-38), is

$$\boldsymbol{Y}_2 = 0.00378 + j0.00374 \text{ mhos}$$

The portion of the system to the left of the terminals T_3 is made up of two branches connected in parallel. We therefore compute its admittance by adding the admittances of these branches. Values for one have already been computed. The impedance of the other, which corresponds to the electric system of the transducer, is

$$Z_E = 49.6 + j185.2 \text{ ohms}$$

Its admittance is therefore

$$Y_E = 0.00135 - j0.00504 \text{ mhos}$$

The portion of the system in question is thus found to have the resultant admittance

$$Y_3 = (0.00378 + 0.00135) + j(0.00374 - 0.00504)$$
$$= 0.00513 - j0.00130 \text{ mhos}$$

The corresponding impedance is

$$Z_3 = 183.1 + j46.4 \text{ ohms}$$

Finally, the impedance of the system to the left of the output terminals, T_4, may now be computed as the sum of two impedances, since this portion of the system may be considered as made up of two branches connected in series. This impedance is the output impedance of the equivalent network. It has the value

$$Z_{\text{out}} = Z_4 = (183.1 + 270.0) + j(46.4 + 0)$$
$$= 453.1 + j46.4 \text{ ohms}$$

It is at once evident that there is a significant difference between the output impedance of the transducer and the load impedance of the medium. The transition loss corresponding to this difference may be computed at once by Eq. (4A-10). On the basis of information now available it is seen that

$$r = \frac{453.1}{180.0} = 2.52$$

and

$$\tan \psi = \frac{46.4}{453.1 + 180.0} = 0.0731$$

The transition loss in question is, therefore,

$$N_{\text{tsn}} = \lgt \frac{(1 + 2.52)^2}{(4)(2.52)} + \lgt (1 + 0.0731^2)$$
$$= \lgt 1.23 + \lgt 1.005 = 0.90 + 0.02$$
$$= 0.92 \text{ db}$$

The actual load impedance may be computed by a formula to be found in Ref. 1, of Ch. 2. The transducer in question has an active surface which is a circular piston 50 cm in diameter, vibrating in a rigid baffle. For such a piston the radiation impedance offered by the medium is $(Z_L)_M = 86$ mech ohms. This impedance is a pure resistance, as is the load impedance computed for the equiva-lent circuit. The impedance computed for the load of the equivalent network is, however, $(Z_L)_E = 180$ elec ohms. The conversion factor is, therefore, $(Z_L)_M/(Z_L)_E = 86/180 = 0.478$ mech ohms/elec ohms. The actual output impedance of the transducer is thus seen to be

$$(Z_{\text{out}})_M = (453.1 + j46.4)(0.478)$$
$$= 216 + j22.2 \text{ mech ohms}$$

4-D RESPONSE AS A FUNCTION OF BEARING

The manner in which the acoustic energy sent out by a sonar projector varies with the direction in which it is transmitted, or the manner in which the electric energy delivered by a hydrophone varies with the direction from which acoustic energy is received, are significant characteristics of these sonar system elements. The degree to which a projector concentrates within a narrow sector the energy which it radiates is no less important than the efficiency with which it generates this energy. The extent to which the sensitivity of a hydrophone to a signal received on one bearing exceeds its sensitivity to interference received on others is quite as important as its overall sensitivity. These matters are of great interest to the user of a sonar transducer. They are also of concern to its designer, since it is difficult for him to make an observation of any of the performance characteristics of such a transducer without taking due account of its directivity. We shall, therefore, next examine the directional properties of sonar transducers.

4D-1 Response

The term "response" has been used throughout the preceding sections of this book in its usual sense of a specific action, or effect, resulting from some specific cause. As applied to sonar transducers it will hereafter be advantageous to define this term somewhat more rigorously. We shall, therefore, define the **transmitting response** of a sonar projector, for a given bearing and for a given frequency, as the response measured by the quotient obtained by dividing (1) the index intensity of the sinusoidal acoustic waves of the given frequency radiated on the given bearing by the projector when receiving sinusoidal electric waves of the same frequency by (2) the power of these received electric waves.

The **receiving response** of a hydrophone, for a given bearing and for a given frequency, will be defined as the response measured by the quotient obtained by dividing (1) the available power of the sinusoidal electric waves of the given frequency generated in the hydrophone when receiving over the given bearing plane sinusoidal acoustic waves of the same frequency by (2) the free-field intensity of these received acoustic waves.

These responses have been defined in terms of sinusoidal waves. It is usually in terms of such waves that they are actually measured. Values thus measured, however, are of significance when dealing with waves having continuous spectra. For such waves the transmitting response determines the quotient obtained by dividing an intensity per unit band by a power per unit band. Similarly, the receiving response determines the quotient obtained by dividing a power per unit band by an intensity per unit band. Powers per unit band and intensities per unit band determined in this manner are those associated with the particular frequency at which the value of the response in question applies.

The concept of response is also useful when dealing with energy occupying a finite frequency band. In this case we would define the **transmitting band response** of a sonar projector, for a given bearing and for a given frequency band, as the response measured by the quotient obtained by dividing (1) the index intensity of the acoustic energy radiated on the given bearing and in the given frequency band by the projector when receiving electric energy occupying the same frequency band by (2) the power of this received electric energy.

In a similar manner the **receiving band response** of a hydrophone, for a given bearing and for a given frequency band, may be defined as the response measured by the quotient obtained by dividing (1) the available power of the electric energy generated by the hydrophone in the given frequency band when receiving over the given bearing plane acoustic waves occupying the same frequency band by (2) the free-field intensity of these received acoustic waves.

Transmitting response and receiving response are functions of both direction and frequency. In many problems one of these factors will be constant, usually having some specified value, and the other will be the independent variable. In some problems both will be independent variables. In some problems the parameter, as well as the independent variable, may have a succession of

values which must be properly identified. In order to meet these situations adequately it will be necessary to use two subscripts. The subscript immediately adjoining the symbol for the quantity in question, and contained within brackets enclosing this symbol, will indicate the independent variable of which the quantity designated is a function. The subscript following the bracket will indicate the variable which is being held constant.

These two subscripts will, in general, be used with transmitting and receiving responses and with related relative magnitudes. With other related quantities, however, it may be desirable to replace the subscript indicating the fixed parameter by one carrying other significant information. With absolute magnitudes of rates of energy flow, for example, it may be necessary to indicate whether source, input, output, or load values are represented. To keep the number of subscripts to a minimum a prime (′) is used with symbols for quantities associated with the reception of acoustic energy to distinguish them from those for quantities associated with the radiation of acoustic energy.

In accordance with these conventions, the transmitting response of a sonar projector, for a specified fixed frequency and for any given bearing, will be written as

$$(\mu_d)_f = \frac{(I_d)_L}{P_{\text{in}}} = \frac{(J_d)_L}{U_{\text{in}}} \qquad (4D\text{-}1)$$

where

$(\mu_d)_f =$ the transmitting response of a sonar transducer for any given frequency, here considered to be constant, and for any given bearing, here considered to be the independent variable $(1/\text{cm}^2)$

$(I_d)_L =$ the index value of the load intensity of the sinusoidal acoustic waves, of the given frequency, radiated on the given bearing when electric energy is delivered to the transducer as sinusoidal waves of the same frequency (watt/cm^2)

$P_{\text{in}} =$ the input power of these electric waves (watt)

$(J_d)_L =$ the index value of the load intensity per unit band, at the given frequency, of the acoustic waves radiated on the given bearing when electric energy is delivered to the transducer as waves having a continuous spectrum $(\text{joule/cm}^2 \cdot \text{cyc})$

U_{in} = the input power per unit band, at the given frequency, of these electric waves (joule/cyc)

For hydrophones we have

$$(\mu'_d)_f = \frac{(P'_d)_{out}}{(I'_d)_s} = \frac{(U'_d)_{out}}{(J'_d)_s} \qquad (4D\text{-}2)$$

where

$(\mu'_d)_f$ = the receiving response of a sonar transducer for any given frequency, here considered to be constant, and for any given bearing, here considered to be the independent variable (cm^2)

$(P'_d)_{out}$ = the output power of the sinusoidal electric waves, of the given frequency, generated in the transducer when receiving over the given bearing plane sinusoidal acoustic waves of the same frequency (watt)

$(I'_d)_s$ = the source intensity of these received acoustic waves (watt/cm^2)

$(U'_d)_{out}$ = the output power per unit band, at the given frequency, of the electric waves generated in the transducer when receiving over the given bearing plane acoustic waves having a continuous spectrum (joule/cyc)

$(J'_d)_s$ = the source intensity per unit band, at the given frequency, of these received acoustic waves (joule/$cm^2 \cdot$ cyc)

Similar expressions may be written for the transmitting band response, $(\mu_d)_{\Delta f}$, and for the receiving band response, $(\mu'_d)_{\Delta f}$.

It is to be noted that in the case of a hydrophone the value of the intensity, or of the intensity per unit band, of the received acoustic energy has been specified as a source value. In the case of acoustic waves in water this is equivalent to specifying free-field values. Free-field conditions correspond to those at a junction where source and load impedances have equal resistive components and no reactive components. The specific acoustic impedances of contiguous surfaces in a fluid medium are, in other words, conjugate impedances. The power per unit area measuring the rate of flow of energy at a point in such a medium is thus the available power per unit area at that point, or the **available intensity.** In a similar manner the free-field intensity per unit band may be shown to be an **available intensity per unit band.** Such free-field values may thus be properly described as source values, corresponding to the source power defined in Art. 4A-2.

The intensities, or the intensities per unit band, specified in defining the transmitting and receiving responses of a pair of transducers are the same as those which would appear in the ratio measuring the propagation loss between the two if they were to be used for the transmission and reception of an acoustic signal.

To study variations in response with variations in either direction or frequency it is by no means necessary to report response in terms of absolute magnitudes. Instead, we shall define the **relative transmitting response** of a sonar projector, for any bearing and for any frequency, as the ratio of the transmitting response for that bearing and that frequency to the transmitting response for a specified bearing and a specified frequency. Similarly, the **relative receiving response** of a hydrophone, for any bearing and for any frequency, is the ratio of the receiving response for that bearing and that frequency to the receiving response for a specified bearing and a specified frequency.

When response is considered a function of bearing for a constant frequency this constant frequency is the frequency specified in reporting relative response. The bearing specified in reporting this relative response is then designated as the **reference bearing.** Rates of energy flow along this bearing are the reference rates relative to which rates on other bearings are reported. The usual reference bearing is that for which the response is greater than for any other bearing. It is, in other words, generally the **maximum response bearing** of the transducer. By definition the relative response on a reference bearing is unity.

Band responses, like other transmitting and receiving responses, may be reported as relative responses.

It will be convenient, in many problems, to use the direction of a reference bearing as a reference direction as well as to use the rates of energy flow along it as reference rates. When the direction of any source or receiving point is expressed as the angle between that bearing and the reference bearing this angle will be designated as the **deviation angle** and represented by the symbol β.

When relative response is a function of bearing,

for some specified fixed frequency, the two electric powers appearing in the two transmitting responses forming the ratio measuring a relative transmitting response are the same power. This ratio is, therefore, the ratio of two index intensities. These two intensities are measured at the same frequency, but on two different bearings. If, now, we postulate a homogeneous, isotropic medium of sufficient extent, it is evident that as long as the intensities on these two bearings are measured at equal distances from the projector their ratio is independent of the absolute magnitudes of these distances. The intensities measuring a relative transmitting response need not, in other words, be measured at the standard index distance of one yard, but may be measured at any two equal distances which may be appropriate.

When dealing with waves having a continuous spectrum it may be shown, by similar reasoning, that relative transmitting response may be measured by the ratio of the intensities per unit band at points on the two bearings in question provided that these points are at equal distances from the projector.

In speaking of distance from the projector it must be remembered that any projector has finite dimensions. It is thus necessary to make use of the concept of an **equivalent point source.** For this the **effective center** of a projector is defined as that point at which lines coincident with the direction of propagation, as observed at various points some distance from the projector, appear to intersect. If such a point of intersection exists it will correspond to the source at which acoustic energy, moving along any direction of propagation, appears to originate, as indicated by the variation in intensity with distance. For this reason the effective center is often spoken of as the **apparent source.** The effective center of a hydrophone is assumed to be the point which would be the effective center if the hydrophone were to be used as a projector. For many transducers there is no single point which satisfies the above requirements. In such cases it is usual to designate some suitable point of mechanical symmetry as the effective center.

Given this concept of an effective center the relative response of a projector may be said to refer to variations in acoustic intensity, or intensity per unit band, over the surface of a sphere concentric with this center. This is often described as a **constant distance sphere.**

The two free-field intensities appearing in the two receiving responses forming the ratio measuring a relative receiving response are the intensities of acoustic waves propagated along two different bearings. They are not the same intensity. It is possible, however, to specify that the received acoustic waves be of equal intensity, as well as of equal frequency. In this case the ratio measuring the relative receiving response becomes the ratio of two available electric powers. These powers are observed at different times in a single electric circuit. When dealing with waves having a continuous spectrum a relative receiving response may be measured by the ratio of two available powers per unit band. This requires that the intensities per unit band, at the specified fixed frequency, of the acoustic waves received along two different bearings be made equal.

The relations which have been described in the preceding paragraphs are expressed by the following two equations. The various ratios by which relative transmitting response may be measured are

$$(\eta_d)_f = \frac{(\mu_d)_f}{(\mu_{do})_f} = \frac{(I_d)_L}{(I_{do})_L} = \frac{(J_d)_L}{(J_{do})_L} \qquad (4D\text{-}3)$$

where

$(\eta_d)_f =$ the relative transmitting response of a sonar transducer for a specified constant frequency, considered as a function of bearing
(a numeric)

$(\mu_d)_f =$ the transmitting response of the transducer for the specified constant frequency and for any given bearing
$(1/cm^2)$

$(\mu_{do})_f =$ the transmitting response of the transducer, for the same constant frequency, but for the specified reference bearing
$(1/cm^2)$

$(I_d)_L =$ the load intensity of the sinusoidal acoustic waves, of the specified constant frequency, passing a point on any given bearing at a given distance from the effective center of the transducer when it is receiving sinusoidal electric waves of the same frequency
$(watt/cm^2)$

$(I_{do})_L =$ the load intensity of the sinusoidal acoustic waves, of the same constant frequency, simultaneously passing a point at the same given distance from the effective center of the transducer, but on the specified reference bearing (watt/cm²)

$(J_d)_L$ = the load intensity per unit band, at the specified constant frequency, of the acoustic waves passing a point on any given bearing at a given distance from the effective center of the transducer when it is receiving electric waves having a continuous spectrum (joule/cm² · cyc)

$(J_{do})_L$ = the load intensity per unit band, at the same constant frequency, of the acoustic waves simultaneously passing a point at the same given distance from the effective center of the transducer, but on the specified reference bearing (joule/cm² · cyc)

The ratios by which relative receiving responses may be measured are

$$(\eta'_d)_f = \frac{(\mu'_d)_f}{(\mu'_{do})_f} = \frac{(P'_d)_{out}}{(P'_{do})_{out}} = \frac{(U'_d)_{out}}{(U'_{do})_{out}} \quad (4D\text{-}4)$$

where

$(\eta'_d)_f$ = the relative receiving response of a sonar transducer, for a specified constant frequency, considered as a function of bearing (a numeric)

$(\mu'_d)_f$ = the receiving response of the transducer for the specified constant frequency and for any given bearing (cm²)

$(\mu'_{do})_f$ = the receiving response of the transducer for the same constant frequency, but for the specified reference bearing (cm²)

$(P'_d)_{out}$ = the output power of the sinusoidal electric waves, of the specified constant frequency, generated in the transducer when receiving over any given bearing plane sinusoidal acoustic waves of the same frequency and having a given free-field intensity (watt)

$(P'_{do})_{out}$ = the output power of the sinusoidal electric waves, of the same constant frequency, generated in the transducer when receiving plane sinusoidal acoustic waves of the same frequency and intensity as before, but propagated over the specified reference bearing (watt)

$(U'_d)_{out}$ = the output power per unit band, at the specified constant frequency, of the electric waves generated in the transducer when receiving over any given bearing plane acoustic waves having a given free-field intensity per unit band at the same frequency (joule/cyc)

$(U'_{do})_{out}$ = the output power per unit band, at the same constant frequency, of the electric waves generated in the transducer when receiving plane acoustic waves of the same intensity per unit band at the same frequency as before, but propagated over the specified reference bearing (joule/cyc)

The acoustic intensities appearing in a ratio measuring a relative transmitting response are those of sinusoidal acoustic waves meeting equal acoustic conductances per unit area. This intensity ratio, then, in accordance with Eq. (2A-87), is equal to the ratio of the mean-square acoustic pressures of these waves. Since these intensities are actual load intensities these pressures are actual acoustic pressures. It is thus possible to measure the relative response of a projector in terms of acoustic pressure, as well as in terms of acoustic intensity. When so measured the relative response of a projector is known as its **relative pressure response**. Relative pressure response, like relative transmitting response, may be considered a function of bearing when frequency is constant, or a function of frequency when bearing is constant. A relative pressure response is numerically equal to the square root of a relative transmitting response, as previously defined. When considered a function of bearing a relative pressure response may be written as

$$\frac{(p_d)_f}{(p_{do})_f} = \sqrt{(\eta_d)_f} \quad (4D\text{-}5)$$

where

$\dfrac{(p_d)_f}{(p_{do})_f}$ = the relative pressure response of a sonar transducer for a specified constant frequency, considered as a function of bearing (a numeric)

$(p_d)_f$ = the acoustic pressure of sinusoidal acoustic waves, of the specified constant frequency, passing a point on

any given bearing at a given distance from the effective center of the transducer when it is receiving sinusoidal electric waves of the same frequency
(μb)

$(p_{do})_f =$ the acoustic pressure of sinusoidal acoustic waves, of the same constant frequency, simultaneously passing a point at the same given distance from the effective center of the transducer, but on the specified reference bearing
(μb)

The electric powers appearing in a ratio measuring a relative receiving response are those of sinusoidal electric waves generated in a circuit having a fixed output impedance. Since these powers have been specified to be available powers their ratio, in accordance with Eq. (4A-8), is equal to the ratio of the mean-square values of open-circuit output voltages generated in the hydrophone. The relative response of a hydrophone measured by the ratio of the root-mean-square values of these two voltages is known as its **relative voltage response.** Relative voltage response, like other relative responses, may be either a function of bearing or a function of frequency. A relative voltage response is numerically equal to the square root of a relative receiving response. When considered a function of bearing a relative voltage response may be written as

$$\frac{(e_d)_f}{(e_{do})_f} = \sqrt{(\eta'_d)_f} \qquad (4D-6)$$

where

$\dfrac{(e_d)_f}{(e_{do})_f} =$ the relative voltage response of a sonar transducer, for a specified constant frequency, considered as a function of bearing
(a numeric)

$(e_d)_f =$ the open-circuit voltage of the sinusoidal electric waves, of the specified constant frequency, generated in the transducer when receiving over any given bearing plane sinusoidal acoustic waves of the same frequency and having a given free-field intensity
(volt)

$(e_{do})_f =$ the open-circuit voltage of the sinusoidal electric waves, of the same constant frequency, generated in the transducer when receiving plane sinusoidal acoustic waves of the same frequency and

intensity as before, but propagated over the specified reference bearing
(volt)

Relative pressure and relative voltage responses have been defined in terms of sinusoidal waves. This is because they have been derived from relative responses measured either in terms of intensity ratios, or of power ratios. Pressure ratios and voltage ratios cannot be derived from ratios of intensity per unit band, or of power per unit band. We may, however, apply the concept of relative pressure response or of relative voltage response to continuous waves by deriving these quantities from the equivalent sine wave intensities or equivalent sine wave powers (Art. 2A-9) of the energy in frequency bands of narrow, but finite, width. It is customary to use bands having a width of one cycle per second for this purpose. This has the advantage of making the ratio of the intensities measured for such a band numerically equal to the ratio of the intensities per unit band, measured at some frequency within the band, or of making a power ratio numerically equal to a ratio of powers per unit band. It must be noted, however, that a band having a width of one cycle per second is not a narrow band when located at the lower end of the frequency spectrum.

A relative response, being a ratio of two like rates of energy flow, may be used as a measure of transmission loss. When relative response is considered as a function of bearing the transmission loss thus measured is known as the **deviation loss** of the transducer in question. The deviation loss of a projector is given in terms of its relative transmitting response by the equation

$$N_d = \text{lgt} \frac{1}{(\eta_d)_f} \qquad (4D-7)$$

where

$N_d =$ the deviation loss of a sonar transducer for any given bearing and at a specified constant frequency
(db)

Similarly, the deviation loss of a hydrophone may be written as

$$V'_d = \text{lgt} \frac{1}{(\eta'_d)_f} \qquad (4D-8)$$

where

. $N'_d =$ the deviation loss of a sonar transducer

for any given bearing and at a specified constant frequency

(db)

Certain transducers may be used both as projectors and as hydrophones. When such transducers obey the reciprocity law, as given in Art. 4A-4, they are said to be **reversible**. It may be shown that when the frequency is held constant, and relative response is considered a function of bearing, the relative transmitting response and the relative receiving response of a reversible transducer are equal, for any given bearing.

To demonstrate the truth of this statement consider the system shown diagrammatically in Fig. 4D-1. In this system let PH be a reversible

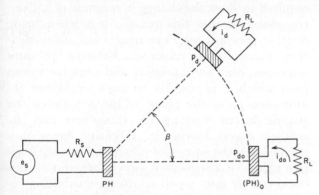

FIG. 4D-1. RECIPROCITY RELATION. Arrangement of transducers for demonstrating reciprocal relations between transmitting and receiving directional responses.

transducer receiving electric energy from a source having the source impedance R_S. Let a second reversible transducer, $(PH)_0$, be located at some distance from PH on a bearing for which the transmitting response of PH, considered as a function of bearing for a given constant frequency, is a maximum. This reference transducer is connected to an electric load having the resistance R_L. When the source voltage of the source is e_S let the free-field acoustic pressure at the position of $(PH)_0$ be p_{do}, and let the corresponding load current in R_L be i_{do}. In accordance with the reciprocity theorem it follows that if a voltage of magnitude e_S were to act in the circuit containing $(PH)_0$ and R_L, and if the original source voltage were to be reduced to zero, there would be a current equal to i_{do} developed in the circuit containing PH and R_S.

Now consider the situation when the reference transducer is moved to a bearing making the angle β with the original bearing, the separation

from PH being the same as before. If the reference transducer has any directional properties it is assumed that its orientation with respect to the line joining it to PH remains unchanged. As before, let the voltage acting in the original source be e_S. The acoustic pressure at the new location of the reference transducer will now be p_d, the ratio p_d/p_{do} being the relative pressure response of PH. The current in the load, R_L, will now be i_d. Under the conditions specified, and assuming the response of the reference transducer to be linear, $i_d/i_{do} = p_d/p_{do}$. If, now, a voltage of magnitude e_S is again allowed to act in the circuit containing $(PH)_0$ and R_L, and the original source voltage again reduced to zero, the current developed in the circuit containing PH and R_S will, by the reciprocity theorem, be equal to i_d.

The magnitudes of the acoustic pressures developed at PH when the voltage e_S acts in the circuit of the reference transducer are equal in the two cases just described, the only difference being that the acoustic waves approach this transducer along different bearings. Since the electric circuit of PH and R_S remains unchanged the open-circuit voltages, e_d and e_{do}, which are developed in this transducer when it is used as a hydrophone must be proportional to the corresponding currents, i_d and i_{do}. Consequently

$$\frac{(p_d)_f}{(p_{do})_f} = \frac{(i_d)_f}{(i_{do})_f} = \frac{(e_d)_f}{(e_{do})_f} \qquad (4D-9)$$

It is thus evident that when the frequency is constant the relative pressure response for any given bearing of the reversible transducer, when used as a projector, is equal to its relative voltage response, for the same bearing, when it is used as a hydrophone. From this it follows at once, by Eqs. (4D-5) and (4D-6), that the relative transmitting response and the relative receiving response of any reversible transducer, when considered a function of bearing at a specified constant frequency, are equal for any given bearing.

4D-2 Directivity Patterns

In order fully to specify the directional characteristics of any transducer it is necessary to consider relative response as a function of direction on a three-dimensional basis. For this purpose it is common practice to specify the orientation of the transducer and the direction of any other transmitting or receiving point in terms of a **reference plane** through the effective center of the transducer and of a **reference direction** in that plane. The direction of any line, OP, as shown in Fig. 4D-2, through the center of the transducer and any point from which acoustic energy is transmitted toward the transducer, or any point to which acoustic energy is transmitted from the

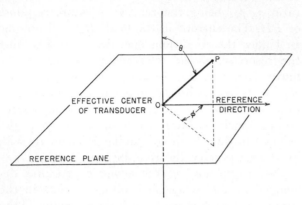

FIG. 4D-2. DIRECTIONAL COORDINATES. The standard system of coordinates used for the three-dimensional specification of the relative response of a transducer.

transducer, is then specified in terms of two angles. One, usually designated as θ, is the angle between the line in question and the perpendicular to the reference plane at the intersection of this line and this plane; the other, usually designated as ϕ, is the angle between a line in the reference plane having the reference direction and the projection on the plane of the line in question.

In practice, variations in relative response are generally shown graphically, against two-dimensional coordinates, by limiting attention to a family of bearings lying in some specified surface. This specified surface is usually the reference plane. It is sometimes a plane making a specified angle with this reference plane. It may, occasionally, be a conical surface. In such cases an effort is made to have the axis of the cone coincide with the perpendicular to the reference plane through the point corresponding to the center of the transducer. For any element of the cone the angle, θ, with this perpendicular is then constant and the value of relative response for any element may be plotted as a function of the angle, ϕ, between the projection of this element on the reference plane and a line having the reference direction.

In the majority of cases relative response is plotted graphically for a family of bearing lines lying in a plane. It is customary, moreover, to select a plane which includes the bearing of maxi-

mum response, and to make this bearing the reference bearing. A chart in which relative response is plotted as a function of bearing in some specified plane, either against rectangular coordinates or against polar coordinates, is known as a **directivity pattern,** or as a **beam pattern.**

In general, it is usually preferable to plot directivity patterns in terms of relative pressure response, or relative voltage response, rather than in terms of relative transmitting response or, relative receiving response. The magnitude of a relative pressure response is the square root of a relative transmitting response. As a relative pressure response decreases in magnitude, therefore, it does so less rapidly than does the corresponding relative transmitting response. The range of values required to show the change in response of a given transducer is, for this reason, less when using relative pressure response than when using relative transmitting response. Relative pressure responses, also, have positive and negative values from which it is possible to draw significant information as to the phase relations between the electric waves reaching the transducer and the acoustic waves leaving it. Intensity, being proportional to the square of pressure, has only positive values. Consequently such information is not conveyed by data as to relative transmitting response. We shall, therefore, describe directivity patterns in terms of relative pressure response or, where more convenient, in terms of relative voltage response, from which similar advantages are derived. In either case, it will be remembered that the two are numerically equal when considered as functions of bearing for a constant frequency.

For many transducers the three-dimensional directivity is such that it may be represented by the surface generated by rotating a two-dimensional directivity pattern about the axis corresponding to the reference bearing of the transducer. This axis may then be described as an **axis of acoustic symmetry,** or, more briefly, as the **acoustic axis.** The acoustic axis of a transducer often corresponds to a bearing of maximum response. In certain types of transducer, however, the three-dimensional representation of variations in relative response is obtained by rotating a two-dimensional directivity pattern about an axis perpendicular to a coordinate identified with a bearing of maximum response. For these transducers the relative response has its maximum value, of unity, for all bearings in the plane corresponding to that generated by the maximum response coordinate, as thus rotated. The generated plane, in other words, is the locus of all bearings of maximum response. Here the axis of acoustic symmetry, about which the directivity pattern has been rotated, may often be an axis of zero response. As in other cases, it corresponds to an axis of mechanical symmetry of the transducer.

Whenever a three-dimensional directivity pattern is generated by rotating a two-dimensional pattern about an axis of acoustic symmetry, lines making a constant angle with this axis are lines of constant deviation angle. If a transducer is so oriented with respect to the reference plane and the reference direction that its reference axis has the reference direction any deviation angle may be expressed in terms of the angles giving direction relative to the reference plane and the reference direction by means of the relation

$$\cos \beta = \sin \theta \cos \phi \qquad (4D-10)$$

Consider, as an example, a transducer having the form of a long cylinder in which the significant motion is a variation in the length of the radii. Such a transducer behaves as though it were, in effect, a straight line source. Assume that a transducer of this type is put into the water so that its mechanical axis lies in a reference plane perpendicular to its reference direction. This orientation is shown in Fig. 4D-3. A constant distance sphere, having the radius r and the effective center of the transducer as its center, will be intersected by the reference plane in a circle, as shown. A plane through the effective center of the transducer and perpendicular to its mechanical axis also intersects this sphere in a circle. Any point

on this last circle has the same positional relation to the active element of the transducer as every other point. Consequently, when the transducer radiates acoustic energy the acoustic pressure is constant over the entire circle. This pressure is the maximum pressure to be found on the surface of the constant distance sphere and will be taken as the reference pressure, designated as p_{do}. Any bearing in the plane perpendicular to the mechanical axis of the transducer, at its effective center, may be considered as a reference bearing.

Now let us draw a conical surface coaxial with the transducer and having its apex at the effective center. All elements of this surface make the same angle, β, with the plane perpendicular to the axis and all bearings having this angle lie in the surface. This conical surface will intersect the spherical surface in two circles the centers of which lie on the axis. As before, any point on either of these two circles has the same positional relation to the active element of the transducer as every other point and the circles are constant pressure circles. This pressure will be designated as p_d. It is evident that however the pressure may vary over the circle formed by the intersection of the spherical surface and the horizontal plane it will vary in an identical manner over any other circle formed by the intersection of the constant distance sphere and a plane through the axis of the transducer. The variation in pressure is, in other words, symmetrical with respect to the mechanical axis of the transducer, which is thus an axis of acoustic symmetry. A directivity pattern in spherical coordinates may be generated by rotating about this axis the polar pattern drawn for any plane through it. The reference axis appearing on this polar pattern would then generate a surface, corresponding to the normal plane, which is the locus of all maximum response values.

Another important example is that of a transducer having the form of a circular plate in which the significant motion is perpendicular to the surface. Assume that a transducer of this type is put into the water with its active surface perpendicular to the reference direction. A spherical surface of radius r, drawn concentric with the transducer as before, will intersect both the reference plane and a plane containing the active surface of the transducer in circles, as shown in Fig. 4D-4. In this case points of maximum pressure, p_{do}, are found on a line, having the reference direction, through the center of the transducer and perpendicular to its active surface. This mechanical

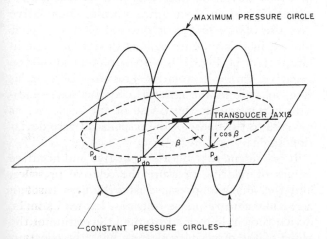

MAXIMUM PRESSURE CIRCLE

TRANSDUCER AXIS

CONSTANT PRESSURE CIRCLES

FIG. 4D-3. LINEAR TRANSDUCER. The geometrical relations between circles of constant pressure and the dimensions of the active element.

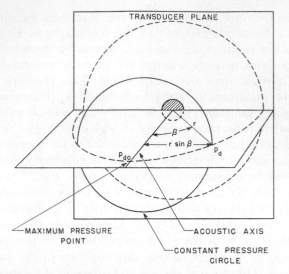

TRANSDUCER PLANE

MAXIMUM PRESSURE POINT

ACOUSTIC AXIS

CONSTANT PRESSURE CIRCLE

FIG. 4D-4. CIRCULAR PLATE TRANSDUCER. The geometrical relations between circles of constant pressure and the dimensions of the active element.

axis of the transducer corresponds, therefore, to the reference axis of the directivity pattern. It is evident that no other point on the spherical surface has the same positional relation to the active surface of the transducer as that of the two thus defined.

As in the previous example a conical surface containing all bearings of a given angle, β, may be drawn concentric with the mechanical axis. As before, all points on the circles formed by the intersection of this conical surface and the constant distance spherical surface exhibit the same pressure, p_d. In the case of this circular plate transducer variations in pressure are symmetrical about the reference axis which must, therefore, be the axis of acoustic symmetry as well. A spherical directivity pattern may therefore be obtained by rotating a plane polar pattern about the reference axis.

Obviously the symmetry observed in the preceding examples exists because the transducers there considered were themselves symmetrical with respect to the axes chosen. If the circular plate of the last example were to be replaced by a rectangular plate it would not be possible to generate the three-dimensional directivity pattern by rotating a two-dimensional pattern about any axis. The three-dimensional pattern would, nevertheless, have a definite symmetry relative to a reference axis which would, as in previous cases, be an axis of mechanical symmetry.

A transducer having maximum response in both directions along a reference axis passing through its center is said to be **bidirectional.** In many practical designs, however, the active surface is mounted in a structure in such fashion that radiation or reception takes place on one side only. In such cases the unit will show maximum response along a single bearing only and is said to be **unidirectional.** The line hydrophone, in its simplest form, shows a uniform response at the maximum value along any radius lying in a plane through the center of the transducer and perpendicular to its mechanical axis. It is sometimes provided with acoustic baffles which give it directional characteristics in this plane as well as in any radial plane passing through its axis. In view of the fact that the majority of significant signal sources lie in a horizontal plane the line hydrophone is frequently spoken of as being bidirectional when it has uniform response in all directions in the perpendicular plane; it is said to be unidirectional when it is more responsive in one horizontal direction than in the other.

A number of conventional directivity patterns are illustrated in Fig. 4D-5. These are drawn from data obtained by computation, using methods to be described later, for a projector having the form of an ideal circular piston the diameter of which is equal to five waves. They show variations in pressure response in a plane passing through the normal to the circular surface at its center. The transducer postulated is assumed to be so mounted that radiation may take place in one direction only.

Although polar plots might appear to be the most appropriate for directivity patterns there are advantages to the use of rectangular coordinates in which deviation angle, as well as relative response, is laid off along a linear scale. The relative pressure of the projector selected as a sample is plotted in this manner against deviation angle in Graph (A) of Fig. 4D-5. In a plot of this type negative values of relative pressure—or of relative voltage, in the case of a hydrophone—indicate a reversal in the phase of the response, as referred to the phase of the response at zero deviation angle.

It is evident that between positive and negative values of relative pressure the relative pressure, and the absolute pressure as well, pass through zero. The zero response bearings, known as **nulls,** divide the circle formed by the intersection of the plane of the directivity pattern with the constant distance spherical surface into a number of sectors. If a three-dimensional representation of the

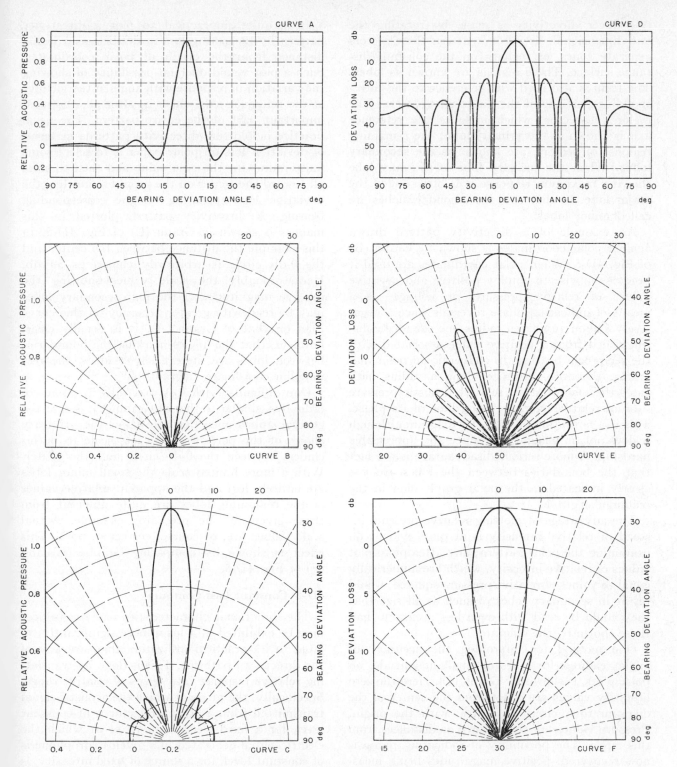

FIG. 4D-5. DIRECTIVITY PATTERNS. Various graphical methods for showing the directivity characteristics of transducers. The data are for a circular plate hydrophone having a diameter of 5λ.

    A. Relative pressure as a function of angle in rectangular coordinates
    B. Relative pressure as a function of angle in polar coordinates
    C. Relative pressure as a function of angle in polar coordinates with the zero pressure coordinate offset
    D. Deviation loss as a function of angle in rectangular coordinates
    E. Deviation loss as a function of angle in polar coordinates for a 50-db scale
    F. Deviation loss as a function of angle in polar coordinates for a 30-db scale

transducer directivity is made by rotating the two-dimensional directivity pattern these sectors generate zones, or regions, on the constant distance surface. These regions are known as **lobes.** The term is also used with reference to the corresponding portions of the directivity pattern. The region, or sector, which includes the reference axis is known as the **primary lobe;** the remaining regions, or sectors, are known as the **secondary lobes.** When the primary lobe is the only lobe showing maximum response it is often called the **major lobe.** In that case the secondary lobes are called **minor lobes.**

An example of a directivity pattern drawn against polar coordinates is shown by Graph (B) of Fig. 4D-5. When polar coordinates are used it becomes unwise to employ positive and negative values of relative pressure—or voltage—as a means of indicating phase reversals since a negative value on any given radius line cannot be distinguished from a positive value associated with the reciprocal bearing. In conventional polar diagrams, therefore, distance along a radius indicates the magnitude of relative acoustic pressure —or of relative voltage—regardless of its phase. This is a limitation of the polar diagram although it does not, in general, introduce any appreciable hardship. A more serious disadvantage is the fact that the boundaries between the lobes are less clearly indicated in the polar graph than in the rectangular graph.

The advantage of plotting relative pressure instead of relative intensity is at once evident on examining the polar pattern; any attempt to plot values of relative intensity, which are numerically equal to values of relative pressure squared, would result in secondary lobes of such small size that they could be read with even less accuracy than those shown by the diagram.

One method for improving the accuracy of angle readings for lobes of small magnitude, on polar plots, is shown by Graph (C). Here the zero intensity values are offset from the center of the diagram to a circle concentric with the origin. Pressure values are then shown as distances from this circle. The possibility of indicating phase is now recovered, positive magnitudes being measured away from the origin and negative magnitudes toward the origin.

The appearance of the graph obtained when a directivity characteristic is plotted as deviation loss, in decibels, against rectangular coordinates, is given by Graph (D) of Fig. 4D-5.

It is quite impractical to plot a directivity pattern by measuring loss in decibels as a radial distance from the origin of polar coordinates. Such a plot would offer no possibility of showing the variation in response with angle in the vicinity of the reference axis which is, after all, the most important part of the entire pattern. The usual practice in plotting directivity patterns in terms of deviation loss on polar paper is to select some finite radius for the zero value and then to scale off toward the center on the proper radius line the deviation loss appearing on the corresponding bearing. A directivity pattern plotted in this manner is shown in Graph (E) of Fig. 4D-5. In this example the distance between the center and the 0-db circle is arbitrarily chosen as 50 db. Unquestionably the scale values showing the relative magnitudes of the four secondary lobes may be read with greater accuracy on this curve than on that of Graph (A). It is equally clear, however, that the angles marking the boundaries between lobes are more easily read on the rectangular coordinate diagram.

One difficulty with loss diagrams in polar coordinates, similar to that of Graph (E), is that the general appearance depends upon the arbitrary choice of the portion of the loss scale to be included between the 0-db circle and the center. With a more limited scale the small minor lobes are entirely lost and the apparent relative values of the remaining lobes are quite different from those given by the preceding example. Actual scale values are, of course, correct in both. This effect is shown by comparing Graphs (E) and (F) of Fig. 4D-5.

4D-3 Constant Loss Contours

The directional characteristics of a transducer may be exhibited in a form more significantly related to its practical utilization than are any of the directivity patterns. This is done by translating relative response into terms of relative range. Specifically, the range at which the acoustic signal transmitted from a given projector is of constant level, for a fixed electric input, or at which the electric signal generated in a given hydrophone is of constant level, for a source of fixed intensity, is computed as a function of angular deviation from the reference axis. To meet either of these conditions the sum, $N_d + N_w$, of the deviation loss in the transducer and the propagation loss in the water must have a constant value; as the loss in the transducer increases with departure from the reference axis the loss in the water must be decreased by decreasing the range. Pairs of range-angle values which satisfy the condition for a constant overall loss may be plotted on polar coordinates. The resulting curve is a **constant loss contour** or a **constant signal level contour.**

An important feature of the constant loss contour, as a method of presenting information regarding the directivity characteristic of a transducer, is that it is a true scalar diagram showing range as radial distance and angle as angle. No arbitrary choice of scale can alter the relative proportions of this diagram. If drawn to the correct scale it may, in fact, be used as a chart overlay to show actual geographical positions to which specified transmission conditions apply. Such a plot is obviously more suitable than a graph drawn to some arbitrary scale of decibels, or to a scale of relative acoustic pressures, in such practical problems as laying out a search procedure for patrol craft or in other tactical maneuvers for which the directivity of the transducer is a significant operational characteristic.

Data for constant loss contours may be derived from data on the transducer, giving deviation loss as a function of angle, and data on the water, giving propagation loss as a function of range. By properly combining these the loss factor, which is common to both, may be eliminated and the range expressed as a function of angle. The actual computation may conveniently be made graphically, as shown in Fig. 4D-6. At the left of this figure is a graph of the directivity characteristic of the circular plate transducer, having a diameter

of 5λ, which served as the basis of the various directivity patterns of Fig. 4D-5. In this graph deviation loss is plotted vertically, in decibels, on rectangular coordinates against angular deviation from the reference axis. At the right is a graph of propagation loss in the water at a frequency of 25 kc/sec. This is plotted vertically, in decibels, against range. The loss scale used for the two graphs must be the same. An increasing loss in the transducer is matched to a decreasing loss in the water by laying off the parallel scales in opposite directions. As thus arranged horizontal lines intersect the two transmission loss scales at values having a constant sum, which is fixed by the relative vertical position of the two graphs. These graphs may be so located, then, as to give the constant value corresponding to the contour line to be computed. In the case shown this is the value which, for the given transducer, would be found on the maximum response axis at a range of 2000 yd. The water loss for this range is given by the propagation loss curve as 77 db. This point on the water curve is set opposite the 0-db point of the transducer curve, which corresponds to the maximum response. It is not necessary to know the absolute magnitude of either the transducer loss or of the total constant loss as we are concerned only with the fact that the latter, whatever it may be, does not change. For the given relative positions of the two curves pairs of range-angle values defining the constant loss contour through the 2000-yd point on the reference axis are obtained directly from their intersections with horizontal lines. The relations defining one such pair of values are shown by the dotted lines in Fig. 4D-6. The results of the complete computation are shown in Fig. 4D-7.

Contour lines separated by any desired **loss interval** may be computed by changing the relative vertical positions of the transducer and water curves by the amount of this interval. Families of such curves will later be found useful in analyzing the performance of sonar equipment for various applications.

It may be shown that if the attenuation loss may be neglected, and if the spreading loss follows the inverse square law, a constant loss contour line is identical with the directivity pattern of the transducer showing relative pressure response as a function of bearing against polar coordinates, using an appropriate scale. This follows at once from the fact that when the inverse square law is stated in terms of acoustic pressure, instead of

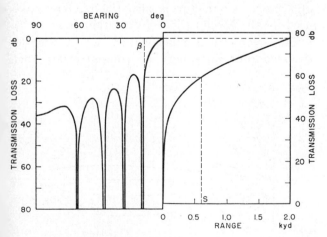

FIG. 4D-6. DETERMINATION OF CONSTANT LOSS CONTOURS. A graphical method for deriving the range, as a function of bearing, at which the combined transmission loss of a directional transducer and of the water has a constant value.

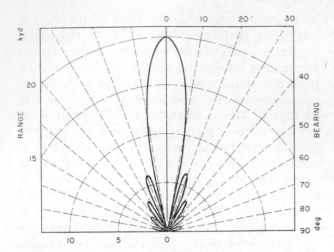

FIG. 4D-7. CONSTANT LOSS CONTOUR. The locus of points from which a constant level source would develop a constant output in a directional transducer, or at which the same transducer would develop a constant intensity signal. Drawn for a circular plate transducer having a diameter of 5λ.

acoustic intensity, it demands that the product of the acoustic pressure by the distance from the source be constant for all points on any given ray path. In a directivity pattern the pressures reported are those for which the distance from the transducer is constant; in a constant loss contour the distances reported are those for which the pressure is constant. For a point on the axis of maximum response and at a given distance from the transducer there will be some definite value of acoustic pressure. This distance may be designated as S_0; it is the reference distance for a constant loss contour passing through the point. The pressure at this point may be designated as p_0; it is the reference pressure for the directivity pattern. For a point at the same distance, S_0, but on a bearing making the angle β with the maximum response axis, the pressure will be p_d, which is less than p_0; the relative pressure for this bearing is then p_d/p_0. There will be a point on this same bearing, but at a distance S_d from the transducer, which is less than S_0, for which the pressure will have its original reference value, p_0; the relative distance for this bearing is then S_d/S_0. Since this bearing corresponds to a ray path the conditions under which the pressure-distance product must be constant, on the assumption that energy is distributed in accordance with the inverse square law, are satisfied when

$$p_d S_0 = p_0 S_d$$

or when

$$\frac{p_d}{p_0} = \frac{S_d}{S_0} \tag{4D-11}$$

The relative distance associated with the bearing in question by the constant loss contour is thus seen to be equal to the relative pressure associated with this same bearing by the directivity pattern; if curves of each are drawn to appropriate scales they will coincide.

In many practical problems it is convenient to be able to visualize a three-dimensional constant loss, or constant signal level, **contour surface.** Such a surface would, for example, indicate the region within which a submerged submarine might be expected to be detectable by a listening surface vessel. A constant loss contour surface may be generated by rotating a constant loss contour line about the axis of acoustic symmetry of the transducer directivity pattern. A surface thus generated is shown in Fig. 4D-8. This surface has been derived from the directivity pattern of a circular plate transducer but has been somewhat simplified with respect to the secondary lobes in order to avoid confusion.

From a constant loss contour surface it is possible to derive constant loss contour lines applying to a source or receiving point lying in a plane other than that defined by the axis of acoustic symmetry of the transducer directivity pattern. These contour lines may be computed either for a plane parallel to the axis of acoustic symmetry or for a plane through the effective center of the transducer and making some specified angle with this axis. For simplicity the method of computation will be described for the case where the axis of acoustic symmetry is also the reference axis used for the specification of deviation angle.

The geometrical relations by which the desired contour lines may be computed are then

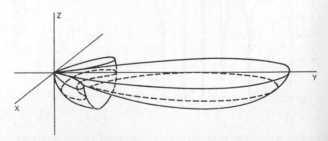

FIG. 4D-8. CONSTANT LOSS CONTOUR SURFACE. The constant signal level surface for a circular plate transducer located near the surface of the ocean.

given by a diagram such as that of Fig. 4D-9. This is drawn for a plane perpendicular to the reference axis through a point at the distance y from the transducer. This plane intersects a constant loss contour surface in the circular arc shown. A line through any point on this circular arc and through the position of the transducer makes the constant deviation angle, β, with the reference axis. Any point on this arc is at the constant distance $S = y/\cos \beta$ from the transducer. The radius of the arc is $S \sin \beta$. The intersection between the plane of this diagram and some specified plane, for which the contour line is desired, is indicated by the line a-a. This line intersects the circular arc in the point P. If the specified plane is parallel to the reference axis the perpendicular distance of this line from the center of the arc is $z = $ a constant. The coordinates of the point P, in this parallel plane, are then

$$y = S \cos \beta$$

and $$\text{(4D-12)}$$

$$x = \sqrt{S^2 \sin^2 \beta - z^2}$$

If the specified plane passes through the transducer at the angle θ with the reference axis the perpendicular distance of the intersection a-a from the center of the circular arc becomes $z = S \sin \gamma$, where $\sin \gamma = \cos \beta \tan \theta$. The coordinates of the point, in the plane thus specified, are then

$$y' = S \frac{\cos \beta}{\sin \theta}$$

and

$$x' = S \sqrt{\sin^2 \beta - \sin^2 \gamma}$$

In situations where the axis of acoustic symmetry is perpendicular to the reference axis it will be necessary to replace the value of β as used in the preceding equations by the value of $[(\pi/2) - \beta]$. This is equivalent to replacing values of $\sin \beta$ by values of $\cos \beta$, and values of $\cos \beta$ by values of $\sin \beta$.

The dotted line appearing in Fig. 4D-8 is the contour line, on the surface there shown, lying in a horizontal plane not passing through the transducer. The curve of Fig. 4D-10 shows a constant transmission loss contour, derived from the same surface, for a plane through the transducer and making the angle $\theta = 10°$ with the acoustic axis. The dotted curve gives, as a reference, the contour line at which the same surface intersects a plane containing the reference axis.

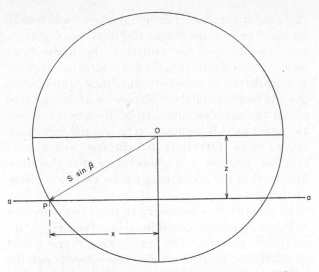

FIG. 4D-9. COMPUTATION OF CONTOUR LINES. The geometrical relations involved when contour lines are to be computed for planes which do not contain the acoustic axis of the transducer.

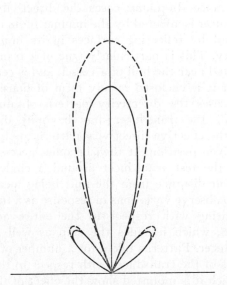

FIG. 4D-10. CONSTANT LOSS CONTOURS. The effect on a constant loss contour, corresponding originally to the dotted line, of swinging the plane of the diagram, about the transducer as a pivot, to make an angle of $\theta = 10°$ with the reference axis.

4D-4 The Measurement of Directivity

The directivity pattern of a transducer used as a projector may be obtained experimentally by setting up a hydrophone at a convenient distance and observing variations in the signal received, for a fixed electric input to the projector, as it is rotated about an axis perpendicular to the line between it and the hydrophone. This gives the directivity pattern in a plane through the line joining the two transducers and perpendicular to the axis of rotation. For a transducer which is to be used as a hydrophone the directivity pattern may be obtained by replacing the hydrophone used as described above by a source of acoustic waves, driven at constant amplitude, and observing the response of the hydrophone as it is rotated about the axis described. In both cases the acoustic signal used is assumed to be a single frequency wave. Since directivity is expressed in terms of relative response it is unnecessary that the absolute level of the acoustic signal be known in either of the two cases.

In practice it is necessary to pay close attention to environmental conditions in observing a directivity pattern. The two transducers would normally be located at the same depth and the unit under test would be rotated about a vertical axis. The directivity pattern would then show variations in response in a horizontal plane. This is generally the pattern of greatest operational significance. In many cases the directivity of a transducer is affected by the manner of its mounting and by reflecting surfaces in its immediate vicinity. This is particularly true of a transducer mounted near the hull of a vessel, and is certainly true if it is enclosed in any form of housing. In such cases the directivity pattern obtained by rotating the transducer may be quite different from the effective directivity pattern applying to any given position. It then becomes necessary to carry the test transducer around a circle, at a constant distance from the unit being measured, and to observe variations in response as a function of bearing with respect to the entire acoustic system, which includes the ship as well as the transducer. Patterns taken for a number of orientations of the transducer with respect to the ship on which it is mounted show the effect of the hull or of any housing on the directivity. In carefully conducted tests, where full account must be taken of all factors, a transducer intended for ship-borne service is mounted in its actual operating position and the ship taken into open water. The test transducer is then mounted on a small boat which circles the ship at a fixed distance. In some instances this fixed distance has been maintained by running a light cable from an unobstructed point on a mast and maneuvering the small boat so that this cable acts as a constant radius.

4-E COMPUTED DIRECTIVITY PATTERNS

For many practical problems it is essential that the directional characteristics of some proposed transducer be predicted prior to construction rather than measured afterwards. It is, in fact, impossible properly to design a transducer for some designated purpose without a clear understanding of the relations between directivity and its design constants. Moreover, in many cases directivity patterns computed on the basis of these relations may well prove to be more representative of a type of tran. ducer than measurements made on any isolated sample.

The relative response of a transducer is a function of certain critical dimensions of the active surface, of the nature of the motion of this surface, and of the wave length of the signal for which the directivity is to be determined. The effects of size and frequency are such that, for a transducer of given form, the relative response is a function of the ratios of the critical dimensions to the wave spacing and is independent, within limits, of the absolute value of either. Detailed methods for computing the directivity patterns of a number of typical transducer forms will be discussed in the following articles.

4E-1 Uniformly Spaced Point Sources

The factors which determine the directive properties of any transducer may be considered most logically by first examining the behavior of a number of discrete receiving points uniformly spaced along a straight line. Such an arrangement is known as a linear **multispot array.** It has great practical utility as well as the theoretical simplicity with which we are, for the moment, concerned.

Let us start with two receiving points at the ends of a line which may be rotated about its center point. Let r be the radial distance of either point from the center of rotation. The angle between a perpendicular to the line connecting the two points at the center of rotation, that is, the normal line, and the direction of propagation of a received wave has been designated as the **deviation angle,** β. This is also the angle between a plane wave front through the center of rotation and the line joining the two points. These geometrical relations are shown in the diagram of Fig. 4E-1 which is drawn to represent the special case where $r = 2.5\lambda$, or where the total separation between the two points is equal to five times the wave spacing of the incoming acoustic signal waves.

When the line joining the two points is perpendicular to the bearing of the source of the

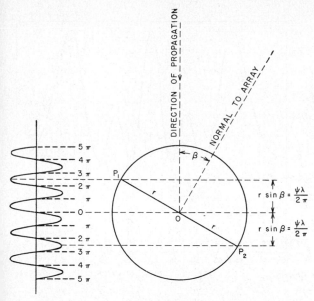

FIG. 4E-1. TWO-ELEMENT RECEIVING SYSTEM. The geometrical relations between an acoustic wave and a pair of
point receiving units, showing the difference in phase between
the responses of these units as a function of the deviation
angle.

test signal, that is, when the deviation angle is
$\beta = 0$, a given wave front will strike both points
simultaneously. The electric outputs of the two,
therefore, will be in phase. Assume the electric
response of either point receiver to be $e_{max} \sin \omega t$.
If the two points are connected together in series
the total response while in this position will be
$2e_{max} \sin \omega t$.

Suppose, now, that the line is rotated, as shown
in Fig. 4E-1. The point P_1 will be advanced
toward the source by the distance $r \sin \beta$ and
the point P_2 will be withdrawn from the source
by the same distance. Since the phase of the
incident signal changes 2π radians per cycle
change in distance from the source, the response of the unit at P_1 will lead the response
which it would have shown in its original position
by the phase angle $\psi = (2\pi r/\lambda) \sin \beta$. This quantity
will be designated as the **phase factor**. The
response at P_2 lags the reference response by
the same phase factor. The response at P_1
then becomes $e_{max} \sin(\omega t + \psi)$ while at P_2 it is
$e_{max} \sin(\omega t - \psi)$. The resulting response when the
two points are connected together is found by
trigonometric identities to be $2e_{max} (\sin \omega t)(\cos \psi)$.
In other words, rotation of the array causes no
progressive phase shift in the total signal obtained by combining the two outputs but does
cause the amplitude to be changed by the factor
$\cos \psi$. For all values of β for which $\cos \psi$ is nega-

tive the resultant response is 180° out of phase
with the reference response, that is, with the
response when $\beta = 0$.

The ratio of the resultant voltage of a pair of
receiving points for any value of the angle β to
the voltage when $\beta = 0$, or the relative voltage, is,
from the foregoing,

$$\frac{e_d}{e_{do}} = \frac{2e_{max}(\sin \omega t)(\cos \psi)}{2e_{max}(\sin \omega t)} = \cos \psi \qquad (4E\text{-}1)$$

where

e_d = the voltage generated by a distant sound
source located on a specified bearing
(volt)

e_{do} = the voltage generated by the same sound
source when at the same distance along
the normal to the array
(volt)

$\psi = (2\pi r/\lambda) \sin \beta$

= the phase factor applying to this pair of
transducers at a specified deviation
angle
(rad)

r = the distance of either of the two receiving
units from the center of rotation
(in)

λ = the wave length of the signal used
(in/cyc)

β = the deviation angle measured between the
normal to the array and the specified
bearing of the sound source
(deg or rad)

Curve (A) of Fig. 4E-2 shows the beam pattern,
as computed by the above equation, of a pair of
point transducers separated by the distance 5λ.
This case is the same as that diagramed in Fig.
4E-1. It will be seen that with this separation
there are six positions, as the array is turned
through 90°, for which the signals at the two
elements are in phase and hence for which the
combined response is a maximum equal to that
at the reference position. Three of these maxima
are positive, indicating that the resultant signal
is of the same phase as that at the center of rotation; three are negative, indicating that the signals are of opposite phase to that at the center.
There are also five positions for which the signal
at one element is exactly 180° out of phase with
that at the other, in consequence of which the
resultant response to sounds arriving from the
specified source is zero.

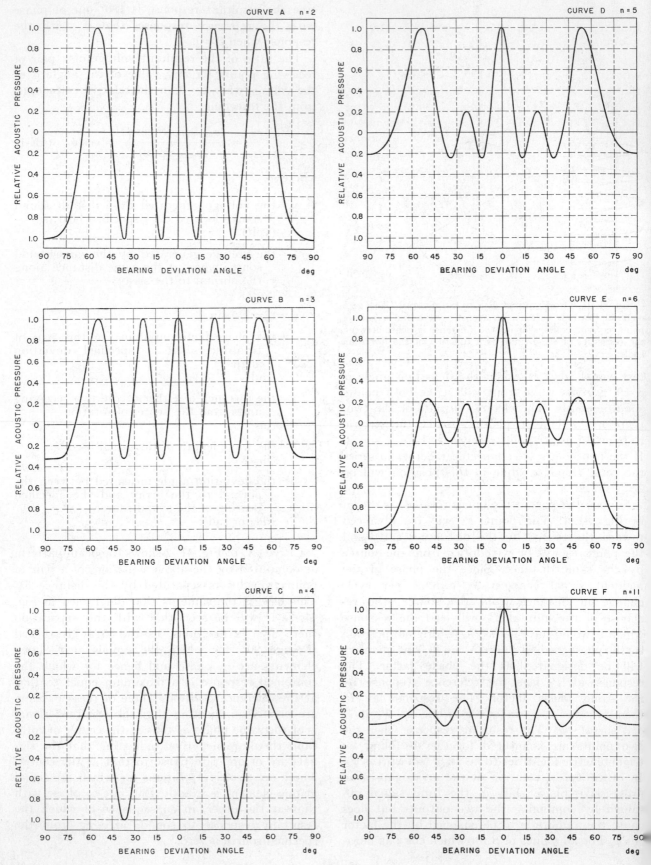

If the array is made up of a number of equally spaced elements these may be grouped into pairs having a common center or into such pairs and a single unit located at the common center. The output for each group may be computed separately. Since the outputs of all groups are in phase or in phase opposition the total output of the combination may be computed by adding algebraically the amplitudes of the several outputs. When the number of unit points becomes large this procedure becomes laborious. It is then simpler to use a general formula which may be derived from Eq. (4E-1) by means of trigonometric relations. This formula is

$$\frac{e_d}{e_{do}} = \frac{\sin n\psi}{n \sin \psi} \qquad (4\text{E-}2)$$

where

$\psi = (\pi s/\lambda) \sin \beta$

$\quad$ = the phase factor applying to the specified array of transducers at a specified deviation angle
$\quad$ (rad)

s = the separation between adjacent elements (in)

λ = the wave length of the signal used (in/cyc)

n = the number of individual elements in the array
$\quad$ (a numeric)

Using the above methods the beam patterns of linear multispot arrays, each having a total length equal to five cycles but differing in the number of elements, have been computed. These beam patterns are shown in Fig. 4E-2. The phase relations between the signals at the individual elements which result in maxima for the relative values of generated voltage, or in complete cancellation, may be examined by constructing diagrams similar to that of Fig. 4E-1. In the diagram there shown the value of β, as drawn, is 30° and the phases of the waves at the two receiving points are such that their combined output is zero through cancellation. A number of useful generalizations may be deduced from Eq. (4E-2).

The first null in the directivity pattern of a linear array occurs when $n\psi = \pi$, and $\sin n\psi = 0$. For this point we may write

$$\psi = \frac{\pi}{n} = \frac{\pi s}{\lambda} \sin \beta_0$$

or

$$\sin \beta_0 = \frac{\lambda}{ns} \qquad (4\text{E-}3)$$

This shows that, for any given frequency, the width of the primary lobe identified with a given number of elements may be reduced only by increasing their separation. For a given array the width of this lobe decreases with increasing frequency.

By differentiating the relative voltage, as given by Eq. (4E-2), with respect to the phase factor, ψ, values of the phase factor, and hence of the deviation angle, β, at which the several lobe maxima occur may be found. This shows that these maxima occur when

$$n \tan \psi = \tan n\psi \qquad (4\text{E-}4)$$

The relations thus defined may be examined graphically by plotting these two quantities against the deviation angles for the quadrant from $\beta = 0$ to $\beta = \pi/2$. For this region the phase factor has values between $\psi = 0$ and $\psi = \pi s/\lambda$. Such a plot is shown in Fig. 4E-3 for a multispot array having $n = 11$ elements spaced uniformly along a line of length $l = 5\lambda$. The spacing is thus $s = \lambda/2$. Those values of deviation angle for which $n\psi = [(2k+1)/2]\pi$ have been marked with the several values of this quantity corresponding to the several values of the integer k which are possible in this case. As may be seen from the figure, the maximum response for any secondary lobe of an array having a number of elements occurs at approximately the deviation angle for which the phase factor is $\psi = [(2k+1)/2](\pi/n)$. This approximation introduces a negligible error, for our present purpose, provided the number of elements is in excess of $n = 10$. When the number is $n = 5$, for example, the first secondary maximum occurs at a phase factor of $\psi = 0.291\pi$ instead of at $\psi = 0.3\pi$, as obtained by placing $k = 1$ in the

FIG. 4E-2. DIRECTIVITY PATTERNS. The directivity patterns for multispot arrays having various numbers of elements uniformly spaced over a fixed distance of 5λ.

Curve	A	B	C	D	E	F
Number of elements	2	3	4	5	6	11
Spacing, in waves	5	5/2	5/3	5/4	1	1/2

above expression. The error resulting from this approximation becomes less as the deviation angle increases or as the number of elements increases.

When any of the values of phase factor thus indicated are substituted into the right hand side of Eq. (4E-2) the numerator becomes $\sin n\psi = 1$. Under these conditions the values of the several secondary maxima are given approximately as

$$\left[\frac{e_d}{e_{do}}\right]_{max} \approx \frac{1}{n \sin \psi} \qquad (4E\text{-}5)$$

The first secondary maximum occurs when $\psi \approx (3\pi/2n)$. If now, the number of elements, n, is large a further approximation may be made by writing, for this maximum,

$$\sin \frac{3\pi}{2n} \approx \frac{3\pi}{2n}$$

whereupon

$$\left[\frac{e_d}{e_{do}}\right]_{max} \approx \frac{2}{3\pi} \qquad (4E\text{-}6)$$

This is in close agreement with the fact that the maximum value of relative voltage for the first secondary lobe, as shown by the several directivity patterns of Fig. 4E-2, approaches the value $e_d/e_{do} = 0.212$ as the number of elements increases.

Regardless of the closeness of the approximation of Eq. (4E-5) it is evident that the associated maxima decrease in magnitude as long as the quantity $1/(n \sin \psi)$ decreases. This quantity does, in fact, approximate closely to the envelope of the directivity pattern under the conditions here assumed as to the number of elements in the array. If the constants of the array and of the signal are such that this quantity begins to increase before the deviation angle has reached the value $\beta = \pi/2$ the maxima will begin to increase. In order that this shall not take place, and that the maximum value of any secondary lobe shall be less than that of the preceding lobe, it is necessary that $\sin \psi = 1$ for no value of $\beta < (\pi/2)$. This condition is satisfied if

$$\psi \leqq \frac{\pi}{2} \geqq \frac{\pi s}{\lambda} \qquad (4E\text{-}7)$$

or if the spacing is one half cycle or less. In any array intended for service use it is customary to require that this condition be satisfied for the shortest wave length.

Although of secondary importance as compared with their heights and widths the number of the secondary lobes is sometimes of interest. It may be demonstrated by rigorous analytical methods that the number of secondary lobes in one quadrant of the directivity pattern of a linear array is equal to the quantity

$$\frac{(n-1)s}{\lambda} = \frac{l}{\lambda} \qquad (4E\text{-}8)$$

This fact might have been deduced by an examination of the relations between the dimensions of the array and the successive cycles of an approaching acoustic wave, as illustrated by Fig. 4E-1, and the corresponding directivity patterns as given in Fig. 4E-2. From this it is apparent that the number of secondary lobes is independent of the spacing of the elements provided the array is of constant length.

These generalizations are of great help in indicating the direction along which to proceed in designing a multispot array for some specified purpose. In many practical applications of these arrays the signal to be received may cover a band of frequencies. From the foregoing it is evident that the width of the primary lobe may be made less than some prescribed value, at all frequencies, by choosing the length to be some suitable multiple of the longest wave spacing. It is also evident that, having specified a linear array as the general form to be used, it is futile to lay down any requirements as to the minimum height of secondary lobes since these have been shown to be almost independent of the design constants of the array. It is, however, proper to demand that the secondary lobes shall decrease, with increasing deviation from the reference axis, for all values of deviation angle. To meet this requirement at all frequencies it is necessary that the element spacing be one half the shortest wave spacing, or less. The spacing, then, is determined by the highest frequency to be used, the length of the array by the lowest, and the number of elements by the ratio of these two quantities.

In the next article we shall examine the beam patterns of a transducer which is the equivalent of a multispot array having an infinite number of elements separated by infinitesimal intervals.

4E-2 Linear Transducers

It has already been indicated that a transducer having the form of a long cylindrical tube, the motion of which is radial, may be treated as an ideal straight-line source if the radius is small as compared with a wave space. In fact, when the transducer is used as a projector the radius need not be small so long as the motion of the tubular surface remains the same as that which a wave sent out by an ideal line of the same length would have at the same radial distance. Transducers of this form have wide application in listening for sounds in the audible portion of the acoustic spectrum. They are generally known as **line hydrophones.** We have already considered some features of their three-dimensional directivity.

When a line hydrophone receives acoustic energy along some specified bearing the relative voltage is

$$\frac{e_d}{e_{do}} = \frac{\sin \psi}{\psi} \qquad (4E\text{-}9)$$

where

$e_d =$ the voltage developed by acoustic energy, of given intensity, arriving along a given bearing
(volt)

$e_{do} =$ the voltage developed by acoustic energy of the same intensity arriving along a normal to the cylindrical axis of the hydrophone, which is here the reference axis
(volt)

$\psi = (\pi l / \lambda) \sin \beta$

= the phase factor applying to the specified transducer at a specified deviation angle
(rad)

$l =$ the effective length of the transducer
(in)

$\lambda =$ the wave length of the signal used
(in/cyc)

$\beta =$ the angle between the reference axis and the bearing in question, in the plane of the transducer axis
(deg or rad)

This formula, like others to follow, is obtained by a method analogous to that described for the computation of the resultant response of a multi-element array. A general expression is first derived for the response due to a single infinitesimal element of the transducer. The phase and amplitude of this response are expressed as functions of the position of the element with respect to a distant transmitting or receiving point. The sum of

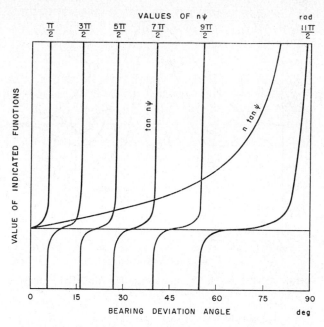

FIG. 4E-3. RELATIONS IN A MULTISPOT ARRAY. Values of the functions $n \tan \psi$ and $\tan n\psi$, where $\psi = (\pi s/\lambda) \sin \beta$, plotted as functions of the deviation angle, β, for a multispot array having $n = 11$ elements separated by half wave intervals. The relative response has a maximum at any value of β for which these two functions are equal.

all such elementary responses for the transducer considered as a whole is then obtained by suitable integration. The result appears as a function of the phase factor identified with the form and dimensions of the transducer and of the bearing deviation angle.

Values of the relative voltage computed by this equation for one quadrant on each side of the maximum response axis are shown graphically in Fig. 4E-4. The curves drawn are for hydrophone lengths which are one, two, and five times the length of the signal wave. It is at once evident that the voltage, e_{do}, corresponding to the perpendicular through the center is the maximum value to be found for any bearing, in each case. The fact that all three curves pass through the same point for $\beta = 0$ does not, of course, indicate that the absolute value of this maximum voltage is the same for all ratios of the length of the transducer to the length of a wave; it merely follows from the fact that, in each case, the unknown voltage for that bearing is used as a reference voltage.

The first minor lobe of the line hydrophone shows a maximum value of relative voltage which is 0.212 times the reference value of unity, corresponding to the major lobe. This is in agreement with the conclusion which would be reached

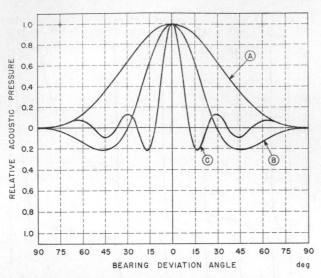

FIG. 4E-4. LINEAR TRANSDUCERS. The directivity patterns for linear transducers having various lengths.

Curve	A	B	C
Lengths in wave spaces	1	2	5

by extending the application of Eq. (4E-6) from the multispot array to the line hydrophone by making the separation of the elements infinitesimally small. Until the quantity l/λ reaches a value so low that the bearing of this first minor lobe maximum vanishes from the directivity pattern this ratio between the two maxima will persist. Its magnitude is, in fact, an important constant of the line hydrophone.

In Fig. 4E-5 the curve of a multispot array, having a total length of 5λ along which point

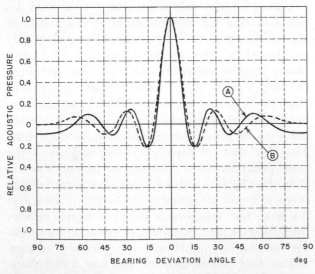

FIG. 4E-5. MULTISPOT AND LINEAR TRANSDUCERS. A comparison of the directivity patterns of (A) a multispot array having elements arranged on a half wave spacing and (B) a continuous, uniform linear transducer. The total length is 5λ in each case.

transducers are spaced at intervals of $\lambda/2$, and the curve of a line hydrophone of the same effective length, which is equivalent to a multispot array having an infinite number of elements, are repeated on a single graph for comparison. It is evident from an inspection of this figure that little is to be gained by providing a multispot array with more elements than are sufficient to give a half-wave spacing; the height of the secondary lobes may be slightly reduced but the width of the main lobe is slightly increased.

4E-3 Ring Transducers

Another type of hydrophone having a simple form is that in which a long cylindrical tube is bent into a circle. This unit may be treated theoretically as equivalent to a circle. Such units, known as **toroidal hydrophones,** or **ring hydrophones,** have been used for direct listening at frequencies in the audible range.

When a ring hydrophone receives acoustic energy of constant intensity but varying direction of propagation the directivity may be described in terms of the electric voltages developed, as in the case of a line hydrophone. The relation between the two-dimensional beam pattern and three-dimensional directivity is the same for this transducer as for the circular plate described by the aid of Fig. 4D-4. The relative voltage from which the two-dimensional pattern may be drawn is

$$\frac{e_d}{e_{do}} = \mathcal{J}_0(\psi) \qquad (4E\text{-}10)$$

where

e_d = the voltage developed by acoustic energy of given intensity arriving along a given bearing
(volt)

e_{do} = the voltage developed by acoustic energy of the same intensity arriving along the normal to the plane of the transducer, at its center, which is here the reference axis
(volt)

$\psi = (\pi d/\lambda) \sin \beta$

= the phase factor applying to the specified transducer at a specified deviation angle
(rad)

d = the diameter of the circle into which the cylindrical tube is bent
(in)

λ = the wave length of the signal used
(in/cyc)

β = the angle between the normal to the plane of the transducer and the bearing in question
(deg or rad)

The symbol $\mathcal{J}_0(\psi)$ indicates that the relative voltage is what is known as a Bessel's function of the phase factor. Although the original derivation of Bessel's functions involves advanced mathematical analysis, their use in computations such as the present is no more difficult than is the use of trigonometric functions. Tables of $\mathcal{J}_0(\psi)$ as a function of ψ are available just as are tables of sin ψ. Actually there is less labor involved in evaluating Eq. (4E-10) than there was in the case of Eq. (4E-9), where it was necessary to reduce ψ from radians to degrees and then to angles less than 90°. Values of $\mathcal{J}_0(\psi)$ as a function of ψ for values of ψ as high as 16 may be found directly in readily available tables of Bessel's functions.[9]

Values of acoustic pressure computed by Eq. (4E-10) are shown graphically in Fig. 4E-6 for one quadrant on each side of the reference axis. The ratios of diameter to wave space used were, as before, equal to one, two, and five. As with the linear transducer the major lobe becomes narrower and the number of minor lobes increases as the critical dimension, in this case the diameter of the transducer, is increased relative to the length of the signal wave. This narrowing of the major lobe may, of course, be effected either by increasing the size of the transducer or by increasing the frequency of the signal.

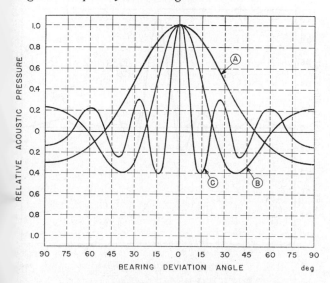

FIG. 4E-6. RING TRANSDUCERS. The directivity patterns for circular ring transducers having various diameters.

Curve	A	B	C
Diameter in wave spaces	1	2	5

A comparison of the beam patterns of ring and linear transducers shows one important effect associated with changes in the basic form of the transducer; the major lobe of the ring transducer occupies a narrower sector than the major lobe of the line transducer, while the minor lobes are considerably higher. As with the linear transducer, it will be noted that the height of the first minor lobe is independent of the ratio of the critical dimension to the wave space so long as this ratio is sufficient to produce a minor lobe. Its relative magnitude is 0.403.

4E-4 Circular Plate Transducers

We have already discussed briefly the three-dimensional properties of transducers having the form of a circular plate. As in the case of the ring-type transducer, the beam pattern in any plane through the center of the plate and perpendicular to its surface is the same as that in any other plane similarly defined. In this case the relative voltage developed as acoustic energy arrives along some given bearing is

$$\frac{e_d}{e_{do}} = \frac{2\mathcal{J}_1(\psi)}{\psi} \qquad (4E-11)$$

where the several variables have the same significance as in the case of Eq. (4E-10). The symbol $\mathcal{J}_1(\psi)$ used in this equation indicates that the functional relationship involved is of the special type known as a Bessel's function of the first order. As in the case of Eq. (4E-10), tables are available for values of $\mathcal{J}_1(\psi)$ as a function of ψ.

Values of relative voltage computed by Eq. (4E-11) for one quadrant on each side of the reference axis, which is also the acoustic axis, are shown graphically in Fig. 4E-7, using the same ratios of diameter to wave space as for the ring transducer.

It will be found that the directivity patterns of the circular plate transducer exhibit the same general characteristics as noted for the other two types. In particular, the main lobe, for a given ratio of critical dimension to wave space, occupies a wider sector than for either of the preceding types examined, while the minor lobes are considerably reduced as compared to the other types. The characteristic height of the first minor lobe of this transducer is 0.132.

4E-5 Rectangular Plate Transducers

The three-dimensional directivity patterns of the typical transducers thus far examined may be

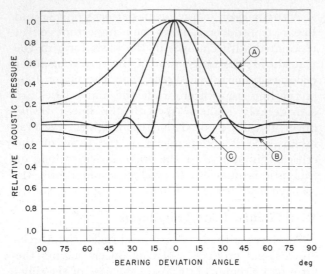

FIG. 4E-7. CIRCULAR PLATE TRANSDUCERS. The directivity patterns for circular plate transducers having various diameters.

Curve	A	B	C
Diameter in wave spaces	1	2	5

derived from the two-dimensional patterns by rotating the latter about suitably chosen axes. This is not possible in the case of square or rectangular transducers. Here the two-dimensional pattern observed in a plane through the center perpendicular to the surface and parallel with one side of the rectangle will be quite different from that in a plane through a diagonal and perpendicular to the surface. Although the transducer does not have an axis of symmetry in the same sense as do the line and circular transducers, a perpendicular to the surface erected at the center may still be regarded as the reference axis. This axis lies in any plane in which it may be desirable to obtain a two-dimensional directivity pattern and will have the maximum response of all bearings in that plane.

For a plane through the reference axis and parallel to one side of a square or rectangle the directivity pattern is the same as that for a line hydrophone, the active element of which coincides with the line of intersection of the transducer surface and the plane in question. The curves of Fig. 4E-4, therefore, may be used as the directivity patterns of a rectangular transducer in a plane through the acoustic axis and parallel to a side. For a plane through the reference axis and the diagonal of a square the relative voltage is

$$\frac{e_d}{e_{do}} = \frac{\sin^2 \psi}{\psi^2} \qquad (4\text{E-}12)$$

where

$\psi = (\pi d/2\lambda) \sin \beta = (0.707\pi l/\lambda) \sin \beta$

= the phase factor applying to this aspect of the specified transducer at the specified deviation angle (rad)

d = the length of a diagonal of the square (in)

l = the length of a side of the square (in)

The ratio of the voltage for any bearing to the voltage corresponding to the reference axis, as given by the above equation, is numerically equal to the square of the voltage ratio found for the case of a linear transducer having a length equal to one half the diagonal of the given transducer.

In Fig. 4E-8 are plotted two directivity patterns for a square transducer, the length of one side of which is five times the length of the signal wave used. One curve, repeating one of those given in Fig. 4E-4, is the directivity pattern lying in a plane parallel to one side of the square; the other is the pattern in a plane intersecting the surface on a diagonal. An unusual feature of the pattern in a diagonal plane is that it has no negative values. In other words, the pressure variations of the several lobes do not show the alternate phase reversals appearing in all other directivity patterns which have been derived up to this point. Another striking fact is that the

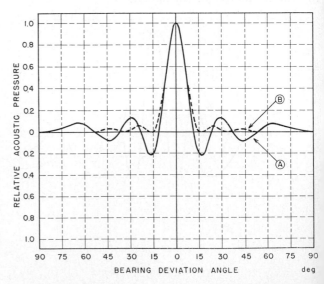

FIG. 4E-8. RECTANGULAR TRANSDUCER. The directivity patterns of a square transducer in (A) a plane parallel to one side and in (B) a plane through one diagonal. The length of the side is 5λ.

heights of the minor lobes in the diagonal plane are considerably lower than any that we have heretofore encountered.

If a plane through the reference axis, and hence perpendicular to the surface, were to be rotated about the acoustic axis there would be four positions at which the directivity pattern corresponds to the "parallel" curve of Fig. 4E-8 and four positions corresponding to the "diagonal" curve. For intermediate positions the directivity pattern would lie somewhere between these two curves and would change shape gradually from one to the other as the plane rotates.

4E-6 Pressure-Gradient Transducers

All of the transducers thus far considered have had an active surface which is either a flat plane or the surface of a cylinder. When used for the reception of acoustic signals the response to a plane wave is proportional to the pressure of that wave. If the acoustical properties of the transducer could be made such that its acoustic impedance matched the acoustic impedance of the water correctly displacements of the active surface would be the same as displacements of the water in contact with it. Suppose, however, that the active element of a transducer is a rigid rectangular block which is supported by an elastic suspension. When used as a hydrophone the resultant force tending to displace such a block is proportional to the difference between the pressures on opposite surfaces perpendicular to the direction in which it is free to move. When such a block is so arranged that its motion generates an electric voltage the device is a hydrophone of the **pressure-gradient** type discussed in Art. 2A-8.

The directional characteristics of a pressure-gradient hydrophone may be deduced from an examination of the diagram given in Fig. 4E-9. Here an active pressure-gradient element is represented by the rectangular solid, having the length s along the direction in which it is free to move. This direction determines the maximum response axis of the device. For any plane wave having a direction of propagation making the angle β with this axis the effective length of the responding unit becomes $s \cos \beta$. The phase difference between the motions of wave fronts at opposite faces of the element and the motion of a wave front at the midpoint is, therefore, $\psi = (\pi s / \lambda) \cos \beta$. The pressures on the two faces are consequently

$$(p_1)_{\text{inst}} = p_{\max} \sin (\omega t + \psi)$$

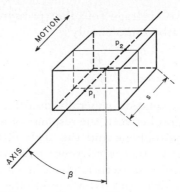

Fig. 4E-9. Pressure-Gradient Hydrophone. The geometrical relations between an acoustic wave and the active element of a pressure-gradient hydrophone showing the phase shift between faces.

and $$(4\text{E-}13)$$
$$(p_2)_{\text{inst}} = p_{\max} \sin (\omega t - \psi)$$

The effective pressure tending to move the element is thus the difference between these two pressures, or

$$(p_1)_{\text{inst}} - (p_2)_{\text{inst}} = 2p_{\max}(\sin \psi)(\cos \omega t) \quad (4\text{E-}14)$$

This last expression is seen to be that of a wave of amplitude $2p_{\max} \sin \psi$ in phase quadrature with the acoustic wave at the center of the element. The relative voltage of a pressure-gradient hydrophone thus becomes

$$\frac{e_d}{e_{do}} = \frac{(p_1 - p_2)_d}{(p_1 - p_2)_{do}} = \frac{\sin \psi_d}{\sin \psi_{do}} \quad (4\text{E-}15)$$

where

$\psi_d = (\pi s / \lambda) \cos \beta$

= the phase factor for a given deviation angle (rad)

$\psi_{do} = \pi s / \lambda$

= the phase factor when the deviation angle is $\beta = 0$ (rad)

It is evident from an inspection of the diagram that, for a plane wave perpendicular to the reference axis, when $s = 1\lambda$ the pressures on the two faces are equal and tend to move the coil in opposite directions. Under these conditions the resultant pressure, as given by Eq. (4E-14), will be zero and the hydrophone will show no response. For values of s which are less than about one sixth of a wave spacing we may write $\sin \psi_d = \psi_d$ and $\sin \psi_{do} = \psi_{do}$. Under these conditions the relative voltage of the pressure-gradient hydrophone becomes simply

$$\frac{e_d}{e_{do}} = \frac{\psi_d}{\psi_{do}} = \cos \beta \qquad (4E\text{-}16)$$

This is the equation generally used for the functional relation between the response of a pressure-gradient hydrophone and the angle of the sound source relative to the reference axis. The associated directivity pattern is given in Fig. 4E-10.

One practical disadvantage of the pressure-gradient hydrophone is the directional ambiguity indicated by the two lobes in Fig. 4E-10. In constructing a hydrophone embodying the pressure-gradient principle an attempt is sometimes made to overcome this objection by combining the response of the pressure-gradient element with the response of a nondirectional element. For a sound source on the maximum response axis the sensitivities of the two elements are adjusted so that their outputs are equal in amplitude and in phase. They therefore combine to give twice the response of either element alone. For sounds arriving from the opposite direction, however, the response of the pressure-gradient element will be in phase opposition to that of the nondirectional element and the two will cancel each other. The directional characteristic of a hydrophone combining pressure-gradient and nondirectional elements to give a response which is nearly unidirectional is shown in Fig. 4E-11. This particular pattern, because of its form, is often spoken of as a cardioid. It is sometimes used for determining the bearing of a source by observing the angle at which the response falls to zero. Its advantage when so used is due to the extreme sharpness of the null point which is clearly far superior to the maximum response point as a means for accurately defining bearing angle.

4E-7 Lobe Reduction and Shading

The secondary lobes which have appeared in every directivity pattern thus far considered often result in a considerable impairment of transducer performance. When the transducer is used as a direct-listening hydrophone the response to sounds coming in on the bearings of the secondary lobes increases the level of interference and hence reduces the range at which a given sound source may be detected. A signal received on a secondary lobe may be mistaken for a signal on the reference axis and incorrect deductions made as to its actual

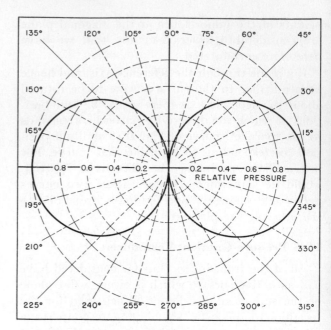

FIG. 4E-10. PRESSURE-GRADIENT HYDROPHONE. The directivity pattern for a pressure-gradient hydrophone.

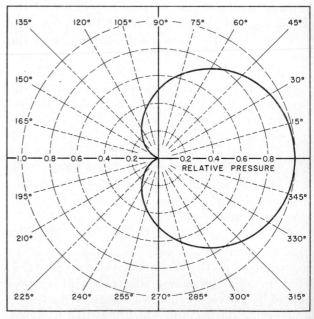

FIG. 4E-11. PRESSURE-GRADIENT HYDROPHONE. The directivity pattern obtained by combining the responses of a pressure-gradient hydrophone and a nondirectional hydrophone.

bearing. When the transducer is used as a sound source the secondary lobes cause a portion of the total acoustic energy put into the water to be directed along bearings where it is not required and where it may, in fact, do appreciable harm. In general, the ideal transducer should have no secondary lobes. Although this ideal can never be completely realized in practice it is possible, by certain modifications known as **lobe reduction** designs, to effect some improvement over the characteristics which would otherwise be obtained.

In discussing the factors involved in lobe reduction it will be convenient to speak in terms of electroacoustic transducers used as projectors. Any conclusions reached as to relative response will, however, be equally applicable to hydrophones, regardless of whether or not they are reversible. For a projector having an active surface lying in a plane, a point on a normal to the surface and at a sufficient distance may be assumed to be equally distant from all points on the projector surface. At such a point the resultant pressure is the sum of the pressures due to the individual elements of the projector surface, acting as point sources. For a linear projector, similarly, the pressure at a point on the normal to the axis is, if the point is at a sufficient distance, the sum of the pressures due to the individual elements of the projector length. For our present purposes the quotient of the pressure at a point equidistant from all elements of a plane surface projector, or from all elements of a linear projector, by the distance of that point from the projector will be designated as the **strength** of the projector. The **strength per unit area** of a plane surface projector is the quotient of the strength of an infinitesimal surface element by the area of that element. The **strength per unit length** of a linear projector is the quotient of the strength of an infinitesimal linear element by the length of that element. The strength of any portion of the surface of a plane surface projector is the integrated value of its strength per unit area taken over that surface. The strength of a transducer used as a hydrophone may be defined as the strength which it would have as a projector if it were ideally reversible.

Lobe reduction processes, as applied to plane surface transducers, may be described in terms of the two-dimensional directivity existing in some assigned plane perpendicular to the surface of the projector. The position of this plane will usually be so chosen as to obtain the maximum length of intersection with the projector surface for the prescribed direction across the surface. All dimensions of the transducer may be referred to this intersection; the length of the intersection will be designated as the length of the transducer and the length of the surface perpendicular to

this intersection as its height. Points on any line perpendicular to the length of a projector have virtually equal separations from a distant point in the assigned directivity plane, regardless of the angle made by the bearing of this point and the normal to the surface of the projector; with respect to acoustic energy delivered to such a distant point the combined effect of all points on such a perpendicular line is the same as though they were concentrated at their projection on the projector length. Any plane surface projector may thus be said to have a strength per unit length, at any point along its intersection with the directivity plane, equal to the strength of a corresponding elementary strip perpendicular to this intersection divided by the width of that strip. This width is understood to be an infinitesimal increment of transducer length. For responses identified with the assigned directivity plane any incremental strip is, in other words, treated as though it were an ideal point source located at its intersection with the plane. For responses restricted to a plane, therefore, plane surface transducers and linear transducers may be treated as equivalent.

For a transducer the active surface of which is a square having constant strength per unit area the strength per unit length for a plane parallel to a side of the active surface is also constant, being proportional to the height and to the strength per unit area. When the directivity plane intersects the surface of such a transducer along a diagonal, however, the heights of the elementary strips are no longer constant but decrease linearly with distance along the length as measured from the center. The strength per unit length in this case varies linearly with length in the same manner. In a transducer the active surface of which is a circular piston of uniform strength per unit area the functional relation of the heights of the strips, and consequently of the strength per unit length, to distance from the center is determined by the circular outline of the active surface.

An examination of the directivity patterns already shown discloses that when the strength per unit length falls off rapidly from the center, as along the diagonal of a square transducer, the maxima of the secondary lobes are less than when this quantity falls off more slowly, as along the diameter of a circular piston. For both of these transducer types the secondary maxima are lower than for a linear transducer, where the strength per unit length does not fall off at all.

This suggests that there may exist a functional relation between strength per unit length and distance along the transducer length for which the secondary maxima may be reduced to negligible values or entirely eliminated. It is to be noted, however, that if the three transducer types mentioned above are listed in the order of decreasing secondary maxima they are also listed in the order of increasing width of primary lobe, as measured at the null points. We will not be surprised, then, to learn that while there is an ideal distribution of strength per unit length for which there are no secondary maxima it results in a main lobe of prohibitive width for a transducer of finite length.

It is evident that if an attempt is made to vary the strength per unit length of a transducer by varying the height of its surface it may be possible to obtain some desired directivity pattern for a specified plane but not for other planes. This is well illustrated by the square transducer, which has a pattern of one character for a plane through either diagonal and patterns of other character for all other planes. In order to design a transducer so that it shall have some prescribed type of directivity pattern in all planes through its center it is necessary to resort to a structure having circular symmetry in which the strength per unit area varies in an identical manner for all radii. The strength per unit length will now vary with distance from the center in the same manner for all diameters and the directivity patterns for all perpendicular planes through the center will be alike.

There are a number of ways in which the strength per unit area may be varied. In general this is accomplished by varying the relative electroacoustic coupling to the several portions of transducer surface. Transducers modified in this manner are said to be **shaded.** For a multi-spot array, or for a transducer having an array of coupling elements, the spacing of the elements may be varied. For a piezoelectric transducer the thickness of the crystals may be varied. When such a transducer is used as a projector, with constant voltage across all crystals, the voltage gradient for any crystal, and hence the force exerted by that crystal, may be made to have some preassigned value relative to the force exerted by other crystals. The same result may be obtained by varying the number of crystals connected in series between the transducer terminals. For a magnetostrictive transducer the

strength per unit area may be varied by using a number of individual magnetostrictive elements, of similar mechanical and magnetic properties, and varying the number of turns in the coils associated with each.

For a circular transducer in which the strength per unit area varies continuously with distance from the center the strength per unit length, at any point along the length corresponding to any plane through the center, would have to be computed by integrating the strength per unit area along the height of the transducer at that point. Since both the height and the manner in which the strength per unit area varies with height are functions of distance along the length of the transducer this problem is one of some complexity. In practice, however, it is unusual to design a transducer so that its strength per unit area varies continuously. Instead, the transducer surface may be arranged in circular zones, each having uniform strength per unit area. In this case the computation of the resulting directional characteristics is greatly simplified. It may be carried out, in fact, merely by combining the response characteristics of the several zones. The manner in which this may be accomplished will be illustrated by the following example.

Let us start with a circular surface of diameter $d_0 = 5\lambda$ and having uniform strength per unit area. The directivity pattern for this surface has already been presented as one of the curves of Fig. 4E-7. It is reproduced as Curve (A) of Fig. 4E-12. From the deductions made on the basis of the directivity patterns of the several transducer forms thus far examined it is suggested that the height of the secondary lobes may be reduced by increasing the strength of the central zone of the circular surface relative to the remainder of this surface. If there were available a supplementary directivity pattern corresponding to this central zone by itself it would be possible, considering the transducer as a projector, to express the pressure at any point due solely to the increased strength of this central zone as a relative pressure in terms of the original reference pressure. Since the relative pressure corresponding to any bearing, as shown by a directivity pattern, is proportional to the absolute value of pressure at that bearing this adjusted supplementary pattern would indicate changes in absolute pressure to the same scale as does the original pattern. It would then be possible to obtain the resultant change in absolute pressure, and hence the re-

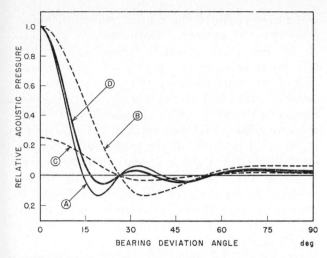

FIG. 4E-12. LOBE REDUCTION. Component and resultant relative response curves used in an empirical attempt to reduce the minor lobes of a circular plate transducer having a diameter of $d=5\lambda$.

(A) Curve for uniform strength over entire plate
(B) Curve for increased strength of central zone having a diameter equal to 56 percent of total diameter
(C) Curve for increased strength of central zone as referred to maximum response of total surface when uniformly driven
(D) Curve for resultant response of shaded surface

sultant relative pressure, by direct addition of the original directivity pattern and the adjusted supplementary pattern. The adjusted supplementary pattern should correspond to pressures developed by the central zone due solely to its increased strength; contributions of this zone corresponding to its original strength are already included in the original directivity pattern.

It is necessary first to decide upon the dimensions of the central zone which is to be given increased strength. To reduce the magnitude of any secondary lobe of the original projector it is obvious that components of pressure due to the increased strength of the central zone, over bearings occupied by each of these lobes, should, if possible, be of opposite phase to the pressure of the original projector. As a step in this direction we shall choose the diameter of the modified central zone so that, by itself, it would have its first null point at the deviation angle for which the original projector had its second null point. From tables of Bessel's functions of $\mathcal{J}_1(\psi)$ it is found that the first null of a circular plate transducer occurs when $\psi_1 = 3.835$ and that the second null occurs when $\psi_2 = 7.015$. The first of these values of phase factor applies to the central zone at a given value of angular deviation; the second applies to the original surface at the same angular

deviation. Since for equal deviation angles values of phase factor for circular plate transducers are proportional to their respective diameters (Art. 4E-4) we may compute the diameter of the desired central zone in terms of the diameter of the original surface as

$$d_z = d_0 \frac{\psi_1}{\psi_2} = \frac{3.835}{7.015}\, d_0 = 0.5467\, d_0$$

In the present example the diameter of the original projector was assumed to be $d_0 = 5\lambda$; the diameter of the proposed central zone is thus $d_z = (5)(0.5467)\lambda = 2.734\lambda$. We may now compute the supplementary directivity pattern for this central zone, in terms of its own reference pressure, in the usual manner, in accordance with Eq. (4E-11). The pattern thus obtained is shown as Curve (B) of Fig. 4E-12. The first null point of this supplementary pattern falls on the second null point of the original pattern as intended.

The second step is to determine the amount by which the strength of the central zone of the projector is to be increased relative to its original strength. This involves a decision as to the pressure which the central zone should develop on any bearing, due solely to this increased strength, relative to the reference pressure of the original surface. An inspection of the original and supplementary response curves shows that at the third null point of the original curve the supplementary curve indicates an appreciable pressure. If the supplementary curve were to be so adjusted as to equal the maximum height of the first minor lobe of the original curve, at the bearing of this maximum, the resultant curve would show an undesirably high second minor lobe. We shall, therefore, attempt to distribute the potential advantages of the supplementary response among the several lobes of the original response. Based on an examination of relations at the first secondary maximum and at the third null of the original curve it appears that if, at these angles, the adjusted supplementary curve, as drawn for pressures relative to the original reference pressure, were to be made approximately 25 percent of the height of the supplementary curve, as drawn relative to its own reference pressure, the resultant curve, as obtained by addition, would have an acceptable characteristic.

If the adjusted curve is to show some fractional value of the supplementary curve at any angle it will show this same fractional value at all angles and hence at the reference angle, $\beta = 0$. In other words, the pressure on the reference axis of the central zone of the projector, due solely to its increased strength, should be brought to 25 percent of the pressure on the reference axis of the original surface. But the ratio of the pressures on the axes of two circular plate projectors driven at equal strengths per unit area is equal to the ratio of their areas, since all surface elements make equal contributions to the resultant pressures. Assuming equal driving powers to be associated with equal surface areas this indicates that the ratio of the two pressures is equal to the ratio of the two driving powers. This may appear, at first sight, to be at variance with the established principle that, since acoustic power is proportional to driving power, acoustic pressure is proportional to the square root of the driving power. It must be remembered, however, that this principle applies to average values of acoustic power, which may be averaged with respect either to time or to space. In the present situation we are not dealing with average values of acoustic power. The specifications of the reference axis of a projector define a unique region of the space-pressure pattern where component pressures, each proportional to the square root of a component driving power, combine by direct addition and the resultant pressure is proportional, by the same factor, to the square root of the sum of the component driving powers. The ratio of the pressure due to the central zone of the projector surface as originally driven to the pressure due to the entire surface as originally driven is thus equal to the ratio of the squares of the diameters of these surfaces, or

$$\frac{p_z}{p_0} = \left(\frac{d_z}{d_0}\right)^2 = (0.5467)^2$$

and

$$p_0 = \frac{p_z}{0.3099}$$

The reference pressure of the central zone is now to be adjusted so that it is increased by an amount equal to 25 percent of the reference pressure of the original projector. This adjusted pressure is consequently

$$p_{adj} = p_z + 0.250\, p_0$$

$$= p_z + \frac{0.250}{0.310}\, p_z = 1.807\, p_z$$

and the strength of the central zone is to be increased by 81 percent. This increase in strength is, by definition, directly proportional to the increase in pressure at any point on the reference axis of the central zone of the projector. But the pressure developed at any portion of a projector surface is proportional to the square root of the acoustic power developed by that surface. Assuming that all elements of the projector surface are equally efficient, then, it appears that the desired objective may be attained if the ratio of the adjusted power of the electric energy delivered to the central zone of the projector to the power of the electric energy originally delivered to this zone is made to be

$$\frac{(P_E)_{adj}}{(P_E)_z} = (1.81)^2 = 3.264$$

The resultant effect of modifying a circular plate transducer as suggested above is shown by Curve (D) of Fig. 4E-12. It is at once evident, by comparison with the original directivity pattern as given by Curve (A), that the secondary lobes have, indeed, been reduced in height. It is not so evident that the overall performance of the transducer has been improved by this shading. The width of the main lobe has clearly been increased. This would indicate that the accuracy with which the bearing of some localized source may be determined has been impaired. In the next section we shall discuss methods for evaluating the directional discrimination of a hydrophone against interference reaching it along bearings other than the maximum response bearing. We shall then be in a position to appraise the effect of shading in terms of this important characteristic.

4-F THE SUMMATION OF DIRECTIONALLY VARIABLE RESPONSE

The information conveyed by a directivity pattern covers in detail the variations in response with bearing which are characteristic of a given transducer at a given frequency. While this information is invaluable for many purposes there are problems for which more concise generalizations are desired. In other words, we need a single comprehensive figure of merit by which to express the integrated effect on its operational performance of the directional properties of any transducer, or array of transducers. Such a figure is given by the **directivity factor** discussed in this section.

4F-1 Directivity Factor

The directivity factor of a sonar transducer used for the transmission of acoustic energy may be defined either in terms of sinusoidal waves or of waves having continuous spectra. When such a transducer is used for the reception of acoustic energy, however, it appears more realistic to deal with waves having continuous spectra. When a transducer is driven by sinusoidal electric waves sinusoidal acoustic waves of identical frequency are radiated on all bearings. When a transducer receives acoustic energy from sources on many bearings, on the other hand, it is somewhat fanciful to postulate that this energy be carried by sinusoidal waves of identical frequency. Later we shall have occasion to consider the integration of the energy transmitted or received by a sonar transducer in some frequency band of given finite width. Here it is necessary to consider waves having continuous spectra. In view of this the directivity factors to be examined in this section will be discussed in terms of waves having continuous spectra. This will permit us to use a single method of analysis for studying the summation of energy which is distributed in bearing and for studying the summation of energy which is distributed in frequency.

The **transmitting directivity factor** of a sonar transducer, for a specified frequency, may be defined as the ratio of (1) the power per unit band of the acoustic energy radiated over all bearings and at the specified frequency by the transducer when receiving electric energy having a given power per unit band at the specified frequency to (2) the power per unit band of the acoustic energy which would be radiated over the same bearings and at the same frequency when receiving the same electric energy, if the transmitting response of the transducer for that frequency were the same for any bearing as for the maximum response reference bearing.

The transmitting directivity factor may also be defined as the ratio of (1) the power of the acoustic energy radiated over all bearings by the transducer when receiving sinusoidal electric waves of the specified frequency and having a given power to (2) the power of the acoustic energy which would be radiated over the same bearings and when receiving the same electric waves, if the transmitting response of the transducer for the specified frequency were the same for any bearing as for the maximum response reference bearing.

The derivation of the relation between directivity factor and relative response, considered as a function of bearing, will be based on the definition expressed in terms of waves having continuous spectra.

The intensity per unit band, at a specified fixed frequency and at a known distance from the projector, of the acoustic energy radiated on any given bearing is, in accordance with the definition for transmitting response (Art. 4D-1),

$$(J_d)_f = (\mu_d)_f (U_E)_f \qquad (4\text{F-1})$$

where

$(J_d)_f$ = the intensity per unit band, at a specified fixed frequency and at a given distance from the effective center of a sonar transducer, of the acoustic energy radiated by the transducer on some given bearing (joule/cm^2·cyc)

$(\mu_d)_f$ = the transmitting response of the transducer for the given bearing and for the specified fixed frequency $(1/\text{cm}^2)$

$(U_E)_f$ = the power per unit band, at the same specified frequency, of the electric energy delivered to the transducer (joule/cyc)

Whenever the directional characteristics of a transducer are such that the directivity patterns in all planes passing through an axis of acoustic symmetry are identical, it is possible to derive an expression for the power per unit band, at some specified frequency, of the energy actually radiated on all bearings in terms of the known relations between intensity per unit band and bearing as given by this two-dimensional pattern. This may be demonstrated by using the circular plate transducer as an example. In Fig. 4D-4 acoustic pressure p_d corresponds to an intensity per unit band $(J_d)_f$, at a specified frequency. This intensity per unit band is constant for each point on the circle formed by the intersection with the constant distance sphere of the conical surface the elements of which make the deviation angle β with the reference axis. Although this intensity per unit band varies continuously with deviation angle, as shown by the directivity pattern of the projector, it may be considered as constant over that portion of the surface having the form of a circular band of infinitesimal width lying adjacent to this constant pressure circle. This band is included between two conical surfaces the elements of which make angles of β and $\beta+\delta\beta$ respectively with the reference axis. Elements of two such conical surfaces are shown in the diagram of Fig. 4F-1. The length of this strip having constant intensity per unit band is equal to $2\pi r \sin \beta$ and its width to $r \, \delta\beta$. The incremental power per unit

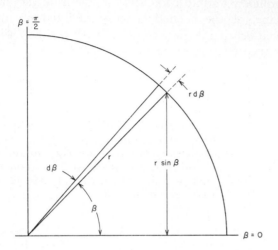

FIG. 4F-1. DIRECTIVITY FACTOR. The geometrical relations between an incremental band of constant intensity and the bearing angle of which the intensity is a function.

band, at the specified frequency, of the energy crossing this incremental strip is then

$$\delta(U_{Ad})_f = 2\pi r^2 (J_d)_f \sin \beta \, \delta\beta$$
$$= 2\pi r^2 (\mu_d)_f (U_E)_f \sin \beta \, \delta\beta \quad (4F\text{-}2)$$

where

$\delta(U_{Ad})_f =$ the power per unit band, at a specified frequency, of acoustic energy having constant intensity per unit band, at the same frequency, radiated through a strip of infinitesimal width on the surface of a sphere concentric with the effective center of a sonar transducer (joule/cyc)

$r =$ the radius of the constant distance sphere (cm)

$\beta =$ the angle between the reference axis of the transducer and a radius of the sphere defining the position of this incremental strip (rad)

$\delta\beta =$ the infinitesimal angle defining the width of this strip (rad)

The power per unit band, at the specified frequency, of the acoustic energy actually put into

the water on all bearings is obtained by taking the sum of all values of this incremental power per unit band as the angle β is varied from zero to π. When the incremental angle, $\delta\beta$, is allowed to approach zero as a limit the power per unit band of this actual acoustic energy may be expressed by the integral

$$(U_A)_{\text{act}} = 2\pi r^2 (U_E)_f \int_0^\pi (\mu_d)_f \sin \beta \, d\beta \quad (4F\text{-}3)$$

The reference power per unit band of the acoustic energy which would be radiated on all bearings in response to the same electric energy, if the transmitting response of the transducer were the same for any bearing as for the maximum response reference bearing, is given at once as the product of the area of the constant distance sphere by the maximum intensity per unit band, $(J_{do})_f = (\mu_{do})_f (U_E)_f$. It is, therefore,

$$(U_A)_{\text{ref}} = 4\pi r^2 (J_{do})_f = 4\pi r^2 (\mu_{do})_f (U_E)_f \quad (4F\text{-}4)$$

The transmitting directivity factor of a sonar transducer for which the axis of acoustic symmetry is also an axis of maximum response thus becomes

$$(\eta_D)_f = \frac{(U_A)_{\text{act}}}{(U_A)_{\text{ref}}} = \frac{1}{2} \int_0^\pi (\eta_d)_f \sin \beta \, d\beta \quad (4F\text{-}5)$$

where

$(\eta_D)_f =$ the transmitting directivity factor, for a specified fixed frequency, of a sonar transducer having an axis of acoustic symmetry which is also a maximum response axis (a numeric)

$(\eta_d)_f = (\mu_d)_f / (\mu_{do})_f$

$=$ the relative transmitting response of the transducer, considered a function of bearing, for the same fixed frequency (a numeric)

In the case of a transducer for which the maximum response bearings form a plane perpendicular to an axis of acoustic symmetry the length of a constant intensity band of infinitesimal width as shown by Fig. 4D-3, is $2\pi r \cos \beta$, instead of $2\pi r \sin \beta$, as for the case previously considered. The constant intensity circle will, in the present case, generate the complete constant distance sphere if the bearing angle is varied from $-(\pi/2)$ to $\pi/2$. The transmitting directivity factor of a projector having an axis of acoustic symmetry perpendicular to its maximum response bearings is therefore

$$(\eta_D)_f = \frac{1}{2} \int_{-\pi/2}^{\pi/2} (\eta_d)_f \cos \beta \, d\beta \qquad (4F-6)$$

It is evident that the average value of the intensity per unit band, taken over the constant distance spherical surface, is expressed in terms of the actual power per unit band appearing in the definition for directivity factor by the relation

$$(U_A)_{\text{act}} = 4\pi r^2 (J_{\text{aver}})_f \qquad (4F-7)$$

From this it follows that the transmitting directivity factor of the transducer may be expressed as

$$(\eta_D)_f = \frac{(U_A)_{\text{act}}}{(U_A)_{\text{ref}}} = \frac{(J_{\text{aver}})_f}{(J_{do})_f} \qquad (4F-8)$$

The radius of the constant distance spherical surface may have the unit value identified with the index magnitudes of radiated acoustic waves. The transmitting directivity factor of a sonar transducer, radiating acoustic energy having a continuous spectrum, may, therefore, be defined as the ratio of (1) the average index value of the intensity per unit band, at a specified frequency, of the acoustic energy radiated on all bearings to (2) the index value of the intensity per unit band, at the same frequency, of the acoustic energy radiated along the maximum response reference bearing. When dealing with sinusoidal waves this factor would be defined as the ratio of (1) the average index intensity of the acoustic energy radiated on all bearings to (2) the index intensity of the energy radiated on the maximum response reference bearing.

The **receiving directivity factor** of a sonar transducer, for a specified frequency, is the ratio of (1) the available power per unit band of the electric energy generated at the specified frequency by the transducer when receiving over all bearings and at the specified frequency acoustic energy having a given free-field intensity per unit band which is the same for all bearings to (2) the available power per unit band of the electric energy which would be generated at the same frequency and when receiving the same acoustic energy over the same bearings, if the receiving response of the transducer for that frequency were the same for any bearing as for the maximum response reference bearing.

We now return to the transducer having an axis of acoustic symmetry which is also a maximum response axis and examine its integrated directional properties when used as a hydrophone. In this case acoustic energy is assumed to reach the transducer from all directions and in such manner that the intensity per unit band of the waves propagated along any bearing is the same as that propagated along any other bearing. It will be assumed that all sources of the acoustic energy reaching the point in question are at such distance that the energy from any one reaches the point in the form of plane waves. This acoustic energy may be evaluated in terms of an imaginary spherical surface having its center at the point to be occupied by the effective center of the transducer. The radius of this spherical surface should be comparable with the dimensions of the transducer, but is not necessarily of any specified magnitude. The geometry of this surface, as it would be used with a transducer of the type postulated, is the same as for the surface shown in Fig. 4F-1.

The available power per unit band of the acoustic energy reaching the transducer through the incremental area of this surface included between the conical loci of bearings making the angles β and $\beta + \delta\beta$ with the reference direction is

$$\delta(U'_{Ad})_f = 2\pi r^2 (J'_H)_f \sin \beta \, \delta\beta \qquad (4F-9)$$

where

$\delta(U'_{Ad})_f =$ the available power per unit band, at a specified frequency, of the acoustic energy reaching a transducer through a narrow strip on the surface of an imaginary sphere having its center at the location to be occupied by the effective center of the transducer (joule/cyc)

$r =$ the radius of this imaginary spherical surface (cm)

$(J'_H)_f =$ the intensity per unit band, at the same specified frequency, of the acoustic waves reaching the transducer through this surface along any bearing (joule/cm²·cyc)

$\beta =$ the angle between any point on one edge of the narrow strip and the reference direction (rad)

$r \, \delta\beta =$ the width of the narrow strip (cm)

The available power per unit band of the electric energy generated in the transducer, when placed in the position assigned, in response to the increment of the total received acoustic energy associated with the waves having the power per unit band defined above, may be written as

$$\delta(U'_{Ed})_f = (k'_d)_f \, \delta(U'_{Ad})_f$$

$$= 2\pi r^2 (J'_H)_f (k'_d)_f \sin \beta \, \delta\beta \quad (4F\text{-}10)$$

where

$\delta(U'_{Ed})_f =$ the power per unit band, at a specified frequency, of the electric energy generated in a sonar transducer in response to acoustic waves reaching the transducer through a given incremental area on an imaginary spherical surface concentric with the effective center of the transducer
(joule/cyc)

$(k'_d)_f =$ a coefficient having a value which is a function of bearing and of frequency
(a numeric)

The available power per unit band of the total energy generated in the transducer is the sum of the available powers per unit band of the incremental components of the energy thus defined. This sum is obtained by making the width of the incremental area of the imaginary spherical surface of the infinitesimal magnitude $r \, d\beta$ and integrating over the entire spherical surface. The quotient of the power per unit band associated with such an infinitesimal area by the infinitesimal area may be described as the power per unit band per unit bearing angle. The available power per unit band of the electric energy actually generated in the transducer is thus written as

$$(U'_E)_{\text{act}} = 2\pi r^2 (J'_H)_f \int_0^\pi (k'_d)_f \sin \beta \, d\beta \quad (4F\text{-}11)$$

The coefficient $(k'_d)_f$ applies to energy reaching the transducer along all bearings differing from the deviation angle β by the incremental angle $\delta\beta$, or less. It is, by definition, the ratio of the available power per unit band of the electric energy generated within the transducer to the free-field value of the power per unit band of the acoustic energy crossing an infinitesimal area defined by these bearings. We may, therefore, write

$$(k'_{d1})_f = \frac{\delta(U'_{Ed1})_f}{(\delta A_1)(J'_{d1})_f}$$

and

$$(k'_{d2})_f = \frac{\delta(U'_{Ed2})_f}{(\delta A_2)(J'_{d2})_f}$$

Since these equations are true for all values of the incremental areas they are true when $\delta A_1 = \delta A_2$. It therefore follows that

$$\frac{(k'_{d1})_f}{(k'_{d2})_f} = \frac{\delta(U'_{Ed1})_f}{(J'_{d1})_f} \frac{(J'_{d2})_f}{\delta(U'_{Ed2})_f} = \frac{(\mu'_{d1})_f}{(\mu'_{d2})_f}$$

This relation is true for any pair of bearing angles. It is, therefore, true when one bearing is the reference bearing and we find that

$$\frac{(k'_d)_f}{(k'_{do})_f} = \frac{(\mu'_d)_f}{(\mu'_{do})_f} = (\eta'_d)_f \quad (4F\text{-}12)$$

For the hypothetical reference condition, where the relative receiving response is assumed to be $\eta'_d = 1$ for any bearing, $k'_d = k'_{do}$ for each bearing. In this case, therefore, if acoustic energy reaches the transducer with constant intensity per unit band from all directions, the reference value of the available power per unit band of the electric energy which would be generated would be

$$(U'_E)_{\text{ref}} = 4\pi r^2 (k'_{do})_f (J'_H)_f \quad (4F\text{-}13)$$

The receiving directivity factor of the transducer is, therefore, in accordance with the definition of this factor,

$$(\eta'_D)_f = \frac{(U'_E)_{\text{act}}}{(U'_E)_{\text{ref}}} = \frac{1}{2} \int_0^\pi \frac{(k'_d)_f}{(k'_{do})_f} \sin \beta \, d\beta$$

$$= \frac{1}{2} \int_0^\pi (\eta'_d)_f \sin \beta \, d\beta \quad (4F\text{-}14)$$

where

$(\eta'_D)_f =$ the receiving directivity factor, at a specified frequency, of a sonar transducer having an axis of acoustic symmetry which is also a maximum response axis
(a numeric)

$(\eta'_d)_f =$ the relative receiving response of the transducer, considered a function of bearing, for the same specified frequency
(a numeric)

$\beta =$ the bearing deviation angle
(rad)

It has been shown in Art. 4D-1 that the relative transmitting response of a reversible transducer, which may be used either as a sonar projector or as a hydrophone, is numerically equal to its relative receiving response. From this it follows at once, by Eqs. (4F-5) and (4F-14), that when such a transducer has an axis of acoustic symmetry which is also an axis of maximum response its transmitting directivity factor and its receiving directivity factor are also numerically equal. In a similar manner it may be shown that the transmitting directivity factor and the receiving directivity factor of a reversible transducer having an axis of acoustic symmetry which is perpendicular to its maximum response bearings also have equal values.

For any hydrophone the utility of its directivity factor is that it furnishes a direct measure of the ability of that hydrophone to discriminate against acoustic interference arriving along bearings other than the bearings of a signal which it is desired to receive. In general, this advantage is defined quantitatively in terms of the response of the hydrophone to acoustic interference reaching its location with equal intensity on all bearings. For a given directional hydrophone it may be described as the factor by which, at any specified frequency, the available power per unit band of the electric waves generated in the hydrophone when receiving such uniformly distributed acoustic energy is less than the available power per unit band of the electric waves which would be generated in a hypothetical hydrophone having a receiving response on each bearing equal to the maximum receiving response of the given hydrophone. If, in this case, the directional hydrophone receives a given signal over its maximum response bearing the responses of the two hydrophones to this signal will be the same, by definition. That is,

$$(U'_s)_{\text{act}} = (U'_s)_{\text{ref}} \qquad (4F\text{-}15)$$

where

$(U'_s)_{\text{act}} =$ the power per unit band, at some specified frequency, of the electric waves generated in a given directional hydrophone when receiving a given acoustic signal over its maximum response bearing
(joule/cyc)

$(U'_s)_{\text{ref}} =$ the power per unit band, at the same specified frequency, of the electric waves generated in a hypothetical nondirectional hydrophone when receiving the same acoustic signal, over any bearing
(joule/cyc)

The response of the directional hydrophone to uniformly distributed interference will, on the other hand, be less than the response of the nondirectional hydrophone because the directional hydrophone has reduced responses on many bearings. The ratio of the available power per unit band of the electric waves generated in the directional hydrophone by this uniformly distributed interference to the available power per unit band of the electric waves which would be generated in the nondirectional hydrophone by the same interference is, also by definition, equal to the directivity factor of the directional hydrophone. We thus have

$$\frac{(U'_n)_{\text{act}}}{(U'_n)_{\text{ref}}} = (\eta'_D)_f \qquad (4F\text{-}16)$$

where

$(U'_n)_{\text{act}} =$ the power per unit band, at some specified frequency, of the electric waves generated in a given directional hydrophone when receiving acoustic interference which is uniformly distributed over all bearings
(joule/cyc)

$(U'_n)_{\text{ref}} =$ the power per unit band, at the same specified frequency, of the electric waves generated in a hypothetical nondirectional hydrophone, having a receiving response on each bearing equal to the maximum receiving response of the given directional hydrophone, when receiving the same uniformly distributed interference
(joule/cyc)

$(\eta'_D)_f =$ the receiving directivity factor of the given directional hydrophone
(a numeric)

By combining these two equations it is evident that

$$\frac{(U'_s)_{\text{act}}}{(U'_n)_{\text{act}}} = \frac{1}{(\eta'_D)_f} \frac{(U'_s)_{\text{ref}}}{(U'_n)_{\text{ref}}} \qquad (4F\text{-}17)$$

In deriving this relation it was convenient to think in terms of a hypothetical nondirectional hydrophone having a definitely specified receiving response on each bearing. As a matter of fact, however, the ratio of the available power per unit band, at some specified frequency, of the energy generated in any nondirectional hydrophone by a signal on any bearing to the available power per unit band, at the same frequency, simultaneously generated by uniformly distributed interference is independent of the absolute value of this receiving response. It is, in fact, the value of signal-to-noise ratio characteristic of the hydrophone location at the time in question. It is thus evident that the value of signal-to-noise ratio observed with any given directional hydrophone is obtained by dividing the signal-to-noise ratio characteristic of the time and place by the directivity factor of the hydrophone.

4F-2 Effective Directivity Factor

The computation, by means of its receiving directivity factor, of the signal-to-noise ratio of the energies generated in a hydrophone, as described in the preceding article, has been predicated on the assumption that the acoustic interference reaches that hydrophone from sources so distributed that the intensity per unit band, at any frequency, of the energy arriving over any bearing is the same as that arriving over any other bearing. This ideal uniform distribution is convenient, or even essential, for the general consideration of the directional discrimination of a hydrophone. It is, however, not the distribution usually found in practice. We may, nevertheless, employ the general relations applying to the ideal case to actual situations. For this we define the **effective directivity factor** of a hydrophone, at a specified frequency, as the ratio of the available power per unit band of the electric waves generated in the hydrophone when oriented in a specified manner in a specified location to the available power per unit band of the electric waves which would be generated, at the same location, in a hypothetical nondirectional hydrophone having a receiving response on any bearing equal to the maximum response of the given directional hydrophone. As in the ideal case, the actual hydrophone and the hypothetical reference hydrophone will respond equally to a signal, provided that signal is on the maximum response axis of the actual hydrophone. Since the signal responses are equal the signal-to-noise ratios vary inversely as the magnitudes of the responses to the interference. The signal-to-noise ratio to be expected when using a directional hydrophone in a given location will, then, be obtained by dividing the signal-to-noise ratio characteristic of that location by the effective directivity factor believed to be applicable to the type of interference distribution likely to exist in that location.

The effective directivity factor of a directional hydrophone is usually measured by comparing its response with the response of a hydrophone known to be virtually nondirectional. The responses of these two hydrophones may, for convenience, be adjusted to be equal when receiving a strong signal from some source on the maximum response bearing of the directional hydrophone. The transmission of energy from this source is then discontinued and the responses to interference observed on each hydrophone. The ratio of the power per unit band available from the directional hydrophone to the power per unit band available from the nondirectional hydrophone is the effective directivity factor of the directional hydrophone in that particular location. It is evident from the foregoing that the effective directivity factor of a given hydrophone in any given location is quite likely to be a function of the orientation of the hydrophone.

It is often convenient to combine the concept of effective directivity factor with the concept of equivalent plane waves. This may be done, for any specified frequency, by designating as the **apparent plane wave intensity per unit band** of the acoustic waves actually received by a given directional hydrophone the intensity per unit band of the plane waves of acoustic energy which, if propagated toward that hydrophone along its maximum response axis, would generate therein electric waves having the same power per unit band as the electric waves actually generated. This apparent plane wave intensity per unit band is related to the receiving response of the hydrophone by the equation

$$(J'_D)_{\text{app}} = \frac{(U'_E)_{\text{act}}}{(\mu'_{do})_f} \qquad (4F\text{-}18)$$

where

$(J'_D)_{\text{app}}$ = the apparent plane wave intensity per unit band, at a specified frequency, of the acoustic waves actually received by a given directional hydrophone from directionally distributed sources (joule/cm²·cyc)

$(U'_E)_{\text{act}}$ = the power per unit band, at the same frequency, of the electric waves actually generated in the given hydrophone by these acoustic waves (joule/cyc)

$(\mu'_{do})_f =$ the receiving response of the given hydrophone, at the same frequency, for its maximum response reference axis
(cm^2)

Now the equivalent plane wave intensity per unit band of these same acoustic waves, as defined in Art. 2A-9, is the apparent plane wave intensity per unit band which would be measured by a nondirectional hydrophone. This equivalent plane wave intensity may, therefore, be written as

$$J'_{\text{equi}} = \frac{(U'_E)_{\text{ref}}}{\mu'_{\text{ref}}} \qquad (4F\text{-}19)$$

By combining these equations

$$\frac{(J'_D)_{\text{app}}}{J'_{\text{equi}}} = \frac{(U'_E)_{\text{act}}}{(U'_E)_{\text{ref}}} \frac{\mu'_{\text{ref}}}{(\mu'_{do})_f} \qquad (4F\text{-}20)$$

But, by the definition of directivity factor, when $\mu'_{\text{ref}} = (\mu'_{do})_{\text{act}}$, $(U'_E)_{\text{act}} = (\eta'_D)_f (U'_E)_{\text{ref}}$. Consequently,

$$(J'_D)_{\text{app}} = (\eta'_D)_f J'_{\text{equi}} \qquad (4F\text{-}21)$$

The apparent plane wave intensity per unit band of the acoustic energy received by a directional hydrophone from sources distributed over many bearings is, therefore, the product of the equivalent plane wave intensity per unit band of these waves and the directivity factor of the hydrophone. If the intensity per unit band of the received waves is not the same for all bearings the directivity factor to be used in this product is the effective directivity factor appropriate to the situation.

4F-3 Directivity Index

The directivity factor of a sonar transducer is, as we have seen, measured by the ratio of two rates of energy flow. It gives the value of a property of an energy transmission system which, like its efficiency, determines the effectiveness with which that system performs certain of its functions. Since the property thus measured has these characteristics it may be evaluated in terms of a transmission loss. The transmission loss measured by the directivity factor of a sonar transducer is known as its **directivity index.**

The relation between the directivity index of a transducer and its directivity factor is similar to that between the efficiency loss of a transducer and its efficiency factor. We thus have

$$N_{DI} = \text{lgt} \frac{1}{(\eta_D)_f} = \text{lgt} \frac{1}{(\eta'_D)_f} \qquad (4F\text{-}22)$$

where

$N_{DI} =$ the directivity index of a sonar transducer, at a specified frequency
(db)

$(\eta_D)_f =$ the transmitting directivity factor of the transducer, at the same specified frequency
(a numeric)

$(\eta'_D)_f =$ the receiving directivity factor of the transducer, at the same frequency
(a numeric)

The directivity index of a projector provides a convenient means for computing the index level of an outgoing signal in terms of the total acoustic energy radiated. By combining Eqs. (4F-7) and (4F-8) and solving for the index value of the intensity per unit band on the maximum response axis we have

$$(J_{do})_f = \frac{(J_{\text{aver}})_f}{(\eta_D)_f} = \frac{(U_A)_{\text{act}}}{4\pi r^2(\eta_D)_f} \qquad (4F\text{-}23)$$

Expressed in terms of transmission levels and transmission gains this gives, when $r = 1$ yd $= 91.44$ cm,

$$L_0 = \text{lgt}\,(J_{do})_f = \text{lgt}\,(U_A)_{\text{act}} + N_{DI} - 50.21 \qquad (4F\text{-}24)$$

where

$L_0 =$ the index level, at a specified frequency, of acoustic energy radiated on the maximum response reference axis of a sonar transducer
(db//1 joule/cm^2·cyc)

$(U_A)_{\text{act}} =$ the power per unit band at this same frequency of the acoustic energy radiated on all bearings
(joule/cyc)

$N_{DI} =$ the directivity index of the projector
(db)

The quantity $\text{lgt}(U_A)_{\text{act}}$ is the transmission level of the radiated acoustic waves, expressed in decibels relative to 1 joule/cyc. The difference between this level and the index level on the maximum response bearing, expressed in decibels relative to 1 joule/cm^2·cyc, is given by the quantity $N_{DI} - 50.21$.

When the radiated acoustic waves have a sinusoidal variation of pressure this same equation may be used to compute the difference between the level of these radiated waves as expressed in decibels relative to one watt and the index level on the maximum response reference axis expressed in decibels relative to one watt per square centimeter. In each of these situations the change in the dimensions of the reference quantity is represented by the term having the constant numerical value 50.21, which has the dimensions of area logits.

For a given directional hydrophone the apparent level of interference, at any location, is given by expressing Eq. (4F-21) in terms of transmission levels and of a transmission loss. When this is done we have

$$(L_n)_{\text{app}} = (L_n)_{\text{equi}} - N_{DI} \qquad (4F-25)$$

where

$(L_n)_{\text{app}}$ = the apparent plane wave level, at a specified frequency, of the acoustic interference reaching a given directional hydrophone from directionally distributed sources (db//1 joule/cm²·cyc)

$(L_n)_{\text{equi}}$ = the equivalent plane wave level, at the same frequency, of this same acoustic interference (db//1 joule/cm²·cyc)

N_{DI} = the directivity index of the given hydrophone (db)

As in similar situations which have been described previously, it is necessary to use the effective directivity index, derived from the effective directivity factor, when the intensity of the received interference varies with bearing.

4F-4 The Effect of Shading

The directivity index of a sonar transducer provides a convenient measure by which to evaluate the resultant effect of shading on the directional properties of that transducer. This use of directivity index may be illustrated by a further consideration of the shaded circular plate transducer which formed the basis for the illustrative example of Art. 4E-7. The effect of the shading described in that article will be evaluated in terms of the difference between the directivity index of the transducer after it had been shaded and its original directivity index. This difference may be

written, considering the transducer as a projector transmitting sinusoidal waves, as

$$(N_{DI})_{\text{shd}} - (N_{DI})_0 = \text{lgt}\,\frac{(I_{\text{shd}})_0}{(I_{\text{shd}})_{\text{aver}}} - \text{lgt}\,\frac{I_0}{I_{\text{aver}}}$$

$$= \text{lgt}\,\frac{(I_{\text{shd}})_0}{I_0} - \text{lgt}\,\frac{(I_{\text{shd}})_{\text{aver}}}{I_{\text{aver}}}$$

In the earlier computations the pressure on the reference axis was increased 25 percent due to the increase in strength of the central zone of the projector. The corresponding value of the ratio of the final and initial intensities on this axis is thus

$$\frac{(I_{\text{shd}})_0}{I_0} = (1.25)^2 = 1.562$$

The ratio of the adjusted energy delivered to the central zone of this projector, in order to bring about this increase in intensity, to the energy originally delivered to this zone was computed to be

$$\frac{(P_E)_{\text{adj}}}{(P_E)_z} = 3.264$$

But the ratio of the energy originally delivered to this zone to the total energy originally delivered to the whole projector was shown to be proportional to the square of the ratio of the diameters of the two surfaces, or

$$\frac{(P_E)_z}{(P_E)_0} = \left[\frac{d_z}{d_0}\right]^2 = 0.3099$$

The adjusted energy finally delivered to the central zone is thus

$$(P_E)_{\text{adj}} = (3.264)(0.3099)(P_E)_0$$

$$= 1.0115(P_E)_0$$

The energy delivered to the outer circular zone of the projector, which is unchanged as a result of shading, is

$$(P_E)_0 - (P_E)_z = (1 - 0.3099)(P_E)_0$$

$$= 0.6901(P_E)_0$$

The ratio of the electric energy delivered to the projector after shading to the electric energy originally delivered is thus

$$\frac{(P_E)_{\text{shd}}}{(P_E)_0} = 1.0115 + 0.6901 = 1.702$$

This ratio is equal to the ratio of the average acoustic intensities before and after shading. The difference between the directivity indexes may therefore be computed as

$$(N_{DI})_{\text{shd}} - (N_{DI})_0 = \text{lgt } 1.562 - \text{lgt } 1.702$$

$$= -0.37 \text{ db}$$

This shows that, when used as a hydrophone, the signal-to-noise advantage of this shaded transducer is not as great as that of the original transducer. It appears, in other words, that the decreased discrimination of the major lobe against uniformly distributed noise has been more than sufficient to offset any improvement due to decreasing the secondary lobes. While the difference between the two conditions is not great in the present example, and would have an almost negligible effect on the performance of the transducer as a listening hydrophone, it is obvious that any proposed lobe reduction scheme should be carefully scrutinized as to its effect on the directivity index.

4F-5 General Formulas for Directivity Factor

Formulas were given in the preceding section for the relative responses of various forms of sonar transducer as functions of bearing. Each of these formulas has stated the relation between the relative response, either transmitting or receiving, and the dimensional constants of the type of transducer to which it applies. The directivity factor of each of these transducers may be derived by substituting the appropriate relative response into an equation of the general form of Eq. (4F-5) and integrating. The results obtained by this process will be given for several of the types of transducer, or transducer assembly, for which formulas for relative response, considered as a function of bearing, have been presented.

The first of these is the two-element array, or dipole. The relative response as a function of bearing, for a specified constant frequency, applicable to this simple arrangement is derived from Eq. (4E-1) as

$$(\eta_d)_f = \cos^2\left[\frac{\pi s}{\lambda}\sin\beta\right] \qquad (4F\text{-}26)$$

A transducer assembly of this type has a directivity pattern for which the axis of acoustic symmetry is perpendicular to the maximum response bearings. The reference bearing, which may be any one of the maximum response bearings, is perpendicular to the line joining the two elements of the dipole. For such an arrangement Eq. (4F-6)

is to be used in computing the directivity factor. On substituting the expression for relative response, as given by Eq. (4F-26), into Eq. (4F-6) and integrating there is obtained

$$(\eta_D)_f = \frac{1}{2}\int_{-\pi/2}^{\pi/2}\cos^2\left[\frac{\pi s}{\lambda}\sin\beta\right]\cos\beta\,d\beta$$

$$= \frac{1}{2}\left[1 + \frac{\sin(2\pi s/\lambda)}{(2\pi s/\lambda)}\right] \qquad (4F\text{-}27)$$

where

$(\eta_D)_f$ = the directivity factor of a dipole (a numeric)

s = the separation between the elements of this dipole (cm)

λ = the wave length of sinusoidal acoustic waves of the frequency for which the directivity factor is applicable (cm/cyc)

The second of the transducer arrangements is that in which similar nondirectional elements are spaced at equal intervals along a straight line. The relative response for this arrangement is derived from Eq. (4E-2) as

$$(\eta_d)_f = \frac{\sin^2 n\left[\dfrac{\pi s}{\lambda}\sin\beta\right]}{n^2\sin^2\left[\dfrac{\pi s}{\lambda}\sin\beta\right]} \qquad (4F\text{-}28)$$

As with the dipole this relative response must be substituted into Eq. (4F-6) to obtain an expression for the directivity factor. Making this substitution and integrating[10] there is obtained

$$(\eta_D)_f = \frac{1}{2}\int_{-\pi/2}^{\pi/2}\frac{\sin^2 n\left[\dfrac{\pi s}{\lambda}\sin\beta\right]}{n^2\sin^2\left[\dfrac{\pi s}{\lambda}\sin\beta\right]}\cos\beta\,d\beta$$

$$= \frac{1}{n} + \sum_{p=1}^{n-1}\frac{(n-p)\sin\left[2p\,\dfrac{\pi s}{\lambda}\right]}{n^2 p\,\dfrac{\pi s}{\lambda}} \qquad (4F\text{-}29)$$

where

$(\eta_D)_f$ = the directivity factor of a linear array of uniformly spaced nondirectional transducers (a numeric)

n = the number of transducer elements (a numeric)

p = any integer between 1 and $n-1$, inclusive

s = the spacing between array elements (cm)

λ = the wave length of sinusoidal acoustic waves of the frequency for which the directivity factor is applicable (cm/cyc)

To compute a directivity factor by this formula it is necessary to take a number of terms in the summation series equal to one less than the number of array elements.

The third type of transducer, like the first, is a limiting case of the general type represented by the second. This is the linear transducer, which may be considered as a multi-element array having an infinite number of elements separated by infinitesimal intervals. When the relative response of this type of transducer, as derived from Eq. (4E-9), is substituted into Eq. (4F-6) and integrated we have

$$(\eta_D)_f = \frac{1}{2} \int_{-\pi/2}^{\pi/2} \frac{\sin^2\left[\dfrac{\pi l}{\lambda}\sin\beta\right]}{\left[\dfrac{\pi l}{\lambda}\sin\beta\right]^2} \cos\beta \, d\beta$$

$$= \frac{\lambda}{\pi l}\left[\mathbb{S}\left(\frac{2\pi l}{\lambda}\right) - \frac{\lambda}{\pi l}\sin^2\frac{\pi l}{\lambda} \right] \qquad (4F\text{-}30)$$

where

$(\eta_D)_f$ = the directivity factor of a linear transducer (a numeric)

l = the length of the transducer (cm)

λ = the wave length of sinusoidal acoustic waves of the frequency for which the directivity factor is applicable (cm/cyc)

The function $\mathbb{S}(2\pi l/\lambda)$, which is known as the Si function, gives the value of the definite integral of $\sin x/x$ taken between the limits $x=0$ and $x=2\pi l/\lambda$. Values of this function are to be found in collections of mathematical tables.

Values of the directivity indexes derived, in accordance with Eq. (4F-22), from the three expressions for directivity factor given above are shown in Fig. 4F-2. These values of directivity index are plotted against values of the quotient l/λ. These values may be converted to values of frequency, applicable to a transducer of given length operating in a given acoustic medium, by multiplying by the constant c/l, where c is the velocity of propagation of acoustic waves in the medium in question. This conversion demonstrates that any value of directivity factor, or any value of directivity index, although computed in terms of relative response considered as a function of bearing for a constant frequency, is, when thus computed for any given transducer, to be considered a function of frequency.

On the graph of Fig. 4F-2 the directivity index of a dipole is shown by the curve marked $n=2$. The index of a multi-element array having five elements is shown by the curve marked $n=5$. The index of a continuous linear transducer is shown by the curve marked $n=\infty$. An examination of these curves suggests that, for many purposes, the formulas given by the preceding equations may be replaced by simpler forms. In the case of the multi-element array, for example, it is evident that when the length of the array is long compared with the length of a wave the directivity factor may be written as

$$(\eta_D)_f \approx \frac{1}{n} \qquad (4F\text{-}31)$$

The formula given by Eq. (4F-29) reduces to this simple form when the quotient s/λ is sufficiently large to make the terms of the summation series negligible in comparison with the term $1/n$. This same approximation may be made in the case of the dipole, since the formula for a multi-element array reduces, as it must, to the formula for a dipole when $n=2$. Values of the quotient s/λ which justify the use of this approximate formula are indicated by the graph. From this it is seen that the error introduced by the approximate formula of Eq. (4F-31) is negligible when the spacing between array elements is ten wave spaces or more. Actually the approximate formula is often used for any spacing in excess of two waves. Beyond this point, although errors exist, they fluctuate between positive and negative values in such manner that their average value is small.

For many practical problems the exact formula for the directivity factor of a linear transducer, like that for a multi-element array, may be reduced to a simpler form. An examination of a table of Si functions shows that when the quotient

l/λ is large we may write

$$\mathcal{S}\left(\frac{2\pi l}{\lambda}\right) \approx \frac{\pi}{2} - \frac{\lambda}{2\pi l}\cos\left(\frac{2\pi l}{\lambda}\right) \quad (4F\text{-}32)$$

We may also write, by trigonometric identities,

$$\frac{\lambda}{\pi l}\sin^2\left(\frac{\pi l}{\lambda}\right) = \frac{\lambda}{2\pi l} - \frac{\lambda}{2\pi l}\cos\left(\frac{2\pi l}{\lambda}\right) \quad (4F\text{-}33)$$

On substituting these two equalities into Eq. (4F-30) an expression for the directivity factor of a linear transducer is obtained which introduces negligible error provided the transducer length is two wave spaces or more. This approximate formula is

$$(\eta_D)_f \approx \frac{\lambda}{\pi l}\left(\frac{\pi}{2} - \frac{\lambda}{2\pi l}\right) \quad (4F\text{-}34)$$

The magnitude of the error resulting from the use of this formula is shown by Fig. 4F-3. In the graph of this figure the directivity index derived from the directivity factor computed by the exact formula of Eq. (4F-30) is shown as a solid line. Values derived from the factor computed by the approximate formula are shown by the curved dotted line.

It is evident that when $\lambda/2\pi l$ is negligible in comparison with $\pi/2$ the approximate formula for the directivity factor of a linear transducer may be further reduced to

$$(\eta_D)_f \approx \frac{\lambda}{2l} \quad (4F\text{-}35)$$

Values of directivity index derived from directivity factors computed by this second approximate formula are shown on the graph of Fig.

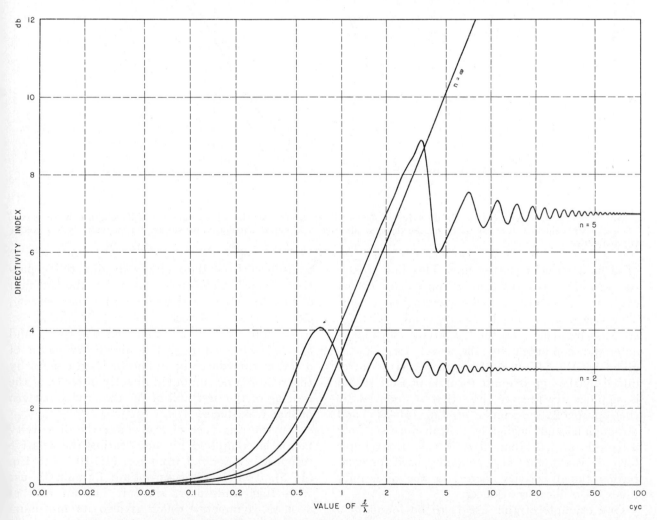

FIG. 4F-2. MULTISPOT ARRAYS. The directivity indexes of multispot arrays, having various numbers of elements, plotted as a function of the length of the array in wave spaces.

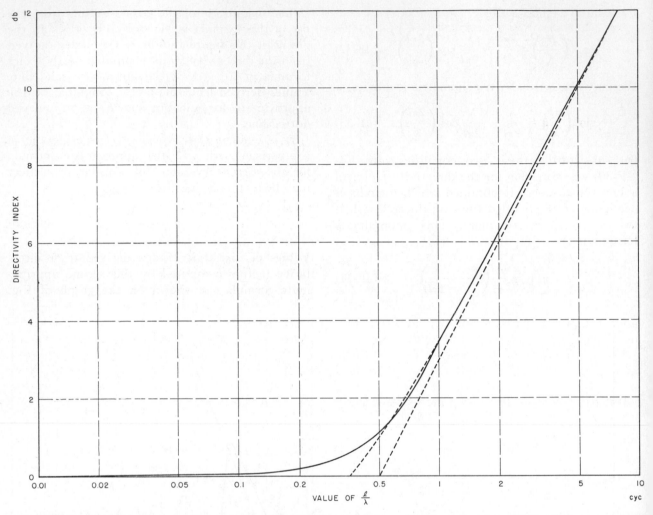

FIG. 4F-3. LINEAR TRANSDUCERS. The directivity index of a linear transducer plotted as a function of its length in wave spaces. The solid curve shows values computed by the theoretically correct formula. The dotted curves are for successively less precise approximations.

4F-3 as a straight dotted line. This line crosses the zero index axis at the point for which $l/\lambda = 0.5$ cyc with a slope of one decibel per frequency logit. This line is approached asymptotically, with increasing frequency, by the directivity index characteristic computed by the exact formula, as given by Eq. (4F-30). Although the error introduced by the approximate formula of Eq. (4F-35) is significantly greater than that introduced by the approximate formula of Eq. (4F-34), and although it is not negligible for transducers having a length of less than five waves, this simple formula is the one most generally used for computing the directivity factor, or the directivity index, of a linear transducer.

One example of this use is to be found in a convenient method for computing the approximate value of the directivity factor of a linear

transducer from data giving its directivity pattern. From Eq. (4E-9) it is seen that the first null of this directivity pattern occurs for that bearing, β_{min}, for which the phase factor is $\pi(l/\lambda) \sin \beta_{min} = \pi$. From this it follows that $\sin \beta_{min} = \lambda/l$, and $\eta_D \approx \lambda/2l = 0.5 \sin \beta_{min}$. The directivity factor of a linear transducer of unknown length may, by this relation, be computed directly in terms of the bearing of the first null of the directivity pattern of that transducer.

For the ring type of transducer the directivity factor is computed by substituting the relative response, as derived from Eq. (4E-10), into Eq. (4F-5). This is the appropriate formula to use with this transducer, since it has an axis of acoustic symmetry which is also its maximum response axis. On making this substitution and integrating[10] we have

$$(\eta_D)_f = \frac{1}{2} \int_0^\pi \left[\mathcal{J}_0 \left(\frac{\pi d}{\lambda} \sin \beta \right) \right]^2 \sin \beta \, d\beta$$

$$= \frac{\lambda}{2\pi d} \left\{ \frac{2\pi d}{\lambda} \mathcal{J}_0 \left(\frac{2\pi d}{\lambda} \right) + \frac{\pi^2 d}{\lambda} \left[\mathcal{J}_1 \left(\frac{2\pi d}{\lambda} \right) \mathcal{H}_0 \left(\frac{2\pi d}{\lambda} \right) - \mathcal{J}_0 \left(\frac{2\pi d}{\lambda} \right) \mathcal{H}_1 \left(\frac{2\pi d}{\lambda} \right) \right] \right\} \qquad (4F\text{-}36)$$

where

$(\eta_D)_f$ = the directivity factor of a ring transducer
(a numeric)

d = the diameter of the ring
(cm)

λ = the wave length of sinusoidal acoustic waves of the frequency for which the directivity factor is applicable
(cm/cyc)

The functions $\mathcal{J}_0(2\pi d/\lambda)$ and $\mathcal{J}_1(2\pi d/\lambda)$ are Bessel functions and the functions $\mathcal{H}_0(2\pi d/\lambda)$ and $\mathcal{H}_1(2\pi d/\lambda)$ are Struve functions. Tables for both are to be found in mathematical handbooks.[9]

As in the case of the linear transducer it is possible to write an approximation to the formula of Eq. (4F-36) which avoids the use of special mathematical tables and which reduces the labor of computation. For the ring transducer this approximate formula is

$$(\eta_D)_f \approx \frac{\lambda}{2\pi d} \left[1 + \sqrt{\frac{\lambda}{\pi^2 d}} \sin \left(\frac{2\pi d}{\lambda} - \frac{\pi}{4} \right) \right] \qquad (4F\text{-}37)$$

A comparison of the results obtained by this formula and the exact formula of Eq. (4F-36) is given by the graph of Fig. 4F-4. Here values of directivity index derived from values of directivity factor are plotted against values of the quotient d/λ. Values of this quotient may be converted to frequency values by multiplying by the constant c/d applicable to a transducer of given diameter. The directivity index of a ring transducer computed by means of the exact formula of Eq. (4F-36) is shown on the graph of this figure as a solid line. Values computed by the approximate formula of Eq. (4F-37) are shown by the curved dotted line. These two curves show that the errors resulting from the use of the approximate formula are negligible when the diameter of the ring is greater than two waves.

From the approximate formula of Eq. (4F-37) it is evident that when the quotient d/λ becomes sufficiently large the directivity factor of a ring transducer reduces to

$$(\eta_D)_f \approx \frac{\lambda}{2\pi d} \qquad (4F\text{-}38)$$

This formula indicates that, for transducer sizes, or for frequencies, which justify its use, the directivity factor of a ring transducer of given circumference is approximately the same as that of a linear transducer having a length equal to that circumference. The directivity index computed from this second approximate formula is shown on the graph of Fig. 4F-4 as the straight dotted line. This line would be the same as the straight line shown on Fig. 4F-3 if the scale of Fig. 4F-4 were laid off in terms of the circumference of the ring instead of in terms of its diameter. Since the second approximate formula for the ring transducer introduces negligible error only when the quotient d/λ is so large that its square root is also large there is a small error in using this formula for a ring transducer having a diameter less than 50 wave spaces. In many practical problems, however, the smooth curve resulting from the use of the approximate formula is fully as useful as the irregular curve resulting from either of the other formulas. The errors represented by the deviations of the exact values of directivity index from the values shown by the smooth curve are not large. They alternate, moreover, between positive and negative values in such manner that their average, taken over a frequency band, is small. The irregularities introduced by following the exact values are, therefore, of little real significance. The smooth curve shows that for the ring transducer, as for the linear transducer, the directivity index increases at the rate of approximately one decibel per frequency logit with increasing frequency.

The directivity factor of a ring transducer, like that of a linear transducer, may be computed in terms of the bearing for which the directivity pattern of the transducer shows its first null. For this relative response a table of Bessel functions shows that the value of phase factor is $\pi(d/\lambda) \sin \beta_{\min} = 2.41$. Consequently, by Eq. (4F-38), the directivity factor is

$$(\eta_D)_f \approx \frac{\lambda}{2\pi d} = 0.208 \sin \beta_{\min}$$

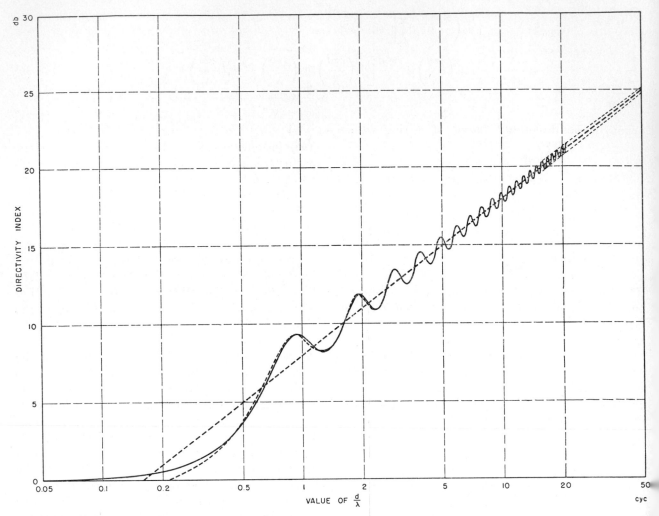

FIG. 4F-4. RING TRANSDUCERS. The directivity index of a ring transducer plotted as a function of the diameter of the ring in wave spaces. The solid curve shows values computed by the theoretically correct formula. The dotted curves are for successively less precise approximations.

The circular plate transducer, which is one of the more commonly used sonar transducers, is usually built so that its responses are restricted to one side of a plane through the active surface. In computing the directivity factor of a transducer of this type, therefore, the relative response, as derived from Eq. (4E-11), is substituted into an equation similar to Eq. (4F-5) but having 0 and $\pi/2$ as the limits of integration. When this integration is carried out[11] the result is

$$(\eta_D)_f = \frac{1}{2} \int_0^{\pi/2} \left[\frac{2 \mathfrak{I}_1 \left(\frac{\pi d}{\lambda} \sin \beta \right)}{(\pi d/\lambda) \sin \beta} \right]^2 \sin \beta \; d\beta$$

$$= \left(\frac{\lambda}{\pi d} \right)^2 \left[1 - \frac{\mathfrak{I}_1 \left(\frac{2\pi d}{\lambda} \right)}{(\pi d/\lambda)} \right] \qquad (4F-39)$$

where

$(\eta_D)_f =$ the directivity factor of a circular plate transducer responsive to bearings on only one side of a plane through its surface
(a numeric)

$d =$ the diameter of the circular plate
(cm)

$\lambda =$ the wave length of sinusoidal acoustic waves of the frequency to which the directivity factor applies
(cm/cyc)

This formula may be replaced by the approximate formula

$$(\eta_D)_f \approx \left(\frac{\lambda}{\pi d} \right)^2 \left[1 - \frac{\lambda}{\pi d} \sqrt{\frac{\lambda}{\pi^2 d}} \sin \left(\frac{2\pi d}{\lambda} - \frac{\pi}{4} \right) \right] \quad (4F-40)$$

198

when the quotient d/λ becomes greater than 0.8 cyc. As the transducer diameter, or the frequency, increases still further this formula may, in turn, be replaced by the even simpler formula

$$(\eta_D)_f \approx \left(\frac{\lambda}{\pi d}\right)^2 \qquad (4F\text{-}41)$$

A comparison of the results obtained by these three formulas for the directivity factor of a circular plate transducer is given by Fig. 4F-5. Here the directivity indexes computed from these factors are plotted as functions of the quotient d/λ. The index corresponding to the exact formula of Eq. (4F-39) is shown as a solid line. The index corresponding to the formula of Eq. (4F-40) is shown by the curved dotted line. The index corresponding to the formula of Eq. (4F-41) is shown by the straight dotted line. This straight line crosses the zero index axis at the point for which $d/\lambda = 1/\pi = 0.3183$ cyc. It has a slope of two decibels per frequency logit. The error in using this line as the directivity index characteristic is negligible when the transducer diameter is greater than three wave spaces. As with other transducers, values of directivity index corresponding to the smooth curve given by the approximate formula are usually of as great interest as those obtained by the exact formula. Errors represented by the difference between the curve computed from the exact formula and the smooth curve computed by the approximate formula given by Eq. (4F-41) are alternately positive and negative and are seldom of practical significance. It must be remembered, however, that as the frequency is reduced below the value at which the approximate formula may be used the directivity factor approaches $(\eta_D)_f = 0.5$, and the directivity index

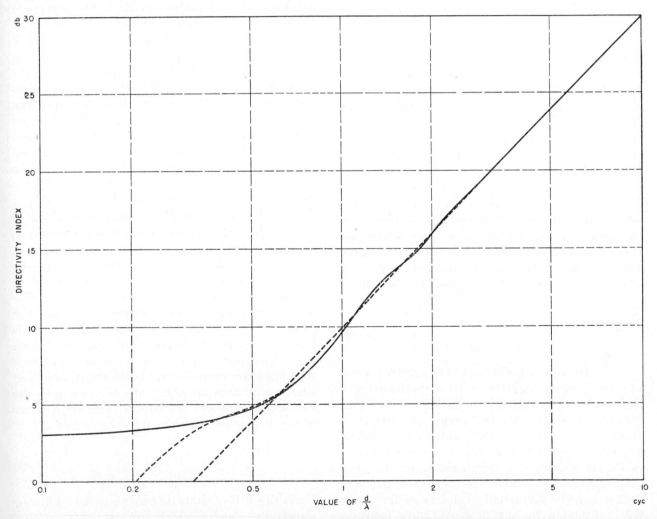

FIG. 4F-5. CIRCULAR PLATE TRANSDUCERS. The directivity index of a circular plate transducer plotted as a function of the diameter of the plate in wave spaces. The solid curve shows values computed by the theoretically correct formula. The dotted curves are for successively less precise approximations.

approaches $N_{DI} = 3$ db. These values are characteristic of any transducer having uniform response for bearings on one side of a plane and no response for bearings on the other side.

The value of the phase factor for which the relative response of a circular plate transducer passes through its first null is $(\pi d/\lambda) \sin \beta_{min} = 3.83$. The formula by which to compute the directivity factor as given by Eq. (4F-41), in terms of the bearing angle of this first null is, therefore, $(\eta_D)_f \approx (\lambda/\pi d)^2 = 0.0682 \sin^2 \beta_{min}$.

The approximate formula for the directivity factor of a circular plate transducer, responsive on only one side of the plane through its active surface, is given by Eq. (4F-41) in terms of the plate diameter. This formula may be rewritten in terms of the plate area by making the substitution $(\pi d)^2 = 4\pi A$. The approximate formula for the directivity factor then becomes

$$(\eta_D)_f \approx \frac{\lambda^2}{4\pi A} \qquad (4F\text{-}42)$$

It has been shown,[12] in connection with the theory of radio antennas, that this formula may be employed for plane surface radiators or receivers which are not circular in shape, provided none of the linear dimensions is less than about two wave spaces. For frequencies which are much lower than those at which this condition is satisfied it is known, since the transducer is assumed to be responsive on only one side of a plane through its surface, that the directivity factor has the constant value $\eta_D = 0.5$. It is possible to derive an empirical formula which gives these values for these conditions and which also approximates the values given by the exact formula for the circular plate at intermediate frequencies. This empirical formula is

$$(\eta_D)_f \approx \frac{\lambda^2}{4\pi A - 2\lambda\sqrt{A} + 2\lambda^2} \qquad (4F\text{-}43)$$

A comparison of the results obtained by the use of this formula and the results obtained for a circular plate transducer by means of the exact formula is shown by the graph of Fig. 4F-6. Here the correct directivity index characteristic has been replotted, as a solid line, against values of the quotient $\sqrt{A}/\lambda$. For a transducer of given area operating in a given acoustic medium these values may be converted to values of frequency by multiplying by the proportionality constant $c/\sqrt{A}$. Values of directivity index computed by

the empirical formula of Eq. (4F-43) are shown on this graph by the curved dotted line. Values computed by the simple formula of Eq. (4F-42) are shown by the straight dotted line.

In general it is not possible to compute the directivity factor of a plane-surface transducer in terms of the bearing of the first null of a directivity pattern. For such a transducer it is not always possible to generate the three-dimensional pattern by rotating a single two-dimensional pattern. Although it is usually possible to compute a directivity pattern for some specified plane perpendicular to the transducer surface this pattern is not a function of the area of the transducer independent of its shape.

In the case of a hydrophone the area appearing in Eq. (4F-42) has an added significance. The product of this area by the free-field plane wave intensity of acoustic energy approaching the hydrophone along a perpendicular to the surface is the power of the acoustic energy available to the hydrophone from the water. It is often possible to measure this available power in terms of known characteristics of the hydrophone. It may, for example, be computed directly from measurements of the electric power available from the hydrophone and of its efficiency as measured by the motional impedance method. In such cases the effective, or apparent, area of the receiving surface may be computed as the quotient of the available power of the acoustic energy divided by its equivalent plane wave intensity, as defined in Art. 2A-9. The value of the area determined in this manner, for a given hydrophone, is known as its **capture area.**

The capture area of a sonar transducer may be thought of as a characteristic constant related to the directivity factor, $(\eta_D)_f$, at a specified frequency, f, and to that frequency through the velocity of propagation, c, of the medium. This relation is derived directly from Eq. (4F-42) on the assumption that for the transducer to which that equation applies the actual active area and the capture area are the same. On this basis the capture area of any transducer is given in terms of the directivity factor of that transducer as

$$A_C = \frac{\lambda^2}{4\pi(\eta_D)_f} = \frac{c^2}{4\pi f^2 (\eta_D)_f} \qquad (4F\text{-}44)$$

From this it is obvious that for transducers having directivity factors which are inversely proportional to the square of the frequency the capture

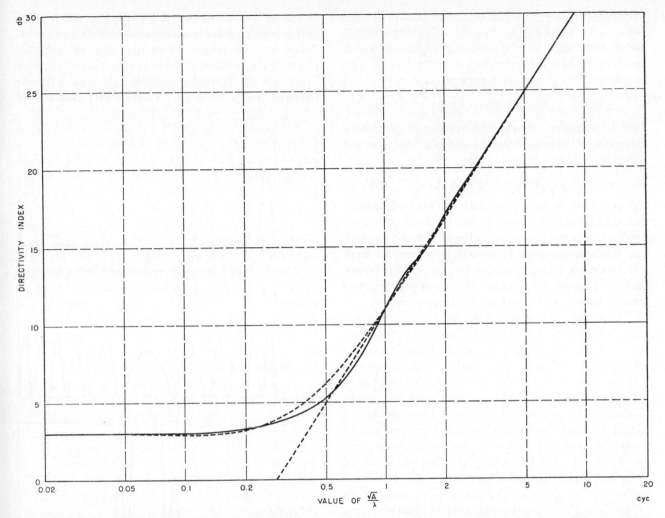

FIG. 4F-6. PLANE-SURFACE TRANSDUCERS. The directivity index of a plane-surface transducer plotted as a function of the square root of its area in wave spaces. The solid curve shows values computed by the theoretically correct formula. The dotted curves are for successively less precise approximations.

area is independent of frequency. When the directivity factor is inversely proportional to the first power of the frequency, as for a line hydrophone, the capture area must also be inversely proportional to the first power of the frequency.

4F-6 The Evaluation of Directivity Factor

In many cases it is necessary or desirable to compute the directivity factor of a transducer from a series of observed values of relative response measured during its calibration. This may be done graphically when the transducer is of a type for which the three-dimensional directivity may be represented by rotating a two-dimensional pattern. To determine the power of the total acoustic energy actually put into the water by such a transducer from the results of individual

measurements, at different angles in a plane, it is necessary to plot the power per unit angle of the radiated energy as a function of angle. At any given angle this power per unit angle depends upon the intensity at the surface of a constant distance sphere and also on the area to which this intensity applies. Power per unit angle is given as a function of angle, β, by the term $(2\pi r^2 \sin\beta) I_d$ similar to the term appearing in Eq. (4F-2). If values of this term are plotted against angle on rectangular coordinates the area under the curve is a direct measure of the output power of the total acoustic energy. In general, however, the intensity I_d is not known in absolute units but only in reference to the intensity, I_0, on the reference axis. For practical purposes, then, it is necessary to plot values of the quantity found under

201

the integral sign in an equation such as Eq. (4F-5). This quantity may be called the **directivity function.** The directivity function for a transducer in which the maximum response axis is also an axis of acoustic symmetry is

$$\mathfrak{F}_D(\beta) = (\eta_d)_f \sin \beta \qquad (4F\text{-}45)$$

For a transducer in which a bearing of maximum response is perpendicular to the acoustic axis the directivity function is

$$\mathfrak{F}_D(\beta) = (\eta_d)_f \cos \beta \qquad (4F\text{-}46)$$

When either of these quantities is plotted against angle, in radians, from $\beta = \beta_1$ to $\beta = \beta_2$ the area under the curve gives the value of the corresponding definite integral. It should, however, be kept in mind that this directivity function is the power per unit angle multiplied by a constant determined by the definition of directivity factor.

There are several methods for determining the area under a curve of the directivity function. In calibrating laboratories, where a large number of such computations are made daily, it is customary to use a mechanical device, known as a planimeter, which measures this area in square inches or in square centimeters. The number of square inches covered by a graph for which an ordinate scale of length y inches is equivalent to $\mathfrak{F}_D(\beta) = 1$ and for which an abscissa scale of length x inches is equivalent to $\beta_2 - \beta_1 = \pi$ radians is xy square inches. This area is equivalent to π radians. The **chart constant,** in other words, is π/xy radians per square inch. The number of radians corresponding to an area under the curve of C square inches is then

$$\frac{\pi C}{xy} = \int_{\beta_1}^{\beta_2} \mathfrak{F}_D(\beta)\, d\beta \qquad (4F\text{-}47)$$

If a computing machine is available values of $\mathfrak{F}_D(\beta)$ for successive angles, separated by small intervals, may be added together. The area under the curve is then the product of the sum thus obtained by the length of the interval chosen. This process is based on the assumption that the area is made up of a number of narrow rectangular areas the height of each being equal to the value of $\mathfrak{F}_D(\beta)$ at its mean angular value. If values of $\mathfrak{F}_D(\beta)$ corresponding to one-degree intervals are used the width of each strip will be 0.01745 radians.

A curve giving the value of the directivity function, as a function of angle, for a circular plate transducer having a diameter of five wave

spaces is shown by Graph (A) of Fig. 4F-7. This graph is drawn on the assumption that the transducer has no response on one side of a plane through its surface. Curves giving the directivity functions of a ring transducer and of a linear transducer are shown by Graphs (B) and (C) of

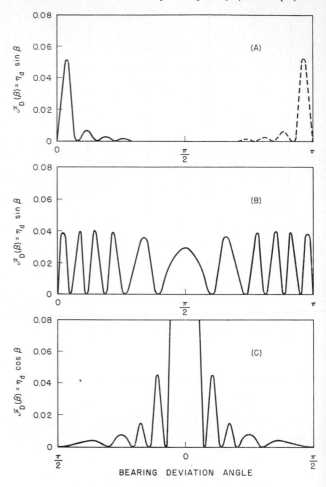

FIG. 4F-7. DIRECTIVITY FUNCTION. Values of the function $\mathfrak{F}_D(\beta) = \eta_d \sin \beta$ or $\mathfrak{F}_D(\beta) = \eta_d \cos \beta$ appearing in the formulas for directivity index.

(A) Circular plate transducer having a diameter of 5λ
(B) Ring transducer having a diameter of 5λ
(C) Linear transducer having a length of 5λ

this same figure. The diameter of the ring and the length of the line are five waves each.

It is to be noted that although each of the transducers for which a directivity function is shown by Fig. 4F-7 has a maximum response at the bearing for which $\beta = 0$ the power per unit angle is zero at this bearing for both the circular plate and the ring transducer. This is because the area per unit angle is zero for this bearing. For the linear transducer, on the other hand, the power per unit angle has its maximum value at the maximum response bearing. This maximum power per unit angle is of such magnitude that less than one tenth of the corresponding value of the directivity function of this transducer can be shown on the graph.

The curves of Fig. 4F-7 throw additional light on the significance of the minor lobes to be found in all transducers. It is apparent that the areas under the curves of the directivity functions of the circular plate and the linear transducer are due almost entirely to the main lobes and that the minor lobes add little to the value of the integral appearing in expressions for the directivity factor.

4F-7 Reverberation Factor and Reverberation Index

When a sonar transducer is used both for the transmission and for the reception of echo-ranging signals the ratio of its response to general reverberation and its response to the echo signal from some localized target is of fundamental significance. The response to reverberation may be expressed quantitatively in terms of the electric response of the transducer to acoustic energy initially transmitted by it and later returned to it by reflection from a concentric spherical surface having uniform reflectivity. We define the **reverberation factor** of a reversible sonar transducer, for a specified frequency, as the ratio of (1) the available power per unit band of the electric energy generated at the specified frequency by the transducer when receiving over all bearings acoustic energy which has previously been radiated over these bearings by the transducer in response to electric energy having a given power per unit band at the specified frequency, and which has then been returned to the transducer by propagation paths of equal length and equal transmission loss, to (2) the available power per unit band of the electric energy which would be generated at the same frequency and when receiving over the same bearings the acoustic energy which would have been radiated over those bearings in response to the same previously received electric energy and returned by the same propagation paths, if the transmitting and receiving responses of the transducer for that frequency were the same for any bearing as for the maximum response reference bearing.

The reverberation factor of a sonar transducer may be expressed in terms of its relative responses, considered as functions of bearing for a specified constant frequency, by an extension of the method used for evaluating receiving directivity factors. By the definition of reverberation factor the ratio of the intensity per unit band of the acoustic energy returned to the transducer on any bearing by a concentric reflecting surface to the index intensity per unit band of the acoustic energy initially radiated on that bearing is constant, independent of the angle of the bearing. This ratio is, in fact, the propagation factor corresponding to the two-way propagation loss between the transducer and the reflecting surface. It may be written as

$$\eta''_w = \frac{(J''_d)_f}{(J_d)_f} = \frac{(J''_d)_f}{(\mu_d)_f (U_E)_f} \qquad (4F\text{-}48)$$

where

$\eta''_w =$ the propagation factor associated with the total propagation path from an echo-ranging transducer to a concentric reflecting surface and back to the transducer
(a numeric)

$(J_d)_f =$ the index intensity per unit band, at a specified frequency, of the acoustic waves radiated by the transducer in question on any given bearing
(joule/cm²·cyc)

$(J''_d)_f =$ the intensity per unit band, at the same specified frequency and for the same given bearing, of the acoustic waves returned to the transducer by the reflecting surface
(joule/cm²·cyc)

$(\mu_d)_f =$ the transmitting response of the transducer for the given bearing and for the specified fixed frequency
(1/cm²)

$(U_E)_f =$ the power per unit band, at the same specified frequency, of the electric energy delivered to the transducer
(joule/cyc)

When the intensity per unit band, $(J''_d)_f$, as given by this expression is used in place of the intensity per unit band, $(J'_H)_f$, appearing in Eq. (4F-11) the power per unit band of the electric energy actually generated in response to reverberation is

$$(U''_E)_{\text{act}} = 2\pi r^2 \eta''_w (U_E)_f \int_0^\pi (\mu_d)_f (k'_d)_f \sin \beta \, d\beta$$

$$(4F\text{-}49)$$

For the specified reference condition the transmitting response has the constant value $(\mu_{do})_f$. Also, as shown by Eq. (4F-12), since the relative receiving response is unity, the coefficient relating the acoustic energy received through an incremental strip on a spherical surface concentric with the transducer and the electric energy generated in the transducer has the constant value $(k'_{do})_f$. The reference value of the available power per unit band of the electric energy which would be generated if the reference conditions were met is then given by an expression similar to that of Eq. (4F-13). This expression is

$$(U''_E)_{ref} = 4\pi r^2 \eta''_w (\mu_{do})_f (k'_{do})_f (U_E)_f \quad (4F-50)$$

The reverberation factor is, therefore, in accordance with its definition,

$$(\eta''_D)_f = \frac{(U''_E)_{act}}{(U''_E)_{ref}}$$

$$= \frac{1}{2} \int_0^\pi \frac{(k'_d)_f (\mu_d)_f}{(k'_{do})_f (\mu_{do})_f} \sin\beta \, d\beta \quad (4F-51)$$

In this expression the ratio $(k'_d)_f / (k'_{do})_f = (\eta'_d)_f$ is the relative receiving response, as shown by Eq. (4F-12). Also, by Eq. (4D-3), the ratio $(\mu_d)_f / (\mu_{do})_f = (\eta_d)_f$ is the relative transmitting response. Finally, by Eq. (4D-9), $(\eta'_d)_f = (\eta_d)_f$. The reverberation factor of a reversible echoranging transducer having an axis of acoustic symmetry which is also an axis of maximum response is, therefore,

$$(\eta''_D)_f = \frac{1}{2} \int_0^\pi (\eta_d)_f (\eta'_d)_f \sin\beta \, d\beta$$

$$= \frac{1}{2} \int_0^\pi (\eta_d)^2_f \sin\beta \, d\beta \quad (4F-52)$$

For a reversible transducer having an axis of acoustic symmetry which is perpendicular to a maximum response axis it may be shown, by a similar process, that the reverberation factor is

$$(\eta''_D)_f = \frac{1}{2} \int_{\pi/2}^{-\pi/2} (\eta_d)^2_f \cos\beta \, d\beta \quad (4F-53)$$

As in the case of the directivity factor of a hydrophone, the situation described in the definition for reverberation factor is such that the actual transducer and the hypothetical reference transducer would respond equally to the echo from some given target. The interference in the reference transducer, resulting from its simultaneous response to reverberation, would, however, equal the interference due to this same cause in the actual transducer multiplied by the reciprocal of the reverberation factor. The reverberation factor of a reversible directional transducer thus gives the signal-to-interference advantage of that transducer when used for echo ranging, relative to a nondirectional transducer.

In many problems it is convenient to express the magnitude of a reverberation factor in terms of the corresponding transmission loss. To this end the **reverberation index** of a reversible sonar transducer is defined as the transmission loss measured by the reverberation factor. The relation between the two is given by the equation

$$N_{RI} = \lgt \frac{1}{(\eta''_D)_f} \quad (4F-54)$$

where

N_{RI} = the reverberation index of a reversible sonar transducer (db)

$(\eta''_D)_f$ = the reverberation factor of that transducer (a numeric)

Although the formula for the reverberation factor of a transducer is obviously related to the formula for its directivity factor, when used either as a projector or as a hydrophone, it is not, in general, possible to compute the reverberation factor directly in terms of directivity factor. Neither are formulas similar to those for directivity factor available for computing the reverberation factor of a transducer of given type. The value of a reverberation factor, or of a reverberation index, may, however, be derived from measured or computed values of relative response, either transmitting or receiving, considered as a function of bearing for a specified constant frequency, provided the three-dimensional directivity pattern of the transducer may be generated by rotating a two-dimensional pattern. In doing so it is necessary to take account both of the variation in power per unit band per unit angle of the received acoustic energy and of the variation in receiving response of the transducer. This may be done by plotting a **reverberation function,** analogous to the directivity function described in Art. 4F-6, as a function of bearing and evaluating the integral of this function by measuring the area under the curve. The reverberation function is the quantity under the integral sign in Eqs. (4F-52) or (4F-53). Typical curves for the reverberation functions of various transducer types are shown in Fig. 4F-8. These apply specifically to the same transducers as do the curves for directivity functions shown in Fig. 4F-7.

The directivity factors and the reverberation factors computed as one half the value, in radians, of the areas under the curves of Figs. 4F-7 and 4F-8 are tabulated in Fig. 4F-9. It is evident from an inspection of the results of these computations that the relation between directivity factor and reverberation factor, or between directivity index and reverberation index, depends greatly on the type of transducer in question. It is to be noted that, although the directivity index of a linear transducer is, to a close approximation, unchanged when the line is bent into a circle, the reverbera-

FIG. 4F-9. COMPUTATION OF DIRECTIVITY AND REVERBERATION INDEXES. Values of the directivity factor and the reverberation factor for a number of transducers and the values of directivity and reverberation indexes computed therefrom. The critical dimension is 5 wave spaces in each case.

Transducer	One-Way Transmission		Two-Way Transmission	
	Directivity Factor	Directivity Index (db)	Reverberation Factor	Reverberation Index (db)
Circular Piston	0.00375	24.3	0.00183	27.4
Ring	0.0299	15.2	0.00323	24.9
Line	0.0984	10.1	0.0677	11.6

tion index would be increased considerably. In general, it has been found that for a plane-surface transducer, responsive on one side only of a plane through its active surface, the reverberation index will be approximately three decibels greater than its directivity index, provided none of its linear dimensions is less than two or three waves.

4-G TRANSMISSION LOSSES OF SONAR TRANSDUCERS

The general concept of transmission loss is as useful when dealing with sonar transducers as elsewhere. For many problems the losses associated with general forms of transducers may be used to advantage with sonar transducers. For other problems it is convenient to define additional losses which are better adapted to the situations encountered. These losses are directly related to other characteristics of sonar transducers which have been discussed in previous sections of this chapter.

4G-1 Projector Loss and Hydrophone Loss

It is usually desirable to evaluate the transmission properties of a sonar transducer as completely as possible without reference to the characteristics of any electric system to which it may be connected. The acoustic characteristics of the water on the opposite side of the transducer are, on the other hand, presumably taken into account in its design. They are not subject to further control. Any transition loss between the transducer and the water is therefore properly included in any report of transducer behavior. This suggests that of all the recognized transmission losses usually associated with a transducer an efficiency

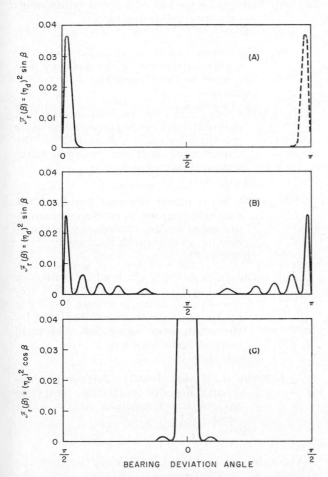

FIG. 4F-8. REVERBERATION FUNCTION. Values of the function $\mathcal{F}_r(\beta) = (\eta_d)^2 \sin \beta$ or $\mathcal{F}_r(\beta) = (\eta_d)^2 \cos \beta$ appearing in the formulas for reverberation index.
  (A) Circular plate transducer having a diameter of 5λ
  (B) Ring transducer having a diameter of 5λ
  (C) Linear transducer having a length of 5λ

loss is the most suitable by which to measure the performance of a projector, and an available power loss the most suitable by which to measure the performance of a hydrophone. If we were content to consider simply the total acoustic energy delivered to the water in one case and the total acoustic energy available from the water in the other, it would be unnecessary to go further; our requirements would be fully met by transmission losses already formally defined. These losses are, however, not the most useful in this particular situation.

What is required is a pair of losses each of which is contiguous, on one side, to the propagation loss of the acoustic path through the water adjoining the transducer and, on the other side, to the transition loss of the junction between the transducer and the electric transmitting or receiving system. As thus described each of these losses is contiguous on one side to a transmission loss measured in terms of a power ratio and on the other side to a transmission loss normally measured in terms of an intensity ratio. This would appear to require that such a loss be measured by a quotient obtained by dividing a power by an intensity, or an intensity by a power. This would, however, be a violation of the accepted definition of transmission loss, which requires that such loss be measured by a dimensionless ratio.

To avoid this conflict we shall define the **projector loss** of a sonar transducer, used for the transmission of acoustic energy, at a specified frequency, as the transmission loss measured by the ratio of (1) the input power of the electric energy delivered to the transducer to (2) the resulting load power of the acoustic energy delivered by the transducer to a water surface having an area of one square centimeter and lying perpendicular to the maximum response reference axis of the transducer at its index point. This definition of projector loss falls wholly within the definition of efficiency loss given in Art. 4A-6. It is less general than the previous definition only insofar as the specification of the transducer load is restrictive. The propagation loss of the water path between a given sonar projector and a distant receiving point on a propagation path leaving the projector along its maximum response reference axis may be made contiguous with the projector loss of the projector by expressing its magnitude in terms of the powers of acoustic waves passing through unit areas of water surface perpendicular to this path at its index point and at the receiving point. The

propagation loss thus expressed will be the same as the propagation loss measured in terms of the acoustic intensities falling on these unit areas. It is assumed that the acoustic intensity throughout either of these areas is constant.

This discussion of projector loss has been in terms of the powers of sinusoidal waves having a specified frequency. Losses thus measured may be used for waves having continuous spectra. In this latter case the losses are expressed in terms of the powers per unit band of these waves at specified frequencies. The projector loss of a sonar projector may therefore be written as

$$N_P = \operatorname{lgt} \frac{P_{\text{in}}}{A_L (I_{do})_L} = \operatorname{lgt} \frac{U_{\text{in}}}{A_L (J_{do})_L} \qquad (4\text{G-1})$$

where

$N_P =$ the projector loss of a sonar transducer, at a specified frequency
(db)

$P_{\text{in}} =$ the input power of sinusoidal electric waves, of the specified frequency, delivered to the transducer
(watt)

$(I_{do})_L =$ the index value of the load intensity of sinusoidal acoustic waves, of the same specified frequency, radiated by the transducer along its maximum response reference axis
(watt/cm²)

$U_{\text{in}} =$ the input power per unit band, at the specified frequency, of electric energy delivered to the transducer as waves having a continuous spectrum
(joule/cyc)

$(J_{do})_L =$ the index value of the load intensity per unit band, at the same specified frequency, of acoustic waves having a continuous spectrum and radiated by the transducer along its maximum response reference axis
(joule/cm²·cyc)

$A_L =$ the unit area of water surface perpendicular to the maximum response axis of the transducer at its index point
(cm²)

A simple and useful relation exists between the projector loss of a sonar transducer and its efficiency loss. This efficiency loss, like that of any other transducer, is measured by the ratio of the input power of the energy delivered to the transducer by its source to the load power of the energy delivered by the transducer to its load. The efficiency loss of a sonar transducer used as a projector, at some specified frequency, may, therefore, be written as

$$(N_{eff})_P = \operatorname{lgt} \frac{P_{in}}{P_L} \qquad (4G\text{-}2)$$

where

$(N_{eff})_P =$ the efficiency loss of a sonar projector, at a specified frequency (db)

$P_{in} =$ the input power of the electric energy delivered to the projector (watt)

$P_L =$ the load power of the total acoustic energy delivered by the projector (watt)

The load power of the total acoustic energy delivered by the projector is related through the directivity index of the projector to the index intensity $(I_{do})_L$ of this energy, as measured on the maximum response reference axis of the projector, by the equation

$$N_{DI} = \operatorname{lgt} \frac{4\pi r^2 (I_{do})_L}{P_L} \qquad (4G\text{-}3)$$

In this expression the quantity $4\pi r^2 (I_{do})_L = (P_A)_{ref}$ is the reference power specified in the definition of directivity factor, the distance r being the index distance. The load power $P_L = (P_A)_{act}$ is the actual acoustic power specified in the definition of directivity factor. By combining Eqs. (4G-1), (4G-2), and (4G-3) we obtain

$$(N_{eff})_P - N_P - N_{DI}$$

$$= \operatorname{lgt} \left[\frac{P_{in}}{P_L} \frac{A_L (I_{do})_L}{P_{in}} \frac{P_L}{4\pi r^2 (I_{do})_L} \right]$$

$$= \operatorname{lgt} \frac{A_L}{4\pi r^2} \qquad (4G\text{-}4)$$

Since the area appearing in the expression for projector loss is $A_L = 1$ cm², and the index distance appearing in the expression for directivity factor is $r = 91.44$ cm, the efficiency loss of the projector is

$$(N_{eff})_P = N_P + N_{DI} - 50.22 \text{ db} \qquad (4G\text{-}5)$$

The **hydrophone loss** of a sonar transducer, used for the reception of acoustic energy, at a specified frequency, may be defined as the trans-

mission loss measured by the ratio of (1) the source power of the free-field acoustic energy available as plane sinusoidal waves from a water surface having an area of one square centimeter and lying perpendicular to the direction of the maximum response reference axis of the transducer at the point to be occupied by its effective center to (2) the resulting output power of the electric energy available from the transducer. This definition falls wholly within the definition of available power loss as given in Art. 4A-6. It is less general than the previous definition only insofar as the specification of the transducer source is restrictive. The propagation loss of the water path by which acoustic energy reaches a transducer is made contiguous to the hydrophone loss of that transducer by expressing its magnitude in terms of the powers of acoustic waves passing through unit areas, as in the case of a propagation loss contiguous to a projector loss.

As in the case of projector losses, hydrophone losses measured in terms of the available powers of sinusoidal waves may be used also with waves having continuous spectra. These losses may, therefore, be written as

$$N_H = \operatorname{lgt} \frac{A_S (I'_{do})_S}{(P'_{do})_{out}} = \operatorname{lgt} \frac{A_S (J'_{do})_S}{(U'_{do})_{out}} \qquad (4G\text{-}6)$$

where

$N_H =$ the hydrophone loss of a sonar transducer, at a specified frequency (db)

$(I'_{do})_S =$ the free-field source intensity of the acoustic energy available from the water as plane sinusoidal waves, of the specified frequency, propagated along the direction of the maximum response axis of the transducer (watt/cm²)

$(P'_{do})_{out} =$ the output power of the electric energy available from the transducer as sinusoidal waves of the same specified frequency (watt)

$(J'_{do})_S =$ the free-field source intensity per unit band, at the specified frequency, of the acoustic energy available from the water in the form of plane waves having a continuous spectrum and propagated along the direction of the maximum response reference axis of the transducer (joule/cm²·cyc)

$(U'_{do})_{\text{out}}$ = the output power per unit band, at the same specified frequency, of the electric energy available from the transducer
(joule/cyc)

A_S = the unit area of water surface perpendicular to the direction of the maximum response reference axis of the transducer at the point to be occupied by the effective center of the transducer
(cm²)

This hydrophone loss may be related to an available power loss in a manner analogous to that by which a projector loss is related to an efficiency loss. The available power loss of a sonar transducer used as a hydrophone, at some specified frequency, may be written as

$$(N_{\text{avl}})_H = \text{lgt} \frac{(P'_{do})_S}{(P'_{do})_{\text{out}}} \qquad (4G\text{-}7)$$

where

$(N_{\text{avl}})_H$ = the available power loss of a hydrophone, at a specified frequency
(db)

$(P'_{do})_S$ = the source power of the total acoustic energy available to the hydrophone, at the specified frequency
(watt)

$(P'_{do})_{\text{out}}$ = the output power of the electric energy available from the hydrophone, at the same specified frequency
(watt)

The source power of the total acoustic energy available to the transducer is related to the free-field intensity, $(I'_{do})_S$, of this energy through the capture area, A_C, of the transducer by the equation

$$(P'_{do})_S = A_C (I'_{do})_S \qquad (4G\text{-}8)$$

On combining Eqs. (4G-6) and (4G-7), we obtain

$$(V_{\text{avl}})_H - N_H = \text{lgt} \left[\frac{(P'_{do})_S}{(P'_{do})_{\text{out}}} \frac{(P'_{do})_{\text{out}}}{A_S (I'_{do})_S} \right] \qquad (4G\text{-}9)$$

or, substituting the equality of Eq. (4G-8),

$$(N_{\text{avl}})_H = N_H + \text{lgt} \frac{A_C}{A_S} \qquad (4G\text{-}10)$$

In the power ratio determined by the efficiency loss of a projector one of the powers is the load power of the total energy delivered to the water. A considerable portion of this total energy is distributed to loads other than that specified in the definition of projector loss. The effect of the energy thus diverted is the same as an increase in the dissipation loss of the transducer, when considered as the connection between the electric driving system and the index point of the acoustic propagation path. This increase is measured by a transmission loss which must be added to the efficiency loss to obtain the projector loss. This loss is $50.22 - N_{DI}$ db. The efficiency loss of a sonar projector may thus be said to be a component of the projector loss.

In the power ratio determined by the available power loss of a hydrophone one of the powers is the source power of the total energy available from the water. A considerable portion of this total energy is collected from sources other than that specified in the definition of hydrophone loss. The effect of the energy thus collected is the same as a decrease in the dissipation loss of the transducer, when considered as the connection between a point on the acoustic propagation path and the electric receiving system. This decrease is measured by a transmission gain which must be subtracted from the available power loss to obtain the hydrophone loss. This gain is $\text{lgt}\,(A_C/A_S)$ db. In the case of a projector the efficiency loss was seen to be a component of the projector loss; in the case of a hydrophone the situation is reversed and the hydrophone loss is a component of the available power loss. In practice it will often be found that the hydrophone loss is such a small portion of the available power loss that it has a negative value and thus appears to be a transmission gain.

4G-2 Response and Transmission Loss

The projector and hydrophone losses defined in the preceding article are directly related to the transmitting and receiving responses defined in Art. 4D-1.

From Eq. (4D-1) the transmitting response of a sonar transducer, when using sinusoidal waves, is given as

$$(\mu_d)_f = \frac{(I_d)_L}{P_{\text{in}}}$$

From Eq. (4G-1) the projector loss of the same transducer is given as

$$N_P = \text{lgt} \frac{P_{\text{in}}}{A_L (I_{do})_L}$$

It is thus clear that the projector loss may be written in terms of the transmitting response applying to the maximum response reference axis as

$$N_P = \text{lgt} \frac{1}{(\mu_{do})_f} - \text{lgt} \, A_L \qquad (4\text{G-}11)$$

In a similar manner it may be shown that the hydrophone loss of a sonar transducer is given in terms of the receiving response of that transducer applying to its maximum response reference axis as

$$N_H = \text{lgt} \frac{1}{(\mu'_{do})_f} + \text{lgt} \, A_S \qquad (4\text{G-}12)$$

From these two equations the advantage of making the two small areas specified in the definition of projector loss and of hydrophone loss of unit magnitude, $A_L = A_S = 1$ cm², is obvious. In this case the ratio measuring a projector loss is numerically equal to the reciprocal of the quotient measuring a transmitting response, and the ratio measuring a hydrophone loss is numerically equal to the reciprocal of the quotient measuring a receiving response.

In addition to the transmitting and receiving responses defined in Art. 4D-1 there are a number of other responses which have been defined by the American Standards Association. The following definitions for these quantities are quoted from the **American Standard Acoustical Terminology**.[13]

The **transmitting power response** of an electroacoustic transducer used for sound emission is the ratio of the mean-square sound pressure apparent at a distance of 1 meter in a specified direction from the effective acoustic center of the transducer to the electric power input.

The **transmitting voltage response** of an electroacoustic transducer used for sound emission is the ratio of the sound pressure apparent at a distance of 1 meter in a specified direction from the effective acoustic center of the transducer to the electric signal voltage applied to the electric input terminals of the transducer.

The **transmitting current response** of an electroacoustic transducer used for sound emission is the ratio of the sound pressure apparent at a distance of 1 meter in a specified direction from the effective acoustic center of the transducer to the current flowing at the electric input terminals.

The **free-field voltage response** of an electroacoustic transducer used for sound reception is the ratio of the voltage appearing at the output terminals of the transducer when the output terminals are open-circuited to the free-field sound pressure existing at the transducer location prior to the introduction of the transducer in the sound field.

The **free-field current response** of an electroacoustic transducer used for sound reception is the ratio of the current in the output circuit of the transducer when the output terminals are short-circuited to the free-field sound pressure existing at the transducer location prior to the introduction of the transducer in the sound field.

Each of these definitions is followed by the statement that the response in question is usually expressed in decibels above a reference response of like kind and of unit magnitude. This appears to indicate that a quantity designated as a "response" may be either a numerical coefficient or the logarithm of such a coefficient. In general, the term "response" will, in this book, be restricted to numerical coefficients; quantities which are said to be in decibels will be either transmission losses or transmission level differentials.

It is evident that the electric power, the electric voltage, and the electric current specified in the first three definitions quoted above are, respectively, the input power, the input voltage, and the input current specified in Art. 4A-4. Similarly, the voltage and the current specified in the last two definitions quoted are, respectively, the output voltage and the output current specified in that same article. It is thus evident that in addition to the five quantities officially defined there is a sixth which is a logical member of this family. This would be described, in conformity with the preceding definitions, as the **free-field power response.** It would be defined, also in conformity with the preceding definitions, as the ratio of the power in the output circuit of the transducer when the output terminals are connected to an impedance which is the conjugate of the electric impedance of the transducer to the mean-square value of the sound pressure existing at the transducer location prior to the introduction of the transducer in the sound field.

Since the quantities described above are in wide use it is desirable that we have at hand formulas showing the relations between these quantities and the projector and hydrophone losses already defined. In carrying out a conversion by such a formula it is necessary to keep in mind that the index distance specified in definitions given in earlier articles, in conformity with standard usage in the U. S. Navy, is one yard, whereas the distance specified in the official American Standard Definitions, in conformity with efforts to introduce the MKS system of units, is one meter. The factor taking account of this dissimilarity will be included in the formulas about to be derived.

Relations between the projector loss of a sonar transducer and the three quantities which have been defined above in connection with the manner in which such a transducer radiates acoustic energy are derived by substituting one or more of the following equalities into Eq. (4G-1).

$$P_{in} = e^2_{in}(G_E)_{in} = i^2_{in}(R_E)_{in}$$

and   (4G-13)

$$(I_{do})_L = \frac{(1.0936)^2(p^2_{do})_L \cdot 10^{-7}}{\rho c}$$

where

P_{in} = the input power of the electric energy delivered to the transducer as sinusoidal waves of specified frequency (watt)

e_{in} = the input voltage of this electric energy (volt)

i_{in} = the input current of this electric energy (amp)

$(G_E)_{in}$ = the conductive component of the electric input admittance of the transducer (mho)

$(R_E)_{in}$ = the resistive component of the electric input impedance of the transducer (ohm)

$(I_{do})_L$ = the one yard index value of the load intensity of the acoustic energy radiated along the maximum response reference axis of the transducer (watt/cm²)

$(p_{do})_L$ = the one meter index value of the load pressure of this acoustic energy (μb)

$1/\rho c$ = the acoustic conductance per unit area of the medium (spec acous mho)

1.0936 = the dimensional conversion factor necessary because of the unlike index distances (yd/m)

By making the appropriate substitutions the projector loss may be written as

$$N_P = \operatorname{lgt} \frac{P_{in}}{A_L(I_{do})_L}$$

$$= \operatorname{lgt} \frac{P_{in}\,\rho c}{(1.0936)^2(p^2_{do})_L\,A_L \cdot 10^{-7}}$$

$$= \operatorname{lgt} \frac{e^2_{in}(G_E)_{in}\,\rho c}{(1.0936)^2(p^2_{do})_L\,A_L \cdot 10^{-7}}$$

$$= \operatorname{lgt} \frac{i^2_{in}(R_E)_{in}\,\rho c}{(1.0936)^2(p^2_{do})_L\,A_L \cdot 10^{-7}} \quad (4G\text{-}14)$$

When the acoustic conductance per unit area of the medium is $1/\rho c = 6.5 \cdot 10^{-6}$ spec acous mhos, and the small area of water surface specified in the definition of projector loss is $A_L = 1$ cm²,

$$\operatorname{lgt} \frac{(1.0936)^2 A_L \cdot 10^{-7}}{\rho c} = 121.09 \text{ Gl//1 acous mho}$$

The above equations may then be written as

$$N_P = -\operatorname{lgt} \frac{(p^2_{do})_L}{P_{in}} + 121.09$$

$$= -2\operatorname{lgt} \frac{(p_{do})_L}{e_{in}} + \operatorname{lgt}(G_E)_{in} + 121.09$$

$$= -2\operatorname{lgt} \frac{(p_{do})_L}{i_{in}} + \operatorname{lgt}(R_E)_{in} + 121.09 \quad (4G\text{-}15)$$

where

N_P = the projector loss of a sonar transducer, applying to the one yard index point (db)

$(p^2_{do})_L/P_{in}$ = the transmitting power response of the transducer applying to the one meter index point on its maximum response reference axis (μb²/watt)

$(p_{do})_L/e_{in}$ = the transmitting voltage response of the transducer applying to the one meter index point on its maximum response reference axis (μb/volt)

$(p_{do})_L/i_{in}$ = the transmitting current response of the transducer applying to the one meter index point on its maximum response reference axis
(μb/amp)

Relations between the hydrophone loss of a sonar transducer and the three quantities which have been defined in connection with the manner in which such a transducer receives acoustic energy are derived by substituting one or more of the following equalities into Eq. (4G-6).

$$(P'_{do})_{out} = \frac{(e^2_{do})_{out}}{4(R_E)_{out}} = \frac{(i^2_{do})_{out}}{4(G_E)_{out}}$$

and   (4G-16)

$$(I'_{do})_S = \frac{(p^2_{do})_S \cdot 10^{-7}}{\rho c}$$

where

$(P'_{do})_{out}$ = the output power of the electric energy generated in the transducer when receiving acoustic energy as plane sinusoidal waves of specified frequency propagated along the maximum response reference axis
(watt)

$(e_{do})_{out}$ = the output voltage of this electric energy
(volt)

$(i_{do})_{out}$ = the output current of this electric energy
(amp)

$(R_E)_{out}$ = the resistive component of the electric output impedance of the transducer
(ohm)

$(G_E)_{out}$ = the conductive component of the electric output admittance of the transducer
(mho)

$(I'_{do})_S$ = the source intensity of the acoustic energy propagated as plane sinusoidal waves along the maximum response axis
(watt/cm²)

$(p_{do})_S$ = the source pressure of this acoustic energy
(μb)

$1/\rho c$ = the acoustic conductance per unit area of the medium
(spec acous mho)

By making the appropriate substitutions the hydrophone loss may be written as

$$N_H = \lgt \frac{A_S(I'_{do})_S}{(P'_{do})_{out}}$$

$$= \lgt \frac{(p^2_{do})_S A_S \cdot 10^{-7}}{(P'_{do})_{out} \rho c}$$

$$= \lgt \frac{(p^2_{do})_S 4(R_E)_{out} A_S \cdot 10^{-7}}{(e^2_{do})_{out} \rho c}$$

$$= \lgt \frac{(p^2_{do})_S 4(G_E)_{out} A_S \cdot 10^{-7}}{(i^2_{do})_{out} \rho c} \qquad (4G-17)$$

When the acoustic conductance per unit area of the medium is $1/\rho c = 6.5 \cdot 10^{-6}$ spec acous mhos, and the small area of water surface specified in the definition of hydrophone loss is $A_S = 1$ cm²,

$$\lgt \frac{4A_S \cdot 10^{-7}}{\rho c} = -115.85 \text{ Gl}//1 \text{ acous mho}$$

The above equations may then be written as

$$N_H = -\lgt \frac{(P'_{do})_{out}}{(p^2_{do})_S} - 121.87$$

$$= -2\lgt \frac{(e_{do})_{out}}{(p_{do})_S} + \lgt(R_E)_{out} - 115.85$$

$$= -2\lgt \frac{(i_{do})_{out}}{(p_{do})_S} + \lgt(G_E)_{out} - 115.85 \quad (4G-18)$$

where

N_H = the hydrophone loss of a sonar transducer
(db)

$\dfrac{(P'_{do})_{out}}{(p^2_{do})_S}$ = the free-field power response of the transducer applying to its maximum response reference axis
(watt/μb²)

$\dfrac{(e_{do})_{out}}{(p_{do})_S}$ = the free-field voltage response of the transducer applying to its maximum response reference axis
(volt/μb)

$\dfrac{(i_{do})_{out}}{(p_{do})_S}$ = the free-field current response of the transducer applying to its maximum response axis
(amp/μb)

4G-3 The Reciprocity Relation

The manner in which acoustic energy is propagated away from a projector is quite different from the manner in which it is propagated toward a hydrophone. The transmission losses of a reversible sonar transducer are, nevertheless, independent of the direction of transmission provided the impedances terminating the transducer on either side remain unchanged. This condition is not met in the case of the projector and hydrophone losses of a reversible transducer since the acoustic load specified for one differs from the acoustic source specified for the other. The load to which the normal efficiency loss of a transducer refers when it is used as a projector is, however, identical with the source to which its normal available power loss refers when it is used as a hydrophone. Furthermore, the efficiency loss of any reversible transducer for a given direction of transmission is, as shown in Art. 4A-7, equal to its available power loss when energy is transmitted in the other direction between the same terminating impedances. For this reason the normal efficiency loss of a reversible sonar transducer when used as a projector, at a given frequency, is equal to the available power loss of the same transducer when used as a hydrophone at the same frequency. We may, therefore, equate the efficiency loss as given by Eq. (4G-4) to the available power loss as given by Eq. (4G-10) to obtain a relation between the projector and hydrophone losses of a reversible sonar transducer. This relation is

$$N_P + N_{DI} - \lgt \frac{4\pi r^2}{A_L} = N_H + \lgt \frac{A_C}{A_S} \quad (4G\text{-}19)$$

The above expression contains a term depending on the capture area, A_C, of the transducer. By definition (Art. 4F-5) the capture area of a given sonar transducer is directly related to the directivity factor of that transducer for any given frequency, and to the wave length corresponding to that frequency. We may, therefore, by Eqs. (4F-22) and (4F-42), express the directivity index in terms of the capture area by the equation $N_{DI} = \lgt[(4\pi A_C)/\lambda^2]$. The substitution of this equality into Eq. (4G-19) gives

$$N_P = N_H + \lgt \frac{\lambda^2 r^2}{A_L A_S} \quad (4G\text{-}20)$$

When the areas specified in the definitions of projector loss and of hydrophone loss are given the values $A_L = A_S = 1$ cm² the relation between the two losses may be written, making the substitution $\lambda r = cr/f$, as

$$N_P = N_H + 2\lgt \frac{cr}{f} \quad (4G\text{-}21)$$

Finally, if the velocity of propagation is assumed to be $1.5 \cdot 10^5$ cm/sec, and the index distance to be $r = 91.44$ cm, this reduces to

$$N_P = N_H - 2\lgt f + 142.74 \quad (4G\text{-}22)$$

where

N_P = the projector loss of a reversible sonar transducer, at a specified frequency (db)

N_H = the hydrophone loss of that transducer, at the same specified frequency (db)

f = the specified frequency (cyc/sec)

The preceding equation expresses what is known as the **reciprocity relation**, applying to a reversible sonar transducer, in terms of transmission losses. This relation may also be expressed in terms of the transmitting and receiving responses defined in Art. 4D-1. By substituting the power ratios measuring projector loss and hydrophone loss, as given by Eqs. (4G-1) and (4G-6), into Eq. (4G-21), and making $A_L = A_S = 1$, as before, it is found that

$$\frac{P_{in}}{(I_{do})_L} = \frac{(I'_{do})_S}{(P'_{do})_{out}} \left(\frac{cr}{f}\right)^2 \quad (4G\text{-}23)$$

In this expression the quotient

$$\frac{P_{in}}{(I_{do})_L} = \frac{1}{(\mu_{do})_f}$$

is, by Eq. (4D-1), the reciprocal of the transmitting response applying to the maximum response reference axis of the transducer. Similarly, the quotient

$$\frac{(I'_{do})_S}{(P'_{do})_{out}} = \frac{1}{(\mu'_{do})_f}$$

is, by Eq. (4D-2), the reciprocal of the receiving response, applying to the same reference axis. We may, therefore, write

$$(\mu'_{do})_f = (\mu_{do})_f \left(\frac{cr}{f}\right)^2 \quad (4G\text{-}24)$$

Now, by Eq. (4D-3), $\mu_{do} = \mu_d/\eta_d$, where μ_d is the transmitting response, and η_d the relative transmitting response, applying to any given bearing

Also, by Eq. (4D-4), $\mu'_{do} = \mu'_d / \eta'_d$, where μ'_d is the receiving response, and η'_d the relative receiving response applying to the same given bearing. Finally, by Eq. (4D-9), $\eta_d = \eta'_d$. On substituting these equalities into Eq. (4G-24) it is found that

$$(\mu'_d)_f = (\mu_d)_f \left(\frac{cr}{f} \right)^2 \qquad (4G\text{-}25)$$

where

$(\mu'_d)_f =$ the receiving response of a reversible sonar transducer, at a specified frequency, and for a given bearing (cm²)

$(\mu_d)_f =$ the transmitting response of the same transducer, at the same specified frequency, and for the same given bearing (1/cm²)

$c =$ the velocity of propagation of the medium (cm/sec)

$r =$ the distance from the effective center of the transducer at which radiated acoustic energy is measured (cm)

$f =$ the specified frequency (cyc/sec)

In expositions of theoretical acoustics the reciprocity relation for a reversible electroacoustic transducer is usually developed in terms of its transmitting current response and its free-field voltage response. This relation is usually established on the basis of a reciprocity theorem similar to that stated in Art. 4A-4, but applying to an electroacoustic transducer rather than to an electric transducer. The reciprocity relation between transmitting current response and free-field voltage response may, however, be obtained directly from the relation, given by Eq. (4G-25), between the transmitting and receiving responses defined in Art. 4D-1. This requires simply that the following equalities be substituted into that equation.

$$P_{\text{in}} = i^2_{\text{in}} R_E \qquad (P'_{do})_{\text{out}} = \frac{(e^2{}_{do})_{\text{out}}}{4R_E}$$

$$(I_{do})_L = \frac{(p^2{}_{do})_L \cdot 10^{-7}}{\rho c}, \text{ and } (I'_{do})_S = \frac{(p^2{}_{do})_S \cdot 10^{-7}}{\rho c}$$

When these substitutions are made it is found that

$$\frac{(e_{do})_{\text{out}}}{(p_{do})_S} = \frac{(p_{do})_L}{i_{\text{in}}} \frac{2r \cdot 10^{-7}}{\rho f} \qquad (4G\text{-}26)$$

Now, by Eq. (4D-9),

$$(e_{do})_{\text{out}} = (e_d)_{\text{out}} \frac{(p_{do})_L}{(p_d)_L}, \quad \text{when} \quad (p_{do})_S = (p_d)_S$$

When these equalities are substituted into Eq. (4G-26) there results

$$\frac{(e_d)_{\text{out}}}{(p_d)_S} = \frac{(p_d)_L}{i_{\text{in}}} \frac{2r \cdot 10^{-7}}{\rho f} \qquad (4G\text{-}27)$$

The ratio of the free-field voltage response of a reversible sonar transducer to the transmitting current response of the same transducer, at some specified frequency and for any given bearing, is thus seen to be equal to the quantity $(2r/\rho f) \cdot 10^{-7}$. This quantity is generally known as the **reciprocity parameter.** Its dimensions are watts per microbar squared.

The reciprocity relation stated by Eq. (4G-20) may be used to confirm the relation, stated by Eq. (3D-7), between the propagation loss between two points at which the velocities of propagation are not equal and the direction in which acoustic energy is propagated between these points. The total transmission loss between a source delivering electric energy to an electroacoustic transducer at point P_a and a load receiving electric energy from an electroacoustic transducer at point P_b is

$$(N_\Sigma)_{a/b} = (N_{\text{tsn}})_a + (N_P)_a + (N_w)_{a/b}$$
$$+ (N_H)_b + (N_{\text{tsn}})_b$$

The electric driving force is now removed from the transducer at P_a and applied to the transducer at P_b, the electric systems connected to these transducers being otherwise unchanged. The total transmission loss between the source now delivering electric energy to the transducer at P_b and the load now receiving electric energy from the transducer at P_a is

$$(N_\Sigma)_{b/a} = (N_{\text{tsn}})_b + (N_P)_b + (N_w)_{b/a}$$
$$+ (N_H)_a + (N_{\text{tsn}})_a$$

The transition losses at the electric terminals of the transducers are each independent of the direction of energy flow, as shown in Art. 4A-3. Also, as shown in Art. 4A-7, the resultant losses, being the losses of a passive linear network between fixed impedances, are equal. That is,

$(N_\Sigma)_{a/b} = (N_\Sigma)_{b/a}$. Finally, by the reciprocity relation of Eq. (4G-21),

$$(N_P)_a = (N_H)_a + 2 \lgt \frac{c_a r}{f}$$

and

$$(N_P)_b = (N_H)_b + 2 \lgt \frac{c_b r}{f}$$

When these equalities are substituted into the original equations, and the resulting expressions equated to each other, it is evident that

$$(N_H)_a + 2 \lgt c_a + (N_w)_{a/b} + (N_H)_b$$
$$= (N_H)_b + 2 \lgt c_b + (N_w)_{b/a} + (N_H)_a$$

That is,

$$(N_w)_{a/b} = (N_w)_{b/a} + 2 \lgt \frac{c_b}{c_a}$$

as was to be shown. In Art. 3D-1 this relation was established solely on the basis of the consequences of Snell's Law, as applied to the propagation of acoustic energy through an acoustic medium in which the velocity of propagation was not constant. Here it has been established solely on the basis of the manner in which acoustic energy passes between an electroacoustic transducer and an acoustic medium. The identity of the two conclusions may be looked upon as a demonstration of the infallibility with which mathematical processes close the circle of a series of statements of the relations between physical quantities.

4G-4 Reciprocity Calibrations

Although a projector loss or a hydrophone loss is identified with a power ratio in the conventional manner one of the two power magnitudes in any given ratio refers to electric energy and one to acoustic energy. Any direct measurement of either of these two losses, then, implies determinations of absolute magnitudes of electric and acoustic powers. By means of the reciprocity relation it is possible to measure the projector loss and the hydrophone loss of a reversible transducer by comparisons with the known transmission losses of an electric network without knowing the actual value of either the electric power or the acoustic power. Measurements made in this manner are known as **reciprocity calibrations.** Once a transducer has been calibrated by this method it may

thereafter be used for determining absolute values of acoustic power in terms of measured values of electric power. The following example will show how a reciprocity calibration may be carried out. At the same time it will afford an opportunity to demonstrate the utility of some of the quantities which have been defined in this chapter.

The equipment required for the calibration of a reversible transducer by the reciprocity method includes an auxiliary projector, an auxiliary hydrophone, a source of electric energy, an electric power indicator, and an adjustable attenuation network. There is also required a suitable water path between two points separated by a known fixed distance; one point will be designated as the projector position and one as the hydrophone position. It will be necessary to know the electric impedance of the transducer to be calibrated at each frequency for which a determination of its characteristics is desired. Neither the impedances nor the losses of the auxiliary transducers need be known. If either of the auxiliary transducers is directional it will be convenient, although not necessary, to know the direction of its major response axis. The adjustable attenuator must be accurately calibrated since it supplies the known values of transmission loss against which the losses of the transducer are compared. The computations involved in this measurement will be simplified if the output impedance of the source and the input impedance of the indicator are equal to the characteristic resistance of the attenuation network at all frequencies. The power available from the source need not be known except as may be desired to insure that the transducer being calibrated is driven, when used as a projector, at a suitable level.

Adjustments and observations must be made on four apparatus arrangements in order to carry out this calibration. The first arrangement is shown schematically in Diagram (A) of Fig. 4G-1. Here the transducer to be calibrated is placed at the projector position and connected to the source through the adjustable attenuator. The auxiliary hydrophone is placed at the hydrophone position and connected to the electric power indicator. If the transducer to be calibrated is directional its axis of maximum response should coincide with the line joining the projector and hydrophone positions. The attenuator should be adjusted so that the transducer is driven, as a projector, at some suitable amplitude. The elec

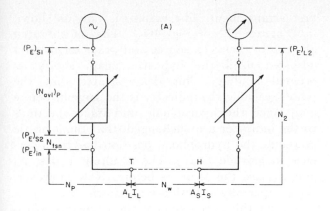

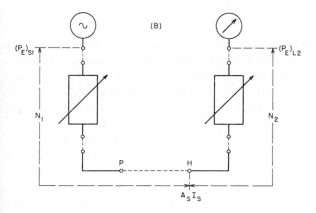

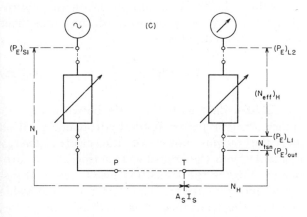

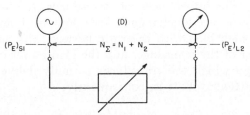

FIG. 4G-1. RECIPROCITY CALIBRATION. The arrangements of equipment by which the transmission losses of a reversible transducer may be measured in terms of the known transmission losses of a calibrated electric attenuation network. The unknown transducer is represented by T, an auxiliary hydrophone by H, and an auxiliary projector by P.

tric power indicator should next be adjusted so that the reading due to the hydrophone response is of such magnitude that it may be accurately reproduced. The effective response of the auxiliary hydrophone should be less than the response of the transducer under calibration when used as a hydrophone. This may be brought about, if necessary, by the use of a resistance pad in the hydrophone output. Neither the loss nor the impedance of this pad are significant; a simple series resistor will suffice.

The total transmission loss, in decibels, between source and indicator measures the ratio between the source power of the energy available from the source and the load power of the energy delivered to the indicator. This loss may be written as

$$N_\Sigma = \text{lgt } \frac{(P_E)_{S1}}{(P_E)_{L2}} \qquad (4G\text{-}28)$$

For the first arrangement expressions may be written for a number of the contiguous losses making up this total transmission loss. Assuming the attenuator to be matched to its source but not to its load (Art. 4A-7) its setting gives the available power loss,

$$(N_{\text{avl}})_P = \text{lgt } \frac{(P_E)_{S1}}{(P_E)_{S2}} \qquad (4G\text{-}29)$$

between the actual source and the transducer terminals. This loss is identified with the ratio between the power of the electric energy available from the source and the power of the electric energy available from the attenuator. The transition loss,

$$N_{\text{tsn}} = \text{lgt } \frac{(P_E)_{S2}}{(P_E)_{\text{in}}} \qquad (4G\text{-}30)$$

between attenuator and transducer is computed (Art. 4A-6) from the known characteristic resistance of the attenuator and the known impedance of the transducer. This loss is identified with the ratio between the power of the electric energy available from the attenuator and the power of the electric energy actually delivered to the transducer. The projector loss of the transducer, which is yet to be determined, is identified with the ratio between the power of the electric energy delivered to the transducer and the power of the acoustic energy through a small area of water surface at a point one yard from the effective center of the transducer. The projector loss is written as

$$N_P = \lgt \frac{(P_E)_{\text{in}}}{A_L I_L} \qquad (4\text{G-}31)$$

The propagation loss of the water path,

$$N_w = \lgt \frac{A_L I_L}{A_S I_S} \qquad (4\text{G-}32)$$

is computed from the known distance between the projector and hydrophone positions. When the areas appearing here have the value $A_L = A_S = 1$ cm² this loss determines the ratio between the acoustic intensity one yard from the transducer and the acoustic intensity at the hydrophone position.

The source power, $A_S I_S$, of the acoustic energy available to an area, $A_S = 1$ cm², of water surface at the hydrophone position will be used as a fixed reference power. It is not required that the absolute magnitude of this power be known. The resultant transmission loss,

$$N_1 = \lgt \frac{(P_E)_{S1}}{A_S I_S} \qquad (4\text{G-}33)$$

between the source and the hydrophone position is identified with the ratio of the source power of the electric energy available from the source to this reference power. The resultant transmission loss,

$$N_2 = \lgt \frac{A_S I_S}{(P_E)_{L2}} \qquad (4\text{G-}34)$$

between the hydrophone position and the indicator is identified with the ratio of this reference power to the load power of the electric energy delivered to the indicator. The total transmission loss between source and indicator is the sum of these two resultant losses. The resultant loss, N_1, between the source and the hydrophone position has been evaluated with the transducer to be calibrated at the projector position. It is given by the sum of the contiguous losses defined by Eqs. (4G-29) to (4G-32).

In the second apparatus arrangement the transducer being calibrated and the calibrated attenuator are replaced by the auxiliary projector, which is located exactly at the original projector position, and by an uncalibrated attenuator. The auxiliary hydrophone remains in the hydrophone position and is connected to the indicator exactly as in the first arrangement. The system is now as shown in Diagram (B) of Fig. 4G-1. The uncalibrated attenuator, between source and projector, is next adjusted until the indicator again shows its original reading. This demonstrates that the power reaching the indicator is the same as before and, since the hydrophone and its connections to the indicator are unchanged, that the acoustic power at the hydrophone position has the reference magnitude, $A_S I_S$. The resultant losses, N_1 and N_2, are the same as before. Now, however, the components of both are unknown.

For the third arrangement the auxiliary hydrophone is replaced by the transducer being calibrated. The arbitrarily chosen pad between the hydrophone and the indicator is replaced by the calibrated attenuator. This arrangement is shown in Diagram (C). The calibrated attenuator is now adjusted until the indicator is once more brought to the original reading. Once more, also, since the resultant loss N_1 is unchanged, the reference power has its original magnitude. With this power and the power of the energy delivered to the indicator both at their original values the resultant loss N_2 is also the same as before.

The components making up this loss may now be evaluated. The first component is the hydrophone loss, as yet unknown, of the transducer being calibrated. This is

$$N_H = \lgt \frac{A_S I_S}{(P_E)_{\text{out}}} \qquad (4\text{G-}35)$$

and is identified with the ratio between the reference acoustic power at the hydrophone position and the output power of the electric energy available from the transducer, acting as a hydrophone. Next is the transition loss between transducer and attenuator. This has the same value as when the transducer was used as a projector, since the impedances of transducer and of attenuator are unchanged. This loss is, however, now identified with the ratio between the output power of the transducer and the load power of the energy which the transducer actually delivers to the attenuator. It is, consequently,

$$N_{\text{tsn}} = \lgt \frac{(P_E)_{\text{out}}}{(P_E)_{L1}} \qquad (4\text{G-}36)$$

Since the attenuator is connected to a matching load but is mismatched to its source the loss measured by the box is an efficiency loss. This may be written as

$$(N_{\text{eff}})_H = \lgt \frac{(P_E)_{L1}}{(P_E)_{L2}} \qquad (4\text{G-}37)$$

It shows the ratio between the load power of the energy delivered to the attenuator and the load power of the energy delivered by the attenuator to the indicator.

The fixed resultant loss, N_2, between the hydrophone position and the indicator has now been evaluated with the transducer to be calibrated at the hydrophone position. It is given by the sum of the contiguous losses defined by Eqs. (4G-35) to (4G-37).

We may now express the total loss as the sum of the series of contiguous losses known to be equivalent to the constant resultant loss between source and hydrophone position and the constant resultant loss between hydrophone position and indicator. The sum of these contiguous transmission losses is

tain known quantities. By substituting the value of projector loss as given by Eq. (4G-22) there is obtained

$$N_\Sigma = (N_{\text{avl}})_P + (N_{\text{eff}})_H + 2N_{\text{tsn}} + N_w$$
$$+ 2N_H - 2\lgt f + 142.74 \qquad (4\text{G-}39)$$

The hydrophone loss of the reversible transducer, at any frequency, is thus given in terms of known transmission losses as

$$N_H = \tfrac{1}{2}[N_\Sigma - (N_{\text{avl}})_P - (N_{\text{eff}})_H - N_w]$$
$$- N_{\text{tsn}} + \lgt f - 71.37 \qquad (4\text{G-}40)$$

The projector loss may be computed at once by Eq. (4G-22).

It is thus evident that the two transmission losses which have been designated as projector loss and hydrophone loss, and which are identified with ratios between electric and acoustic powers, may be determined by comparison with the known

$$N_\Sigma = N_1 + N_2 = \lgt \left[\frac{(P_E)_{S1}}{(P_E)_{S2}} \frac{(P_E)_{S2}}{(P_E)_{\text{in}}} \frac{(P_E)_{\text{in}}}{A_L I_L} \frac{A_L I_L}{A_S I_S} \frac{A_S I_S}{(P_E)_{\text{out}}} \frac{(P_E)_{\text{out}}}{(P_E)_{L1}} \frac{(P_E)_{L1}}{(P_E)_{L2}} \right]$$
$$= (N_{\text{avl}})_P + N_{\text{tsn}} + N_P + N_w + N_H + N_{\text{tsn}} + (N_{\text{eff}})_H \qquad (4\text{G-}38)$$

It is seen that, with the exception of the initial source power of the energy available from the source and the final load power of the energy delivered to the indicator, all power magnitudes appearing in the several ratios here multiplied together cancel. This verifies the condition of contiguity required by the method here employed.

The value of the total transmission loss may be measured in terms of an attenuator setting by connecting source and indicator directly by a calibrated attenuation box as shown in Diagram (D) of Fig. 4G-1. When this box is adjusted to give the same indicator reading as that maintained for all previous arrangements it shows the value, N_Σ, of the sum of the transmission losses appearing in Eq. (4G-38).

All quantities in this equation except the desired transducer characteristics are therefore known, either as readings of the attenuator box, as the transition loss between attenuator and transducer, or as the propagation loss of the water path between projector and hydrophone positions. Were it not for the reciprocity relation we should be in the position of having a single equation with two unknowns. By means of this relation, however, it is possible to replace either the projector loss or the hydrophone loss by an expression containing only the other loss and cer-

transmission losses of an electric network, which are identified with ratios involving only electric powers.

4-H RESPONSE AS A FUNCTION OF FREQUENCY

When the relative responses of a sonar transducer are considered as functions of bearing, at a single fixed frequency, it is evident that the efficiency of the transducer is not a significant factor. Although this efficiency affects the magnitude of the total acoustic energy radiated at any given frequency it has no effect on the manner in which this energy is distributed in bearing. When our attention is restricted to a single bearing, and we wish to examine the manner in which the energy of the acoustic waves radiated by a sonar projector on that bearing varies with frequency, it is found that the rate of energy flow at one frequency relative to that at another depends upon the relation between the rate of flow of the received electric energy and frequency, upon the relation between the efficiency of the transducer and frequency, and upon the relation between the directional characteristics of the transducer and frequency. A similar group of relations determines the distribution of energy as a function of frequency in the electric waves generated in a hydrophone when receiving acoustic waves over any given bearing. It is with the effect of the directional characteristics of the transducer on the relation between response and frequency, when bearing is held constant, that we are now chiefly concerned.

4H-1 The Effect of Transducer Directivity

When a sonar transducer is used as a projector the efficiency with which it converts electric energy to acoustic energy has one, and only one, value for any specified frequency. When used as a hydrophone, however, the efficiency with which it converts acoustic energy to electric energy, at any specified frequency, has no fixed value but depends upon the directional distribution of the energy of the received acoustic waves. The transmitting efficiency of a reversible transducer, in other words, is a unique property of that transducer, whereas its receiving efficiency depends upon circumstances which are wholly independent of the transducer as well as upon its characteristics. It is thus evident that the efficiency of any sonar transducer is expressed most simply in terms of its performance as a projector.

In Sec. 4-E there are given a number of formulas for relative response as a function of bearing. Each of these leads to the ratio of the response of a transducer for any given frequency and for any given bearing to the response of the same transducer for the same frequency but for a specified reference bearing. All of these indicate, as an inspection will show, that such a ratio is a function of frequency as well as a function of bearing. These formulas do not, however, afford a means for the direct computation of useful values of relative response as a function of frequency. If a succession of ratios is computed, by any of these formulas, for a succession of values of frequency, the value of bearing being held constant, each ratio will represent the magnitude of the response at the given bearing and at the given frequency relative to the magnitude of some other response, of like kind, at the same frequency. The reference response, in other words, as well as the response being evaluated, is a function of frequency. Since the value of this reference response is itself a variable relative magnitudes thus computed are not direct measures of the changes in transducer response accompanying changes in frequency. To obtain such direct measures it is necessary that the response at each frequency be referred to a fixed response, applicable

to the bearing in question. This response may be that at any suitable frequency, which would then be known as the **reference frequency.** We must, therefore, derive additional formulas by which to compute, for any given bearing, relative responses which are referred to a reference response which remains fixed as frequency is varied.

Response was defined in Art. 4D-1 in terms of the power of sinusoidal electric waves, and of the intensity of acoustic waves. The waves encountered in situations which require that response be considered a function of frequency are likely to be those having continuous spectra. For this reason it will be more convenient if the responses with which we now deal are evaluated in terms of power per unit band and intensity per unit band. It has already been shown that responses applying to sinusoidal waves of given frequency also apply, at that frequency, to waves having continuous spectra.

A general formula for relative response as a function of frequency, when bearing is held at some specified constant value, may be developed in the following manner.

Let

$(U_{in})_f =$ the input power per unit band, at a specified constant frequency, of the energy delivered to a sonar transducer as electric waves having a continuous spectrum (joule/cyc)

$(\eta_{EA})_f =$ the electroacoustic efficiency of the transducer at the specified frequency (a numeric)

Then

$$(U_L)_f = (\eta_{EA})_f (U_{in})_f$$

$=$ the load power per unit band, at the specified frequency, of the total acoustic energy delivered by the transducer (joule/cyc)

Let

$$(J_{aver})_f = \frac{(U_L)_f}{4\pi r^2}$$

$=$ the average intensity per unit band, at the specified frequency, of the acoustic energy passing through a spherical surface, of radius r cm, concentric with the effective center of the transducer (joule/cm²·cyc)

$(\eta_D)_f$ = the directivity factor of the transducer at the specified frequency (a numeric)

Then

$$(J_{do})_f = \frac{(J_{aver})_f}{(\eta_D)_f}$$

= the intensity per unit band, at the specified frequency and at the distance r from the effective center, of the acoustic energy radiated on the maximum response reference axis of the transducer (joule/cm² · cyc)

Let

$(\eta_d)_f$ = the relative transmitting response of the transducer, for the specified frequency and for any given bearing, considered as a function of bearing when the specified frequency is held constant (a numeric)

Then

$$(J_d)_f = (\eta_d)_f (J_{do})_f$$

= the intensity per unit band, at the specified frequency and at the distance r from the effective center of the transducer, of the acoustic energy radiated on the given bearing (joule/cm² · cyc)

Let

$$(\mu_d)_f = \frac{(J_d)_f}{(U_{in})_f}$$

= the transmitting response of the transducer, at the specified frequency and for the given bearing (1/cm²)

By combining the equalities given above it is found that the transmitting response of the transducer, for the specified frequency and for the given bearing, may be written as

$$(\mu_d)_f = \frac{(\eta_d)_f}{(\eta_D)_f} \frac{(\eta_{EA})_f}{4\pi r^2} \qquad (4\text{H-1})$$

Since this relation applies at any frequency it applies at the frequency which may be selected to be the reference frequency. The response at this reference frequency, which is, by definition, the reference response for the given bearing, is then written as

$$(\mu_d)_{fo} = \frac{(\eta_d)_{fo}}{(\eta_D)_{fo}} \frac{(\eta_{EA})_{fo}}{4\pi r^2} \qquad (4\text{H-2})$$

The relative transmitting response of a sonar transducer is defined in Art. 4D-1 as the ratio of the transmitting response for any bearing and for any frequency to the transmitting response for a specified bearing and for a specified frequency. It applies, therefore, both to relative responses considered as functions of bearing for a single specified frequency and to relative responses considered as functions of frequency for a single specified bearing. The equations immediately preceding give expressions for the transmitting response of a transducer for any bearing and for any frequency, and the transmitting response of the same transducer and the same bearing, but for a specified reference frequency. Since this latter response is constant, for the given bearing, the ratio of these two responses is the relative transmitting response of the transducer for this given bearing, considered as a function of frequency. This relative transmitting response may be written as

$$(\eta_f)_d = \frac{(\mu_f)_d}{(\mu_{fo})_d} = \frac{(\mu_d)_f}{(\mu_d)_{fo}}$$

$$= \frac{(\eta_d)_f}{(\eta_d)_{fo}} \frac{(\eta_D)_{fo}}{(\eta_D)_f} \frac{(\eta_{EA})_f}{(\eta_{EA})_{fo}} \qquad (4\text{H-3})$$

where

$(\eta_f)_d$ = the relative transmitting response of a sonar transducer for any given bearing and for any given frequency, but considered a function of frequency for that bearing and referred to the transmitting response of the transducer for that same bearing but for a specified reference frequency (a numeric)

$(\eta_d)_f$ = the relative transmitting response of the same transducer for the same given bearing and for the same given frequency, but considered a function of bearing for that frequency and referred to the transmitting response of the transducer for that same frequency but for a specified reference bearing (a numeric)

$(\eta_d)_{fo}$ = the relative transmitting response of the same transducer for the same given bearing and for the frequency specified as the reference frequency, considered a function of bearing for that reference frequency and re-

219

ferred to the bearing specified as a reference bearing
(a numeric)

$(\eta_D)_f$ = the directivity factor of the transducer for the given frequency
(a numeric)

$(\eta_D)_{fo}$ = the directivity factor of the transducer for the frequency specified as the reference frequency
(a numeric)

$(\eta_{EA})_f$ = the electroacoustic efficiency of the transducer for the given frequency
(a numeric)

$(\eta_{EA})_{fo}$ = the electroacoustic efficiency of the transducer for the frequency specified as the reference frequency
(a numeric)

It is to be noted here that any absolute value of the response of a given sonar transducer, unlike a relative response, is a unique function of bearing and frequency. The question of whether one of the two variables is an independent variable and one a fixed parameter is without significance. When dealing with absolute values of response the response for a given bearing and frequency represented symbolically as a function of bearing for a fixed frequency and the response for the same bearing and frequency, but represented as a function of frequency for a fixed bearing, are the same response.

In the preceding equation the ratio of the two directivity factors and the ratio of the two electroacoustic efficiencies have values which are characteristics of the transducer. Each is a function of frequency, independent of bearing. The two relative transmitting responses, however, apply to a specified bearing at two different frequencies. In computing the value of either it is considered a function of bearing for the frequency to which it applies. The value thus computed is a unique value determined both by the bearing and by the frequency. One of these relative transmitting responses is a fixed reference response, applying to a specified bearing at a specified frequency. The other applies to the same bearing but to a frequency which is considered to be an independent variable. The ratio of the two may, therefore, properly be considered a function of frequency for this specified bearing.

For the maximum response reference bearing the relative responses considered as functions of bearing appearing in Eq. (4H-3) are

$$(\eta_d)_f = (\eta_{do})_f = 1$$

and

$$(\eta_d)_{fo} = (\eta_{do})_{fo} = 1$$

Consequently, for this bearing, the relative transmitting response considered as a function of frequency is

$$(\eta_f)_{do} = \frac{(\eta_D)_{fo}}{(\eta_D)_f} \frac{(\eta_{EA})_f}{(\eta_{EA})_{fo}} \qquad (4H-4)$$

The relative receiving response of a sonar transducer is defined in Art. 4D-1 as the ratio of the receiving response for any bearing and for any frequency to the receiving response for a specified bearing and for a specified frequency. For our present purposes we wish to determine the relative receiving response as a function of frequency for a specified fixed bearing, referred to a reference receiving response for that same bearing but at a specified reference frequency. By definition $(\mu_d)_f = (\mu_f)_d$, and $(\mu_d')_f = (\mu_f')_d$. Consequently, by substituting these equalities into Eq. (4G-25) the receiving response for the specified fixed bearing and for the frequency which is to be considered the independent variable is given at once as

$$(\mu'_f)_d = (\mu_f)_d \left(\frac{cr}{f}\right)^2 \qquad (4H-5)$$

The receiving response for the same bearing, but for the frequency which is specified as the reference frequency, may, in a similar manner, be written as

$$(\mu'_{fo})_d = (\mu_{fo})_d \left(\frac{cr}{f_0}\right)^2 \qquad (4H-6)$$

From these two equations it follows at once that the relative receiving response of a sonar transducer considered as a function of frequency for a specified constant bearing is

$$(\eta'_f)_d = \frac{(\mu'_f)_d}{(\mu'_{fo})_d} = (\eta_f)_d \left(\frac{f_0}{f}\right)^2 \qquad (4H-7)$$

where

$(\eta'_f)_d$ = the relative receiving response of a reversible sonar transducer for any bearing and for any frequency, but considered a function of frequency for that bearing and referred to the receiving response of the transducer for

that same bearing but for a specified reference frequency
(a numeric)

$(\eta_f)_d$ = the relative transmitting response of the same transducer for the same bearing and for the same frequency, also considered a function of frequency for that bearing and referred to the transmitting response of the transducer for that same bearing but for the same specified reference frequency
(a numeric)

f = the value of the independently variable frequency
(cyc/sec)

f_0 = the value of the specified reference frequency, for which the transmitting and receiving responses for the bearing in question are the reference responses
(cyc/sec)

Two marked differences are to be noted between relative responses which are functions of bearing for a constant frequency and relative responses which are functions of frequency for a constant bearing. For responses which are functions of bearing for a constant frequency the relative transmitting response and the relative receiving response of a reversible transducer are always equal. For responses which are functions of frequency for a constant bearing the relative transmitting response and the relative receiving response of a reversible transducer are equal, in general, only for the frequency specified as the reference frequency. The second conspicuous difference is that relative responses which are functions of bearing are independent of the efficiency of the transducer. Relative responses which are functions of frequency depend both on the directional characteristics of the transducer and on the manner in which its efficiency varies with frequency.

The effect of the directional characteristics of a given type of transducer on relative responses considered as functions of frequency may be evaluated by the simple expedient of assuming the efficiency to be independent of frequency. This is equivalent to postulating a hypothetical transducer having the directional characteristics of the type of transducer in question but having a constant electroacoustic efficiency.

4H-2 Spectrum Patterns

A graph showing the relative response of a sonar transducer as a function of frequency for some specified bearing may be described as a **spectrum pattern.** Spectrum patterns bear the same relation to relative response considered as a function of frequency that directivity patterns bear to relative response considered as a function of bearing. For a given transducer, designed to operate over some given frequency band, relative response may be plotted directly against values of frequency. When considering general types of transducer, however, some other quantity, providing what is, in effect, a generalized frequency scale, may be more appropriate.

To illustrate some of the factors of significance in connection with a consideration of relative response as a function of frequency the transmitting and receiving spectrum patterns for a linear transducer will be examined. For a transducer of this type it is convenient to plot relative response as a function of the length of the transducer as measured in wave spaces. For a transducer of given length values of the quantity l/λ, in cycles, are converted to values of frequency, in cycles per second, by multiplying by c/l, where c is the velocity of propagation in the medium postulated. It will be recalled that this is the method used in plotting directivity index in Art. 4F-5. To obtain a spectrum pattern which is determined by the directional characteristics of the transducer, but which is independent of any variations in overall efficiency, it will be assumed that the electroacoustic efficiency is constant, or that $(\eta_{EA})_f = (\eta_{EA})_{fo}$.

The relative response of a linear transducer, considered as a function of frequency, or of a quantity such as l/λ which is proportional to frequency, will first be examined for the maximum response reference axis. For this bearing $\beta = \beta_0 = 0$, and $(\eta_d)_f = (\eta_d)_{fo} = 1$. The relative transmitting response as given by Eq. (4H-3) then reduces to

$$(\eta_f)_{do} = \frac{(\eta_D)_{fo}}{(\eta_D)_f} \qquad (4H\text{-}8)$$

Under the same conditions the relative receiving response given by Eq. (4H-7) reduces to

$$(\eta'_f)_{do} = (\eta_f)_{do}\left[\frac{f_0}{f}\right]^2$$

$$= \frac{(\eta_D)_{fo}}{(\eta_D)_f}\left[\frac{\lambda}{\lambda_0}\right]^2 \qquad (4H\text{-}9)$$

To compute these relative responses for values of l/λ between $l/\lambda = 2$ cycles and $l/\lambda = 10$ cycles it is evident from Fig. 4F-3 that the approximate formula for directivity factor given by Eq. (4F-34) may be used. On making the appropriate substitutions the relative transmitting response of a linear transducer, considered as a function of frequency for the maximum response reference bearing, is found to be

$$(\eta_f)_{do} = \frac{\lambda_0}{\lambda} \frac{\pi^2 - (\lambda_0/l)}{\pi^2 - (\lambda/l)} \qquad (4H\text{-}10)$$

The corresponding relative receiving response is

$$(\eta'_f)_{do} = \frac{\lambda}{\lambda_0} \frac{\pi^2 - (\lambda_0/l)}{\pi^2 - (\lambda/l)} \qquad (4H\text{-}11)$$

In carrying out computations by these formulas it is, of course, necessary to select some suitable frequency as the reference frequency. The curves shown in Fig. 4H-1 have been computed by these formulas using the frequency corresponding to the upper limit of the range covered. For this reference frequency $l/\lambda_0 = 10$ cycles.

Little significance is to be attached to the relation between values of relative transmitting response and values of relative receiving response. Values of these two responses are, by definition, equal at the point corresponding to the reference frequency. This is true regardless of what frequency is selected as the reference frequency. In any case, for the linear transducer relative transmitting response increases with increasing frequency and relative receiving response decreases with increasing frequency. If the frequency corresponding to the lower limit of the range in question had been chosen as the reference frequency the two relative responses would have been equal at the point for which $l/\lambda = 2$ cycles, and the relative receiving response would have been less than the relative transmitting response for all other points.

The effect of the directional characteristics of the transducer on relative responses considered as functions of frequency will be more evident if these responses are examined for some bearing other than the maximum response reference bearing. For this more general case the relative transmitting response of a linear sonar transducer, considered as a function of frequency, is obtained by substituting Eqs. (4E-9) and (4F-34) into Eq. (4H-3). The corresponding relative receiving response is obtained from values thus computed by means of Eq. (4H-7). If we compute, by the formulas thus derived, the responses for the bearing $\beta = 25°$ it is found that the relative transmitting response passes through a maximum when $l/\lambda = 3.4$ cycles. This corresponds to the frequency for which the first secondary maximum falls on this bearing when relative response is considered a function of bearing. At this bearing and this frequency the relative transmitting response and the relative receiving response, considered as functions of bearing, have the value $(\eta_d)_f = (\eta'_d)_f = (0.212)^2$, as stated in Art. 4E-2.

In selecting a reference frequency it is not unreasonable to choose that frequency for which the bearing in question is the bearing of the first secondary maximum of the directivity pattern. When this frequency is chosen $l/\lambda_0 = 3.4$ cycles. This choice has the effect of assigning the value unity to both the relative transmitting response and to the relative receiving response, both considered as functions of frequency, occurring for this value of the independent variable.

Spectrum patterns corresponding to the conditions here postulated are shown in Fig. 4H-2. From these curves it is seen that the relative transmitting response passes through a maximum of unity at the reference frequency. The relative receiving response, on the other hand, passes through a maximum, which is greater than unity, at a lower frequency.

It is to be noted that as the quantity l/λ approaches 2 cyc the relative responses both show rapidly increasing values. This is because the bear-

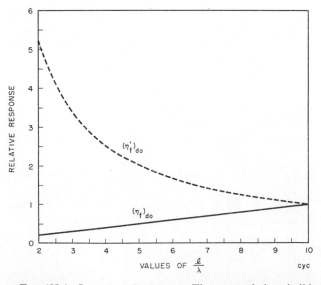

FIG. 4H-1. SPECTRUM PATTERNS. The transmitting (solid line) and receiving (dotted line) spectrum patterns of a linear transducer applying to its maximum response reference bearing, plotted as a function of the factor l/λ, which is proportional to frequency. The reference frequency is that corresponding to the highest value of this factor.

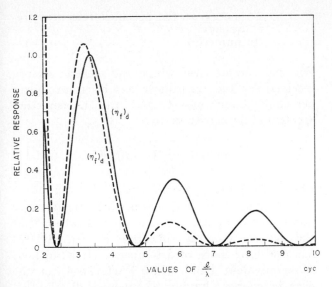

FIG. 4H-2. SPECTRUM PATTERNS. The transmitting (solid line) and receiving (dotted line) spectrum patterns of a linear transducer applying to that bearing which is the bearing of the first minor lobe when $l/\lambda = 3.4$ cycles, plotted as a function of the factor l/λ. The reference frequency is that at which this factor has this value.

ing in question is, by the corresponding reduction in frequency, being brought within the major lobe of the directivity pattern.

4H-3 Spectrum Factor and Spectrum Index

For reasons similar to those which make it desirable to evaluate the integrated effect of the directional characteristics of a sonar transducer it is desirable to evaluate the integrated effect of the manner in which the responses of such a transducer vary with frequency. For this purpose the **transmitting spectrum factor** of a sonar transducer, for a specified bearing, for a specified frequency band, for a specified distribution of energy in that band, and for a specified reference frequency, is defined as the ratio of (1) the index intensity of the acoustic energy radiated over the specified bearing and in the specified frequency band by the transducer when receiving electric energy having a power per unit band which varies with frequency in the specified manner to (2) the index intensity of the acoustic energy which would be radiated over the same bearing and in the same frequency band when receiving the same electric energy if the transmitting response of the transducer for that bearing were the same for any frequency as for the specified reference frequency.

Spectrum factors might be so defined as to

make them unique properties of the transducer, independent of the manner in which energy is distributed throughout some frequency band. This would be accomplished, in the case of the transmitting spectrum factor, by postulating that the received electric energy have a constant power per unit band, independent of frequency. It appears desirable, however, to employ more general definitions and thus to establish general expressions for the integrated responses of the transducer as functions of frequency. An evaluation of the transducer alone may then be obtained by making appropriate simplifications.

The similarities between the definitions for transmitting spectrum factor and for transmitting directivity factor are apparent. There are, however, two important differences between spectrum factors and directivity factors which should be noted in addition to the effect of the manner in which the energy passing through the transducer is distributed in frequency. In the case of a directivity factor the integration is always carried out over the entire surface of a sphere enclosing the transducer; it is, therefore, unnecessary to specify the limits of integration in each individual case. In the case of a spectrum factor it is impossible to fix the limits of integration once for all; it is, therefore, necessary that they be specified, or clearly understood, whenever a value of spectrum factor is to be computed or reported. The second difference is of the same character as the first. In the case of directivity factors the reference bearing is always the maximum response bearing; it need not, therefore, be explicitly specified in each individual case. For spectrum factors, however, the reference frequency, unlike the reference bearing, cannot be established once for all; it, too, must be definitely specified in each use of this quantity.

In deriving an expression for the transmitting spectrum factor of a sonar transducer, for some specified fixed bearing, it will be assumed that the electric energy delivered to that transducer has a continuous spectrum, and that the power per unit band of this energy, at any frequency, is

$$U_{Ef} = \eta_{Ef} U_{Efo} \qquad (4\text{H-}12)$$

Here the quantity η_{Ef} is a relative power per unit band. Its reference magnitude is the power per unit band, U_{Efo}, at the reference frequency, f_0, of the electric energy in question. This relative power per unit band is a function of frequency. In a number of situations encountered in practice

$\eta_{Ef}=(f/f_0)^n$, where n is a fixed exponent, usually negative.

The index value of the intensity per unit band of the acoustic energy radiated on a specified bearing, at any given frequency, is

$$(J_f)_d = (\mu_f)_d\, U_{Ef} = (\mu_f)_d\, \eta_{Ef}\, U_{Efo} \quad (4\text{H-}13)$$

In this equation $(\mu_f)_d$ is the transmitting response of the transducer for the specified fixed bearing and for the given frequency.

The index intensity of the acoustic energy actually radiated on the specified bearing, in the band between the frequencies f_a and f_b, is obtained by integrating the intensity per unit band given by Eq. (4H-13) over the spectrum interval between these two frequencies. The index intensity thus computed is

$$I_{act} = U_{Efo} \int_{f_a}^{f_b} (\mu_f)_d\, \eta_{Ef}\, df \quad (4\text{H-}14)$$

For the reference value of index intensity specified in the definition for transmitting spectrum factor the transmitting response has the constant value $(\mu_{fo})_d$. The reference intensity is, therefore,

$$I_{ref} = (\mu_{fo})_d\, U_{Efo} \int_{f_a}^{f_b} \eta_{Ef}\, df \quad (4\text{H-}15)$$

The transmitting spectrum factor, which is the ratio of these two intensities, is thus seen to be

$$(\eta_F)_d = \frac{I_{act}}{I_{ref}} = \frac{\displaystyle\int_{f_a}^{f_b} (\eta_f)_d\, \eta_{Ef}\, df}{\displaystyle\int_{f_a}^{f_b} \eta_{Ef}\, df} \quad (4\text{H-}16)$$

where

$(\eta_F)_d =$ the transmitting spectrum factor of a sonar transducer, for a specified bearing, a specified frequency band, a specified distribution of energy within that band, and a specified reference frequency (a numeric)

$(\eta_f)_d = (\mu_f)_d/(\mu_{fo})_d$

     = the relative transmitting response of the transducer, considered as a function of frequency, for the specified bearing (a numeric)

$\eta_{Ef} =$ the relative power per unit band, at any frequency, of the electric energy delivered to the transducer referred to the power per unit band of this electric

energy at the specified reference frequency (a numeric)

For the special case where the electric energy received by the transducer has constant power per unit band $\eta_{Ef}=1$ and the transmitting spectrum factor reduces to

$$(\eta_F)_d = \frac{1}{\Delta f}\int_{f_a}^{f_b} (\eta_f)_d\, df \quad (4\text{H-}17)$$

where $\Delta f = f_b - f_a$ cyc/sec.

It is evident by inspection, since the relative power per unit band, η_{Ef}, is dimensionless, that the definite integral appearing in Eq. (4H-15) has the dimensions of a frequency. It is, in fact, the equivalent band width (Art. 2B-4) of the electric energy, having a specified distribution throughout a specified frequency band, for which the spectrum factor is to be computed. That this integral is, indeed, this equivalent band width is seen by examining Eq. (4H-15). Here the quotient $(I_{ref})/(\mu_{fo})_d$ is the power of the electric energy occupying the given frequency band and having the given distribution in this band. This power is, by the definition of equivalent band width, the product of the power per unit band at a specified reference frequency and the equivalent band width. The definite integral must, therefore, be this equivalent band width. This equivalent band width is equal to the actual band width, as shown by Eq. (4H-17), when the relative power per unit band is $\eta_{Ef}=1$.

The expression for transmitting spectrum factor may be said to bear a family resemblance to the expression for directivity factor given by Eq. (4F-5). Where the relative transmitting response of the transducer considered as a function of frequency for a constant bearing appears in the latter, the relative transmitting response considered as a function of bearing for a constant frequency appears in the former.

The **receiving spectrum factor** of a sonar transducer, for a specified bearing, for a specified frequency band, for a specified distribution of energy in that band, and for a specified reference frequency, is the ratio of (1) the available power of the electric energy generated in the specified frequency band by the transducer when receiving over the specified bearing acoustic energy having a free-field intensity per unit band which varies with frequency in the specified manner to (2) the available power of the electric energy which would be generated in the same frequency band and when receiving the same acoustic energy over the same bearing if the receiving response of the transducer for that bearing were the same for any frequency as for the specified reference frequency.

In establishing an expression for the receiving spectrum factor of a sonar transducer we are concerned only with acoustic energy reaching that transducer along a single fixed bearing. It is assumed that this energy arrives in the form of plane waves having a continuous spectrum, and that its free-field intensity per unit band, at any frequency, is

$$(J'_f)_d = \eta'_{Af}(J'_{fo})_d \qquad (4H\text{-}18)$$

Here the quantity η'_{Af} is a relative intensity per unit band. Its reference magnitude is the intensity per unit band, $(J'_{fo})_d$, at the reference frequency, f_0, of the acoustic energy reaching the transducer. This relative intensity per unit band, like the relative power per unit band, η_{Ef}, appearing in Eq. (4H-12), is a function of frequency which is often of the form $\eta'_{Af} = (f/f_0)^n$. For general water noise the nominal value of the exponent is $n = -5/3$.

The available power per unit band, at any given frequency, of the electric energy generated in the transducer in response to the acoustic energy propagated along the specified bearing is

$$(U'_{Ef})_d = (\mu'_f)_d(J'_f)_d = (\mu'_f)_d\,\eta'_{Af}(J'_{fo})_d \quad (4H\text{-}19)$$

The available power of the electric energy actually generated in response to the acoustic energy propagated along the specified bearing and occupying the specified frequency band is obtained by integrating this available power per unit band over the specified band. It is, therefore,

$$(P'_E)_{act} = (J'_{fo})_d \int_{f_a}^{f_b} (\mu'_f)_d\,\eta'_{Af}\,df \quad (4H\text{-}20)$$

For the reference value of available power specified in the definition for receiving spectrum factor the receiving response has the constant value $(\mu'_{fo})_d$. The reference available power is, therefore,

$$(P'_E)_{ref} = (\mu'_{fo})_d(J'_{fo})_d \int_{f_a}^{f_b} \eta'_{Af}\,df \quad (4H\text{-}21)$$

The ratio of these two available powers, which, by definition, is the receiving spectrum factor of the transducer, is

$$(\eta'_F)_d = \frac{(P'_E)_{act}}{(P'_E)_{ref}} = \frac{\int_{f_a}^{f_b} (\eta'_f)_d\,\eta'_{Af}\,df}{\int_f^{f_b} \eta'_{Af}\,df} \quad (4H\text{-}22)$$

where

$(\eta'_F)_d$ = the receiving spectrum factor of a sonar transducer, for a specified bearing, a specified frequency band, a specified distribution of energy within that band, and a specified reference frequency
(a numeric)

$(\eta'_f)_d = (\mu'_f)_d/(\mu'_{fo})_d$

= the relative receiving response of the transducer, considered as a function of frequency for the specified bearing
(a numeric)

η'_{Af} = the relative intensity per unit band, at any frequency, of the acoustic energy reaching the transducer along the specified bearing referred to the intensity per unit band of this acoustic energy of the specified reference frequency
(a numeric)

Here the definite integral appearing in the denominator is the equivalent band width of the acoustic energy received in a specified band and having a specified distribution in that band. When the relative intensity per unit band characteristic of this distribution is $\eta'_{Af} = 1$ this equivalent band width is equal to the actual band width and the receiving spectrum factor reduces to

$$(\eta'_F)_d = \frac{1}{\Delta f}\int_{f_a}^{f_b} (\eta'_f)_d\,df \quad (4H\text{-}23)$$

These expressions differ, as might have been expected, from those for the transmitting spectrum factor only in the substitution of the relative receiving response for the relative transmitting response and in the substitution of a relative intensity per unit band for a relative power per unit band. Since these two relative responses are, in general, not equal, as shown by Eq. (4H-7), and since the relative rates of energy flow are also likely to be different, the transmitting and receiving spectrum factors of a reversible sonar transducer will, in general, not be equal. It will be recalled that the transmitting and receiving directivity factors of a reversible sonar transducer are always equal.

It is sometimes desirable to transmit an echo-ranging signal which, over some limited frequency band, has a continuous spectrum. To provide for this situation the **echo spectrum factor** of a reversible sonar transducer, for a specified bearing, for a specified frequency band, for a specified distribution of energy in that band, and for a specified reference frequency, is defined as the ratio of (1) the available power of the electric energy generated in the specified frequency band by the transducer when receiving over the specified bearing acoustic energy which has previously been radiated over that bearing by the transducer in response to electric energy having a power per unit band which varied with frequency in the specified manner, and which has then been returned to the transducer by a propagation path of given length and given transmission loss, to (2) the available power of the electric energy which would be generated in the same frequency band and when receiving over the same bearing the acoustic energy which would have been radiated over that bearing in response to the same previously received electric energy and returned by the same propagation path, if the product of the transmitting and receiving responses of the transducer for that bearing were the same for any frequency as for the specified reference frequency.

The reference condition specified in this definition requires that the transmitting response of the hypothetical transducer, for the specified bearing, be proportional to frequency and that the receiving response, for the same bearing, be inversely proportional to frequency. This follows from the relation given by Eq. (4G-24). By this relation, when $(\mu_f)_d(\mu'_f)_d = (\mu_{fo})_d(\mu'_{fo})_d$,

$$(\mu_f)^2{}_d\left(\frac{cr}{f}\right)^2 = (\mu_{fo})^2{}_d\left(\frac{cr}{f_0}\right)^2$$

or the transmitting response is

$$(\mu_f)_d = (\mu_{fo})_d(f/f_0) \qquad (4\text{H-}24)$$

Similarly, for the same condition the receiving response must be

$$(\mu'_f)_d = (\mu'_{fo})_d(f_0/f) \qquad (4\text{H-}25)$$

When the electric energy delivered to a sonar transducer used for echo ranging has a continuous spectrum, occupying some specified fre-quency band, the intensity per unit band, at any given frequency, of the acoustic energy returned by a target on some specified fixed bearing depends upon the transmission factor, η''_w, for the transmission path between the transducer and target and upon the transmitting response, $(\mu_f)_d$, of the transducer for the frequency and bearing in question. The free-field intensity per unit band, at any given frequency, of this returned acoustic energy may be written as

$$(J''_f)_d = \eta''_w(\mu_f)_d\,\eta_{Ef}\,U_{Efo} \qquad (4\text{H-}26)$$

Here, as in Eq. (4H-12), $\eta_{Ef}\,U_{Efo} = U_{Ef}$ is the power per unit band, at any given frequency, of the energy initially delivered to the transducer as electric waves having a continuous spectrum.

The available power per unit band, at this same given frequency, of the electric energy generated in the transducer in response to this received acoustic energy is

$$U''_{Ef} = (\mu'_f)_d(J''_f)_d = \eta''_w(\mu_f)_d(\mu'_f)_d\,\eta_{Ef}\,U_{Efo} \qquad (4\text{H-}27)$$

The available power of the electric energy actually generated in the specified frequency band is obtained by integrating this power per unit band between the limits of this specified band. This available power is

$$(P''_E)_{\text{act}} = \eta''_w U_{Efo}\int_{f_a}^{f_b}(\mu_f)_d(\mu'_f)_d\,\eta_{Ef}\,df \qquad (4\text{H-}28)$$

For the reference value of available power specified in the definition for echo spectrum factor the product of the transmitting and receiving responses has the constant value $(\mu_{fo})_d(\mu'_{fo})_d$. The reference available power is, therefore,

$$(P''_E)_{\text{ref}} = \eta''_w(\mu_{fo})_d(\mu'_{fo})_d\,U_{Efo}\int_{f_a}^{f_b}\eta_{Ef}\,df \qquad (4\text{H-}29)$$

The ratio of these two available powers, which is the echo spectrum factor of the transducer when used for echo ranging, is thus

$$(\eta''_F)_d = \frac{(P''_E)_{\text{act}}}{(P''_E)_{\text{ref}}} = \frac{\displaystyle\int_{f_a}^{f_b}(\eta_f)_d(\eta'_f)_d\,\eta_{Ef}\,df}{\displaystyle\int_{f_a}^{f_b}\eta_{Ef}\,df} \qquad (4\text{H-}30)$$

Here, as in Eq. (4H-16), the definite integral appearing in the denominator of this equation is the equivalent band width of the electric energy initially delivered to the transducer. When the relative power per unit band of this energy is $\eta_{Ef}=1$ this equivalent band width is equal to the actual band width and the echo spectrum factor reduces to

$$(\eta''_F)_d = \frac{1}{\Delta f}\int_{f_a}^{f_b}(\eta_f)_d(\eta'_f)_d\,df \qquad (4\text{H-}31)$$

The reference intensity of the acoustic waves and the reference power of the electric waves specified in the definitions for the three spectrum factors have been so chosen that they may be computed with relatively little difficulty. Once a reference value has been computed the value of the actual intensity, or of the actual power, is obtained by multiplying directly by the appropriate spectrum factor. Unfortunately, as already mentioned, spectrum factors, unlike directivity factors, are not unique properties of the transducer but depend, as well, on the manner in which the energy in question is distributed in frequency. As an inspection of the three equations for spectrum factor will show, it is not possible when integrating with respect to frequency to obtain a general figure of merit for the transducer which is independent of the nature of this distribution. The transmitting or receiving response of the transducer, or their product, must be multiplied before integration by the factor by which this energy distribution is evaluated to obtain the resultant function of frequency required. The effect of neither of these factors may be integrated separately. Although a single spectrum factor, applicable to all situations, cannot be established for a given transducer the evaluation of spectrum factors identified with specified types of energy distribution and with frequency bands of specified width is, in a number of problems, of much advantage.

In view of the fact that any spectrum factor which may be computed for a given transducer is not a unique characteristic of that transducer there is little to be gained by establishing a series of formulas similar to those given in Art. 4F-5 for directivity factors. Wherever it is required to find the spectrum factor applying to a given transducer under given specified conditions the product of the relative response of the transducer, and the relative rate at which driving energy is delivered to that transducer, may be plotted as a function of frequency for the bearing in question. For this the reference response and the reference

rate are the response and the rate at whatever frequency is most convenient, or most appropriate, as the reference frequency. The area under the curve thus obtained, when measured between limits defining some given frequency band, then gives the value of the integral appearing in the expression for the spectrum factor sought.

By Eq. (4H-14) it is seen that the actual value of the index intensity of the acoustic energy radiated by a given sonar transducer on a given bearing, and in a given specified frequency band, may be written as

$$I_{\text{act}} = (\mu_{fo})_d U_{Efo}\int_{f_a}^{f_b}(\eta_f)_d\,\eta_{Ef}\,df$$

$$= (J_{fo})_d\int_{f_a}^{f_b}(\eta_f)_d\,\eta_{Ef}\,df \qquad (4\text{H-}32)$$

From a consideration of the dimensional relations implicit in this equation it is evident that the quantity represented by the integral is the width of a frequency band of such magnitude that if the acoustic energy contained within it had an intensity per unit band, at any frequency, equal to the intensity per unit band at the specified reference frequency the resulting intensity would be equal to the actual intensity. This integral, in other words, is the equivalent band width, as defined in Art. 2B-4, of the acoustic energy radiated by the transducer in question along a specified bearing. The transmitting spectrum factor is thus seen to be the ratio of the equivalent band width of the acoustic energy radiated by a given sonar transducer on a given bearing to the equivalent band width of the electric energy delivered to this transducer. In evaluating these equivalent band widths it is understood that the actual widths of the bands occupied by the two energies are the same and that the reference frequencies used in the evaluation are the same.

When a sonar transducer is used as a hydrophone the available power of the electric energy actually generated is shown by Eq. (4H-20) to be

$$(P'_E)_{\text{act}} = (\mu'_{fo})_d(J'_{fo})_d\int_{f_a}^{f_b}(\eta'_f)_d\eta'_{Af}\,df$$

$$= U'_{Efo}\int_{f_a}^{f_b}(\eta'_f)_d\eta'_{Af}\,df \qquad (4\text{H-}33)$$

It thus follows that the receiving spectrum factor is the ratio of the equivalent band width of the electric energy generated in the transducer to the equivalent band width of the acoustic energy reaching that transducer as plane waves propagated along some given bearing.

In a similar manner it may be shown that the echo spectrum factor is the ratio of the equivalent band width of the electric energy generated in a given sonar transducer when echo ranging against a target on a given bearing to the equivalent band width of the electric energy initially delivered to the transducer.

In problems where it is more convenient to deal with transmission losses than with multiplying factors the effect of any spectrum factor may be expressed as a transmission loss in the usual manner. A transmission loss computed in this manner may be described as a **spectrum index,** in continuation of the analogy between spectrum factors and directivity factors. The transmitting spectrum index is written in terms of the transmitting spectrum factor as

$$(N_{SI})_d = \text{lgt} \frac{1}{(\eta_F)_d} \qquad (4\text{H-}34)$$

The receiving spectrum index is, similarly, written in terms of the receiving spectrum factor as

$$(N'_{SI})_d = \text{lgt} \frac{1}{(\eta'_F)_d} \qquad (4\text{H-}35)$$

4-I RESPONSE AS A FUNCTION OF BOTH BEARING AND FREQUENCY

In previous sections we have considered the response of a sonar transducer either as a function of bearing for a constant frequency, or as a function of frequency for a constant bearing. In both cases we have expressed response as a relative magnitude. When responses at a given constant frequency are thus expressed the reference response is the response at that constant frequency and for a bearing specified as a reference bearing. When responses at a given constant bearing are thus expressed the reference response is the response for that constant bearing and at a frequency specified as a reference frequency.

Formulas are available for computing the relative responses of many forms of sonar transducer as functions of bearing for a fixed frequency. These lead to the familiar directivity patterns. By means of Eqs. (4H-3) and (4G-25) it is possible to derive from the relative responses given by these formulas relative responses for a fixed bear-

ing and having a reference response at the same bearing but at a specified reference frequency.

There are many advantages to the use of relative magnitudes. It must be remembered, however, that, in general, relative magnitudes do not convey as much information as do absolute magnitudes. In considering the response of a sonar transducer as a function of both bearing and frequency it is, for this reason, believed that a clearer understanding of the nature of the variations encountered will be obtained by first examining their absolute magnitudes.

4I-1 Further Consideration of the Responses of a Linear Array

To study the manner in which the responses of a sonar transducer, or transducer system, vary with both bearing and frequency we shall direct our attention to a specific example. For this we shall postulate an array having $n = 17$ nondirectional elements spaced along a straight line at intervals of $s = 1$ ft.

To compute the absolute magnitude of the response of this, or of any other sonar transducer, for a given bearing and for a given frequency, it is necessary to have, in addition to information derived for a number of frequencies from the appropriate formula for its relative response considered as a function of bearing for a fixed frequency, information as to its electroacoustic efficiency at each of these frequencies. We shall, therefore, further postulate that the electroacoustic efficiency of the array to be examined shall be $(\eta_{EA})_f = 0.004$ at a frequency of $f_0 = 1000$ cyc/sec, and that it shall be directly proportional to frequency. We may, therefore, write the electroacoustic efficiency of our postulated array, at any frequency, as

$$(\eta_{EA})_f = (\eta_{EA})_{f_0} (f/f_0) = 4.0 \cdot 10^{-6} f$$

where f is in cycles per second.

When we were considering relative response as a function of bearing, for a single fixed frequency, it was shown (Art. 4D-1) that the relative transmitting response for any bearing and for any frequency was equal to the relative receiving response for that same bearing and for that same frequency. By Eq. (4H-5) it is evident that the absolute magnitude of the transmitting response at any bearing and frequency is not equal to the absolute magnitude of the receiving response for that same bearing and that same frequency. We shall, therefore, examine these two responses separately.

The transmitting response of our array may be expressed, in accordance with the relation given by Eq. (4H-1), as

$$(\mu_d)_f = (\mu_f)_d = \frac{(\eta_d)_f (\eta_{EA})_f}{4\pi r^2 (\eta_D)_f}$$

A value has already been assigned to the electro-acoustic efficiency, $(\eta_{EA})_f$.

The relative transmitting response, $(\eta_d)_f$, of the array here in question, considered as a function of bearing for each of several fixed frequencies, is computed by a formula derived from Eq. (4E-2). This formula is

$$(\eta_d)_f = \left[\frac{\sin n\psi}{n \sin \psi} \right]^2$$

where

$$\psi = \frac{\pi s f}{c} \sin \beta$$

Here f is a given value of frequency and β is a given value of bearing for which the relative response is to be computed. The velocity of propagation will here be assumed to be $c = 5000$ ft/sec.

Values of the directivity factor, $(\eta_D)_f$, may be computed by the formula of Eq. (4F-29). They may also be obtained by plotting the derivative function $\mathcal{F}(\beta, f) = (\eta_d)_f \cos \beta$ as a function of bearing for each of the frequencies for which values of response are desired and evaluating the definite integral of this function between $\beta = -\pi/2$ and $\beta = \pi/2$. For an array of the form here postulated the characteristic showing directivity index as a function of frequency is similar to those shown in Fig. 4F-2. It is, in fact, approximately the same, for the frequencies here in question, as the characteristic for $n = \infty$ given by that figure. This characteristic is seen to be a straight line having a slope of 1 db/fl for frequencies greater than that corresponding to $l/\lambda = 0.65$ cyc. In our present problem $l = 16$ ft. This point, then, corresponds to a wave length of

$$\lambda = \frac{16}{0.65} \approx 25 \text{ ft/cyc}$$

or to a frequency of

$$f = \frac{c}{\lambda} \approx \frac{5000}{25} = 200 \text{ cyc/sec}$$

It is intended here to examine the response of the postulated transducer system over the frequency interval between $f = 0$ cyc/sec and $f = 1400$ cyc/sec. At the higher frequency the directivity factor of the array is computed by Eq. (4F-29) as $(\eta_D)_f = 0.1041$. Whenever a directivity index characteristic has a slope of 1 db/fl, as in the present case, it is evident that the reciprocal of the corresponding directivity factor is proportional to frequency. For frequencies between 200 cyc/sec and 1400 cyc/sec, therefore, we may determine the value of the reciprocal of the directivity factor needed for our computations as

$$\frac{1}{(\eta_D)_f} = 0.00687 \, f$$

As frequency decreases progressively below 200 cyc/sec the value of this reciprocal becomes progressively greater than that given by this formula. It reaches the value $1/(\eta_D)_f = 1$ when $f = 0$ cyc/sec.

In the formula for the transmitting response $r = 91.44$ cm is the radius of the constant distance spherical surface on which the index intensity, or the index intensity per unit band, of acoustic energy radiated by the transducer is measured.

By making the substitution

$$(\eta_d)_f = \frac{(\mu_d)_f}{(\mu_{do})_f}$$

in this expression for the transmitting response it is seen that

$$\frac{(\eta_{EA})_f}{(4\pi r^2)(\eta_D)_f} = (\mu_{do})_f$$

is the transmitting response which is used as the reference response in expressing some other response at the same frequency, but at a different bearing, as a relative magnitude. This quantity is a function of frequency which is independent of bearing.

Using the relations described in the preceding paragraphs the transmitting response of a linear array of uniformly spaced nondirectional elements meeting the conditions postulated has been computed for bearings between $\beta = 0°$ and $\beta = 90°$, and for frequencies between $f = 0$ cyc/sec and $f = 1400$ cyc/sec. This transmitting response is found to have a maximum value of $(\mu_d)_f = (\mu_f)_d = 5.13 \cdot 10^{-7}$ 1/cm² at a bearing of $\beta = 0°$ and a frequency of $f = 1400$ cyc/sec. The majority of the values computed are much less than this. They are, in fact, so much less that they cannot well be shown on any graph containing the maximum value. They cannot be shown against a logarithmic scale since responses of zero magnitude must be plotted. Any transmitting response is, however, the index magnitude of the intensity of the acoustic energy which would be radiated if the electric energy delivered to the transducer were in the form of sinusoidal waves having a power of one watt. A graphical presentation may, therefore, be obtained by plotting values of the acoustic pressure corresponding to this index intensity. This pressure is computed from the transmitting response by the relation

$$(\mu_d)_f = (\mu_f)_d = \frac{(p_d)^2_f \cdot 10^{-7}}{\rho c \, (P_{Ed})_f}$$

Assuming that the acoustic conductance per unit area has the constant value $1/\rho c = 6.5 \cdot 10^{-6}$ acoustic mhos the acoustic pressure is

$$(p_d)_f = (p_f)_d = 1.24 \cdot 10^6 \sqrt{(\mu_d)_f} \ \mu b$$

Values of acoustic pressure computed in this manner are shown by the three-coordinate graph of Fig. 4I-1.

The receiving response of the array is computed from the transmitting response by the relation, given in Eq. (4G-25),

$$(\mu'_d)_f = (\mu'_f)_d = (\mu_d)_f \left(\frac{cr}{f}\right)^2$$

In applying the conversion factor, $(cr/f)^2$, the velocity of propagation, c, must be in centimeters per second if the radius, r, of the constant distance sphere used in computing transmitting response is in centimeters.

It is to be remembered that the derivation of this relation, as given in Art. 4G-3, is valid, for a system of the type here in question, only over the region where the directivity factor is inversely proportional to frequency. The computation of receiving response will, however, be extended somewhat beyond this region, which is characterized by the fact that, in this particular problem, the receiving response for a bearing of $\beta = 0°$ is independent of frequency. The reason for this extension will be discussed later. It is to be noted, in this connection, that it is not possible to drive a sonar transducer by acoustic energy at a frequency of zero. To do so would require that its

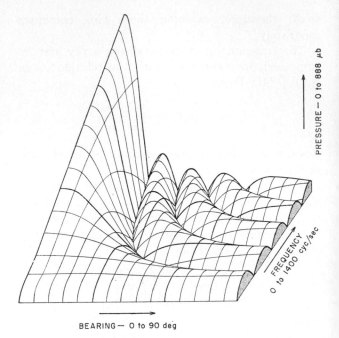

BEARING— 0 to 90 deg

FIG. 4I-1. TRANSMITTING RESPONSE OF A LINEAR ARRAY. The acoustic pressure developed by a linear array of 17 uniformly spaced elements when receiving sinusoidal electric waves of constant power, plotted as a function of the frequency and bearing of the radiated acoustic waves.

active surface be displaced by an infinite amount as shown by Eq. (2A-4). It is, on the other hand entirely possible to drive such a transducer by electric energy at a frequency of zero. All that is required is that its electric terminals be connected to a direct-current generator. When this is done, however, no acoustic energy will be radiated. This is in agreement with the conclusion that the transmitting response is zero at this frequency.

It is desirable that the results of computations of receiving response be presented graphically in a manner similar to that used for transmitting response. This may be done. Any receiving response is the magnitude of the available power of the electric energy which would be generated in a transducer if the acoustic energy received by it were in the form of plane sinusoidal waves having an acoustic intensity of one watt per square centimeter. We wish to plot the open-circuit electric voltage corresponding to this available power. To do so it is necessary to know the resistive component of the electric impedance at each frequency. In general this resistance, unlike the acoustic conductance per unit area used in computing acoustic pressure from acoustic intensity, is not independent of frequency. For our present purposes, however, we may compute the voltage which would be generated if the electric resistance between the terminals of the array were constant. For convenience we will assume that this resistance has a magnitude of $R = 0.25$ ohms. The open-circuit voltage is computed from the receiving response by the relation

$$(\mu'_d)_f = (\mu'_f)_d = \frac{(e_d)^2{}_f}{4R(I_d)_f}$$

Under the conditions assumed it is thus seen to have the value

$$(e_d)_f = (e_f)_d = \sqrt{(\mu'_d)_f}$$

Values of open-circuit electric voltage computed on the basis of these assumptions are shown by the three-coordinate graph of Fig. 4I-2.

It is evident from an examination of the two graphs of Figs. 4I-1 and 4I-2 that the variations of the transmitting response of a sonar transducer differ in a number of respects from the variations of the receiving response. The two are, however, alike with respect to the pairs of bearing-frequency values at which they pass through zero. The

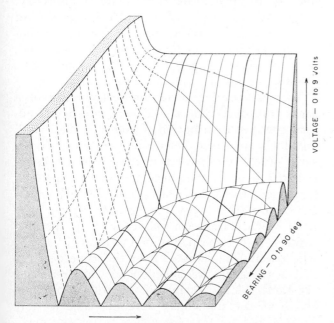

FREQUENCY — 0 to 1400 cyc/sec

FIG. 4I-2. RECEIVING RESPONSE OF A LINEAR ARRAY. The electric voltage developed by a linear array of 17 uniformly spaced elements, having an electric conductance which is independent of frequency and an efficiency as an acoustic radiator which is proportional to frequency, when receiving plane sinusoidal acoustic waves of constant intensity, plotted as a function of the frequency and direction of propagation of these acoustic waves.

traces on the zero pressure and zero voltage planes have values of bearing and of frequency for which the product, $n\psi$, of the phase factor and the number of array elements is equal to an integral multiple of π. Since

$$n\psi = q\pi = \frac{n\pi sf}{c} \sin \beta$$

these traces must pass through points for which

$$f \sin \beta = \frac{qc}{ns}$$

Portions of the traces corresponding to values of $q = 1, 2, 3,$ and 4 may be seen on the graphs.

The three-coordinate graphs showing the pressure and voltage responses of the array are also alike with respect to the shape of the constant frequency contours for any given frequency. These contours correspond directly to the familiar directivity patterns. The relative pressures, or relative voltages, usually plotted as directivity patterns are, in fact, the relative magnitudes obtained by dividing any of the responses indicated by such a contour line by the value corresponding to the point on that contour which falls in the zero bearing plane.

There is a marked difference between the transmitting and receiving responses of a sonar transducer with respect to the manner in which they vary with frequency for a given bearing. If the two constant bearing contours for any given bearing are examined it will be found that they are unlike in shape. They do meet the zero response plane at the same pairs of bearing-frequency values; their maxima, on the other hand, do not occur at the same pairs of bearing-frequency values. Constant bearing contours on either of the two response surfaces lead directly to spectrum patterns. No choice of reference frequency will, however, cause the transmitting spectrum pattern for any given bearing to be the same as the receiving spectrum pattern for that bearing.

An examination of the two response surfaces shown in Figs. 4I-1 and 4I-2 gives some indication as to how best to choose a reference frequency for the computation of relative transmitting and receiving responses as functions of frequency for various constant bearings. The problem of selecting a frequency at which to find the reference response, either transmitting or receiving, to be used for expressing as relative magnitudes other responses at the same bearing has no counterpart when evaluating relative responses for a constant frequency. The bearing at which to find the reference response to be used in expressing as relative magnitudes other responses at the same frequency is always definitely established. It is that bearing on which a point at a distance from the transducer which is large as compared with the dimensions of the transducer may be said to be equidistant from all elements of the transducer. All of the many formulas for directivity patterns are derived in terms of energy leaving from or arriving at such a point. In the case of relative response considered as a function of frequency for a constant bearing the frequency of the reference response is not fixed in any such definite manner. It is, instead, usually a matter of arbitrary choice.

In any problem having to do with the transmission of energy along a single bearing this choice is rarely difficult. It is sufficient to make certain that the frequency selected is one for which the transducer has a finite response on the bearing in question. In many problems, however, we are interested in energy transmitted, or received, over bearings making up some specified angle. An examination of the three-coordinate graphs of Figs. 4I-1 and 4I-2 shows at once that for many frequency bands there may be no single frequency for which there will not be one or more bearings for which the response is zero. There may, in other words, be no single frequency at which a response suitable for use as a reference magnitude is to be found on all bearings. In such cases it may be desirable to employ responses which occur at frequencies which vary with bearing. In many problems, however, it may be simpler to select a reference frequency which is outside the particular frequency band of interest. There is nothing in the derivation of the relations between response, bearing, and frequency which requires that the reference frequency be between the limits defining any band within which these relations actually apply. It is not, indeed, necessary that the response to be used as a reference magnitude be an actual response. It is sufficient that it be the response which would be computed for the selected frequency by an extension of the relations known, or assumed, to apply throughout the frequency band of interest. It is permissible, in other words, to compute relative responses in terms of hypothetical reference responses. The fact that such a response does not exist physically

in no way impairs its utility as a reference magnitude to be used mathematically.

In the case of the array postulated for our illustrative example it is evident that for any frequency less than $f = c/ns = 294$ cyc/sec there will be a response for any bearing between $\beta = 0°$ and $\beta = 90°$. An inspection of Fig. 4I-2 suggests that $f_0 = 200$ cyc/sec would be a convenient reference frequency. As already noted, it is not necessary that a receiving response to be used as a reference magnitude be an actual response. In the region where constant bearing and constant frequency contours are shown by Figs. 4I-1 and 4I-2 as dotted lines the responses are not necessarily actual responses; they are, however, responses which are related to actual responses in a definite and convenient manner.

4I-2 Directivity Factors for Frequency Bands of Finite Width

There are many problems in which it is necessary to consider the integrated response of a sonar transducer, or of an array of transducers, when the acoustic energy radiated or received is distributed with respect to both bearing and frequency. In such problems we find it necessary, in general, to carry out a double integration of the response. The result may be described either as a directivity factor for a finite frequency band, or as a spectrum factor for a finite solid angle. The former description will be used here.

The **transmitting band directivity factor** of a sonar transducer, for a specified frequency band, for a specified distribution of energy in that band, and for a specified reference frequency, is the ratio of (1) the power of the acoustic energy radiated over all bearings and in the specified frequency band by the transducer when receiving electric energy having a power per unit band which varies with frequency in the specified manner to (2) the power of the acoustic energy which would be radiated over the same bearings and in the same frequency band when receiving the same electric energy, if the transmitting response of the transducer were the same for any bearing and for any frequency as for the maximum response reference bearing and for the specified reference frequency.

In deriving expressions for this and other band directivity factors attention will be restricted to transducers having three-dimensional directivity patterns each of which may be generated by rotating a two-dimensional pattern about the maximum response reference axis. Formulas for a transducer having an axis of acoustic symmetry which is perpendicular to a maximum response plane may be obtained at once by modifying formulas thus derived in a manner similar to that by which Eq. (4F-5) is modified to give Eq. (4F-6).

For a transducer in which the maximum response reference axis is an axis of acoustic symmetry the power per unit band, at any frequency, of the acoustic energy radiated on all bearings is

$$(U_A)_f = 2\pi r^2 U_{Efo} \int_0^\pi (\mu_d)_f \, \eta_{Ef} \sin \beta \, d\beta \quad (4\text{I-1})$$

Here, as in formulas for spectrum factors, η_{Ef} is the relative rate at which electric energy is delivered to the transducer at any frequency referred to the rate, U_{Efo}, at the specified reference frequency.

The power of the acoustic energy actually radiated on all bearings and at all frequencies in the specified frequency band is obtained by integrating this power per unit band over the specified band. This second integration gives

$$(P_A)_{\text{act}} = 2\pi r^2 U_{Efo} \int_{f_a}^{f_b} \int_0^\pi (\mu_d)_f \, \eta_{Ef} \sin \beta \, d\beta \, df \quad (4\text{I-2})$$

For the reference value of power specified in the definition for transmitting band directivity factor the transmitting response has the constant value $(\mu_{do})_{fo} = (\mu_{fo})_{do}$ associated with the maximum response reference bearing and with the specified reference frequency. The reference power is, therefore,

$$(P_A)_{\text{ref}} = 2\pi r^2 (\mu_{do})_{fo} U_{Efo} \int_{f_a}^{f_b} \int_0^\pi \eta_{Ef} \sin \beta \, d\beta \, df$$

$$= 4\pi r^2 (\mu_{do})_{fo} U_{Efo} \int_{f_a}^{f_b} \eta_{Ef} \, df \quad (4\text{I-3})$$

When we take the ratio of these two powers there appears, under an integral sign, the relative response $(\mu_d)_f/(\mu_{do})_{fo}$. This is unlike any relative response which we have encountered heretofore. In the present case both the bearing and the frequency of the reference response differ from the bearing and the frequency of the response being expressed as a relative magnitude. This relative response may be written as the product of two

other relative responses, as follows.

$$\frac{(\mu_d)_f}{(\mu_{do})_{fo}} = \frac{(\mu_d)_f}{(\mu_{do})_f} \frac{(\mu_{do})_f}{(\mu_{do})_{fo}}$$

$$= \frac{(\mu_d)_f}{(\mu_{do})_f} \frac{(\mu_f)_{do}}{(\mu_{fo})_{do}} \quad (4\text{I-4})$$

The first of the two ratios on the right of the final expression is the relative transmitting response considered as a function of bearing for the given frequency. The reference response here is the response for the given frequency and for the maximum response reference bearing. The second of the two ratios is the relative transmitting response considered as a function of frequency for the maximum response reference bearing. The reference response here is the response for the maximum response reference bearing and for the specified reference frequency. The relative response in question may, therefore, be written as

$$\frac{(\mu_d)_f}{(\mu_{do})_{fo}} = (\eta_d)_f (\eta_f)_{do} \quad (4\text{I-5})$$

The process which is implicit in this expression may be described graphically in terms of the absolute responses plotted in Fig. 4I-1. The response, $(\mu_d)_f = (\mu_f)_d$, which is to be expressed as a relative magnitude is reported on this graph at the given bearing, β, and the given frequency, f, in terms of the corresponding acoustic pressure. This response is first expressed as a relative magnitude in terms of a reference response, $(\mu_{do})_f$, which is reported in the same constant frequency plane but at the intersection of this plane with the constant bearing plane containing reports of the response on the maximum response reference bearing. The response, $(\mu_{do})_f = (\mu_f)_{do}$, reported at the intersection of the constant frequency plane and the reference bearing plane is then, in its turn, expressed as a relative magnitude in terms of a reference response, $(\mu_{fo})_{do}$, which is reported in the same reference bearing plane but at the intersection of this plane with the constant frequency plane containing reports of responses at the specified reference frequency. The relative response in question is the product of these two relative responses. In this manner the response at any bearing and any frequency may be referred to a reference response at any other specified bearing and any other specified frequency.

It may be shown, both analytically and graphically, that the relative response in question may also be expressed as the product of a relative response considered as a function of frequency for the given bearing and a relative response considered as a function of bearing for a specified reference frequency. This is written as

$$\frac{(\mu_d)_f}{(\mu_{do})_{fo}} = \frac{(\mu_f)_d}{(\mu_{fo})_{do}} = (\eta_f)_d\,(\eta_d)_{fo} \qquad (4I\text{-}6)$$

With these relations in mind we may take the ratio of the two powers given by Eqs. (4I-2) and (4I-3) to obtain expressions for the transmitting band directivity factor. This ratio is thus found to be

$$(\eta_D)_{\Delta f} = \frac{\dfrac{1}{2}\displaystyle\int_{f_a}^{f_b}\int_0^\pi (\eta_d)_f(\eta_f)_{do}\,\eta_{Ef}\,\sin\beta\,d\beta\,df}{\displaystyle\int_{f_a}^{f_b}\eta_{Ef}\,df} \qquad (4I\text{-}7)$$

$$= \frac{\dfrac{1}{2}\displaystyle\int_{f_a}^{f_b}\int_0^\pi (\eta_f)_d(\eta_d)_{fo}\,\eta_{Ef}\,\sin\beta\,d\beta\,df}{\displaystyle\int_{f_a}^{f_b}\eta_{Ef}\,df} \qquad (4I\text{-}8)$$

where

$(\eta_D)_{\Delta f} =$ the transmitting band directivity factor of a sonar transducer for a specified frequency band, for a specified distribution of energy in that band, and for a specified reference frequency
(a numeric)

$(\eta_d)_f =$ the relative transmitting response of the transducer for any bearing and for any frequency, considered as a function of bearing for that frequency and referred to the transmitting response for that same frequency but for the maximum response reference bearing
(a numeric)

$(\eta_f)_{do} =$ the relative transmitting response of the transducer for any frequency but for the maximum response reference bearing, considered as a function of frequency for that bearing and referred to the transmitting response for that same bearing but for the specified reference frequency
(a numeric)

$(\eta_f)_d =$ the relative transmitting response of the transducer for any bearing and for any frequency, considered as a func-

tion of frequency for that bearing and referred to the transmitting response for the same bearing but for the specified reference frequency
(a numeric)

$(\eta_d)_{fo} =$ the relative transmitting response of the transducer for any bearing but for the specified reference frequency, considered as a function of bearing for that frequency and referred to the transmitting response for that same frequency but for the maximum response reference bearing
(a numeric)

$\eta_{Ef} =$ the relative power per unit band of the electric energy delivered to the transducer at any frequency referred to the power per unit band of this electric energy at the specified reference frequency
(a numeric)

$\beta =$ the bearing deviation angle
(rad)

As in Eq. (4H-16) for the transmitting spectrum factor the integral appearing in the denominators of these equations is the equivalent band width of the electric energy, occupying the specified frequency band with the specified distribution, delivered to the transducer.

In the first of these two expressions $(\eta_f)_{do}$ and η_{Ef} are not functions of bearing. By holding frequency constant, therefore, and integrating with respect to bearing we obtain

$$(\eta_D)_{\Delta f} = \frac{\displaystyle\int_{f_a}^{f_b}(\eta_D)_f(\eta_f)_{do}\,\eta_{Ef}\,df}{\displaystyle\int_{f_a}^{f_b}\eta_{Ef}\,df} \qquad (4I\text{-}9)$$

where

$(\eta_D)_f =$ the directivity factor of the transducer, considered as a function of frequency
(a numeric)

In a similar manner, since the quantities $(\eta_d)_{fo}$ and $\sin\beta$ are not functions of frequency, we may hold bearing constant and integrate with respect to frequency to obtain

$$(\eta_D)_{\Delta f} = \frac{1}{2}\int_0^\pi (\eta_F)_d(\eta_d)_{fo}\,\sin\beta\,d\beta \qquad (4I\text{-}10)$$

where

$(\eta_F)_d =$ the transmitting spectrum factor of the

transducer for the specified frequency band and the specified distribution of energy in that band, considered as a function of bearing (a numeric)

We next define the **receiving band directivity factor** of a sonar transducer, for a specified frequency band, for a specified distribution of energy in that band, and for a specified reference frequency, as the ratio of (1) the available power of the electric energy generated in the specified frequency band by the transducer when receiving over all bearings acoustic energy having a free-field intensity per unit band which is the same for all bearings and which varies with frequency in the specified manner to (2) the available power of the electric energy which would be generated in the same frequency band when receiving the same acoustic energy over the same bearings, if the receiving response of the transducer were the same for any bearing and for any frequency as for the maximum response reference bearing and for the specified reference frequency.

It is unnecessary to repeat here the steps by which formulas for the receiving band directivity factor are developed. A comparison of these formulas, as given below, with formulas already derived for directivity factors, for spectrum factors, and for the transmitting band directivity factor, will show that they adhere to a pattern which is now clearly apparent. The formulas for the receiving band directivity factor are

$$(\eta'_D)_{\Delta f} = \frac{\int_{f_a}^{f_b} (\eta'_D)_f (\eta'_f)_{do} \, \eta'_{Af} \, df}{\int_{f_a}^{f_b} \eta'_{Af} \, df} \quad (4I\text{-}11)$$

$$= \frac{1}{2} \int_0^{\pi} (\eta'_F)_d (\eta'_d)_{fo} \sin \beta \, d\beta \quad (4I\text{-}12)$$

where

$(\eta'_D)_{\Delta f}$ = the receiving band directivity factor of a sonar transducer for a specified frequency band, for a specified distribution of energy in that band, and for a specified reference frequency (a numeric)

η'_{Af} = the relative intensity per unit band, at any frequency, of the acoustic energy reaching the transducer along any bearing referred to the intensity

per unit band of this acoustic energy at the specified reference frequency (a numeric)

Other factors appearing in these equations are similar to those appearing in Eqs. (4I-9) and (4I-10) except that they apply to the reception of acoustic energy rather than to its radiation.

The **band reverberation factor** of a reversible sonar transducer, for a specified frequency band, for a specified distribution of energy in that band, and for a specified reference frequency, is the ratio of (1) the available power of the electric energy generated in the specified frequency band by the transducer when receiving over all bearings acoustic energy which has previously been radiated over those bearings by the transducer in response to electric energy having a power per unit band which varied with frequency in the specified manner, and which has then been returned to the transducer over propagation paths of equal length and equal transmission loss, to (2) the available power of the electric energy which would be generated in the same frequency band when receiving over the same bearings the acoustic energy which would have been radiated over those bearings in response to the same previously received electric energy and returned by the same propagation paths, if the product of the transmitting and receiving responses of the transducer were the same for any bearing and for any frequency as for the maximum response reference bearing and for the specified reference frequency.

The receiving band directivity factor may be written as

$$(\eta''_D)_{\Delta f} = \frac{\int_{f_a}^{f_b} (\eta''_D)_f (\eta_f)_{do} (\eta'_f)_{do} \, \eta_{Ef} \, df}{\int_{f_a}^{f_b} \eta_{Ef} \, df} \quad (4I\text{-}13)$$

$$= \frac{1}{2} \int_0^{\pi} (\eta''_F)_d (\eta_d)_{fo} (\eta'_d)_{fo} \sin \beta \, d\beta \quad (4I\text{-}14)$$

where

$(\eta''_D)_{\Delta f}$ = the receiving band directivity factor of a reversible sonar transducer, for a specified frequency band, for a specified distribution of energy in that band, and for a specified reference frequency (a numeric)

$(\eta''_D)_f$ = the reverberation factor of the transducer, considered as a function of frequency
(a numeric)

$(\eta''_F)_d$ = the echo spectrum factor of the transducer, considered as a function of bearing
(a numeric)

The manner in which any of the formulas for band directivity factors may be assembled from the corresponding formulas for directivity factors and spectrum factors will be at once evident when these formulas are compared. The integrand in the formula for the transmitting band directivity factor is seen to be the product of the transmitting directivity factor and the integrand appearing in the formula for the spectrum factor applying to the maximum response reference bearing. It is also the product of the transmitting spectrum factor and the integrand appearing in the formula for the directivity factor applying to the specified reference frequency. If either the directivity factor or the spectrum factor is known, one as a function of frequency and the other as a function of bearing, the computation of the band directivity factor reduces to a single integration. Analogous relations are seen to exist for the receiving band directivity factor and for the band reverberation factor.

As with directivity factors and spectrum factors the relative magnitude associated with a band directivity factor may be expressed in terms of a corresponding transmission loss. Such a transmission loss would be described as a **band directivity index,** in the usual manner.

4I-3 Application of Spectrum Factors and Band Directivity Factors

The use of directivity factors, or of directivity indexes, in expressing the manner in which a directional hydrophone discriminates, at any one specified frequency, against interference arriving along bearings other than the maximum response bearing is discussed in Art. 4F-2. It is there shown that the receiving directivity factor gives at once the improvement in signal-to-noise ratio resulting from this discrimination when the transducer is used for receiving an acoustic signal from a distant source. In a similar manner it has been shown that the reverberation factor gives at once the improvement in echo-to-reverberation ratio resulting when the transducer is used reversibly for echo ranging. When dealing with signals and with interference having continuous spectra, and occupying frequency bands of finite width, the improvement in signal-to-noise ratio, or in echo-to-reverberation ratio, is not given by a single spectrum factor, or by a single band directivity factor. This is due, in part, to the fact that here it is necessary to take fully into account the manner in which both the signal energy and the interfering energy are distributed with respect to frequency.

Stated generally, the problem is to compare the signal-to-interference ratio of the electric energies generated in a given directional hydrophone, when receiving an acoustic signal over its maximum response bearing, with the signal-to-interference ratio of the acoustic energies as they exist in the water at the hydrophone location.

The signal-to-interference ratio existing in the electric output of a given directional hydrophone is the ratio of the available power $(P'_s)_{act}$, of the electric energy generated in response to the acoustic signal received over the maximum response axis to the available power, $(P'_n)_{act}$, of the electric energy generated in response to the acoustic interference received over all bearings. The available power of the electric signal energy is the actual power specified in the definition for the receiving spectrum factor, as this factor applies to the maximum response reference axis of the given hydrophone. The available power of the interfering electric energy is the actual power specified in the definition for the receiving band directivity factor. Each of these factors applies to a specified frequency band and to a specified distribution of energy in that band.

The signal-to-interference ratio existing in the water at the hydrophone location is the ratio of the free-field intensity, I'_s, of the acoustic signal reaching the hydrophone location along a single propagation path to the free-field equivalent plane wave intensity, I'_n, of the acoustic interference reaching the same point from all directions.

We now imagine the given hydrophone to be replaced by an ideal reference hydrophone. This is a nondirectional hydrophone having a receiving response for any bearing and for any frequency which is equal to the receiving response, $(\mu'_{do})_{fo}$, of the given hydrophone for its maximum response reference bearing and for the specified reference frequency. The available power of the electric energy which would be generated in this hypothetical hydrophone in response to the acoustic signal is $(P'_s)_{ref} = (\mu'_{do})_{fo} I'_s$. This is the reference power specified in the definition for the receiving spectrum factor applying to the maximum response axis. The available power of the electric energy which would be generated in response to the acoustic interference is $(P'_n)_{ref} = (\mu'_{do})_{fo} I'_n$. This is the reference power specified in the definition for the receiving band directivity factor. It is evident that the ratio of the powers associated with the electric signal and the electric interference present in the output of the hypothetical reference hydrophone is the same as the ratio of the intensities associated with the acoustic signal and the acoustic interference present in the water. That is,

$$\frac{(P'_s)_{ref}}{(P'_n)_{ref}} = \frac{I'_s}{I'_n} \qquad (4I\text{-}15)$$

To evaluate the signal-to-interference advantage of a directional hydrophone at a single frequency we computed (Art. 4F-1) the ratio of the power per unit band of the electric interference generated in the given hydrophone to the power per unit band of the electric interference which would be generated in a reference hydrophone. In that case the powers per unit band of the electric signals generated in the two were equal. The ratio of the two noise powers per unit band was, in that case, found to be equal to the receiving directivity factor of the given hydrophone. In the present case the powers of the electric signals generated in the given and reference hydrophones are not the same. It is necessary, therefore, to multiply the ratio of the powers of the two interfering energies by the inverse ratio of the two signal energies. The measure of the signal-to-interference advantage of a directional hydrophone receiving acoustic energy occupying frequency bands of finite width is thus found to be

$$\frac{(P'_n)_{act}}{(P'_n)_{ref}} \frac{(P'_s)_{ref}}{(P'_s)_{act}} = \frac{(\eta'_D)_{\Delta f}}{(\eta'_F)_{do}} \qquad (4I\text{-}16)$$

It is, in other words, the receiving directivity factor applying to the interference received over all bearings divided by the receiving spectrum factor applying to the signal received over the maximum response axis of the transducer. Each of these factors applies to energy which is distributed throughout a specified frequency band in a manner which must be definitely specified. In general the two distributions will not be the same. The formula does, in fact, apply when the bands occupied by the signal and by the interference are not the same. This is essential, since

there are circumstances under which the band occupied by a given signal may be significantly less than the band occupied by the interference.

The relations which have been considered in the preceding paragraphs may be examined further in terms of transmission levels and level differentials. For this the intensity of the received acoustic signal energy is written as

$$I'_s = (J'_s)_{fo} \int_{f_a}^{f_b} (\eta'_{Af})_s \, df \qquad (4I\text{-}17)$$

where

$I'_s =$ the intensity of the acoustic energy of the signal received over the maximum response axis of a given hydrophone (watt/cm²)

$(J'_s)_{fo} =$ the intensity per unit band of this acoustic energy at the specified reference frequency (joule/cm²·cyc)

$(\eta'_{Af})_s =$ the relative intensity per unit band of this energy at any frequency, referred to the intensity per unit band at the specified reference frequency (a numeric)

$f_a =$ the lower limiting frequency of the specified frequency band (cyc/sec)

$f_b =$ the upper limiting frequency of this band (cyc/sec)

It will be recalled that the value of the definite integral appearing here is the equivalent band width associated with the acoustic energy in question.

The available power of the electric energy generated in the hydrophone in response to this acoustic signal energy is

$$(P'_s)_{act} = (\eta'_F)_{do}(U'_s)_{fo} \int_{f_a}^{f_b} (\eta'_{Af})_s \, df$$

$$= (\eta'_F)_{do}(\mu'_{do})_{fo}(J'_s)_{fo} \int_{f_a}^{f_b} (\eta'_{Af})_s \, df \qquad (4I\text{-}18)$$

where

$(P'_s)_{act} =$ the available power of the electric energy generated in the given hydrophone in response to the given acoustic signal (watt)

$(\eta'_F)_{do} =$ the receiving spectrum factor of the

given hydrophone applying to the maximum response reference axis of this hydrophone, to the specified frequency band, to the specified distribution of energy in this band, and to the specified reference frequency (a numeric)

$(\mu'_{do})_{fo}$ = the receiving response of the given hydrophone for its maximum response reference axis and for the specified reference frequency (cm²)

It will here be recalled that the product of the receiving spectrum factor and the equivalent band width of the received acoustic energy is the equivalent band width of the generated electric energy.

By combining Eqs. (4I-17) and (4I-18) we obtain

$$(P'_s)_{act} = I'_s(\eta'_F)_{do}(\mu'_{do})_{fo} \qquad (4I-19)$$

The available power of the generated electric energy given by this equation may now be expressed in terms of a transmission level by the relation

$$(L'_s)_E = \lgt (P'_s)_{act} \ db//1 \ watt \qquad (4I-20)$$

The free-field intensity of the received acoustic energy may be similarly expressed by the relation

$$(L'_s)_A = \lgt (I'_s) \ db//1 \ watt/cm^2 \qquad (4I-21)$$

Finally, the receiving spectrum factor may be expressed in terms of a transmission loss by the usual relation between spectrum index and spectrum factor

$$(N'_{SI})_{do} = \lgt \frac{1}{(\eta'_F)_{do}} \ db \qquad (4I-22)$$

The level of the generated electric signal energy is thus written as

$$(L'_s)_E = (L'_s)_A - (N'_{SI})_{do}$$
$$+ \lgt (\mu'_{do})_{fo} \ db//1 \ watt \qquad (4I-23)$$

In a similar manner the level of the generated electric interference may be written in terms of the level of the acoustic interference and the receiving band directivity index as

$$(L'_n)_E = (L'_n)_A - (N'_{DI})_{\Delta f}$$
$$+ \lgt (\mu'_{do})_{fo} \ db//1 \ watt \qquad (4I-24)$$

The signal differential (Art. 2C-2) characteristic

of the electric output of the hydrophone may now be written as

$$(L'_s)_E - (L'_n)_E = [(L'_s)_A - (N'_{SI})_{do}]$$
$$- [(L'_n)_A - (N'_{DI})_{\Delta f}] \ db \qquad (4I-25)$$

On comparing the term $(L'_n)_A - (N'_{DI})_{\Delta f}$ with Eq. (4F-25) it is evident that this term represents the apparent plane wave level of the interference. In a similar manner the term $(L'_s)_A - (N'_{SI})_{do}$ represents the apparent level of the signal. When we were considering the reception of acoustic energy at a single frequency, as we were in Art. 4F-3, the desirability of introducing the concept of an apparent signal level did not arise. There the apparent level of the signal and the actual level were the same.

An expression for the improvement in signal-to-noise ratio resulting from the use of a given directional transducer receiving acoustic energy occupying a frequency band of finite width is obtained by rearranging the terms of Eq. (4I-25). When this is done the amount by which the signal differential as measured at the electric terminals of the directional transducer exceeds the signal differential of the acoustic energy reaching the transducer is found to be

$$(\Delta L'_E)_{s/n} - (\Delta L'_A)_{s/n} = (N'_{DI})_{\Delta f} - (N'_{SI})_{do} \qquad (4I-26)$$

Here the signal differential of the acoustic energy is the amount by which the level of the acoustic signal exceeds the equivalent plane wave level of the acoustic interference as this interference would be measured by a nondirectional hydrophone. It is seen by this equation that the improvement in signal differential is equal to the directivity index applying to the noise in the frequency band in question less the spectrum index applying to the signal occupying the same band. If attention were to be restricted to a single frequency the spectrum index applying to the signal would be zero and this expression for the improvement in signal-to-noise ratio would reduce to the directivity index of the transducer at that frequency. We thus see that Eq. (4I-26) is a more general expression for the relation previously given by Eq. (4F-25).

In a manner similar to that by which Eq. (4I-16) was derived it may be shown that the improvement in echo-to-reverberation ratio provided by a reversible directional transducer used for echo ranging is measured by the ratio of a band reverberation factor to an echo spectrum factor. Here the two factors apply to a specified distribution of the electric energy delivered to the transducer during the radiation of the echo-ranging pulse.

The significance and utility of spectrum factors and of band directivity factors may be demonstrated by computing, with their aid, certain characteristics of a specific transducer system. For this we will return to the array for which transmitting and receiving responses were computed in Art. 4I-1.

We will begin by computing the directivity pattern of this array, as expressed in terms of relative receiving band response, for the band of frequencies between $f_a = 400$ cyc/sec and $f_b = 2400$ cyc/sec. This band has a band ratio of $f_b/f_a = 6$. At the upper frequency, assuming a velocity of propagation of $c = 5000$ ft/sec, the wave length has a magnitude of $\lambda = c/f = 2.08$ ft/cyc. Since the spacing of the array elements is $s = 1$ ft this spacing is slightly less than one-half of the shortest wave space occurring in the signal. Since the number of array elements is $n = 17$ the total length of the array is approximately 7.7 wave spaces at the highest frequency and approximately 1.28 wave spaces at the lowest.

It has been assumed that the electroacoustic efficiency, $(\eta_{EA})_f$, of this array is proportional to frequency, and that the directivity factor, $(\eta_D)_f$, is inversely proportional to frequency. For the present computation it is unnecessary to know the absolute value of either of these quantities.

In reporting the directivity pattern of a transducer, or transducer system, for a band of frequencies it is necessary to specify the distribution of energy in that band. No analogous requirement exists when reporting a directivity pattern at a single frequency. In the present example it will be assumed that the acoustic signal for which the pattern is to be computed reaches the array, when propagated along any bearing, in the form of plane waves having a continuous spectrum. The free-field intensity per unit band of this energy will be assumed to be inversely proportional to the square of the frequency. This corresponds to a spectrum level characteristic having the slope of -2 db/fl common to many acoustic signals generated by ships. For computing the directivity pattern applying to this signal it is unnecessary to know its absolute magnitude. It is sufficient to know that the relative intensity per unit band of the received acoustic energy is $\eta'_{Af} = J'_f/J'_{fo} = (f_0/f)^2$.

The first step toward determining the relative receiving band response of this array as a function of bearing, for this specified signal, is to compute the relative transmitting response as a function of bearing for a number of frequencies. This is done by the formula

$$(\eta_d)_f = \left[\frac{\sin n\psi}{n \sin \psi}\right]^2$$

used in Art. 4I-1.

The second step is to compute the relative receiving response as a function of frequency for a number of bearings. Before taking this step, however, it is necessary to select the reference frequency to be used with these relative responses and, later, with the spectrum factors to be derived from them. This question was discussed briefly in Art. 4I-1. It was there shown that, for the array here in question, it was necessary to go below 295 cyc/sec in order to find a single frequency for which all bearings between $\beta = 0°$ and $\beta = 90°$ would have a finite response, either transmitting or receiving. This frequency is outside the band of frequencies in which we are now interested. It is, however, within the region for which the directivity factor is inversely proportional to frequency. It will simplify the computational work if we choose a reference frequency for which this latter condition is satisfied. The general formula by which to compute the relative receiving response as a function of frequency, which is obtained by combining Eqs. (4H-3) and (4H-7), is

$$(\eta'_f)_d = (\eta_f)_d (f_0/f)^2$$
$$= \frac{(\eta_d)_f}{(\eta_d)_{fo}} \frac{(\eta_D)_{fo}}{(\eta_D)_f} \frac{(\eta_{EA})_f}{(\eta_{EA})_{fo}} \left(\frac{f_0}{f}\right)^2$$

It has already been postulated that

$$\frac{(\eta_{EA})_f}{(\eta_{EA})_{fo}} = \frac{f}{f_0}$$

If, in addition, attention is confined to a region where

$$\frac{(\eta_D)_{fo}}{(\eta_D)_f} = \frac{f}{f_0}$$

the relative receiving response, considered as a function of frequency, becomes

$$(\eta'_f)_d = \frac{(\eta_d)_f}{(\eta_d)_{fo}}$$

This formula may be used if we adopt $f_0 = 275$ cyc/sec as our reference frequency. The fact that this frequency is outside the frequency band for which we wish to compute the relative receiving response of the given array does not prevent us from making this choice. The response which we require as our reference response is one which bears a definite and convenient relation to the actual responses to be integrated. It need not be one of these responses.

Having computed, by the relation given above, the relative receiving response of the array as a function of frequency for a number of bearings the next step is to compute the receiving spectrum factor for these bearings. It is now necessary to introduce the effect of the manner in which the received acoustic energy is distributed with respect to frequency. This is accomplished by plotting as a function of frequency, for each bearing, the derivative function, or integrand, $\mathcal{G}(\beta, f) = (\eta'_f)_d \, \eta'_{Af}$ appearing in Eq. (4H-22). The value of the definite integral

$$\int_{f_a}^{f_b} \mathcal{G}(\beta, f) \, df$$

is then determined between the limits defining the specified frequency band. Typical values of the integrand used for this purpose, plotted for a bearing of $\beta = 30°$, are shown in Fig. 4I-3.

The receiving spectrum factor for each bearing is now computed, in accordance with Eq. (4H-22), by dividing the value of the definite integral thus obtained by the equivalent width of the signal band. On the basis of the assumption that the relative intensity per unit band of the signal, at any frequency, is $\eta'_{Af} = (f_0/f)^2$ this equivalent band width is found to be

$$\int_{f_a}^{f_b} \eta'_{Af} \, df = f_0{}^2 \int_{f_a}^{f_b} \frac{df}{f^2}$$

$$= \frac{f_0{}^2}{f_a f_b} (f_b - f_a) = 157.6 \text{ cyc/sec}$$

It will be noted that the equivalent band width of the signal here in question is less than one-tenth of the actual width. The reason for this is that the reference intensity per unit band, being at a frequency lower than the lowest frequency in the actual band, is greater than the intensity per unit band at any frequency in the actual band.

Values of receiving spectrum factor computed in the manner described above, for bearings be-

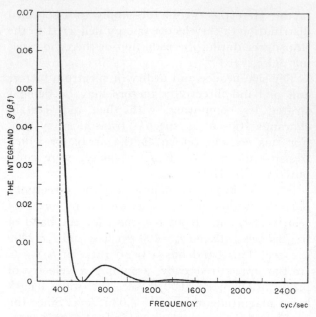

Fig. 4I-3. Evaluation of Spectrum Factor. The value of the integrand appearing in Eq. (4H-22), as computed for the array described in connection with Fig. 4I-2 and for acoustic energy having an intensity per unit band which is inversely proportional to the square of the frequency, plotted as a function of frequency for a bearing of $\beta = 30°$.

tween $\beta_0 = 0°$ and $\beta = 90°$, are shown graphically in Fig. 4I-4.

It remains to compute the relative receiving band response of the given array to the given signal as a function of bearing. In this case the receiving band response to energy occupying the specified band in the specified manner, and propagated along the maximum response reference bearing, $\beta_0 = 0°$, is the reference response.

The available power per unit band of the electric energy generated at the reference frequency in response to the signal as received over any bearing may be written as

$$(U'_{Ed})_{f_0} = (\mu'_d)_{f_0}(J'_d)_{f_0}$$

where

$(\mu'_d)_{f_0} =$ the receiving response for the given bearing and for the specified reference frequency (cm)^2

$(J'_d)_{f_0} =$ the intensity per unit band of the acoustic signal energy received at the specified reference frequency (joule/cm$^2 \cdot$ cyc)

The available power of the electric energy generated in the specified frequency band by the array when receiving this acoustic signal over any

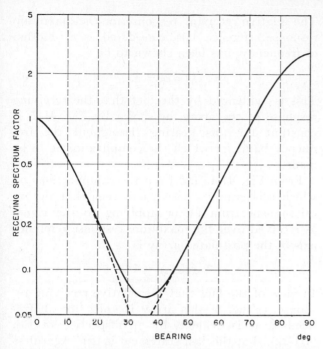

FIG. 4I-4. RECEIVING SPECTRUM FACTOR. The receiving spectrum factor for the array and the acoustic energy postulated in connection with Fig. 4I-3, plotted as a function of bearing.

bearing is, in accordance with the definition for receiving spectrum factor,

$$(P'_{Ed})_{\Delta f} = (\eta'_F)_d (U'_{Ed})_{fo} = (\eta'_F)_d (\mu'_d)_{fo} (J'_d)_{fo}$$

For the maximum response reference bearing the available power of this generated electric energy may be written as

$$(P'_{Edo})_{\Delta f} = (\eta'_F)_{do} (\mu'_{do})_{fo} (J'_{do})_{fo}$$

The desired relative receiving band response is given as the ratio of these two electric powers. It is understood that the signal received on any bearing is the same as that received on the maximum response reference bearing, or that $(J'_d)_{fo} = (J'_{do})_{fo}$. Consequently the relative receiving band response is

$$(\eta'_d)_{\Delta f} = \frac{(P'_{Ed})_{\Delta f}}{(P'_{Edo})_{\Delta f}} = \frac{(\eta'_F)_d}{(\eta'_F)_{do}} (\eta'_d)_{fo} \quad (4I-27)$$

This may be described as the product of the **relative spectrum factor** for the given bearing, referred to the spectrum factor for the maximum response reference bearing, and the relative response for this bearing, considered as a function of bearing for the specified reference frequency. This formula is a general statement of the relations involved. In this particular problem the

receiving spectrum factor for the maximum response reference bearing has been shown to be $(\eta'_F)_{do} = 1$. The equation is, therefore, reduced to a simpler form in view of the specific conditions here postulated.

The relative receiving band response computed for the specified array and for the specified signal is shown graphically in Fig. 4I-5. This graph shows the bearing deviation loss, $(N'_d)_{\Delta f} = -\lg t\ (\eta'_d)_{\Delta f}$, corresponding to the computed relative receiving response, plotted against polar coordinates. This is the type of plot commonly used by transducer measuring facilities in reporting the results of actual measurements made with continuous wave signals occupying frequency bands of finite width.

The response shown for the sector between $\beta = 40°$ and $\beta = 90°$, and for corresponding sectors in other quadrants, is due almost entirely to the first minor lobe of the array. The pattern shows that there is little change in the deviation loss, and hence in the signal magnitude, throughout this region. What the pattern does not show is that the distribution of generated electric energy with frequency varies with bearing. For each bearing in this sector the greater portion of the generated energy is contained within a relatively

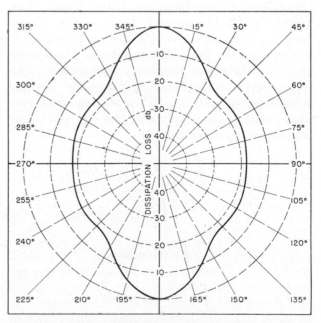

FIG. 4I-5. BAND DIRECTIVITY PATTERN. The dissipation loss of the array postulated in connection with Fig. 4I-2 when receiving acoustic energy having an intensity per unit band which is inversely proportional to the square of the frequency, plotted as a function of bearing for a frequency band between $f_a = 400$ cyc/sec and $f_b = 2400$ cyc/sec.

narrow frequency band, the position of which on the frequency scale is a function of bearing.

The demonstration of the utility of spectrum factors and of band directivity factors will be concluded with the computation of the signal-to-interference advantage of the postulated 17-element array when receiving both an acoustic signal and acoustic interference in the frequency band between $f_a = 400$ cyc/sec and $f_b = 2400$ cyc/sec. This advantage is measured by the ratio, given by Eq. (4I-16), of the receiving band directivity factor applying to the interference received over all bearings to the spectrum factor applying to the signal received over the maximum response reference axis. It will be assumed that the relative equivalent plane wave intensity per unit band of the interference received over all bearings, with uniform directional distribution, is $(\eta'_{Af})_n = (f_0/f)^{5/3}$. This corresponds to the slope of $-5/3$ db/fl typical of the spectrum level characteristic of general water noise.

For computing the receiving band directivity factor applying to the interference we may use either Eq. (4I-11) or Eq. (4I-12). One calls for information as to the receiving directivity factor as a function of frequency and one for information as to the receiving spectrum factor as a function of bearing. From our previous computations this information is available for either factor. The use of Eq. (4I-11) permits the evaluation of the receiving band directivity factor by a simple direct integration, under the conditions which have been postulated for the array in question. The spectrum factor applying to the signal is computed by Eq. (4H-22). By combining these two equations the ratio expressing the signal-to-interference advantage of this array is found to be

$$\frac{(\eta'_D)_{\Delta f}}{(\eta'_F)_{do}} = \frac{\int_{f_a}^{f_b} (\eta'_D)_f (\eta'_f)_{do} (\eta'_{Af})_n \, df}{\int_{f_a}^{f_b} (\eta'_{Af})_n \, df}$$

$$\cdot \frac{\int_{f_a}^{f_b} (\eta'_{Af})_s \, df}{\int_{f_a}^{f_b} (\eta'_f)_{do} (\eta'_{Af})_s \, df} \qquad (4I-28)$$

Under the conditions which have been postulated for this problem the receiving directivity factor of the array, for any given frequency, is

$$(\eta'_D)_f = 145.6 \, f^{-1}$$

The relative receiving response for the maximum response reference axis, considered as a function of frequency, has been shown to be

$$(\eta'_f)_{do} = 1$$

This is evidenced by the fact that the receiving response of the array, as shown by Fig. 4I-2, is constant for this bearing throughout the frequency band for which the computation is to be made.

From Fig. 4I-4, and from the computations on which this graph is based, it is seen that the receiving spectrum factor applying to the signal as received over the maximum response reference axis of the postulated array is

$$(\eta'_F)_{do} = 1$$

In view of the fact that the relative receiving response, $(\eta'_f)_{do}$, of this array is unity for all frequencies it is evident, by an inspection of Eq. (4H-22), that this last statement is true regardless of the manner in which the energy of the acoustic signal is distributed with respect to frequency. It is, in fact, evident from this inspection that for a transducer system having an electroacoustic efficiency which is proportional to frequency, and a directivity factor which is inversely proportional to frequency, the signal-to-interference advantage, when receiving acoustic energy occupying a frequency band of finite width, is measured directly by the band directivity factor applying to the interference. In this special case, as when receiving acoustic energy at a single frequency, the apparent intensity of the acoustic signal and the actual intensity are the same.

On making the appropriate substitutions the ratio measuring the signal-to-interference advantage of the array, when receiving the postulated signal in the presence of the postulated interference, is given as

$$\frac{(\eta'_D)_{\Delta f}}{(\eta'_F)_{do}} = 145.6 \frac{\int_{f_a}^{f_b} (f^{-1})(f^{-5/3}) \, df}{\int_{f_a}^{f_b} (f^{-5/3}) \, df}$$

$$= \frac{2}{5}(145.6) \frac{1}{f_a f_b} \frac{(f^{5/3})_b - (f^{5/3})_a}{(f^{2/3})_b - (f^{2/3})_a} = 0.198$$

The signal-to-interference advantage thus computed may be expressed in terms of transmission level differentials, as in Eq. (4I-25). When expressed in this manner we have

$$(N'_{DI})_{\Delta f} - (N'_{SI})_{do} = \lg t \frac{1}{0.198} - \lg t\, 1 = 7.02 \text{ db}$$

It is interesting to note that this value is approximately equal to the value of the directivity index of the array at a frequency of 720 cyc/sec.

4-J THERMAL EFFECTS IN TRANSDUCERS

In the preceding sections of this chapter we have described a number of properties of electro-acoustic transducers, defined the units by which they are evaluated, and established relations between them. We shall now return to the question of the effect of the thermal agitation of the molecules of the medium in contact with such a transducer and of the thermal agitation of the molecules making up its electric system. These effects will be examined in terms of the quantities already considered since it is in connection with these quantities that thermal effects are of greatest significance to the sonar engineer.

4J-1 Thermal Equivalent Water Noise

For his present understanding of the effect of the thermal agitation of the molecules making up the matter with which he has to deal, the sonar engineer is greatly indebted to the physical chemist. As a result of considerations having to do with the thermodynamics of gases it has been established that the magnitude of the energy associated with each molecule of a gas is proportional to the temperature of that gas. The factor of proportionality is, in fact, one of the fundamental constants of nature. It is known as the **molecular gas constant**, or as **Boltzmann's constant**. Its value is $K = 1.3708 \cdot 10^{-23}$ joules per molecule per degree Kelvin. In terms of this relationship absolute zero is that temperature at which the thermal energy of a molecule is zero. The existence of this thermal energy in the molecules of a gas is manifest by the pressure exerted by that gas.

Thermal energy may also be associated with the molecules of an electric conductor. In this case the energy is manifest by a fluctuating electric potential difference between the terminals of the conductor. When the conductor is connected between the grid and cathode of a thermionic vacuum tube this fluctuating potential causes corresponding fluctuations in the current flowing between anode and cathode. Since these current fluctuations interfere with any signal which it may be desired to amplify by the tube they have come to be known as **circuit noise.** The potential

fluctuations between the terminals of the conductor have, in their turn, been designated as the **thermal noise voltage.** Thermal noise in electric conductors has been investigated by J. B. Johnson,[14] who has shown that the energy associated with the thermal agitation of the molecules of the conductor is directly related to the Boltzmann constant. Johnson's work was followed immediately by a theoretical study by H. Nyquist[15] which established the logical reasons for this relation. The energy originally associated by Boltzmann with the individual molecules of a gas may also be associated with the degrees of freedom of a system made up of molecules. Johnson and Nyquist have shown that in the case of an electric system the band width of the spectrum occupied by any portion of the thermal noise is a direct measure of the number of degrees of freedom of the system with which this thermal noise is associated.

The foregoing paragraphs present a somewhat oversimplified description of the phenomena under consideration. For our present purposes, however, this should suffice. On the basis of relations now well established, it is evident that if the thermal noise voltage appearing between the terminals of an electric conductor is expressed in terms of the corresponding available power, in accordance with Eq. (4A-8), the available power per unit band will be proportional to the absolute temperature, provided only that the conductor obeys Ohm's law. We may, therefore, write this available power per unit band as

$$U_{th} = K T_K \qquad (4J-1)$$

where

$U_{th} = e_{th}{}^2/4R(\Delta f)$

= the available power per unit band corresponding to the thermal noise voltage appearing at the terminals of an electric conductor (joule/cyc)

e_{th} = the thermal noise voltage (volt)

R = the resistance of the conductor (ohm)

Δf = the width of the frequency band (cyc/sec)

$K = 1.3708 \cdot 10^{-23}$ joule/cyc·°K

= the Boltzmann constant

$$T_K = 273.18 + T_C$$

= the temperature of the conductor (°K)

T_C = the temperature of the conductor (°C)

It is to be noted that, although for a given temperature the magnitude of the thermal noise voltage is proportional to the magnitude of the resistance of the conductor, the magnitude of the available power per unit band, defined as indicated, is independent of the magnitude of this resistance and is a unique function of the absolute temperature. It should also be noted that although the concept of the available power of a given source of electric energy assumes that energy may be withdrawn from this source such withdrawal is not possible in the present case. Any electric system which might be connected to a given electric system for this purpose would, itself, have a thermal noise voltage. If the two systems are at equal temperatures the two available powers corresponding to the two thermal noise voltages will be equal. Consequently, any energy which might flow in one direction between the two systems will be exactly equaled by energy flowing in the other direction. This equality is demanded by the law of the conservation of energy. The fact that the energy corresponding to the thermal noise voltage of an electric conductor is not actually available for external use in no way diminishes the validity of the concept of available power. For our present purposes, this available power may be defined simply as the quotient obtained by dividing the mean square value of the open-circuit thermal noise voltage by four times the resistance of the electric system in question. Available power per unit band is then obtained by dividing this quotient by the width of the frequency band in question.

When a hydrophone is in contact with water the thermal agitation of the water molecules exerts a thermal noise pressure on its surface which generates an electric voltage. The magnitude of this generated voltage is exactly equal to the thermal noise voltage of the electric load shown in the equivalent circuits of Figs. 4C-6 and 4C-7. In these equivalent circuits this electric load, shown either as the resistance R_L or as the conductance G_L, takes the place of the medium in contact with the electroacoustic transducer to which the network is equivalent. The magnitude

of the available electric power per unit band corresponding to the thermal noise voltage of this branch of the equivalent network must, therefore, equal the magnitude of the available acoustic power per unit band corresponding to the thermal noise pressure of the medium thus represented.

For the type of problem with which we are likely to be concerned it will be convenient to express this available power per unit band in terms of the intensity per unit band of acoustic waves which, if acting on the transducer in the normal manner, would generate a fluctuating voltage equal to the voltage actually generated by the molecules striking the transducer. This intensity per unit band, which is known as the **thermal equivalent intensity per unit band,** is obtained by dividing the power per unit band, as given by Eq. (4J-1) by the capture area of the transducer. For a nondirectional transducer this capture area is given by Eq. (4F-44) as

$$A_C = \frac{c^2}{4\pi f^2} \qquad (4J-2)$$

The intensity per unit band of plane waves of acoustic energy which would produce an effect equivalent to the effect of the thermal agitation of the water in contact with the hydrophone is, therefore,

$$J_{th} = \frac{U_{th}}{A_C} = \frac{1.3708 \cdot 10^{-23} \, T_K \, 4\pi f^2}{c^2} \qquad (4J-3)$$

where

J_{th} = the thermal equivalent intensity per unit band of the water in contact with a sonar transducer (joule/cm²·cyc)

T_K = the temperature of the water (°K)

f = the frequency at which the value of thermal equivalent intensity per unit band is applicable (cyc/sec)

c = the velocity of propagation of acoustic energy in the medium in question (cm/sec)

It is customary to report the magnitude of this thermal equivalent intensity per unit band in terms of a spectrum level. Such a level would then be designated as the **thermal equivalent spectrum level.** It represents, as stated in Art

2C-3, a lower limit to the water noise of the sea. For a temperature of 60 °F (15.55 °C = 298.73 °K) and for the corresponding velocity of propagation of $1.5 \cdot 10^5$ cm/sec the thermal equivalent spectrum level of water is

$$L_{th} = \lg J_{th}$$

$$= 2 \lg f - 296.86 \text{ db}//1 \text{ joule/cm}^2 \cdot \text{cyc}$$

$$= 2 \lg f - 174.99 \text{ db}//1 \mu b^2 \cdot \text{sec/cyc} \quad (4J\text{-}4)$$

Values of thermal equivalent spectrum level computed in accordance with this formula are shown as the line marked "Thermal Limit" on Fig. 2C-1.

4J-2 Thermal Equivalent Transducer Noise

The thermal equivalent intensity per unit band, and the thermal equivalent spectrum level, discussed in the preceding article are properties of the acoustic medium. Thermal effects are not limited to the medium, however, but occur also in the material of the transducer. If we consider the total equivalent circuit of an electroacoustic transducer there will be a thermal noise voltage between its electric terminals regardless of whether or not it is in contact with an acoustic medium. This thermal noise voltage of the electric system of the transducer is quite as important as the thermal noise pressure of the medium. Actually it is the resultant effect of the two which limits the ultimate performance to be realized. This resultant effect is known as the **transducer noise voltage.** The magnitude of this resultant effect is evaluated in a simple manner.

For our purposes the transducer noise voltage existing at the terminals of a sonar transducer used as a hydrophone may be expressed most conveniently in terms of the magnitude of plane waves of acoustic energy which, reaching the transducer along its maximum response reference axis, and generating a transducer voltage in the normal manner, would generate a voltage equal to the transducer thermal noise voltage. The spectrum level of acoustic waves which would generate in a transducer an open-circuit terminal voltage equal to the transducer noise voltage is known as the **transducer equivalent spectrum level.** The magnitude of this transducer equivalent spectrum level is obtained by substituting into the formula for hydrophone loss, as given by Eq. (4G-6), the available power per unit band corresponding to the transducer noise voltage. When this is done the transducer equivalent spectrum level is found to be

$$(L_{th})_H = \lg (J'_{do})_S = N_H + \lg \frac{(U'_{do})_{out}}{A_S}$$

$$= N_H + \lg \frac{1.3708 \cdot 10^{-23} \, T_K}{A_S} \quad (4J\text{-}5)$$

If we assume the small area of water surface specified in the definition of hydrophone loss to be $A_S = 1$ cm² and, as before, assume the temperature to be 60 °F this spectrum level reduces to

$$(L_{th})_H = N_H - 203.88 \text{ db}//1 \text{ joule/cm}^2 \cdot \text{cyc}$$

$$= N_H - 82.01 \text{ db}//1 \, \mu b^2 \cdot \text{sec/cyc} \quad (4J\text{-}6)$$

This quantity, which has been defined above as the transducer equivalent spectrum level, is sometimes referred to as the **hydrophone threshold.** It is, however, not to be confused with the minimum level of acoustic energy which may be observed, or measured, by the hydrophone. The relation between the **minimum measurable level,** and the transducer equivalent spectrum level depends upon the magnitude of the error due to transducer noise which may be tolerated, or upon the extent to which a correction may be applied. If the hydrophone is to be used for measuring a low-level acoustic signal the error due to thermal noise may be computed by considering the level of this signal and the level of the transducer noise as the two levels to which the curve of Fig. 2B-3 applies. From this curve it is seen, for example, that if the transducer equivalent spectrum level is **17 db** below the spectrum level of the wave to be measured the measurement will be in error by about 0.1 db, unless corrected. For normal operating use the transducer equivalent spectrum level should be of the order of at least 10 db below the spectrum level of the acoustic wave to be measured.

In order that any given hydrophone may function adequately as a device for measuring the magnitude of acoustic waves it is desirable that its transducer equivalent spectrum level should be considerably less than the spectrum level of minimum water noise. The relation between these two levels is conveniently represented graphically, as shown in Fig. 4J-1. In this graph a plot of hydrophone loss is made to serve also as a plot of transducer equivalent spectrum level. To accomplish this all that is required is a supplementary scale, related to the scale of hydrophone loss in accordance with whichever formula of Eq. (4J-6) may be appropriate. In this case, in order that level values shall read in the usual manner it

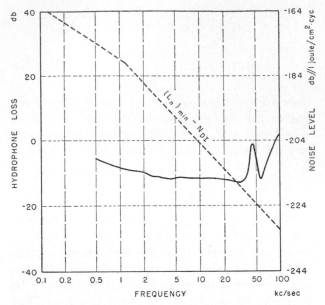

FIG. 4J-1. HYDROPHONE LOSS, THERMAL NOISE, AND WATER NOISE. The hydrophone loss characteristic of a typical hydrophone. The noise level scale permits the spectrum level of the thermal noise of the hydrophone to be read from the hydrophone loss characteristic. The dotted line shows, against this same noise scale, the apparent plane wave spectrum level of minimum water noise for this hydrophone.

appears desirable to lay off values of hydrophone loss to increase upward, instead of downward as is usually done with transmission losses. The spectrum level scale is then added so that the reading at any point on the level scale shall be 204 db (or 82 db) less than the reading of the corresponding point on the hydrophone loss scale. Against this spectrum level scale is then drawn the spectrum level characteristic of minimum water noise, as received by the particular hydrophone to which the hydrophone loss curve applies. This second characteristic is computed, in accordance with Eq. (4F-25), by subtracting the directivity index of the hydrophone in question from the equivalent plane wave level of minimum water noise as received by a nondirectional hydrophone. Nominal values for this minimum water noise are given by the spectrum level characteristic of Fig. 2C-1. This characteristic has a slope of $-5/3$ db/fl. It passes through the following points:

Frequency kc/sec	Spectrum Level db//1 joule/cm²· cyc
0.1	−162.00
1	−178.67
10	−195.33
100	−212.00

The dotted line of Fig. 4J-1 shows the equivalent plane wave level characteristic of minimum water noise as it would be observed with the hydrophone to which the hydrophone loss characteristic appearing on the same graph applies. This hydrophone has no directional discrimination below 1100 cyc/sec. Above this frequency the directivity index increases at the rate of 1 db/fl. The spectrum level characteristic therefore leaves the nominal curve for minimum water noise at the 1100 cyc/sec point and continues for higher frequencies with a slope of $-8/3$ db/fl. The point at which this dotted line crosses the transducer equivalent spectrum level characteristic, obtained by reading the hydrophone loss characteristic against the scale of noise levels, corresponds to the frequency at which the response of the hydrophone to minimum water noise equals its response to thermal noise. These curves show that the hydrophone is of little use, in quiet locations, at any frequency above approximately 11 kc/sec.

REFERENCES

1. E. A. GUILLEMIN, *Introductory Circuit Theory* (John Wiley and Sons, Inc., New York, 1953).
2. J. P. JOULE, "On the Effects of Magnetism upon the Dimensions of Iron and Steel Bars," *Phil. Mag. Series III*, Vol. 30, pp. 76–87 and 225–241, (1847).
3. J. and P. CURIE, "The Development by Pressure of Electric Polarization in Crystals," *Compt. Rend.*, Vol. 91, pp. 294–295 and 383–386, (1880).
4. F. V. HUNT, *Electroacoustics* (Harvard University Press, Cambridge, Mass., 1954). This book contains an excellent review of the early discoveries and researches in both magnetostriction and electrostriction.
5. W. P. MASON, *Piezoelectric Crystals and Their Application to Ultrasonics* (D. Van Nostrand Company, Inc., New York, 1950).
6. W. G. CADY, *Piezoelectricity* (McGraw-Hill Book Company, Inc., New York, 1946).
7. Piezoelectric Crystals Committee, *Proc. I.R.E.*, Vol. 37, No. 12, December 1949.
8. A. E. KENNELLY, *Electrical Vibration Instruments* (Macmillan Company, New York, 1923).
9. JAHNKE and EMDE, *Tables of Functions* (Dover Publications, New York, 1945).
10. This integral was evaluated by MISS RUTH SCULLY while employed at the U. S. Navy Underwater Sound Laboratory, New London, Conn.
11. N. W. MCLACHLAN, *Loudspeakers* (Oxford University Press, 1934).
12. J. C. SLATER, *Microwave Transmission* (McGraw-Hill Book Company, Inc., 1942), p. 260.
13. Sectional Committee Z24, *American Standard Acoustical Terminology* (American Standards Association, Inc. New York, July 31, 1951).
14. J. B. JOHNSON, "Thermal Agitation of Electricity in Conductors," *Phys. Rev.*, Second Series, Vol. 32, pp. 97–109 July, 1928.
15. H. NYQUIST, "Thermal Agitation of Electric Charge i Conductors," *Phys. Rev.*, Second Series, Vol. 32, pp. 110 113, July, 1928.

CHAPTER 5

TRANSDUCER SYSTEMS

In the preceding chapter our interest has been chiefly with individual transducers and their characteristics. We have, it is true, given some thought to multispot arrays. In these, however, the individual units have been ideal nondirectional elements introduced primarily for the purpose of studying the directional characteristics of various transducer forms of which they may be considered as infinitesimal portions. In the present chapter we shall examine the characteristics of systems made up of a number of actual transducers, each of which will have definite directional characteristics determined by its form and size.

Transducer systems are usually designed with either or both of two objectives in view. One is to provide directional characteristics which are not readily obtainable with a single transducer; the other is to provide means whereby information may be obtained as to the deviation of the bearing of some sound source, or echo target, from the reference axis of the system.

5-A DELAYED-RESPONSE DIRECTIONAL SYSTEMS

The directional characteristics of an array of transducers, or of a transducer having finite dimensions, are, as shown in Chapter 4, determined by the manner in which the phases of the responses of the individual elements vary with the direction of the source or of the receiving point. These phase relations may conveniently be expressed in terms of the time delays associated with the differences in the lengths of the acoustic paths between such a distant point and the several portions of the array or transducer. If, in addition to these time delays introduced in the acoustic system because of its configuration and orientation, the responses of the individual elements are further delayed by electric networks, prior to their combination to give a single resultant response, there will be a modification of the directional characteristics. Delay networks may be used to give directivity to an array, such as one in which the elements are arranged in a circle, in some plane in which it would otherwise be nondirectional, or to alter the bearing for which a

fixed directional array, or transducer, has its maximum response. Systems designed for the latter purpose are known as **electrically trained,** or as **electrically steered,** systems. Electrical training is used for multispot arrays made up of a number of individual transducers, or for a single transducer made up of a number of separately connected elements. Examples of the large multispot array are to be found in shore-controlled installations or in hull-mounted ship installations. Electrical steering is used whenever the transducer system is so large that mechanical training presents difficult structural problems or when it is desired to train at speeds so high that mechanical motion of the system becomes impractical.

The relation between the time delay introduced either by a difference in length of water path or by an electric network and the response of the element at some point where it combines with other responses is easily derived. One complete cycle of a sinusoidal wave represents a time interval of $t = 1/f$ seconds; it represents a phase shift of $\psi = 2\pi = \omega/f$ radians. The relation between phase and time is thus

$$\psi = \omega t \qquad (5A\text{-}1)$$

If a complex wave is to be delayed in time without altering the relations between its several components each component must be delayed by the same amount as every other component. It is at once evident from the relation given above that this is equivalent to requiring the phase shift to be proportional to the frequency.

If the equalities $t = l/c$, and $\omega = 2\pi f = 2\pi c/\lambda$, are substituted into the above equation the familiar relation,

$$\psi = \left(\frac{2\pi c}{\lambda}\right)\left(\frac{l}{c}\right) = \frac{2\pi l}{\lambda} \qquad (5A\text{-}2)$$

between phase and distance is obtained. The quantity $2\pi/\lambda$ is, as noted earlier, the change in phase, in radians, per unit length of ray path.

5A-1 Delayed Linear Arrays

The geometric relations between wave fronts arriving along a given direction of propagation

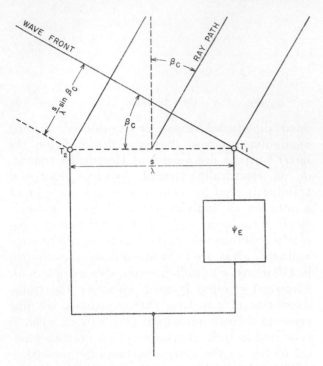

FIG. 5A-1. ELECTRIC COMPENSATION. The connection of an electric delay network to compensate for the acoustic delay due to a difference between the distances of two transducers from a remote point.

and a pair of transducer elements, which may be considered as forming a portion of a multispot array, are shown in Fig. 4E-1. If a wave front arrives along a path making the angle β_C with the normal to the line joining these two elements the individually generated electric voltages may be made to combine in phase by inserting in series with the element nearer the source, as shown in Fig. 5A-1, an electric network the phase delay of which exactly offsets the difference in the travel times between the source and the two elements. If the separation between elements is s/λ wave spaces the difference in the lengths of the two paths is $(s/\lambda) \sin \beta_C$ wave spaces. This follows from the fact that the angle between the wave front and the line joining the elements is equal to the angle between the ray path and the normal to this line. This difference in path length, then, results in a phase shift of $\psi = (2\pi s/\lambda) \sin \beta_C$ radians. It may therefore be said that the insertion of an electric phase delay of this amount, which compensates for the acoustic delay, causes the position of the maximum response axis to be altered by the angle β_C. This angle is, in consequence, known as the **compensation angle.**

Assume that the electric delay connected in the output of one element of a transducer pair

has the value $\psi_E = (2\pi s/\lambda) \sin \beta_C$ and that sound energy arrives along a bearing making the angle β_D with the line joining this pair. The phase shift between the acoustic signals at the two points, due to the difference between the lengths of the two water paths, is such that the signal at the more distant lags behind the signal at the nearer by the acoustic phase delay $\psi_A = (2\pi s/\lambda) \sin \beta_D$. This is also the phase difference between the electric voltages generated in the two elements. Because of the electric network, however, which is connected to introduce a compensating delay, the phase difference between the electric signals at the point where they are combined is

$$\psi_A - \psi_E = \frac{2\pi s}{\lambda} (\sin \beta_D - \sin \beta_C) \qquad (5A\text{-}3)$$

The several transducer elements of a linear array may be connected together by electric delay networks, as shown in Fig. 5A-2, and the combined outputs taken from one end of the resulting system. The series of networks of a system of this type is generally known as a **lag line.** The combination of a lag line and a switching mechanism by which the amount of delay may be adjusted is known as a **compensator.** For a uniformly spaced array the individual elements of the lag line introduce equal delays and each has an effect similar to that of the single delay circuit shown in Fig. 5A-1. In Art. 4E-1 an expression has been given for the resultant relative voltage of a series of elements, each delayed in response behind the preceding element, as a function of the phase factor defining the relation between the component voltages contributed to the resultant output by two adjoining elements. This expression, as given by Eq. (4E-2), is

$$\frac{e_d}{e_{do}} = \frac{\sin n\psi}{n \sin \psi}$$

Here n is the number of transducer elements in the array and ψ is the phase factor applying to a system of this type. It is, for such systems, equal

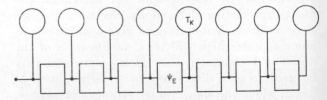

FIG. 5A-2. THE ELECTRIC LAG LINE. The connection of a series of delay networks to a multispot array to provide electric compensation.

to one-half the amount of the phase difference between the outputs of adjoining elements. In the case of a linear array in which the elements are connected by delay networks the value of this phase factor may be written as

$$\psi = \frac{\pi s}{\lambda}(\sin \beta_D - \sin \beta_C) \qquad (5A\text{-}4)$$

Using this value the relative response of such an array may be computed as a function of the deviation angle, β_D, between the direction of propagation of the wave and the normal to the line of the array, for any value of compensation angle, β_C, as a parameter.

Directivity patterns for a linear array, taken in a plane through its mechanical axis, are shown in Fig. 5A-3. The curves given in this figure are computed for an array of 17 uniformly spaced elements and for sinusoidal signals of such frequencies that the separations between adjacent elements have the values $\lambda/2$, $\lambda/4$, and $\lambda/8$. For all curves, then, the arrangement satisfies the condition specified in Art. 4E-1 that the spacing be one half wave or less. For the highest frequency the length of the array is eight wave spaces; for the lowest it is two wave spaces. Curves are drawn for values of electric network delays corresponding to compensation angles of 0, 30, 60, and 90 degrees. The relative voltage responses plotted in these patterns are referred, as usual, to the maximum response. Since, however, this maximum occurs when $\beta_D = \beta_C$ instead

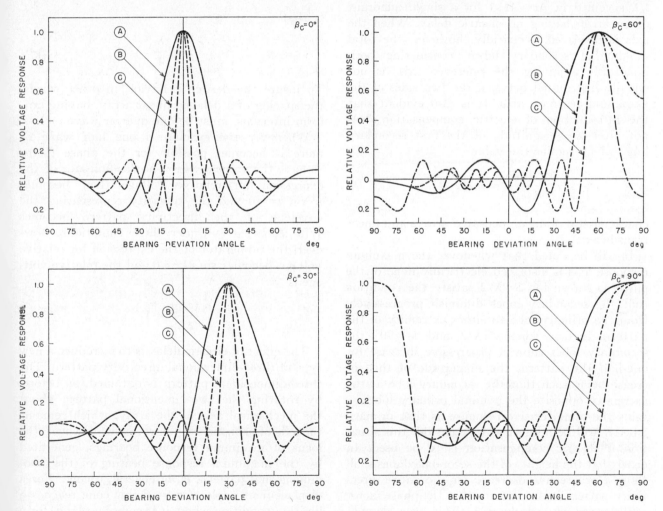

Fig. 5A-3. Directivity Patterns of Compensated Array. Patterns for a linear array of 17 elements uniformly spaced by intervals of length s, for various compensation angles, β_C, and for signals of various wave lengths.

Curve	Spacing
A	$s = \lambda/8$
B	$s = \lambda/4$
C	$s = \lambda/2$

of when $\beta_D = 0$, as we have been accustomed to find it, the relative response should be written as

$$\frac{(e_d)_D}{(e_d)_C}$$

For a compensation angle of $\beta_C = 0$ there are, of course, no delays required in the lag line. Under these conditions the directional characteristics are the same as for any linear array having the number of elements and the spacing described. It will be noted that the number of secondary lobes for a compensated array is the same, in every case, as when the maximum response axis is not electrically displaced. The total number of secondary lobes in the two quadrants adjacent to the reference axis is, in fact, equal to twice the number l/λ specified in Art. 4E-1 for a single quadrant of an array having no electric delay. When the axis is displaced electrically, however, the total number of secondary lobes, considering both quadrants adjoining the reference axis, is not equally distributed between the two sides of the maximum response axis. It is also evident that the introduction of electric compensation does not alter the magnitude of the first secondary lobe, which retains the value

$$\frac{(e_d)_D}{(e_d)_C} = 0.212$$

characteristic of uncompensated arrays and linear transducers.

It will be noted that whenever the maximum response axis is displaced electrically none of the patterns shown for $S = \lambda/2$ satisfy the condition that the secondary lobes diminish progressively from the primary lobe to either extremity of the pattern. In fact, when $s = \lambda/2$, and $\beta_C = 90°$, the secondary lobes show a progressive increase for one-half the pattern, the magnitude of this increase being such that the secondary lobe at the extremity opposite the nominal primary lobe attains the same relative response as that primary lobe. It will be necessary to reconsider this situation if electric compensation is to be used. In order that the heights of the secondary lobes shall show a progressive decrease for the entire directivity pattern it is necessary that the phase factor shall never exceed $\psi = \pi/2$. This was demonstrated in Art. 4E-1, where it was shown that the quantity $(1/n) \sin \psi$, appearing in Eq. (4E-5), represents very closely the envelope of the directivity pattern. This envelope has its first mini-

mum, the value of which is $1/n$, when $\sin \psi = 1$ for the first time. In the present case this condition must be satisfied for all deviation angles between $\beta_D = +(\pi/2)$ and $\beta_D = -(\pi/2)$, and for all compensation angles between $\beta_C = +(\pi/2)$ and $\beta_C = -(\pi/2)$. The maximum value of phase factor thus occurs when $\beta_D = +(\pi/2)$ and $\beta_C = -(\pi/2)$, or when $\beta_D = -(\pi/2)$ and $\beta_C = +(\pi/2)$, and is

$$\psi_{max} = \frac{\pi s}{\lambda}\left(\sin\frac{\pi}{2} + \sin\frac{\pi}{2}\right) = \frac{2\pi s}{\lambda} \quad (5A-5)$$

In order that this value shall not exceed the limit specified above it is necessary that

$$\psi_{max} \leqq \frac{\pi}{2} \geqq \frac{2\pi s}{\lambda}$$

or that

$$s \leqq \frac{\lambda}{4} \quad (5A-6)$$

To insure the desired behavior, in other words, the spacing of a delayed linear array, having uniform intervals, must be one quarter wave or less.

Whenever the spacing is one half wave or more it becomes possible for the phase factor to have the value $\psi = k\pi$. The denominator of the expression for relative voltage then becomes $n \sin k\pi = 0$ and the quantity representing the envelope of the directivity pattern becomes $1/(n \sin k\pi) = \infty$. Under these conditions, however, the numerator of the expression for relative voltage becomes $\sin nk\pi = 0$ and the relative voltage is

$$\frac{(e_d)_D}{(e_d)_C} = 1$$

The effect of electric delay is to introduce a new type of three-dimensional directivity pattern. The three-dimensional pattern is obtained, as before, by rotating the two-dimensional pattern about the mechanical axis of the array, which remains the axis of acoustic symmetry. Now, however, the locus of maximum response bearings, generated by the maximum response bearing of the two-dimensional pattern, is, in general, a cone. For a displacement angle of $\beta_C = 0°$ this cone reaches a limiting condition where it becomes a plane; for a displacement angle of $\beta_C = 90°$ it becomes a straight line. When the electric delay networks are adjusted to produce this last condition the array is said to be **end-fired.** When so compensated the array has its nominal maximum response for sounds traveling along its mechanical axis in one direction only. In order that this performance be realized it is, of course, necessary that the spacing be less than one half wave and preferably not more than one quarter wave.

It is evident from an inspection of the several directivity patterns of Fig. 5A-3 that, for any frequency, the major lobe becomes progressively broader as the displacement angle is increased by adjustment of the electric delay network. This promptly raises a question as to the effect of electrical steering upon the directivity index. It will be recalled that the value of this index depends upon the three-dimensional distribution of transducer response. The situation existing in the case of a linear array, such as we are here considering, is illustrated by the diagram of Fig. 4D-3. It is at once apparent from this diagram that the circum-

ference of the circle corresponding to the intersection of the locus of maximum response bearings with a spherical surface concentric with the transducer, or array, diminishes as the compensation angle is increased. The combined effect of increased lobe width and decreased circular arc may be investigated by plotting the directivity function applying to this type of transducer system, as given by Eq. (4F-46). The four curves of Fig. 5A-4 show values of this function as computed for the four values of compensation angle used for the directivity patterns of Fig. 5A-3 in the case where the separation between elements is one half wave space; that is, for the case where $s = \lambda/2$. These computations show that as the range of deviation angles occupied by the major lobe increases with increasing compensation, the magnitude of the function simultaneously decreases. In general, the areas under curves of the direc-

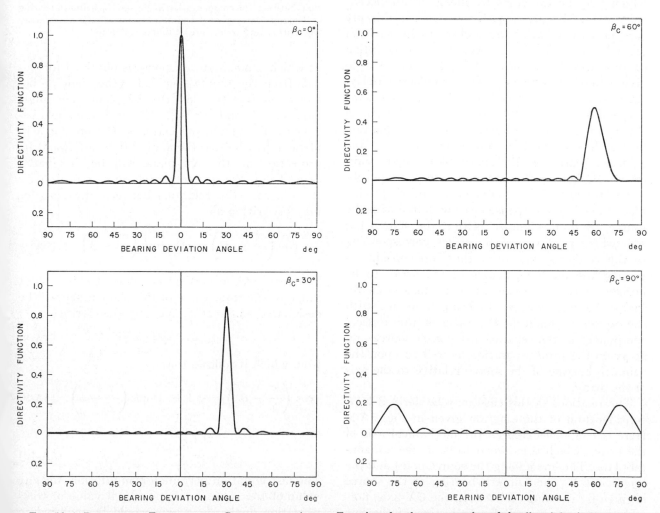

FIG. 5A-4. DIRECTIVITY FUNCTIONS OF COMPENSATED ARRAY. Functions for the computation of the directivity indexes of a linear array of 17 elements spaced at half wave intervals, for various compensation angles, β_C.

tivity function plotted for various compensation angles decrease with increasing angle. For a compensation angle of $\beta_C = 90°$ the area is, except for spacings near $s = \lambda/2$, about one-half the area when $\beta_C = 0°$. The directivity index of an end-fired array, in other words, is approximately 3 db more than for the same array when operated without compensation. At the frequency for which the spacing is $s = \lambda/2$, however, the response of an end-fired array due to the lobe at $\beta_D = -90°$ is equal to that of the lobe, normally considered the main lobe, at $\beta_D = +90°$. For this particular frequency, therefore, the area under the curve and the directivity index are both restored to the values applying to the array when uncompensated.

The location of the maximum response bearing on a conical locus, for compensation angles between 0° and 90°, is accompanied by an ambiguity with respect to the direction of any source which may be traversed by means of an electrically steered linear array. If sounds from a deeply submerged submarine are picked up by such an array located near the surface, and the orientation of this array in a horizontal plane adjusted to give a maximum response with no electric delay, the bearing of the source is known to lie in a plane perpendicular to the axis of the array. Although this furnishes no information as to the inclination of the line connecting source and receiver the azimuth bearing of the source is correctly indicated. If, however, a maximum response is obtained by adjusting a compensator to bring a displaced maximum response bearing in line with the source all that is known is that the source lies somewhere on the conical surface corresponding to the compensation angle thus introduced. Assuming the mechanical axis of the array to be horizontal the displacement of its maximum response bearing required to bring it in line with the source depends on the ratio of the vertical component of the separation between source and array to the total separation as well as upon the azimuth bearing of the source relative to the axis of the array.

The relations in this case may be derived by a consideration of the diagram given in Fig. 5A-5. Here OY is considered as the mechanical axis of the array, which is assumed to be in the horizontal plane. The line joining the source point and the origin is OP. The azimuth bearing of the source is given by the angle ϕ between the OX-axis, normal to the array, and the projection of the line OP on the XY-plane. The compensation angle

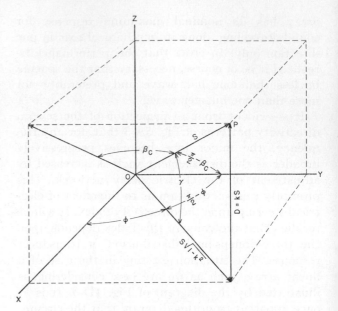

Fig. 5A-5. Geometry of a Compensated Array. The relations between the compensation angle and the azimuth bearing of a sound source giving maximum response on a linear array when array and source are at different depths.

at which a maximum response is obtained for signals from the source specified is the angle β_C between the line OP and the XZ-plane. The angle between OY and OP is $[(\pi/2) - \beta_C]$; the angle between OY and the projection of OP on the XY-plane is $[(\pi/2) - \phi]$; the angle between OP and its projection on the XY-plane will be designated as γ. From the geometric relations indicated by the diagram the relations between these angles may be written as

$$\cos\left(\frac{\pi}{2} - \beta_C\right) = \cos\gamma \cos\left(\frac{\pi}{2} - \phi\right) \qquad (5A\text{-}7)$$

The ratio of the vertical component of the slant range to the total value of this slant range will be designated as $k = D/S$. We may then write

$$\cos\gamma = \sqrt{1 - k^2} \qquad (5A\text{-}8)$$

from which it follows that

$$\cos\left(\frac{\pi}{2} - \beta_C\right) = \sqrt{1 - k^2} \cos\left(\frac{\pi}{2} - \phi\right) \qquad (5A\text{-}9)$$

or

$$\sin\beta_C = \sqrt{1 - k^2} \sin\phi \qquad (5A\text{-}10)$$

The last equation permits a computation, for any value of the ratio, k, of the actual value of compensation angle, β_C, which would be required to show a maximum response when the azimuth bearing has the value ϕ. The significance of this relation may be appreciated by an examination of Fig. 5A-6, in which the maximum response bearing has been plotted as a function of actual azimuth bearing for three values of the ratio stated above. It is evident that the more serious discrepancies occur for azimuth bearings in the neighborhood of 90° and that the error in indicated bearing decreases rapidly as the range becomes large as compared with the difference in depth between source and array. For operations where the ranges are likely to be many times this

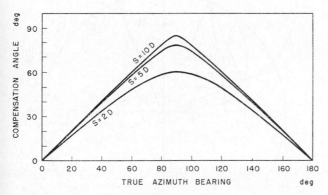

FIG. 5A-6. BEARING ERRORS IN COMPENSATED ARRAY. The compensation angle of a linear array giving maximum response, plotted as a function of the actual azimuth bearing of the source with the ratio of the vertical component of slant range to the slant range as a parameter.

difference in depth, and where great bearing accuracy is not required, corrections due to this effect may usually be neglected. For close-range operations, however, particularly where attempts are made to estimate range by triangulation, using bearings taken from two points, the errors may well become prohibitive.

Constant loss, or constant signal level, contour lines may be drawn from the directivity patterns of electrically steered arrays as well as from other types of directivity pattern. These contour line diagrams may be rotated about the axis of acoustic symmetry to give constant loss contour surfaces similar to those described in Art. 4D-3. In the case of a linear array it must be remembered that the axis of acoustic symmetry is perpendicular to the reference axis from which deviation angles are measured. The general appearance of the region from which signals giving responses in excess of some specified value will be obtained may be deduced from a knowledge of the shapes and positions of the maximum response loci. For a

compensation angle of $\beta_C = 0°$ it is symmetrically disposed about a plane perpendicular to the mechanical axis of the array; as the compensation angle increases it is identified with a conical surface coaxial with the array; when the compensation angle reaches $\beta_C = 90°$ it corresponds to a beam centered on the mechanical axis.

Three-dimensional contour surfaces are particularly useful as a means of deriving a plan view of the region within which a sound source at one depth may be detectable to a horizontal array at a different depth. In Fig. 5A-7 is shown a constant signal contour line drawn for a 17-element array operated at a frequency for which the spacing between elements is one half wave and with the axis of maximum response displaced 60° from the reference axis. This corresponds to a difference of 200 yd between the depths of the source and of the array. The method by which such lines may be computed has been described in Art. 4D-3. The effect on the indicated source bearing of a difference in depth between source and array is shown by the difference between the bearing at which the range is a maximum and the 60° displacement angle for which the contour is drawn. An interesting feature of this contour is the manner in which the main lobe covers bearings in the vicinity of the vertical plane through the axis of the array; a source below the level of the array but near this axis would produce a response only because of the existence of a secondary lobe.

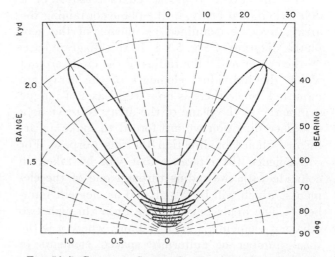

FIG. 5A-7. CONSTANT SIGNAL CONTOUR FOR COMPENSATED ARRAY. The constant signal contour line obtained from the directivity pattern of a linear array of 17 elements spaced by half wave intervals when delayed to a compensation angle of 60° and when source and array differ in depth by 200 yd.

5A-2 Delayed Circular Arrays

If a number of similar nondirectional transducers are positioned at equal intervals around the circumference of a circle the resulting array will have no uniquely defined directivity in the plane of the circle. This will, indeed, be true even though the transducers have directivity in planes perpendicular to the plane of the circle. If the individual elements are nondirectional the directivity in any plane perpendicular to the circle will approach that of a ring transducer, in the same manner that the pattern of a linear multispot array approaches that of a linear transducer. Such an array may be given directivity in the plane of the circle by the use of delay networks, which may be connected to compensate the acoustic delays identified with propagation along any bearing in this plane. Because of the symmetry of the system in this plane the directivity pattern will be independent of whether the system is trained electrically through 360° and measured by a transducer maintained on some given bearing, or whether the network maintains the maximum response axis on this same bearing as the measuring transducer is moved along a circular path concentric with the array. In either case, however, the pattern will depend upon the relation between the fixed bearing and the elements of the array; the pattern for a fixed bearing coincident with a radius through one element differs from the pattern for a fixed bearing coincident with a radius passing between two elements.

The directional response characteristics of a delayed circular array, in the plane containing the array, may be examined by means of the geometric diagram of Fig. 5A-8. In this diagram let O be the center and r the radius of the circle around which the individual elements of the array are mounted. Since there is no natural axis of unique symmetry in the plane of the array to serve as a reference direction we are forced to make an arbitrary choice of direction for this purpose. For convenience the reference axis will be taken to coincide with the radius through one of the elements, which will be designated as element number 1. The angle between the radii through two adjacent elements is $2\pi/n$ radians, where n is the total number of uniformly spaced elements in the array. If T is the position of element number k the angle between the radius through T and the reference axis will be $2k\pi/n$ radians.

Assume that an acoustic wave approaches the

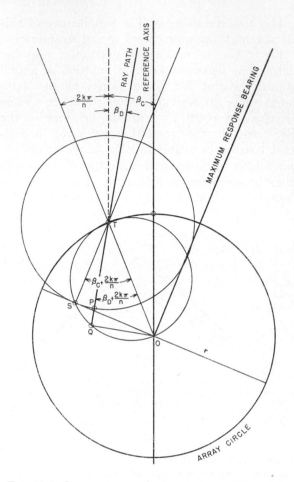

FIG. 5A-8. GEOMETRY OF A CIRCULAR ARRAY. The relations between the element positions and the path lengths corresponding to various acoustic and electric delays. The circle through P is a locus of equivalent response positions; the circle through Q is a locus of equivalent phase reference positions.

array along a line making the angle β_C with the specified reference axis. At the instant when this wave reaches the center of the array it will coincide with the diameter perpendicular to the direction of propagation. The projection of the point T on this diameter will be designated as S. The phase of the wave at the center of the array circle will be taken as the reference phase. For a wave traveling in the specified direction the point T will be in advance of this phase reference point by the distance

$$TS = r \cos\left(\beta_C + \frac{2k\pi}{n}\right)$$

The response of the element at T will be brought to the reference phase if it is delayed by the phase angle

$$\frac{2\pi r}{\lambda} \cos\left(\beta_C + \frac{2k\pi}{n}\right)$$

radians, the coefficient $2\pi/\lambda$ being the rate of phase shift in radians per unit length of ray path. Under these conditions the delayed response is the same as though the transducer had been moved, in the direction of propagation, until it reached its projection, S, on the diameter of the circle perpendicular to this direction. If the response of each element is delayed by the amount

$$\frac{2\pi r}{\lambda} \cos\left(\beta_C + \frac{2k\pi}{n}\right)$$

radians, k being the number of the element, the effect, for a wave propagated along a path making the angle β_C with the reference axis, will be the same as though each element were located at its projection on the diameter perpendicular to this direction. Since all elements would, in that case, respond in phase unison to a wave traveling in this direction it must be the direction of maximum response. The angle β_C appearing in the phase-delay term given above is thus the compensation angle, relative to the designated reference direction.

Consider, now, the situation when a wave approaches the array along a direction making the angle β_D with the designated reference axis. This direction of approach makes the angle $\beta_D + (2k\pi/n)$ radians with the radius through the element at T. In the diagram of Fig. 5A-8 a circle has been drawn on the line OT as a diameter. A line through the center of the array, at O, and perpendicular to the new ray path through the element, at T, intersects this ray path at a point on this circle which has been designated as Q. The line OQ thus coincides with a wave front traveling along the path in question at the instant when it has reached the phase reference position. The phase of the wave at the intersection of the ray path and this circle is thus identical with the phase of the wave at the reference point. The circle may, in consequence, be looked upon as a locus of equivalent phase reference positions for rays passing through the element for which it is drawn. The length of ray path between its intersection with this locus and the element through which it passes is, as seen from the geometry of the diagram,

$$TQ = r \cos\left(\beta_D + \frac{2k\pi}{n}\right)$$

An associated locus of equivalent response positions is formed by a circle having the length

$$TS = r \cos\left(\beta_C + \frac{2k\pi}{n}\right)$$

as a radius and the element position, T, as a center. The length of ray path between its intersection, shown as the point P, with this locus and the element through which it passes is

$$TP = TS = r \cos\left(\beta_C + \frac{2k\pi}{n}\right)$$

the distance for which compensation has been provided. The distance by which the length of ray path between the position of the element and the locus of equivalent phase reference positions exceeds the length of path between this same element position and the locus of equivalent response positions is

$$PQ = TQ - TP$$

$$= r\left[\cos\left(\beta_D + \frac{2k\pi}{n}\right) - \cos\left(\beta_C + \frac{2k\pi}{n}\right)\right] \quad (5A\text{-}11)$$

From this it follows that the response of any transducer element of a circular array, when delayed by the amount

$$\frac{2\pi r}{\lambda} \cos\left(\beta_C + \frac{2k\pi}{n}\right)$$

leads the reference phase by the angle

$$\psi_k = \frac{2\pi r}{\lambda}\left[\cos\left(\beta_D + \frac{2k\pi}{n}\right) - \cos\left(\beta_C + \frac{2k\pi}{n}\right)\right] \quad (5A\text{-}12)$$

where

ψ_k = the phase factor applying to a single element of a compensated circular array (rad)

r = the radius of the array (in)

λ = the wave length of the sinusoidal acoustic wave to which the phase factor applies (in/cyc)

β_C = the angle between the direction of propagation for which compensation is provided and the reference axis through element number 1 (rad)

β_D = the angle between any direction of propagation and the same reference axis (rad)

k = the number of the element to which the phase factor applies

n = the number of elements in the array

This equation may be given in terms of element spacing, as measured by the length of arc between adjacent elements, instead of in terms of the radius of the array circle. Since the circumference of this array circle is ns the radius is $r = ns/2\pi$, or

$$4\pi r = 2ns \qquad (5A\text{-}13)$$

To compute the resultant response of the total number of elements making up an array it is necessary that due account be taken of their relative phases in adding their individual responses. If the magnitude of the voltage generated by each element is given the value $1/n$ the phasor associated with this voltage, as delayed acoustically and electrically, is

$$e_k = \left(\frac{1}{n}\right)(\cos\psi_k + j\sin\psi_k) \qquad (5A\text{-}14)$$

The maximum response due to the combined effect of n elements operating in phase, as they do when a wave approaches at the angle for which compensation has been provided, will be $(e_d)_C = 1$. The total relative voltage response for any angle, β_D, is then given as that voltage the voltage phasor of which is the sum of the voltage phasors of the responses of all of these elements to a wave approaching at this angle. This relative response is thus

$$\frac{(e_d)_D}{(e_d)_C} = (e_d)_D = \frac{\sqrt{(\Sigma\cos\psi_k)^2 + (\Sigma\sin\psi_k)^2}}{n} \qquad (5A\text{-}15)$$

For any value of deviation angle, β_D, the summations of values of $\cos\psi_k$ and of $\sin\psi_k$ are to be made from $k=1$ to $k=n$, where n is the total number of elements in the array.

Whenever the angle $\beta_C + (2k\pi/2)$, between the radius through any transducer element and the direction of propagation for which the acoustic delays have been compensated is between $\pi/2$ and $3\pi/2$ its cosine and the related acoustic phase delay

$$\frac{2\pi r}{\lambda}\cos\left(\beta_C + \frac{2k\pi}{n}\right)$$

are negative. Although negative electric delays

are impossible physically, they present no difficulty mathematically. In any actual system the response of each element would be delayed electrically by $2\pi r/\lambda$ radians more than the amount indicated above. This would have an effect equivalent to moving each element, for a wave approaching along the direction of maximum response, by the additional distance r in the direction of propagation, or from the diameter described above to a line parallel thereto but tangent to the array circle. To express the magnitudes of the delays actually introduced, and the relative phases of the actual responses as thus delayed, by the equations given above the reference phase, which may be selected at will, would be one which lags the acoustic wave at the center of the array by $2\pi r/\lambda$ radians. Since we are here concerned with the effects of compensating networks, rather than with their design, it is permissible, and more convenient, to retain the center of the array as the phase reference point.

It can be shown, either by trigonometric identities or by geometric relations similar to those illustrated in Fig. 5A-8, that the response of one of a pair of diametrically-opposed elements leads the reference phase corresponding to the wave at the center of the array by exactly as much as the response of the other lags it. In other words, $\cos\psi_k = \cos\psi_{(k+n/2)}$ and $\sin\psi_k = -\sin\psi_{(k+n/2)}$ for any value of k. The resultant response for the pair, then, has the voltage phasor

$$e_k + e_{(k+n/2)} = \frac{2}{n}\cos\psi_k \qquad (5A\text{-}16)$$

The relative voltage for an assembly of such pairs has a voltage phasor which is the sum of the voltage phasors of the $n/2$ pairs making up the array and is, therefore,

$$\frac{(e_d)_D}{(e_d)_C} = \frac{2}{n}(\Sigma\cos\psi_k) \qquad (5A\text{-}17)$$

The summation of values of $\cos\psi_k$ is taken, in this case, from $k=1$ to $k=n/2$.

Although the formulas given above have been derived in terms of received acoustic energy it is, of course, understood that they apply also to the relative pressures developed by the array when used for transmission.

The directivity pattern for a compensated circular array may be computed by carrying out the summation indicated above in the same manner that the pattern for a linear array may be computed by summing the terms represented by the formula of Eq. (4E-1). Although the equations for the individual responses appear to be identical in the two cases, they differ with respect to the manner in which the phase factor changes from pair to pair. In the linear array the separation between elements is the independent variable; in the circular array the aspect of the pair relative to the direction of propagation is the independent variable. Because of the dependence of the phase factor on angle it is not possible to derive a simple expression for the relative response of a compensated circular array analogous to Eq. (4E-2), which applies to the linear array. It is, however, possible to simplify the labor of computation which, for an array having a large number of elements, is a task of some magnitude. Those skilled in the manipulation of Bessel functions have succeeded in transforming the series represented by Eq. (5A-17) into another series each term of which is a Bessel function of a quantity determined, as is the phase factor, by the dimensions of the array and by the compensation and deviation angles.[1] This equation is

$$\frac{(e_d)_D}{(e_d)_C} = \mathcal{J}_0\left[\frac{4\pi r}{\lambda}\sin\frac{\beta_D - \beta_C}{2}\right] + 2\sum\mathcal{J}_{np}\left[\frac{4\pi r}{\lambda}\sin\frac{\beta_D - \beta_C}{2}\cos\frac{np(\beta_D - \beta_C)}{2}\right] \qquad (5A-18)$$

The quantity np, appearing as a subscript to the symbol $\mathcal{J}$, designating a Bessel function, indicates the order of that function. Tables containing orders as high as $np = 60$ may be found in various mathematical handbooks. The summation indicated by this equation is to be carried out for a series of terms beginning with that for which $p = 1$ and continuing with successive terms, for each of which this coefficient is increased by 1, until a point is reached at which the contribution of the next term would be negligible. Beyond this point all other terms are negligible. From the theory of Bessel functions it may be shown that any term may be neglected if the quantity, known as the argument, of which the Bessel function is to be taken is not greater than

$$np - 2 \qquad (5A-19)$$

This is based on the fact that

$$\mathcal{J}_{np}(np - 2) < 0.07 \qquad (5A-20)$$

for all positive values of np. The error in the relative voltage—or relative pressure—cannot, there-

fore, be greater than twice this amount if the above condition is satisfied. Now it is evident that the maximum possible value of the argument appearing in any of the terms of the series to be summed is

$$\frac{4\pi r}{\lambda} = \frac{2ns}{\lambda}$$

Since any term may be neglected if

$$\frac{2ns}{\lambda} \leqq np - 2$$

it follows that if the spacing in waves is

$$\frac{s}{\lambda} \leqq \frac{p}{2} - \frac{1}{n} \qquad (5A-21)$$

the term to which the value of p applies need not be included. In particular, the entire summation series may be disregarded if

$$\frac{s}{\lambda} \leqq \frac{1}{2} - \frac{1}{n} \quad \text{or} \quad n \geqq \frac{4\pi r}{\lambda} + 2 \quad (5A-22)$$

In this case the approximation equation reduces to

$$\frac{(e_d)_D}{(e_d)_C} \approx \mathcal{J}_0\left[\frac{2ns}{\lambda}\sin\frac{\beta_D - \beta_C}{2}\right]$$

$$\approx \mathcal{J}_0\left[\frac{4\pi r}{\lambda}\sin\frac{\beta_D - \beta_C}{2}\right] \qquad (5A-23)$$

The advantage of the approximate method of solution over the method required by Eq. (5A-17) is evident. Although rigorously correct, the summation of cosine terms requires the computation of as many terms, for every value of deviation angle for which a solution is desired, as there are pairs of elements in the array; for many practical array designs the expression of Eq. (5A-23) gives an adequate approximation. It is noted that although this equation becomes more and more exact as the number of elements in an array of given dimensions is increased, and applies without error when the spacing is infinitesimal, it is not the same as the equation for a circular ring transducer given by Eq. (4E-10). The reason for the difference is that the earlier equation applies to a plane perpendicular to the transducer circle whereas the present equation applies to the plane containing this circle.

In selecting sample directivity patterns for circular arrays it will be informative if the constants chosen are related to those of the linear array for which patterns are available. With this in mind we shall consider a circular array having 16 elements uniformly spaced around the circumference of a circle of such dimensions that the spacing is one half wave. The circumference of this circle, in other words, is equal to the length of the linear array identified with one group of the directivity patterns shown in Fig. 5A-3. On applying the criterion of negligibility to the first term of the summation series of Eq. (5A-18) it appears that

$$\frac{s}{\lambda} = \frac{1}{2} > \frac{1}{2} - \frac{1}{16}$$

or that the term may not be disregarded. In the directivity pattern shown in Fig. 5A-9 the contributions of the zero order term, corresponding to Eq. (5A-23), and of the first term of the summation series, which is of the order $np = 16$, are shown separately so that the importance of this latter term may be appraised. In computing these curves it has been assumed that the compensation angle is $\beta_C = 0°$, or that the axis of maximum response coincides with the radius through an element of the array.

It will be noted that the directivity patterns

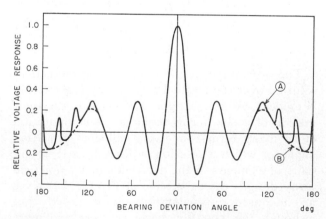

FIG. 5A-9. DIRECTIVITY PATTERN OF COMPENSATED ARRAY. The pattern of a circular array of 16 elements uniformly spaced at half wave intervals as compensated to bring the maximum response axis into the plane of the array.
  A. Resultant pattern
  B. Pattern omitting second term of Eq. (5A-18)

of a compensated circular array are drawn for the two quadrants on either side of the reference axis instead of for a single quadrant, as in patterns shown previously. This is required because the compensated circular array lacks the symmetry relative to an axis perpendicular to the reference axis which has characterized the arrays and transducers examined heretofore; the pattern for the second and third quadrants, therefore, does not repeat that for the first and fourth.

In any circular array for which the relative response on any bearing in the plane of the array is given to a sufficiently close approximation by Eq. (5A-23) the relation between the design constants and the width of the primary lobe is easily derived. Reference to a table of Bessel functions shows that a Bessel function of order zero has the value $\mathcal{J}_0(a) = 0$ when the argument is $a = 2.405$. In the present problem, then, placing $\beta_C = 0°$ for convenience,

$$\frac{4\pi r}{\lambda} \sin \frac{\beta_D}{2} = 2.405$$

or

$$\sin \frac{\beta_D}{2} = \frac{2.405\,\lambda}{4\pi r} = \frac{2.405\,\lambda}{2ns} \qquad (5A\text{-}24)$$

This shows, as do analogous formulas for other types of arrays or for transducers, that the width of the primary lobe depends on the dimensions of its configuration as measured in wave spaces, which is the same as saying that for a configuration of given dimensions the width of the lobe depends on the frequency. It is independent of the spacing or of the number of the elements so long as the configuration and frequency remain constant.

Tables of Bessel functions also show that the magnitude of the first secondary maximum, corresponding to the relative voltage of the first secondary lobe, has the value 0.403. This is identical with the maximum relative voltage of the first secondary lobe of the directivity pattern for a ring transducer in a plane perpendicular to the plane of the ring.

Provided the spacing and the number of elements of a compensated circular array satisfy the condition stated by Eq. (5A-21) the amplitudes of the secondary lobes will diminish progressively as their angular deviation from the primary lobe increases. This follows as a consequence of the fact that successive maxima of a zero order Bessel function are each of smaller magnitude than the preceding maximum. It is only when terms containing higher order functions are required that the possibility of a minimum, and hence of a subsequent increase, in the height of the envelope of the directivity pattern arises.

It is evident that under conditions which permit the use of Eq. (5A-23) the shape of the directivity pattern is independent of the compensation angle, β_C. The quantity $\sin\left[(\beta_D-\beta_C)/2\right]$ goes through normal sinusoidal variations regardless of the value of this angle, which simply determines the value of deviation angle, β_D, at which the initial zero occurs. It is only when subsequent terms contribute to the value of the resultant voltage that the directivity pattern, for fixed compensation, depends upon the angle between the fixed axis of maximum response and a radius through one of the transducer elements.

It is noted that the number of secondary lobes between the deviation angles $\beta_D=\beta_C$ and $\beta_D=\beta_C\pm\pi$ is equal to twice the diameter of the array circle in wave spaces.

In the case of a compensated circular array there is no axis of acoustic symmetry about which a two-dimensional directivity pattern may be rotated to generate the complete three-dimensional pattern. For this reason it is impossible to compute the directivity index for such an array from data furnished by a two-dimensional pattern. It has, however, been demonstrated that the directivity index of a circular array when compensated to have directivity in the plane of the array is approximately the same as the index for the uncompensated array. In either case the directivity index increases at the rate of 1 db/fl with increasing frequency. The index for the uncompensated array may be computed from the two-dimensional pattern taken in a plane through the normal to the array, at its center, since rotation of this pattern about this normal generates the three-dimensional pattern. Although we have a formula in Eq. (4E-10) from which to compute such a pattern in the case of a ring transducer, this may not be used for a circular array unless the number of elements is large and the separation between them small. It is desirable, then, to obtain a general formula for the relative response of a compensated circular array which may be used for any bearing.

Assume the circular array to be made up of an even number of elements uniformly spaced around a circle of radius r located in the XY-plane of a system of three-dimensional rectangular

coordinates with its center at the origin. Let x_D, y_D, and z_D be the angles between any direction of propagation and the X-, Y-, and Z-axes. Let x_C, y_C, and z_C be the angles between these same coordinate axes and the direction of propagation for which the relative acoustic delays of the several elements have been compensated electrically. These last three angles, then, define the direction of maximum response. We shall make use of the abbreviation

$$\mathfrak{F}(\beta_D, \beta_C)$$
$$= \sqrt{(\cos x_D-\cos x_C)^2+(\cos y_D-\cos y_C)^2} \quad (5A\text{-}25)$$

We shall also define the angle γ by the relations

$$\tan\gamma = \frac{\cos x_D - \cos x_C}{\cos y_D - \cos y_C} \quad (5A\text{-}26)$$

It may be shown by methods similar to those previously employed, but carried out in three dimensions rather than in two, that the response on any bearing relative to the maximum response is given in terms of these quantities by the relation

$$\frac{(e_d)_D}{(e_d)_C} = \frac{2}{n}\sum\cos\left\{\left[\frac{2\pi r}{\lambda}\mathfrak{F}(\beta_D, \beta_C)\right]\right.$$
$$\left.\cdot\left[\sin\left(\gamma+\frac{2k\pi}{n}\right)\right]\right\} \quad (5A\text{-}27)$$

In this case the summation is to be carried from $k=0$ to $k=(n/2)-1$.

As with Eq. (5A-17), the solution of this equation requires the computation of as many terms, for any given direction of propagation, as there are pairs of elements in the array. Since we are now concerned with directions in three dimensions the labor involved is even greater than before. Fortunately this series, also, may be transformed by the aid of Bessel functions into a shorter series. The alternative equation in this case is

$$\frac{(e_d)_D}{(e_d)_C} = \mathfrak{J}_0\left[\frac{2\pi r}{\lambda}\mathfrak{F}(\beta_D, \beta_C)\right]$$
$$+ 2\sum\mathfrak{J}_{np}\left[\frac{2\pi r}{\lambda}\mathfrak{F}(\beta_D, \beta_C)\right]\cos np\gamma \quad (5A\text{-}28)$$

As with Eq. (5A-18) the summation is to be carried from the term for which $p=1$, through terms for each of which this integer is increased by 1, until further terms become negligible. The same test of negligibility may be employed as before, namely, that the argument of the term in question shall not exceed the value $np-2$. In fact, Eqs. (5A-21) and (5A-22) may be applied in this case exactly as in the case of Eq. (5A-18), since the maximum possible value of the argument of the Bessel function is the same in each.

If there is no electric compensation connected to the elements of the array the direction of maximum response will coincide with the Z-axis. In this case $x_C = y_C = \pi/2$. The directivity pattern in the XZ-plane may be computed by placing $y_D = \pi/2$ and allowing the angle between the direction of propagation and the X-axis to vary from $x_D = 0$ to $x_D = \pi/2$. Under these conditions $\mathcal{F}(\beta_D, \beta_C) = \cos x_D$. The maximum value which the argument of the first term of the summation series may have is $2\pi r/\lambda$; this term may be neglected if

$$\frac{2\pi r}{\lambda} \leqq n - 2$$

or if

$$n \geqq \frac{2\pi r}{\lambda} + 2$$

It is thus apparent that if the array has a sufficient number of elements to permit the summation terms of Eq. (5A-18) to be disregarded it has more than enough to permit a similar simplification to be made in Eq. (5A-28). Under these conditions the equation reduces to

$$\frac{e_x}{e_{\pi/2}} = \mathcal{J}_0\left[\frac{2\pi r}{\lambda} \cos x_D\right] \quad (5A-29)$$

If we measure the angle indicating the direction of propagation, in the XZ-plane, from the Z-axis, which is the axis of maximum response, and designate it as β_D in the usual manner, we have $\beta_D = (\pi/2) - x_D$ and $\cos x_D = \sin \beta_D$ whence

$$\frac{(e_d)_D}{(e_d)_C} = \mathcal{J}_0\left[\frac{2\pi r}{\lambda} \sin \beta_D\right]$$

which is identical with Eq. (4E-10).

By means of Eq. (5A-28) the directivity pattern of a compensated circular array having its maximum response axis in the plane of the array may be computed for a plane through the maximum response axis and perpendicular to the array. The various fixed angles are the same as for the derivation of Eq. (5A-29) except that the angle between the compensated direction and the X-axis is now $x_C = 0°$. When the proper substitutions are made Eq. (5A-28) reduces to

$$\frac{(e_d)_D}{(e_d)_C} = \mathcal{J}_0\left[\frac{2\pi r}{\lambda} (\cos x_D - 1)\right] \quad (5A-30)$$

In Fig. 5A-10 the directivity patterns for a plane perpendicular to a compensated circular array and for the plane of the array are compared. The array for which these curves are computed is of the same diameter as that assumed in computing the curves of Fig. 5A-9. The number of elements has, however, been increased to be in excess of $n = (4\pi r/\lambda) + 2$ as required by Eq. (5A-22). It will be noted that with respect to the number and heights of its secondary lobes this pattern is the same as that for the plane of the array. With respect to their location and width, however, there are marked differences between the two. The difference between the widths of the primary lobes is conspicuous.

5A-3 Universal Compensators—Directivity Plotting Machines

In many situations it may be impossible, or undesirable, to use an array having a symmetrical arrangement of elements. For example, the difficulty of two maximum response bearings in a linear array of elements uniformly spaced by half wave intervals may be avoided if the elements are positioned along a line which is not straight, or if the elements are not uniformly spaced. Under certain conditions structural considerations may make it impossible to obtain equal responses from all members of a given array. This is usually the case with electrically steered transducers or with large arrays which are hull-

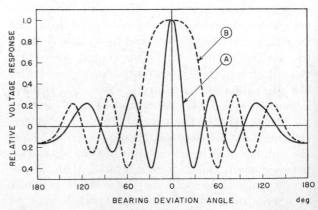

FIG. 5A-10. DIRECTIVITY PATTERN OF COMPENSATED ARRAY. The pattern for a circular array of 16 elements uniformly spaced at half wave intervals, compensated to bring the maximum response axis into the plane of the array.
A. As taken in the plane of the array
B. As taken in a plane perpendicular to the array

mounted in such manner that some elements are shielded from waves traveling in certain directions. When adjusting the delay circuits to direct the maximum response axis along a given bearing it is preferable, in such cases, to connect only those elements which are suitably exposed. In arrangements of this type the computation of the amounts of delay required, or of the directivity patterns to be expected, becomes a matter of considerable complexity. Fortunately both of these arduous tasks may be avoided by a simple mechanical arrangement of the lag line connections.

The diagram of Fig. 5A-11 shows, at A, a plan view of an array for which it is desired to provide electric compensation. Although a circular array has been chosen for this illustration the method to be described is applicable to an array having any configuration in a plane, or having any distribution of elements within that configuration. The ray paths between the array and a remote point, for a given direction of propagation, may be represented by straight lines parallel to this direction and passing through the positions of the individual transducer elements. A perpendicular to this direction drawn near the array on the side away from the remote point is a locus of points equidistant from the remote point and may be used as a reference line. The lengths of ray path, shown by arrows on the diagram, between this reference line and the several element positions are proportional to the amounts of acoustic delay by which the waves at these positions lead the wave at the reference position. If electric delays proportional to these lengths of ray path are introduced into the outputs of the individual elements the delayed response of each will be the same as though it had been moved to its projection on this line. All delayed responses will, under these conditions, be in phase with the acoustic wave at this reference line and will consequently be in phase with each other. The direction of propagation for which the ray paths have been drawn would thus be a direction of maximum response.

Means for obtaining amounts of electric delay proportional to the lengths of ray path between the individual transducer elements and a constant distance locus, perpendicular to some given direction of propagation, is provided by a **network commutator,** or **universal compensator.** This consists of a flat plate made of a number of thin conducting bars laid parallel to each other and separated by even thinner insulating strips. Successive bars are connected to successive points along an electric lag line, as shown at B in Fig. 5A-11. If the total amount of electric delay associated with the number of bars in one inch of plate length is 1/4800 sec the electric delay per inch of plate will be equal to the acoustic delay per foot of water. A model of the array which is to be compensated is built to whatever scale is used for the commutator plate. The positions on this model which

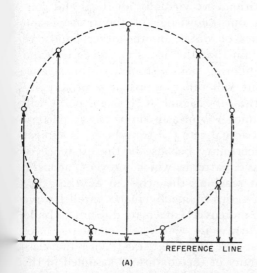

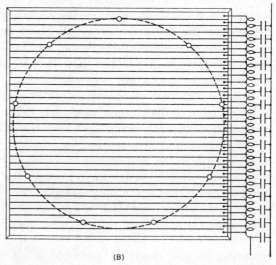

FIG. 5A-11. UNIVERSAL COMPENSATOR.
(A) The lengths of ray path for which equivalent electric delays must be provided in order that the delayed responses of all transducers to an acoustic signal traveling in the indicated direction shall be in phase
(B) The arrangement of a commutator plate and a lag line which connects the required delay into each transducer for any desired compensation angle

correspond to the positions of the transducer elements are occupied by small contactor elements. Each transducer element is connected to its corresponding contactor element. The combination of contactor array and lag-line commutator constitutes the compensator. Assume the contactor array to be so oriented that the bearing which corresponds to the desired maximum response bearing of the transducer is perpendicular to the commutator bars and directed away from the last bar of the plate. This last bar is connected to the output end of the lag line and the response of any transducer element connected to it suffers no electric delay; the amount of delay associated with any other bar is proportional to its distance from this terminal bar. The amount of delay connected to any given transducer element is thus proportional to the length of commutator plate between its associated contactor element and this terminal bar. By virtue of the scalar relations between the compensator and the transducer array this length of commutator plate is, in turn, proportional to the length of ray path between the actual transducer element and a constant distance locus corresponding to the terminal bar. The amounts of lag line connected to the several transducer elements by their associated contactors consequently introduce the amounts of delay required to make the specified bearing a bearing of maximum response. The direction of maximum response may be shifted to another bearing merely by reorienting the contactor array relative to the commutator plate. That bearing of the transducer array corresponding to the bearing of the contactor array which is perpendicular to the commutator bars, and which is directed away from the terminal bar, is always the bearing of maximum response.

It is evident that the position of the contactor array relative to the commutator plate determines the position of each transducer element relative to the direction of propagation for which it is desired to make the response a maximum. It is, therefore, a simple matter so to arrange the commutator plate that it not only connects the proper amount of electric delay for any given bearing of maximum response but that it also disconnects any element which should be prevented from contributing to the resultant response when transmitting or receiving on that bearing.

A universal compensator of the type just described has obvious practical advantages in connection with the design of steerable arrays for service use. Our present task, however, is not concerned with designing operating equipment so much as with studying the manner in which various forms of equipment behave. For our present purposes the utility of this device results from the assistance which it is able to give in the plotting of directivity patterns.[2]

In its normal use the compensator selects electric delays which are the differences between certain variable acoustic delays and a fixed acoustic delay. This fixed delay may correspond to a point between the array and the source as well as to a point beyond the array. If an electric signal is supplied to one end of the lag line the phases of the voltages appearing at the several contactor elements will be the same as the phases of plane progressive acoustic waves, received from a distant source, at the corresponding positions of the elements of the acoustic array of which the contactor array is a scale model. For the purpose of obtaining directivity patterns the electrical counterpart of an acoustic array is to be preferred to the actual array. The saving in time and money required to make or to modify the electrical version, as compared with the actual acoustical version, is obvious. In addition to these advantages, the results are incomparably superior. The relations between the electric signals in the lag line and commutator plate simulate ideal acoustic relations more closely than they may ever be attained by acoustic signals in water. The magnitudes of the electric signals at the several element positions are virtually identical and constant; from our knowledge of the transmission characteristics of water, on the other hand, we may be certain that the acoustic signals received at two neighboring points from a distant transmitting point will differ appreciably at any instant and that the signal at a single point will vary with time. Any measured directivity pattern taken on an actual array of transducers is subject to great uncertainty because of the existence of standing-wave patterns which prevent acoustic energy from reaching the array in anything approaching a series of ideally plane parallel wave fronts. It is, moreover, extremely difficult to build an actual array in which all elements have identical response characteristics. With the electric array many of the conditions assumed in the computation of directivity patterns may be achieved with little difficulty.

An analog computer for generating directivity patterns may be constructed by using a pair of

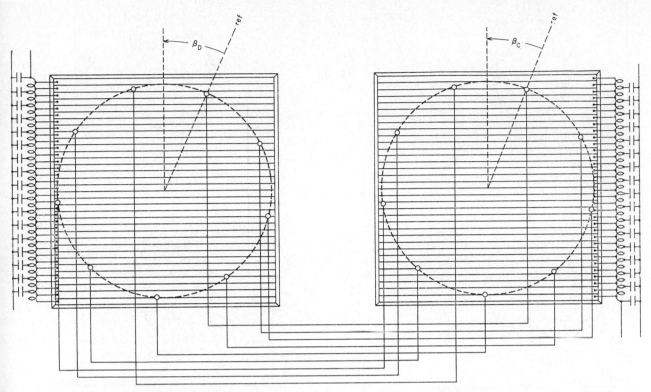

FIG. 5A-12. DIRECTIVITY-MEASURING COMPENSATOR. An arrangement of universal compensators for measuring the relative response of a plane array of any configuration as a function of deviation and compensation angles.

lag lines, each provided with a commutator, and each having a suitable scale model of the array for which patterns are desired. In this computer each contactor of one commutator is connected to the corresponding contactor of the other. Patterns are generated by supplying a signal to one lag line and observing the resulting voltage developed in the other as one of the array models is rotated. Motion of the counterpart array is equivalent to moving a distant source of acoustic energy along a circular path concentric with the array in question; motion of the compensating array is equivalent to training the system electrically with reference to a fixed source. A single-frequency directivity pattern is obtained by supplying the analog computer with a sinusoidal signal. Patterns may be taken with equal facility for signals having continuous spectra and for signals occupying frequency bands of finite width.

Data obtained from such an analog computer may be plotted automatically by any of several methods. They may, for example, be presented on the screen of a cathode ray oscilloscope. Permanent records may be obtained in either polar or rectangular coordinates by properly relating the motion of the coordinate paper used in a suitable recorder to the rotation of either of the contactor arrays while a moving stylus records the magnitude of the response. Patterns may be drawn in terms of relative pressure or relative voltage by using a conventional linear amplifier to drive the recording stylus. They may be drawn in terms of deviation loss, in decibels, by using a logarithmically responding circuit.

Band directivity patterns made with an analog computer of the type described are shown in Fig. 5A-13. These patterns[3] are for linear arrays of uniformly spaced elements. The signal used in obtaining these patterns occupied a frequency band having a band ratio of one octave. Within this band the power per unit band of the signal was constant. The compensation angles for which electric delays were introduced are the same as those shown in Fig. 5A-3 for a single-frequency signal. For one series of these patterns the array was made up of $n = 36$ elements spaced at intervals of $s/\lambda = 0.25$ cyc, the wave length being computed at the geometric mean frequency of the band. For the other series of patterns the number of elements was $n = 18$ and the separation was $s/\lambda = 0.5$ cyc. The length of the array was thus $8.75\,\lambda$ in one case and $8.50\,\lambda$ in the other.

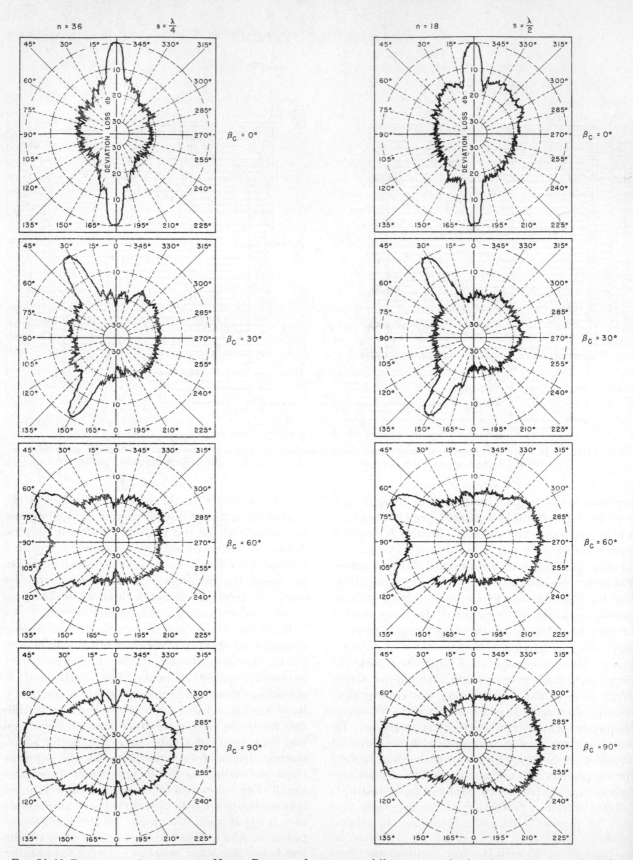

FIG. 5A-13. DIRECTIVITY PATTERNS FOR NOISE. Patterns of compensated linear arrays, having the numbers, *n*, and spacings, *s*, of elements indicated. The source used emitted a noise spectrum occupying one octave and having an essentially constant spectrum intensity. Spacings apply to the geometric mean frequency of the band.

264

It is interesting to note that a second lobe having a maximum relative response of unity fails to appear in any of these patterns. Such a lobe is conspicuous in the directivity pattern of an end-fired linear array having a half wave spacing, when $\beta_C = 90°$, as shown in Fig. 5A-3. The reason that such a lobe does not appear with a wide-band signal is not because it does not exist but because its contribution to the total response is too small as compared to the contributions of all other components. The presence of such a lobe might, however, be detected by the ear when listening to a complex signal by means of an array for which it exists; because of the high selectivity of the ear it is possible to identify the response to any one component should it exceed the responses to other components considered individually.

The patterns obtained by means of the analog computer are seen to agree, in general, with the form of the pattern obtained by computation and shown in Fig. 4I-5. The pattern obtained by computation, like all computed patterns, is a smooth curve because identical elements and ideal continuous variability are assumed. The patterns obtained by the computer show the effects of finite discontinuities. In any actual array the elements are never sufficiently identical, nor are the increments of the delay line sufficiently small, to avoid irregularities similar to those in the pattern generated by the computer.

In any problem in which the transmission or reception of complex signals is involved it is evident that directivity patterns of the type here considered have greater utility than do single-frequency patterns. In many cases they show that it is unnecessary to provide as many elements for a multispot array as would have been thought required on the basis of single-frequency patterns. They also show that it is by no means always necessary to insist that the envelope of the directivity pattern shall decrease progressively, with increasing deviation angle, all the way to its outer extremities; this requirement may well be relaxed for a portion of the frequency band without seriously impairing the directivity pattern applying to the band as a whole.

5A-4 Performance Characteristics of Arrays

In problems having to do with the design and use of arrays it is desirable to be able to express their performance characteristics in terms of those of the individual elements of which they are composed. In deriving relations for this purpose it will be assumed that the elementary transducers making up a directional array are themselves directional and that each has a directivity index $(N_{DI})_1$. Attention will be limited to cases where these elementary transducers are so mounted that bearings of equal relative response are parallel. Their directivity patterns, in other words, will all be oriented in the same manner. Under these conditions the relative response of the array, for any bearing, is given as the product of the relative response of a single element by the relative response of the array which would result from replacing each of the directional elements of the actual array by a nondirectional element. The validity of this statement, which is known as the **product theorem,** has been well established in connection with the directivity patterns of arrays of directional antennas. The directivity index, $(N_{DI})_\Sigma$, of an array of n directional transducers may be computed from the three-dimensional directivity characteristics obtained by the aid of this theorem. If the three-dimensional pattern is such that it may be generated by rotating a two-dimensional pattern about some axis of acoustic symmetry this computation may be effected by evaluating a directivity function, as described in Art. 4F-6. Where lack of symmetry makes this impossible a double integration will be required. An example of this process will be found in Chapter 8. In many cases the directivity index of an array of directional transducers is the sum of the indexes of one of its individual transducers and of the array when formed of nondirectional elements.

The following discussion will also be limited to cases where the maximum response axis which a given array would have if formed of nondirectional elements is parallel to the maximum response axes of the directional elements of which it is actually composed. This would, of course, be the logical arrangement to use since it gives the greatest prominence to the major response. To illustrate this point consider a number of linear transducers to be so disposed that their mechanical axes coincide with the elements of a cylinder. The plane of the array would then be identified with a section of the cylinder perpendicular to its axis and passing through the effective centers of the individual transducers. Under these conditions the maximum response planes of the individual transducers would all lie in the plane of the array. The maximum response axis of the array when formed of nondirectional elements would lie along the axis of the cylinder. The array pattern may, however, be given a maximum response axis in its own plane by means of delay networks. This axis of compensation will then be parallel to a maximum response bearing of each of the individual elements, thus satisfying the postulated requirements. The array of directional elements may show little, if any, response along the axis of the cylinder; if the relative response of an individual element is negligible in this direction its multiplication by the relative response of the array when formed of nondirectional elements will also be negligible. In this manner the maximum response axis of the array, as developed in the plane of the array by compensation, is made more prominent by using directional elements than it would be with nondirectional elements.

For an array of directional elements meeting the conditions specified above the relation between the hydrophone losses of the array and of its elements serves as a convenient connection between the other performance characteristics. For an individual element the hydrophone loss may be written, in accordance with Art. 4G-1, as

$$(N_H)_1 = \lg \frac{4A_S I_S R_1}{(e_{out})_1{}^2} \qquad (5A\text{-}31)$$

Here the intensity I_S is that of a plane wave reaching the element along its maximum response axis. The resistance R_1 is that of a single element and the open-circuit voltage $(e_{out})_1$ is that generated in this element by the given plane wave. When a number, n, of these hydrophone elements are connected in series the resistance of the array is $R_\Sigma = nR_1$. If the maximum response axis of the array coincides with the direction of propagation of the wave of intensity I_S the open-circuit voltage resulting from the response of all elements will be $(e_{out})_\Sigma = n(e_{out})_1$. This follows from the fact that, for the conditions here specified, all elements of the array are responding in phase. The hydrophone loss of the array is thus

$$(N_H)_\Sigma = \lg \frac{4A_S I_S R_\Sigma}{(e_{out})_\Sigma{}^2}$$

$$= \lg \frac{4A_S I_S R_1}{n(e_{out})_1{}^2}$$

$$= (N_H)_1 - \lg n \qquad (5A\text{-}32)$$

The same relation is obtained by considering a parallel connection of elements since then the array resistance is $R_\Sigma = R_1/n$ and its open-circuit voltage is $(e_{out})_\Sigma = (e_{out})_1$.

The projector loss of an array and the projector loss of one of its elements may each be written in terms of a corresponding hydrophone loss, assuming the elements to be reversible. By using the relation between these hydrophone losses as given above the relation between the projector losses is found to be

$$(N_P)_\Sigma = (N_P)_1 - \lg n \qquad (5A\text{-}33)$$

In a similar manner the transducer equivalent spectrum level (Art. 4J-2) of an array is given in terms of the transducer equivalent spectrum level of one of its elements as

$$(L_{th})_\Sigma = (L_{th})_1 - \lg n \qquad (5A\text{-}34)$$

The efficiency loss for an array of n similar elements may be written, in accordance with Eq. (4G-5), as

$$(N_{eff})_\Sigma = (N_P)_\Sigma + (N_{DI})_\Sigma - 50.22$$

$$= (N_P)_1 - \lg n + (N_{DI})_\Sigma - 50.22 \quad (5A\text{-}35)$$

But, by this same equation,

$$(N_P)_1 = (N_{eff})_1 - (N_{DI})_1 + 50.22 \quad (5A\text{-}36)$$

Hence

$$(N_{eff})_\Sigma = (N_{eff})_1 - \lg n$$

$$+ [(N_{DI})_\Sigma - (N_{DI})_1] \quad (5A\text{-}37)$$

This shows that the efficiency loss of an array is not the same as the efficiency loss of its elements unless the amount by which the directivity index of the array exceeds the directivity index of a single element is equal to the quantity $\lg n$. In certain types of array this condition is satisfied almost ideally. For example, the directivity index of an array of n linear transducers of length l placed along a straight line end-to-end is $(N_{DI})_\Sigma = \lg(2nl/\lambda)$. The index for a single element is $(N_{DI})_1 = \lg(2l/\lambda)$. The difference is thus $(N_{DI})_\Sigma - (N_{DI})_1 = \lg n$ and the efficiency loss and the efficiency of this array are the same as those of one of its elements.

We have already expressed the relations between the transducer equivalent spectrum level of an array and that of one of its elements. The relations between the responses to acoustic interference as measured by the levels of its equivalent plane waves is of equal significance. By reference to Eq. (4F-25) we may write equations showing the apparent level of acoustic waves corresponding to a directionally distributed interference of level $(L_n)_{\text{equi}}$. For a single element of an array the equation is

$$(L_{\text{app}})_1 = (L_n)_{\text{equi}} - (N_{DI})_1 \qquad (5A\text{-}38)$$

and for an array of n of these elements it is

$$(L_{\text{app}})_\Sigma = (L_n)_{\text{equi}} - (N_{DI})_\Sigma \qquad (5A\text{-}39)$$

Let $(e_n)_1$ be the response of a single hydrophone of an array to an apparent plane wave of level $(L_{\text{app}})_1$. Let $(e_n)_\Sigma$ be the response of the entire array to an apparent plane wave of level $(L_{\text{app}})_\Sigma$. The response of a single element to this latter wave is $[(e_n)_\Sigma]/n$, assuming a series connection, or $(e_n)_\Sigma$ assuming a parallel connection. For the series connection, then, since the ratio, expressed in voltage-squared logits, between the voltage responses of a single element to plane waves of different levels is equal to the difference between these levels, in decibels,

$$2 \operatorname{lgt} \frac{(e_n)_\Sigma}{(e_n)_1} = 2 \operatorname{lgt} n + [(L_{\text{app}})_\Sigma - (L_{\text{app}})_1] \quad (5A\text{-}40)$$

By substituting the value for the difference between the apparent levels obtained by subtracting Eq. (5A-38) from Eq. (5A-39) this becomes

$$2 \operatorname{lgt} \frac{(e_n)_\Sigma}{(e_n)_1} = 2 \operatorname{lgt} n - [(N_{DI})_\Sigma - (N_{DI})_1] \quad (5A\text{-}41)$$

For the parallel connection this becomes simply

$$2 \operatorname{lgt} \frac{(e_n)_\Sigma}{(e_n)_1} = [(N_{DI})_\Sigma - (N_{DI})_1] \qquad (5A\text{-}42)$$

These equations furnish a convenient method for determining the effective directivity index, $(N_{DI})_\Sigma$, of an array of directional elements, provided the effective value of the directivity index, $(N_{DI})_1$, of a single element is known. This latter value may be determined, as described in Art. 4F-2, by comparing the responses of the directional element and of a nondirectional element to the directionally distributed noise existing in some given location. The effective directivity index of the array is determined in a similar manner by comparing the responses of the array and of a single element, which may here be considered as the reference hydrophone.

From the equations developed above it is possible to determine the hydrophone loss which may be permissible in the individual transducers used in an array. The diagram of Fig. 4J-1 shows the relation between the transducer equivalent spec-

trum level of a transducer, as computed from its hydrophone loss by Eq. (4J-6), and the apparent plane wave level of minimum water noise as measured by the same transducer. In general it is desirable that the apparent plane wave level of water noise exceed the transducer equivalent spectrum level by some definite amount. This difference, for the array as a whole, may be written as

$$\Delta L_{n/\text{th}} = (L_{\text{app}})_\Sigma - (L_{\text{th}})_\Sigma \qquad (5A\text{-}43)$$

The maximum permissible hydrophone loss of the array for which this condition is realized is, in accordance with Eq. (4J-6),

$$(N_H)_\Sigma = (L_{\text{th}})_\Sigma + 203.88 \qquad (5A\text{-}44)$$

On substituting Eq. (5A-43) this becomes

$$(N_H)_\Sigma = (L_{\text{app}})_\Sigma - \Delta L_{n/\text{th}} + 203.88 \quad (5A\text{-}45)$$

This may be expressed in terms of the equivalent plane wave level of water noise, $(L_n)_{\text{equi}}$, by substituting Eq. (5A-39). This gives

$$(N_H)_\Sigma = (L_n)_{\text{equi}} - (N_{DI})_\Sigma$$
$$- \Delta L_{n/\text{th}} + 203.88 \qquad (5A\text{-}46)$$

If a single element of the array is to be used by itself, and is to meet this same condition, its allowable hydrophone loss is

$$(N_H)_0 = (L_n)_{\text{equi}} - (N_{DI})_1$$
$$- \Delta L_{n/\text{th}} + 203.88 \qquad (5A\text{-}47)$$

By combining these last two equations,

$$(N_H)_\Sigma = (N_H)_0 - [(N_{DI})_\Sigma - (N_{DI})_1] \quad (5A\text{-}48)$$

By substituting Eq. (5A-32) the maximum allowable loss which may be tolerated in a single element of the array is now obtained in terms of the hydrophone loss which would be tolerated in the same element if it were to be used singly as

$$(N_H)_1 = (N_H)_0 + \operatorname{lgt} n - [(N_{DI})_\Sigma - (N_{DI})_1] \ (5A\text{-}49)$$

5A-5 Frequency-Dependent Compensation

In the compensated arrays considered in the preceding articles the time delay introduced by the delay line has been independent of frequency. This condition was imposed in order that all components of a broad-band signal might be delayed equally. For arrays compensated in this manner the major lobes of directivity patterns taken at various frequencies coincide. There is a second basic type of compensated array in which the time delay is inversely proportional to frequency.

Delay lines having the form of confluent band filters give delay times which vary in this manner. For arrays compensated by such lines the maximum response bearing varies with frequency.

Arrays of this type may be used for the transmission and reception of narrow-band signals such as those encountered in echo ranging. For this use they have the advantage that the amount of compensation, and therefore the bearing of the maximum response axis, may be altered by adjusting the signal frequency instead of by adjusting the components of the delay line. When the signal transmitted by such an array occupies a broad frequency band its energy is distributed in bearing in accordance with its initial distribution in frequency and with the constants of the array. Because of the analogy between this directional distribution and the formation of a spectrum by an optical prism, arrays having frequency-dependent compensation have been described as **acoustic prisms.** The use of broad-band signals with arrays of this type permits echo-ranging operations to be carried out on a number of bearings simultaneously. The bearing of a given target is, with such a system, indicated by the frequency of its echo.

The characteristics of an array having frequency-dependent compensation will be examined in terms of a linear array of uniformly spaced elements, each of which, considered individually, is nondirectional. When sinusoidal plane waves of acoustic energy are received by an array of this type the phase difference between the acoustic pressures simultaneously present at two points lying on a single propagation path and separated by the projection on that path of the distance between adjoining array elements is the same as for an array of the type already considered. This phase difference, which appears in the derivation of Eq. (5A-3), is $\psi_A = (2\pi s/\lambda) \sin \beta_D$. In the arrays previously considered the phase difference between the electric voltages simultaneously present at the two ends of a section of delay line through which sinusoidal waves of electric energy are being propagated is proportional to frequency. This is required in order that the delay time which, as given by Eq. (5A-1), is $t = \psi/2\pi f$ shall be independent of frequency. For arrays having frequency-dependent compensation the time delay associated with a given section of delay line is inversely proportional to frequency. The phase shift taking place in such a section is therefore constant. It is thus evident that for arrays having

frequency-dependent compensation the electric phase shift associated with a pair of adjoining array elements may be written as $\psi_E = 2k\pi$ where k is a constant independent of frequency. By combining the acoustic and electric delays associated with a pair of adjoining elements as was done in deriving Eq. (5A-4) the phase factor of an array having frequency-dependent compensation is seen to be

$$\psi = \frac{\psi_A - \psi_E}{2} = k\pi \left(\frac{s}{k\lambda} \sin \beta_D - 1 \right) \quad (5A\text{-}50)$$

The array here under consideration, like all other arrays, is fully compensated for plane acoustic waves of given frequency propagated along a given bearing provided the phase factor for that frequency and that bearing is $\psi = 0$. For this type of array there is no single maximum response bearing. We shall, therefore, arbitrarily select a bearing of $\beta_0 = 90°$ as the reference bearing. The conventions regarding geometry are the same as in Fig. 5A-1; the reference bearing, in other words, coincides with the line of the array. At the frequency for which the reference bearing is compensated $\lambda = \lambda_0$, $\beta_D = \beta_0 = 90°$, $\psi = 0$, and, by Eq. (5A-50), $k = s/\lambda_0$. By substituting this equality into Eq. (5A-50) the general expression for phase factor is given as

$$\psi = \frac{\pi s}{\lambda_0} \left[\frac{\lambda_0}{\lambda} \sin \beta_D - 1 \right]$$

$$= \frac{\pi s}{\lambda_0} \left[\frac{f}{f_0} \sin \beta_D - 1 \right] \quad (5A\text{-}51)$$

Here f is any fixed frequency and f_0 the frequency at which the reference bearing is compensated. This latter frequency will be considered the reference frequency.

The value of phase factor given above may be used for computing relative response as a function of bearing for a single fixed frequency. For the linear array the relative voltage response as a function of bearing is obtained by substituting this value of phase factor into Eq. (4E-2).

At the frequency for which some bearing other than the reference bearing is compensated $f = f_C$, $\beta_D = \beta_C$, $\psi = 0$, and, by Eq. (5A-51),

$$\frac{f}{f_0} = \frac{f_C}{f_0} = \frac{1}{\sin \beta_C} \quad (5A\text{-}52)$$

This relation is obviously of basic significance. It shows that for a linear array of uniformly spaced elements having frequency-dependent compensation there is a unique relationship between the compensated bearing and the relative frequency. This relationship is independent of the number and spacing of the array elements and of the absolute value of frequency. If the reference bearing, $\beta_0 = 90°$, is compensated at the reference frequency, f_0, the frequency at which the compensated bearing is $\beta_C = 30°$ is $f_C = 2f_0$.

By substituting Eq. (5A-52) into Eq. (5A-51) the phase factor is seen to take the form

$$\psi = \frac{\pi s}{\lambda_0}\left[\frac{\sin \beta_D}{\sin \beta_C} - 1\right] \qquad (5A\text{-}53)$$

It is interesting to compare this equation with that of the phase factor of an array having compensation which is independent of frequency, as given by Eq. (5A-4).

In dealing with arrays having frequency-dependent compensation it is particularly useful to be able to compute relative response as a function of frequency for a given bearing. Such computations may be carried out as described in Sec. 4-H. Relative transmitting response considered as a function of frequency for any bearing would be computed by Eq. (4H-3). In carrying out this computation it is necessary first to compute the relative transmitting response for the given bearing considered as a function of bearing for each frequency at which a solution is desired. In carrying out such a computation it is usually convenient to select the frequency at which the given bearing is compensated as the reference frequency. It is also necessary to compute the directivity factor of the transducer as a function of frequency. In order to show relative response as a function of frequency in the form of a spectrum pattern the electroacoustic efficiency may be considered constant.

The receiving response as a function of frequency is derived from the transmitting response by multiplying by the square of the reciprocal of the relative frequency as shown in Eq. (4H-7).

Spectrum patterns for a linear array of 20 uniformly spaced elements are shown in Fig. 5A-14. Relative transmitting response is shown as a relative pressure and relative receiving response as a relative voltage as is customary with both directivity patterns and spectrum patterns.

5-B BEARING-DEVIATION INDICATORS

The bearing of some sound source causing a

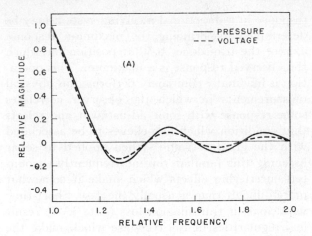

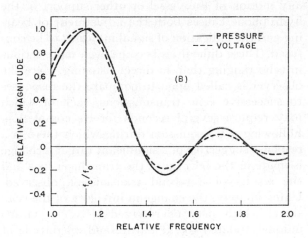

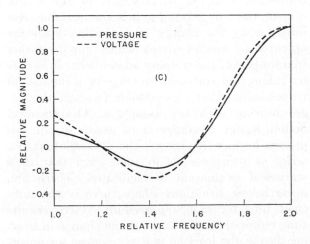

Fig. 5A-14. Spectrum Patterns. Spectrum patterns for a linear array of 20 uniformly spaced elements having frequency-dependent compensation.

(A) For a bearing of $\beta = 90°$

(B) For a bearing of $\beta = 60°$

(C) For a bearing of $\beta = 30°$

response in a directional receiving system may be determined by bringing the maximum response axis of the transducer to that position for which the observed response is a maximum. This operation is like many commonly performed in physical measurements in which the observer correlates some response with some adjustment and selects that condition which he believes to be associated with the greatest value. When applied to sonar listening this familiar routine frequently encounters interfering effects which make it somewhat more difficult than is usually the case. Short-time variations in transmission loss (Art. 3A-7) result in irregularities in the response which make the selection of the maximum uncertain. In addition, any motion of the vessel or other support of the hydrophone causes both the adjustment of bearing and the indication of signal intensity to be confused. These difficulties become even more serious in echo ranging than in direct listening. Here the observer is called upon to compare the responses to successive echo transmissions, each of which may require several seconds for its completion. Following a transmission during which there is a response suggestive of a significant target a change is made in the bearing of the transducer axis and the results of a second transmission observed. Unfortunately, the change in intensity of the echo signal which may be received is by no means uniquely related to the nature and magnitude of the change in angle between target bearing and transducer axis. It is, however, in the simple system, the only form of indication available. Not infrequently the change in indication leads the operator to manipulations which impair, rather than improve, the training adjustment. It is only by taking the statistical average of a number of transmissions that it is possible to select the target bearing with any assurance. The chemical Sound Range Recorder is of assistance in this process because it presents the data relative to a series of transmissions in such form that their statistical evaluation is facilitated. There are, nevertheless, situations where there is not sufficient time for such a procedure. Moreover, the time required is so great that the change in bearing during the interval is itself a cause for uncertainty. In some situations the delay in bringing the transducer axis directly to the bearing of a target giving a faint indication results in failure to maintain a potential contact.

These effects are of sufficient importance to make some method of indicating the direction of the deviation between transducer and target bearings highly desirable. By directing the operator to the correct adjustment of the transducer bearing such an indication insures more speedy and more accurate determinations of target bearing and reduces the chance of failing to maintain a poor contact. Systems which show the direction of the angular difference between the bearing of a sound source, or of an echo target, and the bearing of some critical response axis of a transducer system are known as **bearing-deviation indicators** (BDI). They are sometimes spoken of as **lobe-comparison** systems or as lobe-comparison indicators. In addition to directing the operator to the bearing of a sound source or target their use tends to make the determination of bearing more precise; it does not always make it more accurate. It will be found that they have the further advantage, under certain methods of operation, of effectively increasing the directional discrimination of the system against randomly distributed noise. A lobe-comparison system may also be arranged to provide an electric voltage, or other force, the polarity of which is so identified with the direction of the displacement of the transducer from the bearing of some sound source that it offers a means of automatically maintaining the axis of the transducer system on the target bearing.

The basic process underlying lobe-comparison systems consists in making two observations simultaneously, the two being identified with two transducer responses which are differently affected by the change in bearing of a distant source point. This may be done by providing, in effect, two separate directionally-responsive receiving systems. These receive sounds concurrently from some given source or from some given reflecting target. Uncertainties due to variations in the source level of the signal and due to variations in the transmission characteristics of the water path are thus largely avoided. The closer the two transducers are located at a common point the less will be the differences between the signals reaching them. The relation between the two responses is, then, a reliable and prompt indication of deviations from a symmetrical orientation of the receiving system relative to the source bearing.

In a simple arrangement of this kind comparisons of the two responses indicate no more than the sign—that is, the direction—of the bearing deviation. It is such arrangements which are classed as bearing-deviation indicators. It is possible to devise systems in which the indication discloses the magnitude of the angular deviation as well as its sign. These are known as **proportional-deviation indicators.** Methods for obtaining such indications will be discussed later.

5B-1 Amplitude-Difference Method

For a first examination of the factors to be considered in the design and operation of a bearing-deviation indicator we shall assume a dual system having two similar transducers mounted one above the other on a common vertical shaft so that their maximum response axes form some suitable horizontal angle. This will be designated as the **separation angle** and represented by the symbol β_Δ. In the ideal case it will be assumed that the signals falling on these two transducers are of equal magnitude. With this arrangement the problem of determining which of the two transducers is trained more nearly in the direction of the signal source is one of comparing the relative magnitudes of two electric signals. These electric signals will differ in amplitude, as a function of bearing, in a manner which may be deduced from the directivity pattern applying to both transducers and from the separation angle. If the acoustic signal is a single-frequency wave it will be sufficient to consider only the directivity pattern applying at that frequency; if the signal is a complex wave it will be necessary to consider the pattern applying to the band in question.

The relative voltages of the electric signals in a pair of similar transducers, as functions of the bearing of a signal source, are shown in Fig. 5B-1. It is understood that these patterns, which are for the horizontal plane, apply at one frequency only. They have been computed on the basis of rectangular transducers and for that frequency at which the wave space is one-fifth the horizontal dimension. The two curves are shown displaced by a separation angle of $\beta_\Delta = 8°$. The bearing at which the two major lobes intersect is seen to be an axis of symmetry of the system. Deviations in source bearing are referred to this axis.

There are many arrangements of apparatus by which the magnitudes of two electric signals may be compared. Details of circuit design will be considered here only insofar as they determine the relations between the fundamental parameters and operating performance. It is, of course, desirable that the effects of the two electric signals be combined to cause a single response indicative of the direction of the bearing deviation. The

ordinates of the curves of Fig. 5B-1 are proportional to sinusoidally varying voltages which, in the ideal case, are either in phase or in phase opposition. If combined differentially the resultant voltage, as a function of bearing, would be proportional to the algebraic difference between these curves. This algebraic difference would be zero for a source on the reference axis, would be of one sign for deviation angles on one side of this axis, and of opposite sign for deviation angles on the other side. Actually, the two voltages are unlikely to be exactly in phase or in phase opposition. If the sound source is not in the horizontal plane midway between the two transducers the

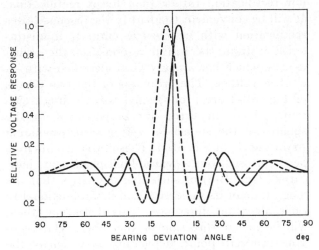

Fig. 5B-1. Lobe-Comparison Patterns. The directivity patterns of a pair of linear transducers, having lengths of $l = 5\lambda$, mounted with their maximum response axes displaced to either side of a reference axis to provide means for indicating bearing deviation by the amplitude-difference method.

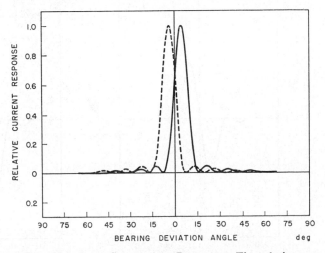

Fig. 5B-2. Lobe-Comparison Patterns. The relative responses, as functions of deviation angle, β_D, of the transducers for which directivity patterns are shown in Fig. 5B-1 as they appear at the outputs of square-law rectifiers.

signal at one transducer will differ in phase from the signal at the other by an amount proportional to the difference between their distance from the source. The resultant voltage due to a differential connection of the transducers would then correspond to the phasor difference between the individual voltages. This resultant would not be of zero magnitude for any deviation angle, although it would pass through a minimum value with changes in deviation angle. The effect of phase displacements may, however, be avoided if the electric signals from the two transducers are rectified before being combined. It will be found preferable, although not necessary, to use square-law rectification rather than linear rectification. It will be convenient to identify the response after rectification with an electric current, to distinguish it from the initial response of the transducers, which has already been identified with an electric voltage. The ordinates of the two curves of Fig. 5B-2 are proportional to two direct currents which, in turn, are proportional to the squares of the sinusoidal voltages corresponding to the curves of Fig. 5B-1. These two currents may be impressed on a variable-displacement indicator (Art. 6B-5) of such characteristics that the magnitude of its deflection will be proportional to their algebraic difference. This deflection, then, will be in one direction or the other, relative to a central zero point, depending on which of the two is the larger. Curves showing the sign and magnitude of the differential current thus indicated are given in Fig. 5B-3. These are drawn for

separation angles, β_Δ, between the maximum response axes of the transducers of 4, 8, and 20 degrees. For these curves the magnitude of the differential current is plotted as a relative value, referred to the maximum value of rectified current identified with the maximum response of either transducer alone. They are plotted against deviation angle, β_D, referred to the reference axis bisecting the maximum response axes, for the first 30° either side of the reference axis.

The angular separation between the maximum response axes of the two transducers is obviously one of the important variables in this problem. Together with the directional characteristic of the individual transducers it determines the significant behavior of the system. This behavior may be appraised on the basis of three important factors: the slope of the differential-response curve at the reference bearing, the magnitude of the relative response for bearings in the vicinity of this reference bearing, and the range of bearings for which an indication is given. The greater the slope of the differential-response characteristic the greater will be the precision with which the bearing of a sound source is given by the null indication. This applies, of course, to operation under ideal conditions; the magnitudes of errors due to departures from the ideal will be investigated separately. The greater the response for a source near the reference bearing the greater is the likelihood that it will be detected. Before the bearing of any source may be determined it is first necessary that it be discovered. The proba-

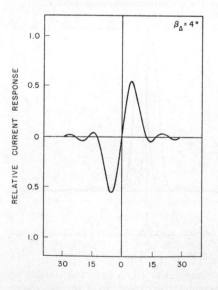
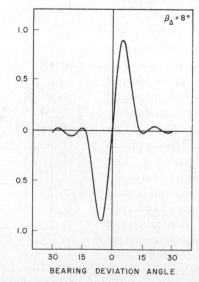
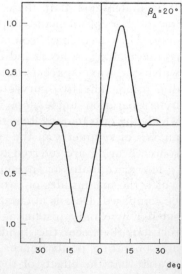

FIG. 5B-3. BEARING-DEVIATION INDICATIONS. The relative magnitudes, as functions of deviation angle, β_D, of the difference between the rectified currents shown in Fig. 5B-2, for various displacement angles, β_Δ.

bility of detection is also improved by increasing the range of deviation angle over which a significant indication is obtained. In this respect the desirable characteristics of a differential-response pattern are unlike those of the directivity pattern of a single transducer. When bearing is to be indicated by the maximum response of a simple system it is desirable that the arc covered by the primary lobe be as restricted as possible; when bearing is indicated by a differential null it is unnecessary to impose this requirement and the angle over which the system is responsive may be increased, thereby improving its search characteristics.

The directional discrimination of differentially responsive systems against randomly distributed interference is not measured by the angle over which it is responsive in the same manner as the discrimination of a single transducer is measured by its directivity index. In the differential system the response to noise corresponding to the negative half lobe tends to neutralize the response corresponding to the positive half lobe. The two would cancel completely if the interference were uniformly distributed with respect to bearing, time, and frequency. In fact, the average values of the positive and negative responses tend to show fewer and smaller differences as the widths of the lobes are increased. However, in order to discriminate against a localized source, as is required when determining the bearings of two targets separated by a small bearing angle, it is necessary that the arc covered by the positive and negative lobes be small.

An inspection of the three curves of Fig. 5B-3 shows that the choice of the most suitable value of separation angle is more a matter of judgment than of the selection of a critically defined optimum condition. The curves show, for example, that the slope of the differential-response characteristic is not seriously affected by the angle of separation over a considerable range of values. For separations of less than four or five degrees, however, the maximum value of differential response is small. It approaches a relative magnitude of unity, as compared with the maximum response due to a single transducer, near eight degrees and retains this magnitude for larger separations. If the separation angle were to be made greater than about twenty degrees the sound source would pass out of the arc of one major lobe before entering that of the other; there would still be a right-or-left indication but the

rate of change of deflection with bearing at the axis of symmetry would be negligibly small.

Since the two transducers must, in the arrangement here considered, occupy different positions it is more than probable that the signal acting on one will not be identical, either in magnitude or in phase, with the signal acting on the other. Impairment of performance because of phase irregularities has been avoided by rectifying the two signals before comparing them. We must, however, consider the consequences of amplitude irregularities due to differences between the transmission characteristics of the two separate receiving channels. The effect of amplitude unbalance may be studied graphically by considering portions of superimposed directivity characteristics in the neighborhood of the reference axis. Such characteristics are given by the curves of Fig. 5B-4. One family of curves gives the angular variation of the square-law response of one transducer for a reference condition and for conditions differing by 2-db increments in signal level, or in system transmission loss. The second family gives the angular variation of square-law response, under the reference condition, for a transducer orientation differing from that of the first by four-degree increments of separation angle. For any of the values of separation angle thus shown the error in indicated bearing is given as the difference between the deviation angle at which the appropriate curve of this second family intersects the reference curve of the first and the deviation angle at which it intersects the curves correspond-

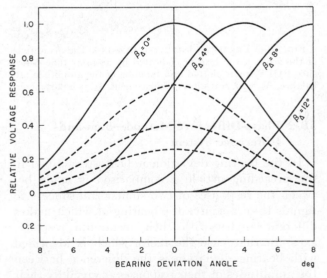

FIG. 5B-4. UNBALANCED LOBE-COMPARISON PATTERNS. Curves showing the effect on the patterns of Fig. 5B-2 of amplitude unbalance in the transducer responses.

ing to the various amplitude unbalances. It is immaterial whether the amplitude unbalance appears as a decrease in the output of one transducer, as an increase in the output of the other, or as a change in both. The only difference between these conditions is in the magnitude of the differential response for bearings at which this response is not zero. The bearing at which it is zero remains unchanged.

The results of the above considerations are expressed graphically in Fig. 5B-5. The curves show clearly that the amount of the angular error per decibel unbalance is considerably less for the larger separations than for the smaller. This factor thus appears to be of greater significance in the selection of the angular separation than do those previously examined.

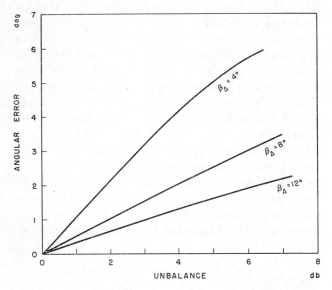

FIG. 5B-5. ERRORS IN INDICATED BEARING. The magnitude of the error in the bearing indicated by an amplitude-difference BDI system, plotted as a function of the amplitude unbalance, N_k, with transducer displacement, β_Δ, as a parameter.

5B-2 Phase-Difference Method—Sum-and-Difference System

In the bearing-deviation indicator described in the preceding article a comparison is made between the responses of two similar transducers to signals from a source the bearing of which makes different angles with their maximum response axes. In that case the factor which is identified with bearing deviation is the difference between the amplitudes of their responses as given by their directional characteristics. The complementary scheme is one in which a comparison is made between the responses of two transducers to signals from a source at different distances from their effective centers. In this case the significant factor is the relative phase of their responses, as given by the delay time associated with the difference in path length.

The relative phase of the signals may be made a function of bearing deviation by mounting the two transducers with their active surfaces in a single vertical plane and with some suitable horizontal separation between their effective centers. Since the orientations of these transducers relative to the bearing of this source are the same, regardless of the value of this bearing, their deviation losses are always equal and there is no difference between the amplitudes of their responses under ideal conditions. The effective centers of these transducers are equidistant from a distant source of acoustic energy located on the normal to their plane. For a source on this bearing the response of each transducer is equal in both magnitude and phase to the response of the other. As the transducers are rotated through an angle, β_D, about the vertical axis of their common support one is advanced toward the source by the distance $r \sin \beta_D$ and the other is withdrawn by an equal distance. The quantity $r = s/2$ is the radius of the circle along which the effective centers move. The response of one transducer is thus advanced by the phase factor $\psi' = (\pi s/\lambda) \sin \beta_D$ while the response of the other is retarded by an equal amount. By combining voltages having instantaneous values which are the sum and the difference of the instantaneous values of the individual transducer voltages it is possible to obtain the desired indication of the sign of the bearing deviation. An arrangement for accomplishing this is known as a **sum-and-difference system.**

Let the instantaneous value of the response of either transducer be $(e_{\text{inst}})_0 = (e_{\text{max}})_0 \sin \omega t$ when the deviation angle is zero. The phase of this response will be the reference phase used throughout the remainder of this discussion. When the deviation angle has a finite value the response of the unit nearer the source becomes $(e_{\text{inst}})_1 = e_{\text{max}} \sin (\omega t + \psi')$. Here the voltage e_{max} is the peak voltage generated in either transducer when the source is on a bearing deviating by the angle β_D from the maximum response axis. The phase factor, $\psi' = (\pi s/\lambda) \sin \beta_D$, is that applying to the pair of transducers, as determined by the separation between their effective centers. It is independent of the phase factor applying to the individual units. The response of the unit at the greater distance from the source is, in a similar manner, $(e_{inst})_2 = e_{max} \sin (\omega t - \psi')$.

If these two responses are combined so that the resultant voltage is equal to their sum this resultant is

$$(e_{inst})_1 + (e_{inst})_2 = 2(e_{max} \cos \psi')(\sin \omega t) \quad \text{(5B-1)}$$

in accordance with established trigonometric relations. This shows the sum voltage to have the peak value $2e_{max} \cos \psi'$. This voltage is in phase with the phase reference voltage when the sign of this quantity is positive and in phase opposition when this sign is negative. The relations here are the same as those for the two-element array discussed in the early paragraphs of Art. 4E-1, except that now the elements are themselves directional. Since the rms values of the sum voltage and of the individual transducer voltages are proportional to the peak values the rms value of the sum voltage may be written, for any deviation angle β_D, as

$$(e_D)_\Sigma = 2e_D \cos \psi' \quad \text{(5B-2)}$$

where e_D is the rms voltage generated in either transducer.

The second required voltage is obtained by combining the outputs of the two transducers differentially, in a circuit separate from that in which they are combined additively. The resultant voltage is thus the difference of the two constituent voltages. Its instantaneous value may be written as

$$(e_{inst})_1 - (e_{inst})_2 = 2(e_{max} \sin \psi')(\cos \omega t) \quad \text{(5B-3)}$$

This voltage leads the phase reference voltage by 90° when the sign of this quantity is positive and lags it by 90° when this sign is negative. The rms value of this difference voltage may be written as

$$(e_D)_\Delta = 2e_D \sin \psi' \quad \text{(5B-4)}$$

Suppose, now, that the sum and difference voltages are impressed on a phase-sensitive rectifier of such characteristics that the resulting output is a direct current proportional to the product of their absolute magnitudes multiplied by the sine of the angle between them. Since the usual types of phase-sensitive rectifiers develop a current proportional to the cosine of the phase angle between two input voltages it will be necessary to include in this portion of the system a delay network for shifting the phase of one of the input voltages by

90°. We shall assume that the difference voltage is delayed by this amount. The system arrangement by which the various voltages and currents described above may be obtained is shown schematically in Fig. 5B-6.

The value of the direct current delivered to an indicator by a system of this type may be written as

$$i_D = g(e_D)_\Delta (e_D)_\Sigma \sin (\psi_\Delta - \psi_\Sigma) \quad \text{(5B-5)}$$

where g is a constant of proportionality. The angle ψ_Δ gives the phase between the differential voltage and the reference voltage; the angle ψ_Σ gives the phase between the sum voltage and the reference voltage. By substituting Eqs. (5B-2) and (5B-4) into Eq. (5B-5) the rectified current is seen to be

$$i_D = 4ge_D^2 \sin \psi' \cos \psi' \sin (\psi_\Delta - \psi_\Sigma)$$
$$= 2ge_D^2 \sin (2\psi') \sin (\psi_\Delta - \psi_\Sigma) \quad \text{(5B-6)}$$

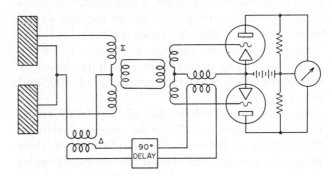

Fig. 5B-6. Bearing-Deviation Indication System. The functional arrangement of elements in a BDI system operating by virtue of the phase difference between the responses of two transducers. Voltages having phasors which are the sum and the difference of the phasors of the individual transducer voltages are impressed on a phase-sensitive rectifier.

A reference current may be specified having the value

$$i_0 = 2ge_0^2 \quad \text{(5B-7)}$$

where e_0 is the voltage generated in either transducer. The value of the rectified current, relative to the specified reference current, is thus given in terms of the relative voltage response of either transducer as

$$\frac{i_D}{i_0} = \left(\frac{e_D}{e_0} \right)^2 \sin (2\psi') \sin (\psi_\Delta - \psi_\Sigma) \quad \text{(5B-8)}$$

When the transducers are of the rectangular or linear form the relative voltage is as given by Eq. (4E-9). Substituting this equation into the expression for relative current, there is obtained

$$\frac{i_D}{i_0} = \frac{\sin^2 \psi}{\psi^2} \sin (2\psi') \sin (\psi_\Delta - \psi_\Sigma) \qquad (5B\text{-}9)$$

Here $\psi = (\pi l/\lambda) \sin \beta_D$ is the phase factor applying to each rectangular transducer, as determined by its length, l, perpendicular to the axis of rotation of the transducer system. Under ideal conditions the responses of the two transducers are equal in magnitude; one leads the phase reference by the angle $\psi' = (\pi s/\lambda) \sin \beta_D$ and the other lags by an equal amount. The angle $2\psi' = (2\pi s/\lambda) \sin \beta_D$ is thus the relative phase of the two transducer responses. The phase angle $(\psi_\Delta - \psi_\Sigma)$ appearing in the final term of this equation may be evaluated by considering the relations between the voltage phasors, e_1 and e_2, generated in the transducers, their phasor difference, Δe, and their phasor sum, Σe. These relations are shown in Fig. 5B-7, where diagrams are drawn for phase factors, ψ', falling in each of the four quadrants. From these diagrams it is clear that when ψ' is in either the first or the third quadrant the difference voltage leads the sum voltage by 90° and $\sin (\psi_\Delta - \psi_\Sigma) = +1$; when ψ' is in either the second or the fourth quadrant the difference voltage lags the sum voltage by 90° and $\sin (\psi_\Delta - \psi_\Sigma) = -1$.

In studying the behavior of a pair of transducers arranged to indicate bearing deviation by the difference between the amplitudes of their responses curves were drawn for various angular separations between their maximum response axes. When the same transducers are arranged to indicate bearing deviation by the difference in phase of their responses the comparable variable is the horizontal separation between their effective centers. Curves of the relative value of rectified current, as given by Eq. (5B-9), plotted as a function of deviation angle, β_D, for 30° either side of the reference axis, are shown in Fig. 5B-8. These curves are for rectangular transducers having a length $l = 5\lambda$ perpendicular to the axis of rotation. The separations, s, assumed between effective centers are $l/2$, l, and $2l$.

Since the transducers postulated for the curves of this figure are the same as those to which the curves of Fig. 5B-3 apply it is possible, by comparing the two figures, to obtain some idea of the relative characteristics of the amplitude-difference and the phase-difference methods for indicating bearing deviation. In addition to the slope at the reference bearing, and the height and spread of the primary lobes, mentioned in Art. 5B-1, we must here consider also the heights of the secondary lobes. When the system is used for indicating the direction of a bearing deviation any high secondary lobe having a different sign than the primary lobe on the same side of the reference axis may result in a false indication. It is evident from the curves of Fig. 5B-8 that the characteristic obtained when the separation is appreciably greater than the transducer length is quite unsatisfactory in this respect. The relative advantages of separations equal to or less than the transducer length are by no means as clearly defined. For search purposes the broadening of the primary lobe accompanying a decrease in separation might well offset the concurrent decrease in its height. From the practical standpoint, a separation which is equal to the transducer length is most frequently used, since this permits the two units to be placed end-to-end. It is, in fact, customary to use a single transducer structure having two electric systems, each associated with one half of the active surface. For this separation the phase factors appearing in the preceding equations are equal, that is, $\psi' = \psi$.

The equations derived in the preceding paragraphs, and used for the computation of the representative response characteristics shown, apply, as pointed out, only under ideal conditions. Under these conditions the signals falling on the two transducers are equal in magnitude and differ in phase by $2\pi/\lambda$ times the difference between

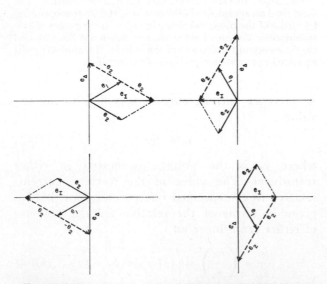

Fig. 5B-7. Phasor Relations in BDI System. The phasors of voltages generated in the individual transducers of a phase-difference BDI system and their sums and differences, relative to a reference response at the point midway between the effective centers of the transducers. These diagrams are drawn to show the leading voltage in each of the four quadrants.

their distances from the source. Under ideal conditions, also, the responses of the two transducers to these signals are equal in magnitude and have the same phase difference as do the signals. We must now consider the consequences if these conditions are not fulfilled. Attention must also be given to the significance of any failure of the circuit used in connection with the phase-sensitive rectifier to delay the difference voltage by exactly 90°. In considering bearing-deviation errors resulting from unbalanced responses, or from incorrect phase delays within the system, attention will be confined to deviation angles in the vicinity of the maximum response axis of the transducer system. It is understood, of course, that at a distance from this system the individual maximum response axes may be represented by a single reference axis perpendicular to the plane of the transducers.

For the analysis of this problem, phase unbalance will be measured as the angle, θ, by which the relative phase of the transducer responses exceeds the phase delay corresponding to the difference between the distances of the two transducers from the source. The phase angle between the responses of the transducers is thus $2\psi' + \theta$. The excess delay will be assigned to the transducer at the greater distance from the source when the deviation angle has a positive value. The amplitude unbalance will be measured by the ratio, k, between the magnitudes of the voltages generated in the two transducers. This may be expressed in decibels by the relation $N_k = 2 \lg t\, k$. When these unbalances exist the phasors representing the voltages generated in the transducers are

$$e_1 = e_{max} \cos \psi' + j e_{max} \sin \psi' \qquad (5\text{B-}10)$$

and

$$e_2 = k e_{max} \cos (\psi' + \theta) - j k e_{max} \sin (\psi' + \theta) \qquad (5\text{B-}11)$$

The sum and the difference of these phasors are then

$$\Sigma e = e_{max} \lfloor \cos \psi' + k \cos (\psi' + \theta) \rfloor \\ + j e_{max} [\sin \psi' - k \sin (\psi' + \theta)] \qquad (5\text{B-}12)$$

and

$$\Delta e = e_{max} \lfloor \cos \psi' - k \cos (\psi' + \theta) \rfloor \\ + j e_{max} [\sin \psi' + k \sin (\psi' + \theta)] \qquad (5\text{B-}13)$$

By the usual relations of complex numbers the phase angles of these voltages, relative to the reference phase identified with the axis of rotation, are given by the expressions

$$\tan \psi_\Sigma = \frac{\sin \psi' - k \sin (\psi' + \theta)}{\cos \psi' + k \cos (\psi' + \theta)} \qquad (5\text{B-}14)$$

and

$$\tan \psi_\Delta = \frac{\sin \psi' + k \sin (\psi' + \theta)}{\cos \psi' - k \cos (\psi' + \theta)} \qquad (5\text{B-}15)$$

The various phasors appearing here are shown diagrammatically in Fig. 5B-9.

It is evident that if there is any difference between the magnitudes of the voltages generated in

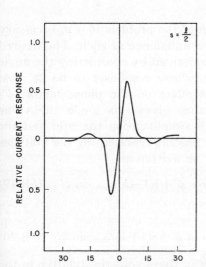
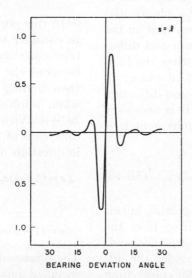
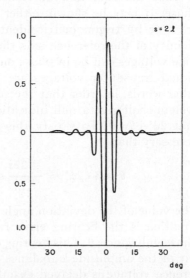

FIG. 5B-8. BEARING-DEVIATION INDICATIONS. The relative magnitudes, as functions of deviation angle, β_D, of the output of a phase-sensitive rectifier in response to the sum and difference voltages of a phase-difference BDI system, for various separations, s, between the effective centers of transducers of length l.

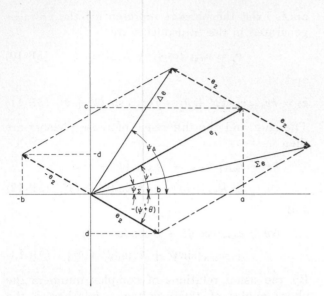

FIG. 5B-9. PHASOR RELATIONS IN UNBALANCED BDI SYSTEM. The phasors, e_1 and e_2, of the voltages generated in the individual transducers of a phase-difference BDI system, their sum, Σe, and their difference, Δe, when there are amplitude and phase unbalances in the individual responses.

$$a = e_{max} \cos \psi'$$
$$b = k e_{max} \cos (\psi' + \theta)$$
$$c = j e_{max} \sin \psi'$$
$$d = j k e_{max} \sin (\psi' + \theta)$$

the two transducers the difference voltage, $(e_D)_\Delta$, can never be zero, regardless of the phase relations between these voltages. The output current of the phase-sensitive rectifier, as given by Eq. (5B-6), will, in that case, be zero only when $\sin(\psi_\Delta - \psi_\Sigma) = 0$. This requires that $\psi_\Delta - \psi_\Sigma = 0$, or that the sum and difference voltages be in phase. It may be shown, either by a phasor diagram or by trigonometric identities, that in the vicinity of the reference axis the sum and difference voltages can be in phase only when the individual transducer voltages are also in phase. In other words, in order that the sum-and-difference system shall give a null indication it is necessary that $2\psi' + \theta = 0$. To satisfy this requirement it is necessary that

$$\theta = -2\psi' = -\frac{2\pi s}{\lambda} \sin \beta_D \quad (5B\text{-}16)$$

The value of the deviation angle appearing in this equation is the bearing error resulting from the phase unbalance, θ. This bearing error is independent of the amplitude unbalance provided the difference voltage is delayed exactly 90° more than the sum voltage, as it is impressed on the phase-

sensitive rectifier. Since the bearing error due to phase unbalance is small it will be permissible to assume that $\sin \beta \approx \beta$, or that the bearing error may be computed as

$$\beta_D \approx -\frac{\lambda \theta}{2\pi s} \quad (5B\text{-}17)$$

If the phase unbalance is given in degrees the bearing error is also in degrees. For transducers having a separation between effective centers of $s = 5\lambda$ this equation becomes $\beta_D = -0.0318 \, \theta$.

The function of the delay network of the phase-sensitive rectifier is to bring voltages nominally in quadrature into exact phase coincidence in order that the resulting rectified current shall be a maximum. A null indication occurs whenever the two voltages, as finally impressed on the rectifier, are in quadrature. The conclusion reached in the preceding paragraphs that a null indication occurs only when the sum and difference voltages are in phase is predicated on the assumption that they will be brought into a quadrature relation by a shift of exactly 90°. A more general statement is that the sum of the angle between the sum and difference voltages and the actual delay angle of the network must equal 90° for the rectified current to be zero. If the actual delay in the network is represented as the angle ϕ the condition for a null indication may be written as

$$(\psi_\Delta - \psi_\Sigma) + \phi = \frac{\pi}{2} \quad (5B\text{-}18)$$

In this portion of the problem it is unnecessary to consider phase unbalance as such. The desired relations may be derived by considering the angle between the transducer responses to be $2\psi'$ and then finding the effect on the phase factor, ψ', when an unbalance gives this angle the value $2\psi' + \theta$. With this simplification the sum and the difference of the phasors representing the voltages in question may be written as

$$\Sigma e = (1+k)e_{max} \cos \psi' + j(1-k)e_{max} \sin \psi' \quad (5B\text{-}19)$$

and

$$\Delta e = (1-k)e_{max} \cos \psi' + j(1+k)e_{max} \sin \psi' \quad (5B\text{-}20)$$

The phase angles of these voltages, relative to the specified phase reference, are then given by the relations

278

$$\tan \psi_{\Sigma} = \frac{1 - k}{1 + k} \tan \psi' \qquad (5\text{B-}21)$$

and

$$\tan \psi_{\Delta} = \frac{1 + k}{1 - k} \tan \psi' \qquad (5\text{B-}22)$$

Instead of solving for the error resulting from a given incorrect value of phase delay it will be simpler to start with an assumed error and determine the value of delay which will result in a null indication. This delay may be computed as follows. For assigned values of phase factor, ψ', and of amplitude unbalance, k, find the phase angle, $\psi_{\Delta} - \psi_{\Sigma}$, between the sum and difference voltages using the relations just derived. For the assigned value of phase factor find also the corresponding deviation angle, β_D, using the relation $\sin \beta_D = \lambda \psi' / \pi s$. This deviation angle is the error in indicated bearing corresponding to an error of $90° - \phi$ in the delay network. In carrying out this computation it will be found that, for any assigned value, k, of amplitude unbalance, the required relative phase of the sum and difference voltages passes through a maximum as the phase factor, ψ', increases with increasing deviation angle. This shows that, for the amplitude unbalance in question, there is no deviation angle giving a null indication for any phase delay error, $90° - \phi = \psi_{\Delta} - \psi_{\Sigma}$, which is greater than this maximum.

When there is no amplitude unbalance Eqs. (5B-21) and (5B-22) show that the angle between the sum and difference voltages is always 90°, provided neither voltage is zero. This confirms the conclusion reached by means of the phasor diagrams of Fig. 5B-7. In this case the rectified current will be zero only when the sum or the difference voltage is zero, regardless of the amount of phase shift in the delay network. Inaccuracies in the delay network, then, result in bearing errors only when there are amplitude unbalances. The magnitude of these errors, as computed for transducers having a separation of $s = 5\lambda$ between effective centers, is shown in Fig. 5B-10. In this graph bearing error is plotted as a function of the angle, $90° - \phi$, by which the delay network fails to alter the phase relations of the sum and difference voltages by exactly 90°. The individual curves correspond to amplitude unbalances of 2, 6, and 12 decibels. When there is phase unbalance between the transducer responses, as well as amplitude

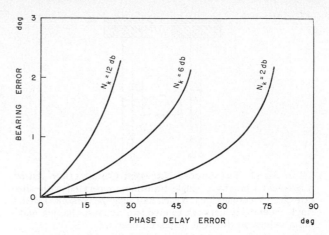

Fig. 5B-10. Errors in Indicated Bearing. The magnitude of the error in the bearing indicated by a phase-difference BDI system, plotted as a function of the amount by which the network of the phase-sensitive rectifier fails to delay the difference voltage by exactly 90°, with amplitude unbalance, N_k, as a parameter.

unbalance, the resultant error is the algebraic sum of any error due to a faulty phase shift and the error due to phase unbalance as given by Eq. (5B-16).

5B-3 Delayed-Response Directional Indicators

Bearing-deviation indications may be obtained from transducer arrays using electric compensation. In such systems the two directionally characterized responses which are compared are derived from a single transducer system through two compensating networks. This may be done by so connecting the contactor arrays of two compensators, such as are described in Art. 5A-3, to a common control shaft that their maximum responses to a given source occur at indicated bearings separated by some suitable horizontal angle. If the array is made up of a large number of separate transducers, spaced at approximately half wave intervals, the performance may be described as similar to that of two transducers giving a differential amplitude indication, as analyzed in Art. 5B-1. The multispot transducers have an apparent advantage over the two separate transducers since the transducers associated with one receiving channel are identical, with respect to both position and response, with those of the other. This does not, unfortunately, eliminate all effects due to time or space variations in signal amplitude.

One form of bearing-deviation indicator much used in practice displaces the maximum response

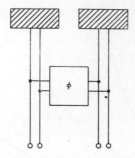

FIG. 5B-11. TRANSDUCER-NETWORK COMBINATION. An arrangement whereby a single transducer, operated with separate electric connections to each half, may be combined with a single fixed delay network to give two responses having maximum values on different displaced bearings.

axis of a mechanically trained transducer by means of a single fixed delay network connected between vertically separated halves. The general arrangement of this system is as shown in Fig.

The resultant voltage is represented by the sum of these component voltage phasors, or by

$$(e_1)_1 + (e_2)_1$$
$$= e_{max}[\cos \psi' + \cos (\psi' + \phi)]$$
$$+ je_{max}[\sin \psi' + \sin (\psi' + \phi)] \quad (5B\text{-}25)$$
$$= 2e_{max} \cos \left(\psi' + \frac{\phi}{2}\right) \cos \frac{\phi}{2}$$
$$- 2je_{max} \cos \left(\psi' + \frac{\phi}{2}\right) \sin \frac{\phi}{2} \quad (5B\text{-}26)$$

The rms values of voltage appearing at this terminal pair, relative to twice the maximum voltage due to either half alone, or to the maximum voltage, e_0, of the transducer when used without the delay network, then becomes

$$\frac{(e_D)_1}{e_0} = \frac{2e_D}{e_0} \sqrt{\cos^2 \left(\psi' + \frac{\phi}{2}\right) \cos^2 \frac{\phi}{2} + \cos^2 \left(\psi' + \frac{\phi}{2}\right) \sin^2 \frac{\phi}{2}} = \frac{2e_D}{e_0} \cos \left(\psi' + \frac{\phi}{2}\right) \quad (5B\text{-}27)$$

5B-11. Each half of the transducer is provided with a pair of terminals to which it is directly connected; it is connected to the terminals of the other half through the delay network, which is thus connected between the two sides and which transmits electric energy in both directions.

Let the phase shift in the fixed delay network be designated as ϕ. The phasor representing the voltage developed at one pair of terminals by the half of the transducer to which it is directly connected is given at once by Eq. (5B-10) as

$$(e_1)_1 = e_{max} \cos \psi' + je_{max} \sin \psi' \quad (5B\text{-}23)$$

Here e_{max} is the peak voltage generated in one half of the transducer when a distant source is on a bearing making the angle β_D with the normal to the transducer. The phase factor, $\psi' = (\pi s/\lambda) \sin \beta_D$, applies to the two transducer halves and is determined by the separation between their effective centers. Under ideal conditions the peak voltage generated in the second half of the transducer also has the value e_{max}, there being no amplitude unbalance. The voltage developed at these same terminals by the half of the transducer to which they are connected by the delay network is then derived from Eq. (5B-11) by substituting $k=1$. This gives

$$(e_2)_1 = e_{max} \cos (\psi' + \phi) - je_{max} \sin (\psi' + \phi) \quad (5B\text{-}24)$$

Here $2e_D/e_0$ is the relative voltage response of either half of the transducer, referred to its own maximum response, $e_0/2$, as given by the conventional directivity pattern.

For a linear or rectangular transducer of length $l=2s$, perpendicular to the vertical axis of rotation, the phase factor of the whole transducer is

$$\psi = \frac{\pi l}{\lambda} \sin \beta_D = \frac{2\pi s}{\lambda} \sin \beta_D = 2\psi' \quad (5B\text{-}28)$$

The phase factor applying to one half of this transducer is one-half of this quantity, or

$$\frac{\psi}{2} = \frac{\pi l}{2\lambda} \sin \beta_D = \frac{\pi s}{\lambda} \sin \beta_D = \psi' \quad (5B\text{-}29)$$

The relative response of one half, as given by Eq. (4E-9), but using the maximum response of the total transducer as the reference, is thus

$$\frac{2e_D}{e_0} = \frac{\sin (\psi/2)}{\psi/2} = \frac{\sin \psi'}{\psi'} \quad (5B\text{-}30)$$

whence the resultant response appearing at the pair of terminals considered above becomes

$$\frac{(e_D)_1}{e_0} = \frac{\sin \psi'}{\psi'} \cos \left(\psi' + \frac{\phi}{2}\right) \quad (5B\text{-}31)$$

When $\phi = 0$ this reduces to

$$\frac{(e_D)_1}{e_0} = \frac{\sin(2\psi')}{2\psi'} = \frac{\sin\psi}{\psi}$$

which is the correct equation for the relative response of the whole transducer used as a single unit.

The component voltages developed at the second pair of terminals by the two transducer halves may be written, in phasor form, as

$$(e_1)_2 = e_{max}\cos(\psi' - \phi) + je_{max}\sin(\psi' - \phi) \quad (5B\text{-}32)$$

and

$$(e_2)_2 = e_{max}\cos\psi' - je_{max}\sin\psi' \quad (5B\text{-}33)$$

The resultant voltage at these terminals is then

$$(e_1)_2 + (e_2)_2$$
$$= 2e_{max}\cos\left(\psi - \frac{\phi}{2}\right)\cos\frac{\phi}{2}$$
$$\quad - 2je_{max}\cos\left(\psi' - \frac{\phi}{2}\right)\sin\frac{\phi}{2} \quad (5B\text{-}34)$$

This has the rms value, relative to the maximum voltage of the whole transducer, of

$$\frac{(e_D)_2}{e_0} = \frac{\sin\psi'}{\psi'}\cos\left(\psi' - \frac{\phi}{2}\right) \quad (5B\text{-}35)$$

The voltages represented by Eqs. (5B-31) and (5B-35) appear simultaneously at the two pairs of terminals of the transducer system. It may be shown, from the phasor relations given above, that under ideal conditions these voltages are in phase. They lag the phase reference, identified with the voltage response of the whole transducer, by a phase angle which is either $\phi/2$ or $(\phi/2) + \pi$.

The bearing of a source for which the resultant voltage at a given pair of terminals is a maximum may be displaced from the normal to the transducer by some suitable amount through proper choice of the phase delay, ϕ, introduced by the electric network. When $\phi = \pi$ the quantity $\cos[\psi' + (\phi/2)]$ appearing in Eq. (5B-31) becomes

$$\cos\left(\psi' + \frac{\pi}{2}\right) = -\sin\psi' \quad (5B\text{-}36)$$

and the relative response at one pair of terminals is

$$\frac{(e_D)_1}{e_0} = -\frac{\sin^2\psi'}{\psi'} \quad (5B\text{-}37)$$

Similarly, the quantity $\cos[\psi' - (\phi/2)]$, in Eq. (5B-35), becomes

$$\cos\left(\psi' - \frac{\pi}{2}\right) = +\sin\psi' \quad (5B\text{-}38)$$

and the relative response at the second pair of terminals is

$$\frac{(e_D)_2}{e_0} = +\frac{\sin^2\psi'}{\psi'} \quad (5B\text{-}39)$$

These equations show that, for this delay, both resultant responses are zero on the reference axis, normal to the transducer, and that they are of equal magnitude but opposite phase for bearings at which they have finite values.

The curves of Fig. 5B-12 show relative values of the resultant responses, as given by Eqs. (5B-31) and (5B-35), at the terminals of a rectangular transducer having a total length of $l = 5\lambda$ which is split into halves and connected by a delay network as shown in Fig. 5B-11. The values of delay angle, ϕ, for which these curves were computed are multiples of $\pi/4$. It is quite evident from these curves that a displacement of the maximum response axis of a transducer brought about in this manner is associated by a marked distortion of the directivity pattern. For small displacements an increase in the electric delay is accompanied by a decrease in the height of the primary lobe as well as by a shift in its bearing. At the same time the maximum value of the secondary lobe which approaches the reference axis increases. When $\phi = \pi$ the heights of these two lobes become equal. For any value of delay, $\phi = \pi + a$, greater than π it can be shown that the curve for the resultant response at one pair of terminals is that which would be obtained by rotating about the origin by 180° the curve for the delay, $\phi = \pi - a$, which is less than π by the same amount. In the region between $\phi = \pi$ and $\phi = 2\pi$, then, the lobe which approaches the reference axis as the delay is increased becomes the primary lobe and increases in height. When $\phi = 2\pi$ the maximum value of relative response indicated by this lobe becomes unity and occurs for a deviation angle of zero. In fact, when $\phi = 2\pi$ the quantity $\cos[\psi' \pm (\phi/2)]$ becomes $\cos(\psi' \pm \pi) = -\cos\psi'$ and the relative responses at the two terminal pairs become equal to each other and equal in magnitude but opposite in sign to the responses corresponding to a delay of $\phi = 0$. This change in sign does not indicate that the phase in one case is opposite to the phase in the

281

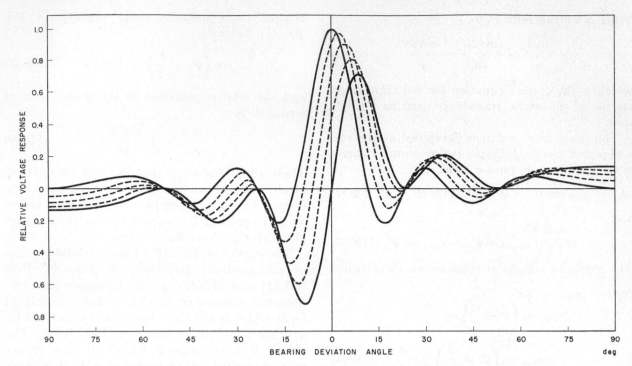

Fig. 5B-12. Displaced Directivity Pattern. The directivity patterns obtained at one of the terminal pairs shown in Fig. 5B-11 as the phase shift of the electric delay network is increased by increments of $\phi = \pi/4$.

other. It will be remembered that a positive value of relative response, as given by Eqs. (5B-31) or (5B-35), indicates a response which lags the phase reference response, corresponding to the maximum response of the whole transducer when operated as a single unit, with no delay, by the phase angle $\phi/2$. When $\phi = 2\pi$, therefore, a negative value for the relative response indicates that it is in phase with the phase reference response. The responses when $\phi = 2\pi$ are, in other words, identical with those obtained when $\phi = 0$. As the delay is increased beyond the point where $\phi = 2\pi$ the relative response patterns repeat the cycle of variation appearing between $\phi = 0$ and $\phi = 2\pi$.

The displacement of the maximum response axis of a split transducer by a single fixed delay network does not result in a simple displacement of the directivity pattern, as does the mechanical displacement of a single transducer or the electrical displacement of the directivity pattern of a circular array obtained by a variable network. For small displacements, however, it is nevertheless possible to use the amplitude-difference method, as described in Art. 5B-1, for obtaining indications of bearing deviation. The curves of

Fig. 5B-13 show the characteristics which would be obtained if the responses appearing at the two pairs of terminals of a transducer-network system similar to that illustrated in Fig. 5B-11 were separately impressed on square-law rectifiers and the resulting direct currents used to produce a

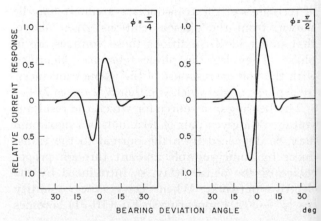

Fig. 5B-13. Bearing-Deviation Indications. The relative magnitudes, as functions of deviation angle, β_D, of the differences between two direct currents which are, respectively, proportional to the squares of the voltages appearing at the two terminal pairs in a transducer-network combination similar to that shown in Fig. 5B-11. These curves are drawn for a split transducer having a total length of $l = 5\lambda$ and for fixed electric delays of $\phi = \pi/4$ and $\phi = \pi/2$.

differential deflection. The curves have been derived from those of Fig. 5B-12 which correspond to delays, ϕ, of $\pi/4$ and $\pi/2$. The curve for $\phi = 3\pi/4$ is identical with that for $\phi = \pi/4$. In fact, it may be shown that the differential response characteristic for any value of displacement angle, $\phi = (\pi/2) + b$, between $\pi/2$ and π is the same as that for a displacement angle of $\phi = (\pi/2) - b$ between 0 and $\pi/2$. It is obvious from the curves of Fig. 5B-12 that the differential response for a delay of $\phi = \pi$ would be zero for all displacement angles. The differential response characteristic for a delay of $\phi = \pi + a$, for any value of a between 0 and π, is the same as that for a delay of $\phi = \pi - a$.

Expressions similar to Eq. (5B-12) may be written for the voltages at the two ends of the delay network when there are amplitude and phase unbalances between the responses of the two halves of the transducer. From these equations it is found that the rms values of the terminal voltages, relative to the maximum voltage of the whole transducer, are

$$\frac{(e_D)_1}{e_0} = \frac{e_D}{e_0}\sqrt{(1+k^2)+2k\cos(2\psi'+\theta+\phi)} \quad (5B\text{-}40)$$

and

$$\frac{(e_D)_2}{e_0} = \frac{e_D}{e_0}\sqrt{(1+k^2)+2k\cos(2\psi'+\theta-\phi)} \quad (5B\text{-}41)$$

Here the amplitude unbalance, k, and the phase unbalance, θ, have the same significance as in Art. 5B-2. When there are no unbalances $k=1$ and $\theta = 0$ and these equations reduce to the forms given by Eqs. (5B-31) and (5B-35), as they should.

When the desired indication of bearing deviation is obtained as the difference between two direct currents proportional to the squares of these voltages a null reading requires that the quantities under the radicals in these two equations be equal. This condition will be satisfied, regardless of the amplitude unbalance, only when $2\psi' = -\theta$. The error due to a phase unbalance is, in other words, the same as for the sum-and-difference method, as given by Eq. (5B-16). For equivalent transducers, however, the separation in the present case is less than in the sum-and-difference case. For a split transducer having a length $l = 5\lambda$ the separation which determines the value of the phase factor is $s = 2.5\lambda$ and the

bearing error as given by Eq. (5B-17) becomes $\beta_D = -0.0159\ \theta$. This consideration of the errors due to unbalance indicates that, although the voltages present at the terminals of a split transducer when joined by a fixed delay network appear similar to those found in the amplitude-difference system, the split transducer system behaves more nearly as a phase-difference system.

There are several other methods for obtaining a bearing-deviation indication from a split transducer and fixed delay network. For example, a voltage may be derived from the outputs of the two transducer halves as they exist ahead of the network. For sources in the vicinity of the reference axis this voltage has a phase which is the same as that previously specified as the reference phase. The voltages at the terminals of the network will lag this voltage either by the angle $\phi/2$ or by the angle $(\phi/2) + \pi$. Each of the network terminal voltages, as given by Eqs. (5B-31) and (5B-35), may be impressed on a separate phase-sensitive rectifier together with the phase reference voltage. Under ideal conditions the two direct currents thus developed would be equal for a source on the reference axis and would indicate by the sign of their difference the direction of any small deviation from this bearing. The performance of any such system may be analyzed more fully by the methods used in the preceding portions of this section.

5B-4 Proportional-Deviation Indicators

All of the bearing-deviation indication systems thus far described show the sign of the deviation but give no information as to its magnitude. This follows from the fact that in each case the final deflection of the indicating system is a function of the signal level as well as of the angular deviation. If the signal at some point in the receiving system is brought to a predetermined level, either by some suitable volume-control arrangement or by a limiter circuit, the magnitude of the final deflection may be made proportional to the magnitude of the deviation provided the sound source is within the region covered by the linear portion of the differential response characteristic passing through the origin.

A relatively simple proportional-deviation indicating system may be set up by taking advantage of the phasor relations between the sum and difference voltages obtained from a pair of transducers mounted end-to-end. These voltages, as shown in Fig. 5B-7, are always in quadrature to each other, provided neither is zero, and provided the amplitudes of the voltages from the two transducers are equal. The peak values of these voltages, as shown by Eqs. (5B-2) and (5B-4), are

$$(e_{max})_\Sigma = 2e_{max} \cos \psi' \qquad (5B-42)$$

and

$$(e_{max})_\Delta = 2e_{max} \sin \psi \qquad (5B-43)$$

If one of these voltages is delayed by 90°, thus bringing it into exact phase, or phase opposition, with the other, and the two are then impressed on the two pairs of deflecting plates of a cathode ray oscilloscope the resulting deflection will be a straight line. If the sum voltage is applied to the vertical deflection plates and the difference voltage to the horizontal deflection plates the components of the spot displacement will be as shown in Fig. 5B-14. It is evident by inspection that under ideal conditions the trace will have a length proportional to the response voltage, e_{max}, and will make the angle $\gamma = \psi'$ with the vertical. The angle by which the sound source deviates from the reference axis, normal to the transducer, may thus be determined at once from the tilt angle of this trace by the familiar relation

$$\sin \beta_D = \frac{\lambda\psi'}{\pi s} = \frac{\lambda\gamma}{\pi s} \qquad (5B-44)$$

For any given transducer a transparent scale, made up of a series of radial lines, may be so positioned relative to the cathode ray trace that the deviation angle may be read directly. For a split transducer having a total length of $l = 5\lambda$ the separation is $s = 2.5\lambda$ and the trace is tilted by approximately $\pi s/\lambda = 7.9$ times the deviation angle. This assumes that the deviation angle is so small that $\beta_D \approx \sin \beta_D$. The diagram of Fig. 5B-15 shows the general appearance of the scale apply-

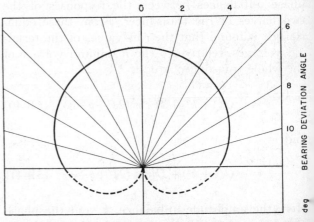

FIG. 5B-15. PROPORTIONAL-DEVIATION INDICATION. The locus of positions occupied by the outer end of a cathode ray trace, similar to that shown in Fig. 5B-14, drawn against a scale of values of the deviation angle, β_D, of the sound source. This scale is laid off to correspond to a split transducer having a total length of $l = 5\lambda$.

ing to a split transducer having a length of $l = 5\lambda$. The curve drawn against this scale is the locus of the end of the cathode ray trace, applying to a signal of constant level, and shows the effect of the directional characteristics of the transducers.

If there are amplitude and phase unbalances in the responses of the two transducers, or of the two transducer halves, the magnitudes of the vertical and horizontal components of the spot displacement, which may be derived from Eqs. (5B-12) and (5B-13), are

$$(e_{max})_\Sigma = e_{max}\sqrt{(1 + k^2) + 2k \cos (2\psi' + \theta)} \quad (5B-45)$$

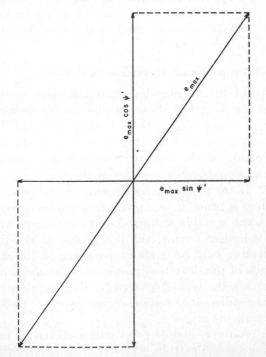

FIG. 5B-14. PROPORTIONAL-DEVIATION INDICATION. The components of displacement occurring when voltages derived from a transducer-network combination similar to that shown in Fig. 5B-11 are impressed on a cathode ray oscilloscope.

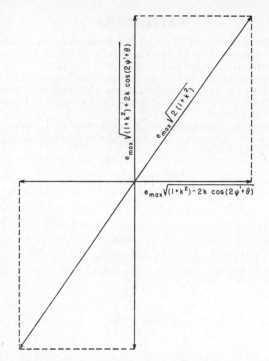

FIG. 5B-16. RELATIONS IN UNBALANCED PDI SYSTEM. The components of displacement occurring when the voltages impressed on a cathode ray oscilloscope by a transducer-network combination are unbalanced in magnitude and phase.

and

$$(e_{max})_\Delta = e_{max}\sqrt{(1 + k^2) - 2k \cos (2\psi' + \theta)} \quad (5\text{B-}46)$$

The constants appearing here have the same significance as in similar problems considered earlier. The components of spot displacement are, in this case, as shown in Fig. 5B-16. Under these conditions the voltages impressed on the oscilloscope will not be in exact phase, or phase opposition, and the trace will not be a straight line. It will, instead, be an ellipse having as one axis a line which represents the phasor sum of the displacements corresponding to the two voltages defined above. It may be reduced to a single straight line by adjustment of the electric phase delay introduced into one of the resultant responses. Actually such correction is rarely necessary, once the system has been properly adjusted, since the unbalances occurring in practice are usually of such short duration that they will appear as momentary deviations from an average trace displacement which is a straight line.

The angle, γ, which this line makes with the vertical is now related to the bearing deviation of

the source, through the phase factor, ψ', by the equation

$$\tan^2 \gamma = \frac{(1 + k^2) - 2k \cos (2\psi' + \theta)}{(1 + k^2) + 2k \cos (2\psi' + \theta)} \quad (5\text{B-}47)$$

This equation gives no information as to the length of the line in question, which varies with the bearing of the source, in accordance with the directional characteristics of the transducers, as well as with the level of the signal. When $\psi' = \pi/2$ the transducers have no response and there is, of course, no displacement of the cathode ray trace.

The value of the tilt angle, γ, as given by this equation is plotted in Fig. 5B-17 as a function of the quantity $2\psi' + \theta$ for various values of amplitude unbalance, k. These curves, like the equation which they represent, give no information as to trace magnitude. Errors due to deviation from ideal conditions may, however, be deduced from this diagram. Against the value of $2\psi' + \theta$ corresponding to a given deviation angle and to some assumed phase unbalance the actual tilt angle may be read on the curve for the assumed amplitude unbalance. The value of $2\psi' + \theta$ read against this same tilt angle on the curve for zero amplitude un-

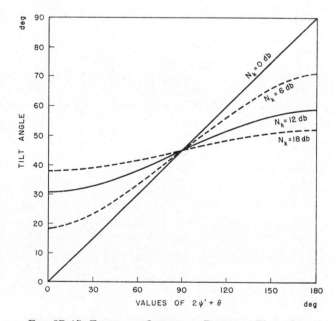

FIG. 5B-17. ERRORS IN INDICATED BEARING. The value of tilt angle, γ, plotted as a function of the quantity $2\psi' + \theta$, with amplitude unbalance as a parameter, resulting when the voltages impressed on a cathode ray oscilloscope by a transducer-network combination are unbalanced in magnitude and phase.

balance is the value of phase factor, $\psi' = (\pi s/\lambda)$ sin β_D, corresponding to the deviation angle, β_D, for which the system has been calibrated. The difference between the given deviation angle and the deviation angle thus indicated is the error associated with the assumed amplitude and phase unbalances. It is evident that this error is a function of the actual deviation angle as well as of the unbalances.

REFERENCES

1. HEINRICH STENZEL, *Leitfaden zur Berechnung von Schallvorgängen* (Guide for the Calculation of Signal Processes) (Julius Springer, Berlin, 1939).
2. This use of the electric compensator was proposed and reduced to practice by C. J. Loda while employed by the U. S. Navy Underwater Sound Laboratory, New London, Connecticut.
3. These directivity patterns were taken by C. J. Loda and E. W. Showalter, Jr., of the U. S. Navy Underwater Sound Laboratory.

CHAPTER 6

INDICATORS AND RECORDERS

The instruments by which sonar signals are given perceptible form may be classified as **indicators,** which exhibit a response only during the existence of the signal, and as **recorders,** which preserve evidence as to certain of its pertinent characteristics. Many recorders function also as indicators insofar as the signal and its recorded effect exist simultaneously. With few exceptions the indicators and recorders used in sonar operate in response to electric energy; they may be said to complete the coupling between the medium and the observer begun by the hydrophone.

Acoustic reproducers, such as headphones and loud-speakers, which are here considered as indicators, generate an acoustic wave in air which has some prescribed relation to an acoustic wave in the water. Although the audible form is, perhaps, a logical one in which to present sonar signals for observation it is not necessarily the most suitable for all purposes. In many applications of sonar it is required to make quantitative observations of signal characteristics which are outside the capabilities of the human ear. In echo sounding, for example, the measurement of signal travel time, which may be less than a second in duration and which must be known to better than a millisecond, requires that the instrument used include some type of automatic timing mechanism. To meet such situations special indicators and recorders have been devised which respond to the received signal in a manner which makes the information sought instantly available. In addition to insuring the needed accuracy these instruments present the information in the most convenient form for the given purpose and thus relieve the observer of much of the burden of interpretation. This is illustrated by the lobe-comparison system (Sec. 5-B) in which the response to the signal is such as to furnish information relative to the angular separation between the direction of signal propagation and the orientation of the receiving transducer. The majority of instruments which report on specific features of the signal give a visible response.

Before examining the detailed arrangement of sonar indicators and recorders, designed for specific purposes, it will be well to consider certain fundamental factors common to all such instruments.

6-A GENERAL TYPES OF INDICATORS AND RECORDERS

6A-1 Audible Presentations

Indicators and recorders used in sonar in which the response is an audio wave in air are, in general, identical with similar instruments used in electric communication. Conventional headphones and loud-speakers are used as indicators and any of the several forms of phonograph as recorders.

In many applications of sonar acoustic reproducers are the primary instrument. They are, of course, the only practical indicator for telephony by means of voice-modulated waves transmitted through the water. They are also well adapted to the reception of telegraphic code transmissions. Their chief use, however, is in direct listening where they make possible the observation of underwater sounds, such as those generated by ships or other primary sources, through their reproduction in the air-borne form. In other applications these acoustic devices are used to supplement some special form of visual indicator. This is to take advantage of the fact that human beings have become accustomed, through long experience, to correlate sounds heard by the ear with stimuli affecting other senses. The actual perception of some event is often due to the aggregate effect of the responses of more than one sense. The use of an acoustic reproducer in conjunction with some other form of indicator makes it possible to utilize this ability of the brain to build up a body of information from fragments each of which, by itself, might be hopelessly inadequate.

6A-2 Visual Presentations

A discussion of the details of those sonar indicators and recorders which present the signal in a visual form can profitably be undertaken only in connection with a study of the specific applications with which they are associated. A brief examination of certain general features of these instruments, however, is necessary in order to understand the relations between the operating requirements to be imposed on the instrument, the characteristic performance of the remainder of the receiving system, the nature and meaning of the signal, and the disturbances which interfere with its observation.

One of the visual indicators widely used in sonar is the Sound Range Recorder. This instrument is, in general arrangement, similar to the recorders used in facsimile transmission by wire or by radio. It was initially developed by the British, as an echo-ranging indicator, prior to the entry of the United States into World War II and was later adopted, with some modifications, by the United States Navy. The paper used in this recorder is chemically treated and is in the form of a long strip wound into a roll from which it is drawn at a constant speed. This paper passes between a fixed metallic platen and a moving metallic stylus which crosses it, in a direction perpendicular to its own motion, at a speed which is also maintained constant. The electric output of the receiving circuits, which is here a current of varying amplitude, flows between stylus and platen, through the paper, and, as a result of electrochemical action, leaves a trace of varying degrees of darkening. At the completion of one transit of the paper the stylus returns to its starting point, without leaving a trace, and begins a new record. The beginning of each transit is coincident with the departure of an echo-ranging signal from the transducer. The distance along the trace at which the record of a returned echo appears is, therefore, a measure of the distance of the target by which it was reflected. This presentation has many advantages in echo ranging and other applications of sonar. For the moment our chief concern is with the nature of the recorded trace. The degree of darkening appearing at any point on this trace depends, in some manner, on the magnitude of the electric current, including both noise and signal, delivered by the receiving circuits. The Sound Range Recorder is representative of one group of indicators and recorders which give a visible trace, or indication, the intensity of which is some function of the magnitude of the acoustic input to the hydrophone. Instruments of this group are known as **variable-intensity** devices. All instruments having an audible response are inherently variable-intensity devices.

The cathode ray oscilloscope is coming into increasing use in sonar where, as in radar, it is ideally suited to plan position indications (PPI). Here the spot moves from some point on the screen, corresponding to the location of the apparatus, in a direction corresponding to the bearing of the acoustic axis of the directional transducer. As in the Sound Range Recorder the beginning of motion of the spot is coincident with the departure of an echo-ranging signal from the transducer. The rate of motion is, as before, adjusted to indicate target range by measuring the signal travel time. The point on the screen at which the response to an echo appears thus establishes both the range and the bearing of the target relative to the position of the apparatus. In this instrument the response to the electric output of the receiving system is an illumination of the screen, the degree of illumination depending on the magnitude of the electric input to the instrument. Like the Sound Range Recorder the cathode ray oscilloscope, when used as a plan position indicator, is clearly a variable-intensity instrument.

The cathode ray oscilloscope may be operated in a manner quite different from that just described. For example, suppose that the spot starts at the left-hand side of the screen, at the instant when an echo-ranging signal leaves the transducer, and moves across the screen at a rate correlated with the time required for the signal to travel to the target and back. As the spot moves horizontally the output of the receiving circuits may be applied in such a manner as to cause the spot to be deflected vertically, or to be drawn out into a vertical line, the vertical motion being related to the magnitude of the acoustic wave received by the transducer. The response in this case is known as a **variable-displacement** indication. It will be shown later that variable-displacement indications have certain marked advantages over variable-intensity indications. They do, however, require that one of the dimensions of a two-dimensional screen be allotted to signal amplitude. They can be used only when there is but one other variable, such as range, to be reported. When it is desired to present information regarding two other variables, such as range and bearing, in addition to signal amplitude, it is necessary to employ the variable-intensity indication.

6-B EVALUATION OF PERFORMANCE

The primary purpose of every indicator or recorder used in sonar is, in some way or other, to make the signal perceptible to the observer. In some cases it is required merely to establish the fact that a signal exists; in others, as in the bearing-deviation indicator, the response to the signal is such that additional information as to the circumstances associated with it may be deduced. Whatever the nature of its response, however, the quantitative evaluation of the performance of the instrument involves defining the limiting conditions under which the effect to be produced is adequately perceptible. This implies that the operation of any instrument is a joint enterprise in which the instrument is one partner and the observer the other. In stating the performance of the instrument quantitatively, therefore, certain physiological and psychological characteristics of human beings are quite as relevant as the nature and behavior of acoustic waves in the sea, or as the properties of the system by which these waves are caused to influence the instrument.

6B-1 Signal Differential and Observed Differential

In the operation of any sonar system we are intimately concerned with signal-to-interference ratios. Some attention has already been given to signal-to-noise ratios in connection with direct listening. When operating an echo-ranging system, as we shall see in a subsequent chapter, the problem is to identify an echo from some specified reflecting target in the presence of general reverberation. Although both originate as a single transmitted signal it will be found convenient to treat part of the returned energy as signal and part as interference. In echo ranging, then, the echo-to-reverberation ratio may be considered in the same manner as the signal-to-noise ratio in direct listening.

The signal and the interference may be considered separately with respect to their origins, to their losses during propagation, and to their effects on a hydrophone. When we come to the response of the indicating instrument, however, the signal may rarely be considered by itself. No indicating instrument or recorder ever presents the signal as a wholly independent quantity; the significant magnitudes in the instrument response are those of the interference alone and of the signal and interference combined. The relation of the resultant response when the signal is present to the response which would be observed if the signal were absent is, therefore, quite as significant as the relation between signal and interference considered individually. It has al-

ready been noted (Art. 2C-2) that the difference between the level, at any point in a sonar system, of the signal energy to be observed, and the level, at the same point, of the energy which interferes with its observation may be designated as the **signal differential.** In a similar manner we shall designate as the **observed differential**, ΔL_{obs}, the difference between the level of the resultant energy of the signal and interference combined and the level of the interfering energy alone.

These two quantities are uniquely related to each other. The signal differential may be written as

$$\Delta L_{s/n} = L_s - L_n = \lg t \frac{P_s}{P_n} \qquad (6B\text{-}1)$$

and the resultant differential as

$$\Delta L_{obs} = \lg t \frac{P_n + P_s}{P_n} = \lg t \left[1 + \frac{P_s}{P_n} \right] \qquad (6B\text{-}2)$$

Both are thus seen to be functions of the signal-to-interference ratio, P_s/P_n, and are, in consequence, functions of each other. The relations here are, in fact, identical with those discussed in Art. 2B-3. The curves of Fig. 2B-3 may be used as a graphical representation of the relation between the two quantities; the abscissas of that diagram correspond to observed differential and the ordinates to signal differential.

6B-2 Recognition Differential

As the level of the signal from some given source is reduced, relative to the level of the interference, a point is ultimately reached below which the reliability with which it may be observed decreases rapidly. The reliability of observation, at any given value of signal differential, may be expressed quantitatively in terms of the percentage of a large number of trials, at that signal differential, which are successful. The value employed is usually the statistical average for a number of observers. The variation of this percentage with change in signal differential shown graphically by the curve of Fig. 6B-1 is typical of the relation between these two quantities. The actual position of such curves with respect to the signal differential scale may vary greatly, depending on the nature of the signal and of the interference, on the means by which the system response is made perceptible, and on the acuity of the observer. The shape of the curve, however, is not greatly affected by changes in any of these factors. Over a

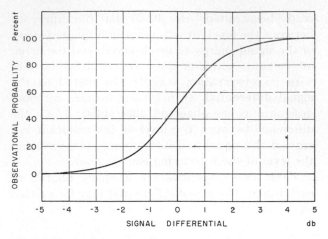

FIG. 6B-1. REGION OF MARGINAL OBSERVATION. A typical curve showing the relation between the change in the percentage of successful attempts at signal observation accompanying changes in signal differential.

wide range of conditions it is safe to assume that the reduction in signal differential responsible for a reduction in the probability of successful observation from 90 percent to 10 percent will be in the neighborhood of 4 db. It is evident that this region within which the reliability of observation changes so abruptly is of the utmost significance to the design and operation of sonar systems.

The location, on the signal differential scale, of this region of marginal reliability may conveniently be identified with the value of signal differential for which the probability of successful observation is 50 percent. This value of signal differential, characteristic of a specified set of conditions, is designated as the **recognition differential.**

It is evident, for a given type of system and for a normally perceptive observer, that the value of the recognition differential is a quantitative measure of the relation between the character of the signal and the character of the interference. Those characteristics which exert a controlling influence on the value of recognition differential may be described as properties of the **signal-interference combination.** This term is to be associated with the quality, or nature, of the signal and of its interference, as distinguished from either their absolute or their relative magnitudes.

When the signal and the interference are alike in character the only indication of the existence of a signal is the change in the magnitude of the total response of the receiving system. In fact,

unless the signal either begins or ends with sufficient abruptness to produce a noticeable change in magnitude there will be no observable clue to its presence. In the case of audible signals, occupying finite frequency bands, it is generally agreed that unless the observed differential is of the order of 3 db or more the signal is likely to pass unnoticed. With speech or music, for example, a change in level of this amount, such as might result from a sudden change in the gain of a reproducing system, is about the least change which may be recognized as such. The minimum detectable change in many types of visually reproduced signals is of the same order of magnitude. From the relation between observed differential and signal differential it is thus seen that the recognition differential is often in the neighborhood of $\Delta L_{\mathrm{rgn}} = 0$ db.

It is by no means uncommon, in practice, to find conditions such that a sudden change in the level of system response is the only possible basis for signal identification. This is, indeed, common experience in echo ranging, as we shall see presently. On the other hand, many continuous signals exhibit some well defined character—or quality—which tends to attract attention at an early stage as they emerge from an obscuring background, or which permits attention to be focused on them once they have been discovered. The rhythmic beat of propellers is, perhaps, the most familiar example in sonar. A pronounced concentration of energy in a single-frequency component, or in components forming a sound having some distinctive tonal quality, may also give significant individuality to a signal. These effects are exhibited by the whine of propulsion gears or by the resonant singing of propeller blades. Examples are to be found in echo ranging as well as in direct listening. If the target from which an echo-ranging signal is reflected is in motion the echo will suffer a different shift in frequency, due to the Doppler effect, than does the reverberation. In an echo-ranging system having an audible response, then, the echo will be reproduced at a different pitch than the reverberation and will be more easily identified than would otherwise be possible. Whenever there is a perceptible difference in quality between a signal and its interference the recognition differential is considerably less than the value $\Delta L_{\mathrm{rgn}} = 0$ db characteristic of the case where they are alike in character.

If the interference preceding a change representing a signal is not constant but shows irregular variations, of any rate or magnitude, it is obvious that the change will pass unnoticed unless it causes a greater change than might normally be expected. This condition is almost always encountered in echo ranging. It is illustrated in Fig. 6B-2 in which is plotted, as a function of time, the pressure of the acoustic waves falling on the transducer of an echo-ranging system following the transmission of a pulse of ultrasonic

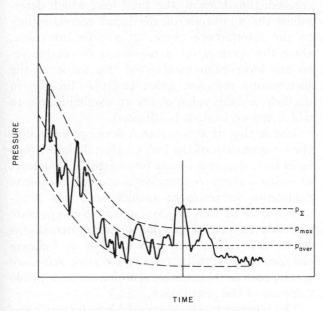

FIG. 6B-2. RESPONSE OF ECHO-RANGING RECORDER. The envelope of the ultrasonic waves falling on a transducer following the transmission of an echo-ranging signal.

p_{aver} = average pressure of interference
$p_{max} - p_{aver}$ = range of random deviations in pressure of interference
p_{Σ} = total pressure due to signal and interference

energy. The curve shown is the envelope of the voltage actually developed in the transducer as recorded by means of a cathode ray oscilloscope.

If the pressure of any signal increases gradually, particularly if it is of the same general character as the interference, the least detectable increase will be much greater than if it had increased suddenly. Many observers have had the experience of failing to detect the approach of a submarine until the stopping of the screws brought about an abrupt change in the level of the total energy received. In such cases the increase in level observed as speed is resumed often indicates that the signal had been well above the noise level. This condition, also, is associated with a recognition differential having a positive value.

6B-3 Incremental Response Index

For any signal-interference combination the recognition differential depends on the characteristics of the instrument by which it is observed. Conversely, differences between recognition differentials obtained with two instruments depends on the signal-interference combination. It will, therefore, be necessary to consider with some care any signal-interference combination selected for establishing a figure of merit indicative of the performance of an indicating or recording instrument with respect to this effect.

In observing the response of an indicator the ear or the eye is inclined to recognize magnitudes on the basis of short-time averages. In some cases the significant magnitudes are expressed in terms of power, in others they may be peak pressures, or average pressures. It is not, in general, possible always to translate the responses of some instrument into terms of signal differential. It is, however, necessary to relate this response to signal differential in some manner since effects such as those due to propagation loss or to transducer directivity, which are of fundamental importance in determining the performance of sonar equipment, must be computed separately for the signal and for the interference.

We may define the **incremental response index** of an indicating or recording instrument as the difference, in decibels, between the level of a single-frequency wave following an abrupt increase above some initial constant level and this initial constant level when the change in level is such as will be detected on 50 percent of a number of trials by a number of observers. It is thus apparent that, although the incremental response index, as defined, is a property of a piece of apparatus, its actual value involves the acuity of perception of the observer.

The test signal specified by this definition is ideally suited to the measurement of incremental response index for two reasons; it represents an accurately reproducible signal-interference combination which may be generated with simple equipment, of a type generally available, and which may be adjusted to any desired relative and absolute magnitudes; it also involves no characteristic difference between signal and interference and hence requires the observer to base his selection of a detectable change in magnitude on magnitude alone.

The measurement of incremental response index may be carried out by means of an arrangement such as that shown in Fig. 6B-3. A test signal, in the form of a sinusoidal wave of constant amplitude, is generated by a vacuum tube oscillator and transmitted to the input terminals of the instrument through two attenuation networks, A and B, connected in series. Both of these networks are variable and may be adjusted to any desired value of transmission loss. The network B is associated with a pair of contacts, 1 and 2, which are carried by a single relay, or other

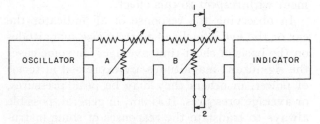

FIG. 6B-3. MEASUREMENT OF INCREMENTAL RESPONSE INDEX. A schematic showing an arrangement of apparatus for obtaining the test signals specified in the definition of incremental response index.

suitable switching mechanism, and so adjusted that when either one opens the other closes. When contact 1 is open and contact 2 closed network B is in the circuit and the signal is attenuated by the transmission loss of both networks. When contact 1 is closed and contact 2 open this network is removed from the circuit and the signal level is increased by the amount of its transmission loss. By this arrangement the level of the test signal may be changed abruptly, but without any interruption in continuity, from one value to another. The initial level of the test signal depends on the level delivered by the oscillator and on the total transmission loss of the two attenuation networks. It is not necessary to know the absolute value of this initial level as it may be specified in terms of the response of the instrument, or in some other arbitrary manner which is of significance in connection with its use. Initial levels are frequently referred to that at which the instrument gives the minimum perceptible response.

The switching of network B is generally controlled automatically in some suitable relation to the operation of the instrument. When applied to the Sound Range Recorder, for example, the loss of this unit is removed momentarily as the stylus is making a transit of the recording paper. It thus causes a change in the recorded trace which has

features representative of the record of an echo signal. Examples of such traces are shown in Fig. 6B-4. The minimum change in power required to produce a detectable change in response is found by increasing the loss of network B, as it is periodically removed from the circuit, until a value is reached at which the change in response may be detected. In order to maintain a constant initial power level it is, of course, necessary to decrease the loss of unit A as that of unit B is increased, thus keeping the total loss, which determines the amplitude of the input corresponding to the interference alone, at a constant value. Once the settings for a minimum detectable response have been established the value of the incremental response index is given directly, in decibels, by the value of the transmission loss to which the network B is adjusted.

The setting of attenuator A does not enter into the computation of the index value. This network is, in fact, simply a means for controlling the level at which a given observation is made; its accurate calibration in terms of transmission loss is required in order that it may be used to compensate correctly for changes in the setting of attenuator B. Its calibration may also be used to indicate changes in level with respect to some reference power, such as that causing a minimum perceptible response of the instrument.

The representation of a signal-interference combination by an electric wave having a sinusoidal variation, as required by the definition of incremental response index, is equivalent to assuming a signal and an interference which are identical in frequency and phase. This condition is quite unlikely ever to be satisfied in practice. It obviously requires that both signal and interference originate at a common source. This might appear to be the situation with echo and reverberation in echo ranging. As will be shown later, however, there are several reasons why the phase of energy reflected from one portion of the environment is different from that of energy reflected from another. In the case of a moving target, as already noted, the Doppler shift of the echo is different from that of the reverberation; signal and interference are, therefore, not of the same frequency, to say nothing of being of the same phase.

In practice the signal and its interference may be assumed to combine in a random manner with respect to the phase relations of the individual components. Under these conditions the total

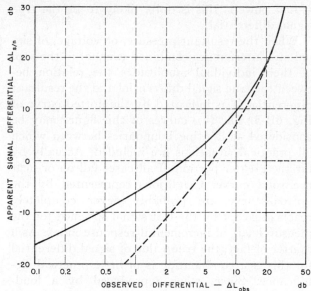

FIG. 6B-5. SIGNAL DIFFERENTIAL. Values of signal differential plotted as a function of observed differential.

power will be the sum of the power associated with the interference alone and the power which would be associated with the signal alone if there were no interference. It is these individual powers which must be taken into account in estimating the signal differentials to be expected in any given situation. The relations here are, in fact, those discussed in Art. 2A-9 in connection with equivalent plane wave intensity.

Uncertainty as to the manner in which the signal and the interference combine, under any given circumstances, makes it impossible rigorously to identify values of signal differential with values of observed differential. We may, however, define the **apparent signal differential** as that which would be deduced from measured values of observed differential. The curve showing this relation, originally presented in Fig. 2B-3, is reproduced as the solid curve of Fig. 6B-5. By means of this curve it is possible to derive a value for the apparent signal differential of any signal-interference combination from the value of observed differential indicated by some given instrument. In the majority of cases, since the signal and interference combine in random phase to give a resultant power which is the sum of their indi-

FIG. 6B-4. INCREMENTAL RESPONSES. Records taken with a Sound Range Recorder when connected to a circuit for measuring its incremental response index.

vidual powers, this is quite likely to be the true signal differential.

When the resultant pressure, or voltage, of signal and interference combined is equal to the sum of their individual amplitudes the relation between the true signal differential and the resultant differential is as indicated by the dotted curve of Fig. 6B-5. The two curves of this figure may be considered as limiting boundaries between which all practical situations are included. Actually by far the greater portion of all cases fall on or near the solid curve. Conditions represented by the dotted curve are probably never completely reached except by the test signal specified for the measurement of incremental response index. As a matter of fact, the true value of signal differential for this test combination is of little practical significance. Since, when reproduced by a loudspeaker, it is heard as a pure tone, and since it is entirely free from random variations in level prior to the change in level representing the signal, it is probable that the recognition value of observed differential will be less than the 3 db cited as the minimum detectable change in level when signal and interference are alike in character. Insofar as it may be said to have an actual value of signal differential this value is less than its apparent value. It would appear, then, that incremental response index is measured by means of a signal-interference combination which is unlike that on which the value of recognition differential is based. This fact in no way impairs the utility of the test signal as a means for establishing a figure of merit for the performance of indicating and recording instruments. Regardless of the phase relations between the signal and the interference the incremental response index correctly associates the marginal value of observed differential, as indicated by any given instrument, for any given signal-interference combination, with the recognition differential. This recognition differential, in turn, establishes the necessary relations between the levels of the signal and of the interference, the transmission losses, and similar significant factors prescribed by some given problem.

The incremental response index finds its greatest utility in connection with visual indicators and recorders, particularly those of the variable-intensity type. With these instruments, more than with others, it is true that the manifestation of the signal is restricted to its effect on the total response. It is just this effect which is measured by the incremental response index. In the Sound Range Recorder, for example, it is apparent that the recognition differential can never be less than the apparent value identified with the incremental response index. Many cases of great practical importance will be found where the recognition differential is fixed solely by the incremental response index of the indicating or recording instrument. For instruments such as loud-speakers or headphones, where the presentation is audible, the listener is often able to perceive the signal independently from the interference. In such cases the incremental response index is of little real significance. This is partly due to the fact that the index is not directly related to critical performance characteristics and partly to the fact that the performance characteristics of the instrument are more than adequate and any limitations which it may impose are negligible in comparison with those fixed by the signal-interference combination.

When incremental response index is plotted against the initial power level of the test signal the resulting curve is an **incremental response characteristic.** Variations with initial level are generally of considerable magnitude and often show that acceptable values of the index are confined to a narrow range of levels. The relation between incremental response index and operating level is thus one of the more important performance characteristics of any indicator or recorder. It not only permits the merit of the instrument to be assessed quantitatively but prescribes the most suitable operating adjustments for the system. Examples of incremental response characteristics are given later in this section.

For instruments giving audible presentations the recognition differential is likely to vary with frequency or with the frequency band to which the system is responsive. Reliable information regarding the effect of frequency on recognition differential is essential to the proper design of detection equipment.

6B-4 Variable-Intensity Responses

In a variable-intensity instrument the response is measured in terms of energy, as the name implies. In the case of an acoustic instrument the acoustic intensity may be measured at some given observation point; for a visual instrument it is possible to measure the intensity of the light radiated from some luminous spot, as in the cathode ray oscilloscope, or absorbed by a darkened trace, as in the Sound Range Recorder. Any variable-intensity instrument would be said to show a **linear response** if the power associated in some prescribed manner with its response were proportional to its input power.

In appraising the performance of a variable-intensity instrument it is necessary to consider the manner in which the observer responds to the energy which he receives from the instrument as well as the manner in which the instrument responds to the energy which it receives from the preceding portion of the system. The physiological behavior of the observer is described by the Weber-Fechner law, according to which the fractional change in any stimulus which results in the minimum detectable change in sensation is a function of the initial value of the stimulus. For many years it was believed that, for any given sense, this minimum detectable fractional change had a constant value. This is, in fact, the basis for the statement that sensation is proportional to the logarithm of the stimulus.

Refined methods of measurement[1] show that the fractional value of the minimum detectable change in stimulating energy, although constant over a considerable range of levels, increases as the initial value of this energy approaches either the threshold of sensation or the limit of toleration. The ratio of the minimum detectable increase in the intensity of any stimulus to the initial value of its intensity is now known as the Fechner ratio.

It is possible for an observer to detect periodic changes in acoustic intensity of as little as 10 percent if the change recurs at the most favorable rate. Under optimum conditions a change in luminous intensity of only 1.5 percent is detectable. These values may be increased tenfold at the threshold of perceptibility. In general, changes in stimulating energy representing the response of a sonar system to a signal must exceed these values by an appreciable factor for reliable detection. A single abrupt change in intensity will seldom be observed unless it is at least 25 percent of the initial constant value; changes of less than 40 percent may easily escape notice. Since we are primarily concerned with the overall performance of sonar equipment our interest in the Fechner ratio is limited to its effect on the incremental response index.

As applied to our immediate problem the Fechner ratio may be written as

$$F = \frac{P_\Sigma - P_n}{P_n} \qquad (6B\text{-}3)$$

where P_n is the initial power measuring the response of some instrument and $P_\Sigma - P_n$ is the least detectable increase in that power. For an instrument having a linear response the magnitude of the response is proportional to the magnitude of the power input. It will be convenient, in this and other cases to follow, to express the relations between input and response in terms of wave amplitudes instead of in terms of power. To facilitate this we shall adopt the expedient of representing the input amplitude as an electric current. Assuming the power measuring the response of an instrument to be proportional to the square of the input current a fundamental relation for a linear variable-intensity indicator may be derived from Eq. (6B-3). This relation is

$$\frac{P_\Sigma}{P_n} = \frac{i_\Sigma{}^2}{i_n{}^2} = (1 + F) \qquad (6B\text{-}4)$$

where i_n and i_Σ are the rms values of the initial and total amplitudes. For an ideal linear instrument, in which the output amplitude is proportional to the input amplitude, the incremental response index would be

$$\Delta L_{IR} = \operatorname{lgt} \frac{P_\Sigma}{P_n} = 2 \operatorname{lgt} \frac{i_\Sigma}{i_n} = 2 \operatorname{lgt} \frac{e_\Sigma}{e_n}$$

$$= \operatorname{lgt} (1 + F) \qquad (6B\text{-}5)$$

This index is thus seen to be a unique function of the Fechner ratio applying to its response and to the nature of the change in this response caused by the signal. In practice it may be expected that the actual incremental response index of any instrument will not be less than 1 or 2 db over any portion of its operating range.

As input levels increase above the threshold value the incremental response index of a variable-intensity instrument may show a variation due to the change in the Fechner ratio. In situations occurring in practice this is likely to be obscured by other effects. The typical incremental response characteristic of a linear variable-intensity indicator may, for positive input levels, be represented as a horizontal line having an index value between 1 and 2 db. Theoretically this should extend to the limit of toleration of the observer;

actually the equipment is certain to fix an upper limit long before any such level is reached. Many instruments have a range of input levels of something like 40 db; some have no more than 20 db; the observer is able to perceive changes in stimulus over a range of levels of nearly 120 db. An incremental response characteristic, for positive input levels, representative of linear variable-intensity indicators is shown by curve (A) of Fig. 6B-6. The reference input level, corresponding to the zero point of the abscissa, is that level for which the total response is the minimum which may be perceived.

For negative input levels, that is, for input powers, P_n, which are less than the reference power, P_0, the increase in level due to the signal input must be sufficient to bring the total input power, P_Σ, to the minimum perceptible value. For this portion of the characteristic, then, $P_\Sigma = P_0$ and the incremental response index must be

$$\Delta L_{IR} = \text{lgt}\, \frac{P_\Sigma}{P_n} = \text{lgt}\, \frac{P_0}{P_n} = -L_{\text{in}} \quad (6B\text{-}6)$$

Theoretically Eqs. (6B-5) and (6B-6) indicate a discontinuity in the characteristic as it passes through zero input level. When $P_n = P_0$ Eq. (6B-6) gives the incremental response index a value of zero whereas Eq. (6B-5) gives it a finite value. In practice it may be assumed that the characteristic enters the quadrant of negative input levels as a continuation of the line appearing in the quadrant of positive input levels; it promptly becomes asymptotic to a straight line passing through the origin and having a negative slope of unity, as required by Eq. (6B-6).

An actual incremental response characteristic, taken for a Sound Range Recorder, is shown in Fig. 6B-7. Records similar to those from which the data for this curve were obtained have already been presented in Fig. 6B-4. It must be remembered, however, that the variations in darkening shown by the original are not reproduced with absolute fidelity. This characteristic, although differing radically from that for an ideal linear indicator, is representative of many taken for visual indicators of the variable-intensity type. Characteristics for variable-illumination devices do not differ greatly in general appearance from those for variable-darkening devices, although the relations between stimulating energy and power input to the instrument are quite different in the two cases. It is not a simple matter to determine, for a variable-darkening instrument, the extent to which the shape of the characteristic is due to failure of the instrument to respond linearly or to variations in the Fechner ratio. For our present purposes, however, it is unnecessary to isolate these two effects.

For the characteristic shown by Fig. 6B-7 the portion indicating the lowest values of incremental response index is seen to be restricted to a narrow range of input levels. It is evident that the receiving system must be so adjusted that the input is brought within the limits of this restricted range if a weak signal is to be most effectively separated from an interfering background.

6B-5 Variable-Displacement Responses

A variable-displacement instrument is said to have a linear response when the deflection of its indicating element is proportional to the amplitude of its input. Conventional ammeters and voltmeters have almost ideal linear responses since the deflections of their needles are as nearly proportional to the currents or voltages impressed on their terminals as it is possible to make them.

The performance of instruments of this type is influenced less by the behavior of the observer than is the case with variable-intensity devices. Here the minimum change in response which may be detected is usually of constant amplitude, in-

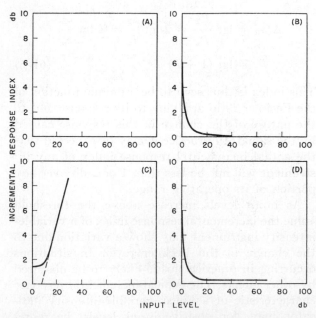

FIG. 6B-6. INCREMENTAL RESPONSE CHARACTERISTICS. Values of incremental response index, plotted as functions of positive input levels, for various types of response.

(A) A linear variable-intensity response
(B) A linear variable-displacement response
(C) A logarithmic variable-intensity response
(D) A logarithmic variable-displacement response

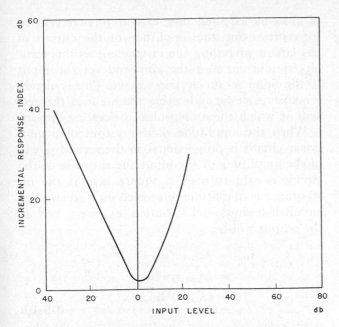

FIG. 6B-7. INCREMENTAL RESPONSE CHARACTERISTIC. A typical characteristic representative of variable-intensity recorders. Taken for a Sound Range Recorder.

dependent of the amplitude immediately preceding the change. Assuming the response to be linear down to zero input this constant difference is also the minimum perceptible input amplitude.

Again using electric current as a representative amplitude the basic relation, in terms of input amplitudes, for an ideal linear variable-displacement indicator is

$$i_\Sigma - i_n = i_0 \qquad (6B-7)$$

The incremental response index of such an instrument may thus be written as

$$\Delta L_{IR} = 2 \lgt \frac{i_\Sigma}{i_n} = 2 \lgt \left[1 + \frac{i_0}{i_n} \right] \qquad (6B-8)$$

The incremental response characteristic of an ideal linear variable-displacement instrument may be derived as follows. Using the minimum perceptible input as a reference amplitude the input level is given directly, by definition, as

$$L_{in} = 2 \lgt \frac{i_n}{i_0} \qquad (6B-9)$$

Since incremental response index and input level are each unique functions of the input amplitude, for a given instrument, each is a unique function of the other. For an instrument having a clearly defined indication the value of the minimum detectable change in deflection is usually somewhere in the neighborhood of 0.5 percent of the full-scale

deflection. This relation may be expressed in terms of input amplitudes, which are proportional to these deflections, as $i_0/i_{max} = 0.005$ where i_{max} is the input amplitude for full-scale deflection. In such an instrument, then, the range of input levels over which the signal may be observed is $2 \lgt (i_{max}/i_0) = 2 \lgt 200 = 46$ db.

When $i_n = i_0$, $L_{in} = 0$, and $\Delta L_{IR} = 6$ db. This value of incremental response index is found in practically all linear variable-displacement indicators at the zero input level. For larger values of input amplitude the characteristic drops in accordance with Eq. (6B-8). An incremental response characteristic illustrating the relations discussed above is shown by curve (B) of Fig. 6B-6. For smaller amplitudes, that is, for negative input levels, the characteristic is the same as that for a variable-intensity instrument; it approaches a straight line passing through the origin and having a negative slope of unity.

In some instruments, such as cathode ray oscilloscopes in which the spot is badly focused, a change of input may not be clearly marked unless it is considerably more than the 0.5 percent of full-scale input assumed above. For a given value of full-scale input, i_{max}, this is equivalent to an increase in i_0, the minimum detectable change in input. It can be seen from the equations that this not only raises the incremental response index, for a given finite value of input, but also reduces the range of input levels over which the instrument may be used; this second effect may be even more serious than the first.

Incremental response characteristics are of little value in connection with instruments such as ammeters and voltmeters, where the interest is in linear variations of input. For sonar indicators and recorders, where the significant amplitudes vary logarithmically, they are a most useful method of reporting the response behavior.

6B-6 Nonlinear Responses

In actual sonar systems it may be advantageous if the relation between the magnitude of the response of the indicating or recording instrument and the magnitude of the acoustic wave acting on the transducer differs from the incremental response characteristic corresponding to either the linear intensity response or the linear displacement response. When such differences are introduced, intentionally or otherwise, the system is said to have a **nonlinear response.** A desired nonlinear characteristic may sometimes be obtained by a suitable choice of design constants for the instrument. It is, however, generally preferable to modify the signal, together with any accompanying interference, in suitable auxiliary circuits forming part of the receiving system preceding the indicator. This arrangement permits of greater freedom in the selection of the resultant characteristic and in its adjustment to given specifications.

When some element of a sonar receiving system shows a nonlinear transmission characteristic it is possible to report its effect on the overall performance in either of two ways. In one the circuit may be considered as modifying the response of the indicator; this would lead to a reevaluation of the effective incremental response index. Alternatively, the circuit may be considered as modifying the relations between the signal and the interference delivered to the instrument; this would be expressed quantitatively as a change in the signal differential. To specify the performance of a nonlinear circuit it is usually necessary to relate the instantaneous amplitude of its output to the instantaneous amplitude of its input. The relations between input and output powers, or between rms or average values of amplitude, therefore, depend on the manner in which the resultant amplitudes of the wave being transmitted vary with time. It is not, in general, possible to derive any simple expression by which the signal differential appearing in the output of a nonlinear circuit may be computed from the signal differential existing at its input. The measurement of incremental response index, on the other hand, is made with a signal wave having a single sinusoidal component. It is possible to obtain input-output characteristics for nonlinear circuits when the wave has this simple form. From these characteristics expressions may be derived for the apparent, or effective, value of the incremental response index as it would be measured at the input to the system. Any relations between signal and interference which may appear in the recognition differential, as the signal-interference combination is observed by some given instrument, will, in general, be modified as the result of transmission through a nonlinear circuit. This will be reflected as a change in the value of the recognition differential. In most cases this effect can best be evaluated by observing the response of the system to the signal-interference combination in question.

In studying the performance of instruments we have adopted the convention of expressing the amplitude of the input to the instrument in terms of an electric current. To study the performance of systems we shall now extend this convention by representing the amplitude of the output of the circuit preceding the instrument as this same electric current and the amplitude of the input to the circuit as an electric voltage. This is merely a convenience for indicating the point in the system at which the amplitudes in question appear.

When the amplitude of the output of a nonlinear circuit is proportional to the second power of the amplitude of the input the response of the circuit is said to obey a **square law.** If the instantaneous amplitude impressed on a square-law circuit is a sinusoidal variation, $e_{\text{inst}} = e_{\max} \cos \omega t$, the output will be

$$
\begin{aligned}
i_{\text{inst}} &= k e_{\text{inst}}^2 \\
&= k e_{\max}^2 \cos^2 \omega t \\
&= \frac{k e_{\max}^2}{2} + \frac{k e_{\max}^2}{2} \cos 2\omega t
\end{aligned}
\qquad (6\text{B-}10)
$$

The output, then, contains a unidirectional component and a sinusoidally varying component of twice the frequency of the variation impressed on the input. We shall assume that the response of the instrument to one of these components is known; its performance may then be deduced in terms of amplitude relations alone.

On the basis of the foregoing the amplitude of the input to an instrument due to interference alone may be written as $i_n = k e_n^2$ and the amplitude following a minimum detectable increase due to the signal as $i_\Sigma = k e_\Sigma^2$. The amplitudes given by these expressions are understood to be rms values. The apparent incremental response index of the system is then

$$
\Delta L'_{IR} = 2 \lg \frac{e_\Sigma}{e_n} = \lg \frac{i_\Sigma}{i_n} = \frac{1}{2} \Delta L_{IR} \qquad (6\text{B-}11)
$$

where ΔL_{IR} is the incremental response index, identified with the initial amplitude, i_n, for the instrument alone. This relation between the effective index of the system and the index of the instrument is a property of the square-law circuit, regardless of whether the instrument is of the variable-intensity type or of the variable-displacement type, and regardless of the linearity of the instrument.

The minimum amplitude of the output of the circuit for which the indicator shows a perceptible response is $i_0 = k e_0^2$. The input level to the system, above or below the reference amplitude, e_0, thus defined, may consequently be written as

$$
L'_{\text{in}} = 2 \lg \frac{e_n}{e_0} = \lg \frac{i_n}{i_0} = \frac{1}{2} L_{\text{in}} \qquad (6\text{B-}12)
$$

where L_{in} is the input level at the instrument.

The relations expressed by Eqs. (6B-11) and (6B-12) at once suggest a method for deriving the effective incremental response characteristic for a system using a square-law circuit ahead of any indicator having a known characteristic; for any point on the known characteristic there will be a point on the derived characteristic the coordinates of which are each one half those of the known point. The use of a square-law circuit, then, does not change the shape of an incremental response characteristic. It does reduce the value of the incremental response index, but at the cost of a reduction in the operating range of input levels.

In general, a circuit forming part of a sonar receiving system may be so arranged that its output amplitude is proportional to any positive power, m, of its input amplitude. The value of this exponent may be greater or less than unity. It may be shown that with such circuits the difference in level between any two amplitudes in the output is m times the difference in level between the corresponding input amplitudes. The incremental response characteristics of systems containing such circuits may be derived from the characteristics of the instruments by the method described above for the square-law circuit, where $m = 2$.

It is possible to arrange an electric circuit so that its output amplitude is a **logarithmic** function of its input amplitude. The characteristic relation in this case may be written as

$$i_x = a \log b e_x \qquad (6B\text{-}13)$$

where a and b are constants of the circuit, and where e_x and i_x are rms values of input and output amplitudes which are valid only when e_x is a sinusoidal variation.

It is obvious that this expression cannot describe the performance of the circuit when the quantity $b e_x$ is less than unity as this would require the output to be negative. Actually the relation never holds down to $b e_x = 1$. The input-output characteristic of a typical logarithmic circuit, for low values of input amplitude, is shown in Fig. 6B-8. The dotted line indicates the relation corresponding exactly to Eq. (6B-13). The portion of the actual curve which departs from this relation may generally be represented reasonably well by a straight line through the origin and tangent to the logarithmic curve, as shown in the figure. The range of input amplitudes for which the logarithmic relation is valid may, in a well designed circuit, cover a difference in level of 60 db. Ranges of 40 db are obtained with relatively little diffi-

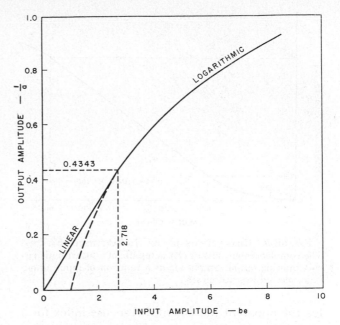

FIG. 6B-8. CHARACTERISTIC OF LOGARITHMIC CIRCUIT. A portion of the input-output characteristic of a logarithmic circuit showing the relations for low input amplitudes. The logarithmic relation between the input and output is given by the equation $i = a \log be$.

culty. A complete input-output characteristic is shown in Fig. 6B-9. In this diagram output amplitude is plotted against the logarithm of the input amplitudes. In the following discussion the limiting values of output amplitude for which Eq. (6B-13) may be used will be written as $i_1 = a \log b e_1$, for the minimum value, and as $i_2 = a \log b e_2$, for the maximum value. As before, i_0 will indicate the amplitude of the circuit output for which the instrument gives the minimum perceptible indication.

The apparent incremental response index of a system using a logarithmic circuit may be written, using logarithms to the base $10^{0.1}$, as

$$\Delta L'_{IR} = 2 \operatorname{lgt} \frac{e_\Sigma}{e_n} = \frac{20}{a}(i_\Sigma - i_n) \qquad (6B\text{-}14)$$

for values of e_Σ and e_n satisfying the conditions for which Eq. (6B-13) is valid. This apparent index has no unique relation to the actual index of the indicating instrument, as was the case with the square-law circuit. It is, however, possible to determine the nature of the incremental response characteristic when a logarithmic circuit is used with either a variable-intensity or a variable-displacement instrument.

By substituting the value $i_\Sigma = i_n \sqrt{1+F}$ for the total output amplitude, as given by Eq. (6B-4), into Eq. (6B-14) there is obtained an expression

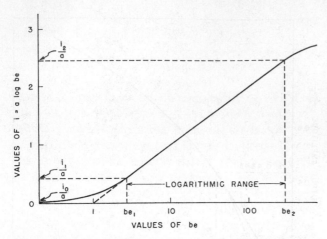

FIG. 6B-9. CHARACTERISTIC OF LOGARITHMIC CIRCUIT. The complete input-output characteristic of a logarithmic circuit showing output amplitude as a function of input amplitude, plotted logarithmically.

for the apparent incremental response index for a system made up of a logarithmic circuit and a linear variable-intensity indicator. This index is

$$\Delta L'_{IR} = \frac{20}{a} \left[\sqrt{1+F} - 1 \right] i_n \qquad (6B\text{-}15)$$

This relation holds for all values of output amplitude between $i_n = i_1$ and $i_n = i_2$.

Referring input levels, for the moment, to the minimum input amplitude, e_1, to which the logarithmic relation applies, the input level to the system may be written as

$$(L'_{\text{in}})_1 = 2 \lgt \frac{e_n}{e_1} = \frac{20}{a} (i_n - i_1) \qquad (6B\text{-}16)$$

If the input-output relations of the circuit are linear below the logarithmic range the difference in level between e_1 and e_0 is $2 \lgt (e_1/e_0) = 2 \lgt (i_1/i_0)$. The input level of the system, referred, in the usual manner, to the minimum perceptible input, is obtained by adding this difference to the level shown in Eq. (6B-16), whereupon

$$L'_{\text{in}} = (L'_{\text{in}})_1 + 2 \lgt \frac{i_n}{i_0}$$

$$= \frac{20}{a} i_n + \left[2 \lgt \frac{i_1}{i_0} - \frac{20}{a} i_1 \right]$$

$$= \frac{20}{a} i_n + N_{\text{sys}} \qquad (6B\text{-}17)$$

The quantity N_{sys}, which is defined by the above equalities, is a constant of the system; it depends on the properties both of the circuit and of the

instrument. For the conditions shown by Fig. 6B-8 it would have the value $N_{\text{sys}} = 16$ db.

For low values of input amplitude, where the output of the circuit is approximately proportional to the input amplitude, the system responds much as a linear variable-intensity indicator would respond. As the input approaches the level at which the logarithmic relation becomes effective the characteristic begins to approach asymptotically to the line defined by Eqs. (6B-15) and (6B-17). The equation for this asymptote, derived by eliminating i_n from the two equations, is

$$\Delta L'_{IR} = (L'_{\text{in}} - N_{\text{sys}})(\sqrt{1+F} - 1) \qquad (6B\text{-}18)$$

Over the region for which this relation is valid the Fechner ratio, F, is quite likely to be constant. For a linear instrument, then, the equation defines a straight line passing through the point $L'_{\text{in}} = N_{\text{sys}}$, $\Delta L'_{IR} = 0$, and having a slope $(\sqrt{1+F} - 1)$. In the quadrant of negative input levels the characteristic has the familiar negative slope of unity.

An incremental response characteristic satisfying the conditions just described is shown by curve (C) of Fig. 6B-6. Its similarity to the incremental response characteristic obtained with the Sound Range Recorder, as shown by Fig. 6B-7, is obvious. This leads to the conclusion that the response of the Sound Range Recorder is more nearly logarithmic than linear. This is true of a majority of all variable-intensity indicators. Since the association of a logarithmic circuit with such an instrument tends to emphasize the more undesirable features of its incremental response characteristic we shall not consider it further.

For a system in which a logarithmic circuit is used with a linear variable-displacement instrument the apparent incremental response index may be written by substituting the value $i_2 - i_n = i_0$, as given by Eq. (6B-7), directly into Eq. (6B-14), whereby

$$\Delta L'_{IR} = \frac{20}{a} i_0 \qquad (6B\text{-}19)$$

This may be put in a more significant form. It will be assumed that the system is so adjusted that full-scale deflection occurs for the maximum logarithmic output, or that $i_2 = i_{\text{max}}$. Also, in any linear variable-displacement instrument, the minimum detectable input may be assumed to be some fixed fraction of the full-scale input. Thus

$$i_2 = i_{max} = K i_0 \qquad (6B\text{-}20)$$

But, from the general equation for the logarithmic circuit, $i_2 = a \log be_2$. Hence

$$\frac{i_0}{a} = \frac{\log be_2}{K} \qquad (6B\text{-}21)$$

Substituting this last equality into Eq. (6B-19) there results

$$\Delta L'_{IR} = \frac{2 \text{ lgt } be_2}{K} \qquad (6B\text{-}22)$$

When the input-output relations of the circuit, for low input levels, are represented by a straight line tangent to the logarithmic curve, as in Fig. 6B-8, the logarithmic range begins at a point for which $i_1/a = 0.4343$ and $be_1 = 2.718$. The quantity $2 \text{ lgt } be_2$ then exceeds the range of input levels for which the circuit is logarithmic by $2 \text{ lgt } be_1 = 8.7$ db.

Over the range of input levels for which the circuit is logarithmic the apparent incremental response characteristic of the system is a horizontal straight line having the index value given by Eq.(6B-22). For input amplitudes below the lower limit of the logarithmic range, but above the minimum required for a perceptible indication, the system is likely to respond approximately as a linear variable-displacement indicator, starting with an incremental response index of 6 db. Below the minimum perceptible input the incremental response characteristic is the same as for other systems. An incremental response characteristic for a system made up of a logarithmic circuit and a linear variable-displacement instrument is given by curve (D) of Fig. 6B-6. It was assumed, in computing this curve, that the ratio between the full-scale input amplitude and the minimum readable input amplitude was $K = i_{max}/i_0 = 100$. It was also assumed that the logarithmic range of the circuit, as measured at its input, was 40 db, and that its input-output characteristic satisfied the conditions represented by the solid curve of Fig. 6B-8. Over the 40-db logarithmic range the incremental response index is 0.5 db.

It is apparent from the foregoing that the characteristic of a system such as this is ideal except for the linear portion corresponding to low values of input level. The relation of this portion of the characteristic to the total response of the system may be determined as follows. From Eq. (6B-13) we have

$$\frac{i_1}{i_2} = \frac{i_1}{i_{max}} = \frac{\log be_1}{\log be_2} \qquad (6B\text{-}23)$$

This is the fraction of the instrument scale which is taken up by the linear portion of the circuit output. In the characteristic shown in Fig. 6B-9, for which $2 \text{ lgt } be_1 = 8.7$ db and $2 \text{ lgt } be_2 = 48.7$ db, the linear response occupies 18 percent of the total instrument scale and the logarithmic portion 82 percent. The latter portion corresponds to the 40-db change in system input level; the initial 18 percent, being linear with respect to input amplitudes, corresponds to a 25-db change in input level when $i_{max} = 100 \, i_0$. These relations are indicated by the points designated on the curve of Fig. 6B-9

The portion of the incremental response characteristic for which the system response is linear may, in effect, be reduced to a negligible portion of the instrument scale by biasing the instrument. Actually this accomplishes little more than removing this portion of the response characteristic from the observer's field of view. The distribution of the logarithmic portion of the response over an increased scale length does, it is true, decrease somewhat the constant index value of the horizontal portion of the incremental response characteristic. This, however, is already so low that any further improvement in performance is negligible. The gain in incremental response index, then, would seem insufficient to justify discarding a portion of the range of input levels at which observations might be made for no other reason than that it is less effective than the remainder of the range.

The system made up of a logarithmic circuit and a linear variable-displacement instrument has obvious advantages over other systems described because of low value of incremental response index and because this low value is maintained over an extensive range of input levels. It will appear later that the system has a second advantage because of the essentially constant value of its incremental response index which permits its responses to be interpreted in terms of range or other quantities which convey significant information relative to the target or sound source observed.

REFERENCE

1. V. O. KNUDSEN, "Sensibility of the Ear to Small Differences of Intensity and Frequency," *Phys. Rev.*, Second Series, Vol. 21, pp. 84–102, January 1923.

CHAPTER 7

DIRECT LISTENING

Direct listening has already been described as the method used in those applications of sonar where the objective is to obtain information having to do with a primary source of acoustic energy by means of the propagated effects of that energy. The information thus obtained may be restricted to an indication of the presence of a sound source, or, in many applications, extended to include data as to the bearing of this source as well. The discussions of the preceding chapters, which may be said to be concerned with factors fundamental to all applications of sonar, have, naturally, included much that is pertinent to direct listening. It is the purpose of the present chapter to consider the interrelations between these and other factors in terms of the overall performance of direct-listening systems.

Any direct-listening system, of the electro-acoustic type, will consist of one or more hydrophones, a transmission system connecting these hydrophones to an observing station, and one or more indicating or recording instruments. The first step in considering the design or performance of any such system is to determine the restrictions imposed by the locations available for the hydrophones and for the observation point. These restrictions affect both the type of hydrophone which may be used and also the type of transmission system by which it may be connected to the indicating instrument. The location of the hydrophone is also of major significance since it determines the nature and the magnitude of the interference to which the signal is exposed. We shall review the various types of direct-listening systems as classified in terms of the conditions under which they must operate.

7-A ENVIRONMENTAL FACTORS IN DIRECT LISTENING

At first sight it might be concluded that the observational advantage in submarine warfare would be enjoyed by the adversary possessing the most effective sonar equipment. Although it is necessary to have superior equipment it is by no means sufficient. The advantage actually rests with the opponent who makes the least noise; he is the least likely to be heard and, at the same time, the most likely to hear. We have already discussed the significance of signal-to-noise ratio sufficiently to have made it clear that the final limit to the range over which reliable operation of sonar gear may be expected depends not so much on the sensitivity of the apparatus as on the level of the interference which disturbs its operation. The noise conditions at any proposed hydrophone location are consequently of major importance in connection with the design and performance of any direct-listening system. Regardless of the type of system proposed it is essential that every precaution be taken to reduce this interference to the lowest possible level.

In Sec. 2-C the so-called minimum water noise to be found in the sea was discussed in some detail. The results of extensive measurements are summarized, as there reported, by the spectrum level characteristic shown in Fig. 2C-1. This represents, as a statistical average, the lower limit to the interference which may be expected during the operation of any direct-listening system. There are many situations in which the actual interference will be considerably above this limit.

One requirement which must be met if the interference, as it exists in the water, is not to exceed the minimum water noise level is that the listening operation shall be carried out in deep water far from shore. It is further necessary that the hydrophone be submerged to at least 20 ft below the surface, that it be motionless in the water, and that there shall be, in its immediate vicinity, no ships or other bodies floating on the surface and no submerged machinery or other primary sources of sound. Obviously it is impossible to realize all of these conditions. They may, however, be approached to a surprisingly close approximation in several situations of tactical significance. These specifications are of most use, perhaps, as a reference base in terms of which to study the sources of interference in various important applications of direct listening.

For our present purposes listening systems may be divided into three basic types: (1) those in which the hydrophone is carried by a supporting mount which is in direct contact with the hull of some vessel, either submarine or surface, (2) those in which it is carried by an independent buoyant support, and (3) those in which it is carried by a tripod or similar support resting on the bottom.

7A-1 Hull-Mounted Hydrophones

The major source of interference for any hull-mounted hydrophone is likely to be the self noise of the vessel which carries it. In addition to the sounds which the vessel puts into the sea, and which reach the hydrophone in the normal manner as water-borne acoustic energy, this interference includes noises due to mechanical vibrations which reach the hydrophone through its supports. Disturbances due to directly transmitted mechanical vibrations may be kept to a low level by the use of vibration-absorbing members in the hydrophone supports. Similar mounts for any machine likely to cause vibrations are also helpful since they reduce the vibration of the hull and hence the sound reaching the hydrophone through the water. This question of machinery noise, although of the utmost importance to the performance of sonar equipment, is a highly specialized branch of engineering which is outside the scope of our present study.

It must be noted at this point that data as to the index level of the sound output of a given vessel tells little about the level of the self-noise interference effective at a hydrophone carried by that vessel. The index level is, in effect, based on observations made at such distances that all components of the total sound output may be considered as originating at a single point. For a receiving point on or near the hull the sources of these components are, relatively, widely distributed in both direction and distance. Intense sounds due to the propeller, for example, may be at some distance from the hydrophone and may be screened by the hull. It may be possible to discriminate against such sources by directional hydrophones. The level of self-noise interference depends on so many factors that it is impractical to assign quantitative values which would be representative of any actual condition. For a given ship and a given hydrophone position, however, the spectrum level characteristic can be measured with little difficulty. The characteristic applying to any permanent installation should, in fact, be determined with some care as a guide to its operational use. This data should be taken as a function of speed and of bearing as well as a function of frequency. Sea state and wind direction, relative to the ship's course, are also pertinent factors in the majority of cases.

For any hydrophone mounted on a vessel under way the motion of the hydrophone through the water may often be the cause of limiting interference. This is certain to be true if the unit is in direct contact with the water and if the speed is sufficient to cause cavitation. The formation and collapse of voids in direct contact with the active surface of the hydrophone, under these conditions, may easily destroy all possibility of useful performance. Fortunately, this type of interference may be somewhat reduced by enclosing the hydrophone in a protective housing, known as a **dome,** which offers little obstruction to the passage of sound waves. Such housings are usually streamlined and are so vented as to be free-flooding. Because of their size and shape the critical speed at which cavitation begins is appreciably higher than for the smaller unprotected hydrophone. When cavitation does occur its increased separation from the hydrophone greatly reduces the level of the resulting noise.

The impact of water against the hull is another powerful source of self-noise interference. This is always serious for any hydrophone carried by a surface vessel. It is likely to be troublesome even when the vessel is lying to, and is usually a limiting factor for a vessel under way. It invariably increases with increasing speed, the intensity generally increasing as some power of the speed. Any attempt at search operations must take careful account of this factor. The **search rate** at which a given area may be covered is given by the product of the range of reliable detection and of the speed. Since this type of interference decreases the range as the speed is increased the optimum speed depends upon the quantitative relation between the two. This relation must be determined for any given installation. Because of this type of interference a moving surface vessel is generally considered to be the worst possible support for a listening hydrophone.

Interference due to wave slap is almost wholly absent for a hydrophone carried by a submerged submarine. For this reason, and because other forms of interference are also low, a submarine provides almost the ideal listening platform. This is true, however, only if machinery and other noises, such as dropped tools and slammed hatches, are reduced to the absolute minimum.

7A-2 Cable-Connected Buoys

One method of reducing some of the more serious components of the interference to which a hydrophone mounted near the hull of a surface vessel is subjected is to support the hydrophone by a buoy at some distance from the vessel. Transmission between the hydrophone and the listening station on the ship may be effected by electric conductors in a cable connecting the two. The use of a cable-connected buoyed hydrophone is usually restricted to operations from a ship which is not under way. It permits a very considerable reduction in all forms of interference classed as own-ship's noise. It will be recalled that the increase in transmission loss due to an increase in separation between source and receiver depends on the ratio of the initial and final separations rather than on the absolute value of either. Consequently, since a hull-mounted hydrophone must be in close proximity to sources of interfering noise, significant reductions may be brought about by only moderate increases in the absolute separation between the vessel and the hydrophone. At separations of something like 200 to 300 yd interference due to surface noise becomes comparable with interference due to the mother ship and further increases in separation usually accomplish little additional reduction in interference level.

In using a buoyed hydrophone precautions must be taken to insure that the rigging used is not itself a source of interfering noise. It must be arranged so that wave motion at the surface causes negligible vertical displacement of the hydrophone. Such motion may be reduced if the hydrophone is supported by a buoy submerged to some distance beneath the surface at a point determined by a weighted sinker which, in turn, is supported by a second float at the surface. The positive buoyancy of the submerged float is only slightly less than the negative buoyancy of the weighted sinker. This gives the combination a very slight negative buoyancy as a result of which it is slow to take up any slack in the length of cable between the surface float and the sinker. Vertical motion at the hydrophone is, therefore, in general, much less than the vertical motion of the surface float. It has been found that both surface noise and tendency to vertical motion are reduced if, instead of a single unit having excess positive buoyancy, the surface float is made up of a series of small floats strung along the conducting cable. This avoids a large area projecting above the surface where it is exposed to impact by moving water masses.

Any horizontal motion of a buoy-supported hydrophone relative to the water may cause serious disturbances. These may be disastrous should the motion be sufficient to set the supporting cable into vibration. Such motion may occur if the mother ship is anchored in water where there are tidal or other currents, or if it is lying to in water through which it is moved by wind pressure on its superstructure.

Because of the restriction that the vessel to which a buoyed hydrophone is connected shall be lying to, this type of support is not widely used. It is, however, sometimes required for the measurement of ambient noise or for similar quantitative investigations.

Hydrophones mounted in this fashion are frequently nondirectional, although for some problems it may be desirable, and possible, to use a line hydrophone, or an equivalent system, as a means of restricting the major response to a horizontal plane. This has a tendency to reduce the response to noise from the surface directly above the hydrophone or to sound energy reaching the hydrophone by nearby surface reflections. The advantages of this scheme are, unfortunately, not great and the method is not of particular significance.

7A-3 Towed Hydrophones

Various attempts have been made to reduce self-noise interference when listening under way by towing a cable-connected hydrophone astern. It has been the usual experience that the signal-to-noise advantage of a hydrophone towed by a surface vessel, as compared with a hull-mounted hydrophone on the same vessel, is not as great as that of a buoy-supported hydrophone connected by cable to a vessel at rest, as compared to a hull-mounted hydrophone on the same vessel. Any towed hydrophone will almost certainly be subject to the turbulence of the ship's wake. This is a source of troublesome self noise and may at the same time act as a partial screen against the signal to be observed.

7A-4 Radio-Sonic Buoys

A radio link between a buoy-supported hydrophone and the vessel from which listening operations are carried out avoids certain of the difficulties associated with the electrically conducting cable. Since the hydrophone and its buoy need not be physically connected to the mother ship, the hydrophone may, with a properly designed buoy, be nearly motionless in the water. The separation between ship and hydrophone may also be increased to considerable distances with little difficulty, particularly if the hydrophone and buoy are of an expendable type which need not be recovered. Hydrophones carried by a radio-sonic buoy may be left in the water in the vicinity of a suspected submerged submarine, where they remain, almost motionless, while the listening vessel proceeds at full speed at such a distance that its self noise causes negligible interference. Listening conditions with an expendable radio-sonic buoy may approach very nearly to the ideal possible in any given location. Because of the great flexibility of its connection to the listening station the radio-sonic buoy may be used from aircraft as well as from surface craft. In fact, the increased elevation of an aerial listening station permits operation over long and rapidly-varying separations.

7A-5 Fixed Hydrophone Installations

Hydrophones for use in connection with shore listening posts may be supported on tripods resting on the bottom and connected to the listening station by submarine cables. Transmission in such installations may be over cables several miles in length, and often calls for the use of equalizers to correct for variations in transmission loss with frequency. Bottom-mounted hydrophones are generally used in water of only moderate depth. In such situations the ambient noise rarely drops to as low a level as the minimum water noise found in the deeper water far from shore. It often includes ship traffic noise or industrial noise originating at nearby shore locations. In addition to these man made disturbances the actual water noise is likely to be considerably above that encountered in the open sea. In some locations where gravelly bottoms are subject to the action of tidal currents the installation of tripod-mounted hydrophones may be quite impractical.

The requirements for fixed hydrophone installation may sometimes be better met by the use of anchored radio-sonic buoys than by the use of cable connections. In general, however, the chief differences between these two types of transmission link have to do with mechanical convenience rather than with any marked difference in acoustic performance.

Directional hydrophones may be mounted on tripods and may be trained by remote control from the distant listening station, either by the mechanical rotation of a directional system or by the adjustment of an electrically steered multispot array.

7-B BASIC DIRECT-LISTENING METHODS

For each of the situations discussed in the preceding section there is inevitably some lower limit to the interference which is fixed by the characteristics of the vessel or other location from which the listening operation is to be conducted. These are factors over which the sonar engineer has no control but which he must take carefully into account. It is possible, however, by judicious design and operation of the system, to provide some measure of discrimination between the signal and the interference, provided there are any characteristic differences between them. Such differences may appear in the frequency distribution or in the directional distribution of the sonic energy, or in the time variation of the intensity level. Much of the discussion of the following articles will be directed toward an examination of the various expedients for improving the signal-to-noise ratio by treatment during the receiving process. This brings us to a consideration of the various methods by which the direct-listening operation may be carried out.

7B-1 Nondirectional Listening

When the equipment used for direct listening has no directional discrimination, either because conditions under which the apparatus must be operated preclude the use of directional hydrophones, or because of the tactical necessity for being able to receive signals from any direction at all times, the chief method of effecting discrimination against the interference is through the choice of the frequency band over which the apparatus is responsive. The possibility of obtaining a high signal-to-noise ratio through selection of a suitable frequency-response characteristic for the receiving system has been noted in connection with the study of spectrum levels of ship sounds and of water noises. The article on recognition differential (Art. 6B-2) has pointed out that an effective signal-to-noise advantage may also be realized because of the ability of the listener to discriminate, on the basis of quality differences, between the signal response and the noise response. As a matter of fact, the marginal value of signal differential, which depends on those qualities of a signal-noise combination which are measured by its recognition differential, and the actual value, which depends on the spectrum level characteristics of the signal and of the noise, are both functions of the receiving characteristic of the receiving system.

One of the early investigations of World War II was an empirical determination of the relation between the frequency-response characteristic of the listening system and the detectability of a faint signal against interfering noise. The evaluation was effected by comparing the ranges at which sounds due to various types of ship could be identified, through representative background noise, by observers listening on high-quality headphones. It was noted that each listener showed an initial tendency to prefer systems responsive over the lower portion of the frequency spectrum, that is, to frequencies in the range below about 3000 cyc/sec. This appeared to result from preconceived ideas of naturalness. It was interpreted to indicate that the sounds as heard agreed with those which the listener expected to hear as a result of his previous experience with air-borne sounds associated with the movement of objects in water. It was soon realized, however, that fidelity, as understood in connection with the high-quality reproduction of sounds by radio or by phonographs, means little with respect to the detection of underwater signals. Actually, listeners have no past experience with such sounds and hence are free to select those systems which are the most advantageous as measured solely by their ability to assist in the detection of faint signals. Once this was recognized it became immediately evident that audio components having frequencies well above 3000 cyc/sec were of considerable value. In fact, systems responsive to frequencies as high as 10,000 cyc/sec appeared more likely to lead to detection, in some cases, than systems incapable of responding to those frequencies. This increase in detectability accompanying an extension of the frequency range upward appears not to be associated with an increase in naturalness—or fidelity—because there are found to be many circumstances under which it is advantageous to exclude wave components having frequencies at the lower end of the audible range.

In interpreting the results of these tests it must be kept in mind that the quality of the signal, and the ability of the ear to recognize the signal because of this quality, is only one of the factors fixing the optimum frequency range. The other is the relation between the frequencies of the wave components selected and the actual value of the signal-to-noise ratio. From our knowledge of the spectrum level characteristics of signals and of noises it appears likely that the maximum value of the signal differential, for a given signal-noise combination at the hydrophone, would be found to exist for a narrow band of frequencies if not, indeed, for a single point on the frequency scale. We are not, however, interested simply in obtaining the highest possible value of signal differential but in establishing those conditions under which the signal reaching the hydrophone may be detected with the greatest margin of acceptability. If the receiving response of some system is restricted to that portion of the frequency scale for which the actual signal differential has a maximum value the marginal value may be increased considerably, due to a low value of recognition differential. The optimum choice of frequency band is that for which the marginal value of signal differential has the lowest possible value. Such a condition permits the greatest reduction in signal level before reaching the limit of detectability and hence gives the maximum range at which dependable signals may be received from the source in question.

No attempt was made in the tests just mentioned to observe the effect of the frequency characteristic of the system on either the actual or the acceptable values of signal differential. In fact these quantities had not, at that time, been formulated nor was there available any comprehensive data as to the spectrum level characteristics of either signals or noise. The tests do, however, have the undeniable merit of having given the information required in terms of the end result. In the light of subsequent data it appears likely that at the range beyond which it was no longer possible to detect a receding vessel the marginal signal differential was somewhere in the neighborhood of -12 db. Later observations indicate that whenever the signal is marked by any pronounced characteristic, or quality, a recognition differential of from -10 to -15 db may be expected.

It may be recalled that reports on underwater sounds indicate that the spectrum level of ship sounds falls off at the rate of 2 db/fl with increasing frequency and that water noise falls off at the rate of only 5/3 db/fl. This appears to be at variance with the conclusions of these tests that the most advantageous listening band, at least for nondirectional listening, extends to the upper end of the audio spectrum and may exclude a considerable portion of the lower end. On the basis of the values given above for the spectrum levels the signal differential should decrease with increasing frequency. As a matter of fact, it should decrease even more than would correspond to the 1/3 db/fl difference between the slopes of the two spectrum level characteristics since, at long ranges, the signal suffers an added loss at the higher frequencies due to increased attenuation. It must be remembered, however, that the interference during these tests was not limited to water noise alone. There were, as always in shallow water, many other sources of interference. These are almost invariably characterized by a predominance of low-frequency energy. In spite of all precautions the proximity of the vessel carrying the listening equipment is certain to introduce disturbing interference which has a large part of its energy at the lower end of the audible spectrum. The spectrum level characteristic of the actual interference, then, is almost certain to have a greater slope than the $-5/3$ db/fl shown by the curves for water noise as given by Fig. 2C-1. It may, in fact, approach the -3 db/fl shown for the noise level of a vessel at low speed.

7B-2 Directional Listening

Directional listening systems have two obvious advantages over nondirectional systems; they permit the bearing of the signal source to be determined and they offer a possibility of discriminating against sources of interference other than those on bearings close to that of the signal source. In addition, they permit the signal differential of the signal-interference combination to be increased materially over that applying to a nondirectional system. Attention has already been called (Art. 6B-2) to the greater difficulty of detecting a signal which increases slowly and continuously from a level well below the background as compared with that of detecting a signal which stops or starts abruptly. With a trainable directional listening system the observer is able to exclude or to receive the signal at will and to change from one condition to the other with sufficient abruptness to increase materially the perceptibility of any small increment of the total response which may be due to the signal. Usually the change in transducer bearing will not be sufficient to cause any concurrent change in the level of interfering noise which might be confused with the change due to the signal. In fact, any abrupt change in total noise with bearing is evidence of the existence of a localized source of acoustic energy which, in the situation here under consideration, is by definition a signal source.

This phase of the problem presents two aspects which are of quantitative significance; the first has to do with the time during which the sound source is within the directional beam of the transducer; the other is the manner in which the signal changes in character during this interval. The ideal situation would be one in which the receiving system shows a constant and uniform response to all components of the signal whenever the source is within the boundaries of the directional beam. Unfortunately neither of these conditions is realized in practice; the response to any one component of the signal is not constant but increases gradually as the source moves toward the major axis of the beam; neither are these increases uniform since the relation between response and bearing deviation varies with the frequency of the component. The net result of these effects is to reduce the apparent abruptness with which the response to a signal begins or ends as the source passes into or out of the beam. There is evidence to show that, if the ideal case described above could be realized in practice, the improvement in signal differential would be a function of the time required for the directional beam to sweep across the source. The improvement would, moreover, show a maximum value for some definite duration of the signal response. If the transit time were less than the optimum value the duration of the response would be too short to permit the detection of weak signals which might otherwise be perceptible; if the transit time were longer than this the rate of increase of the response, as the source entered the beam, would be reduced, again decreasing the detectability of a faint signal. For the ideal case it would appear to be a simple matter to establish once and for all the optimum rate at which to train the transducer. In practice, however, the deviations from this ideal condition are so varied that available data do not permit reliable predictions of the optimum scanning rate.

We are obviously concerned here with subjective psychoacoustic effects. Actually, in the case of many listeners, the ear appears not to recognize the response of a broad-band directional system, when trained across a localized sound source, as a gradual inclusion of components of increasing frequency. Instead it has a tendency to separate these components into two groups; the low-frequency group is heard over a wide arc as though the response of the system could be represented by a single broad directivity pattern applying to this group as a whole; the high-frequency group is heard over a much narrower arc as though there were a separate and distinct directivity pattern for this second group. As a matter of fact, this phenomenon is not without practical advantage. Detection frequently results from responses to the lower group of frequencies; for this purpose a broad directivity band is advantageous. The determination of bearing by observing the setting for maximum response is carried out on the basis of response to the high-frequency group; here the apparent existence of a narrow beam pattern improves the accuracy of setting.

Tests made with line hydrophones, so mounted that an axis of major response could be swept in a horizontal plane across a broad-band sound source, have led to the following conclusions. When listening to a broad band of **sonic** frequencies, extending down to approxi**mately** 300 cyc/sec, the beam width of a 3-ft line hydrophone, at these low frequencies, is so great that it cannot be swept across the target in a sufficiently brief interval to accomplish noticeable improvement in recognition differential. Under similar circumstances improvements of approximately 2 db in recognition differential have been observed as a 4-ft line hydrophone is trained at a rate of 20 to 25 deg/sec. The narrower beam pattern of the 5-ft line hydrophone permits the same results to be obtained at training speeds of from 15 to 20 deg/sec. These data were obtained with sounds from a ship having a fairly well defined propeller rhythm. It appears probable that the improvement in recognition differential would have been greater had there not already been a distinguishable difference between signal and interference. In fact, in the case of attempts to detect approaching torpedoes by listening in a narrow band of ultrasonic frequencies the improvement in recognition differential due to sweeping the target with a directional beam has, on occasion, been as much as 10 to 15 db. Here there is no characteristic by which the signal may be distinguished from the background other than the change in level accompanying the transit of the directional beam.

In order to realize the greatest possible advantage from the ability of the ear to detect a small incremental change in total level it is necessary that the listener be in a position to decide whether some observed change is identified with a definite bearing or whether it is merely one of the ever present random variations in average level. We have already considered (Art. 6B-2) the difference between an abrupt incremental change in level occurring in a signal which is otherwise of constant level and an incremental change which is conspicuously greater than normally expected variations in total level. With a trainable directional listening system it becomes possible to reduce the recognition differential somewhat below the value which would be found if identification were based solely on relative magnitudes (Fig. 6B-1). If the listener has direct control of the orientation of the transducer he may cross and recross any bearing at which some small increase in total level is observed and listen for a recurrence. By swinging back and forth he may, in fact, introduce a rhythmic variation in level, in phase with the motion of the transducer, whenever there is a definitely localized source. Since normal variations in level are not definitely associated with bearing there will be no correspondence between transducer motion and signal level unless there is a localized source.

To apply this technique it is essential that the listener be able to associate what he hears with the motion which he imparts to the training control. This may be done most easily if there is a one-to-one correspondence between the angular motion of the training control and the angular motion of the transducer. If it is necessary to employ a remotely controlled power drive it will be found that a system in which the transducer follows the motion of the manually operated control is to be preferred to one in which a slewing control turns on or off a continuous rotation of the transducer, at fixed speed, in either direction. It is obvious that whenever a follow-up system is used there must be as little deviation as possible between the displacements of the manual control and the transducer.

This is, of course, an example of directional coherence, which was mentioned in Chapter 6. The advantage to be gained by proper attention to this effect is by no means trivial. It is more than sufficient to justify the most careful attention to the design of any training mechanism forming part of a direct-listening system.

It must be noted that the ear may be assisted most effectively by the eye in its search for an obscure signal. One method of providing a visual presentation of the signals received during direct listening is to arrange a cathode ray oscilloscope to be operated in conjunction with a continuously rotating transducer. As the directive beam sweeps the horizon the luminous spot travels along a circular path near the outer circumference of the screen, the angular position of the spot corresponding, at any instant, to the bearing of the transducer axis. The response of the transducer is indicated visually by a radial deflection of the spot toward the center of the screen. Such an arrangement makes it possible to utilize the high incremental response index typical of variable-displacement presentations, and aids in the comparison of incremental changes due to signals with those due to random variations. Experience with this system has demonstrated that by combining the discrimination of the ear and that of the eye an observer is able to identify a faint signal at a much lower value of signal differential than would be possible by either alone.

7B-3 Binaural Listening

The sensation, due to differences between the sounds received by the two ears, which indicates to a listener the direction of a sound source, is known as the **binaural effect.** This has been shown to be due, in part, to the phase difference between components of like frequency caused by the difference in length of the paths from the source to the ears. This is probably the major factor with components in the lower portion of the band of audible frequencies. For components in the upper portion of this band there is considerable evidence to indicate that amplitude differences play an important part. For a source which is not directly in front of, or behind, the listener the head acts as a partial screen for one ear and thus reduces the intensity of the signals which it receives. This screening is more pronounced the shorter the wave length and hence is more effective at the upper portion of the audible spectrum. Our ability to judge the direction of some source of air-borne sound is based on our unconscious recognition of the phase and amplitude differences. It is obvious that our judgments are based on quantitative relations which involve the wave lengths of sounds in air, the separation between our ears, and the acoustic properties of our heads. These relations must, in some way, be preserved if we are to employ this same subjective sense for the observation of underwater sounds.

Direct listening to underwater sounds may be carried out binaurally by using two independent receiving systems, one for each of the listener's ears. This requires two submerged receiving units, either acoustic or electroacoustic, two independent transmission systems, and two ear-pieces. The simplest form of binaural system, for underwater use, consists of two metallic tubes leading to submerged hollow rubber spheres about the size of tennis balls. The inboard ends of these tubes are connected to the ears of the listener by flexible rubber tubes and ear-pieces of the type used by physicians in their stethoscopes. Since the wave length of sound, at a given frequency, is over four times as great in water as in air it appears logical to separate the submerged receiving points by about four times the normal separation between the listener's ears. Experience has indicated, however, that it is possible to enhance the binaural effect by increasing this separation somewhat and thus increasing the amount of phase shift accompanying some given angular deviation of the source from the axis of symmetry of the system. A horizontal distance of between four and five feet gives very satisfactory results.

If the dual receiving system is maintained in a fixed position the listener is aware of a sensation of direction in listening to sounds from some definitely localized source. This sensation appears to differ considerably with the individual. In many cases the sensation is such as would be caused by a source located in close proximity to the head, if not actually in contact with it. When the source is on the perpendicular to the line joining the two submerged receivers one observer may feel that the sound comes from a point near the middle of his forehead; another may place it at the back of his head. There is seldom any inclination to imagine the apparent source at any appreciable distance.

A fixed binaural system has little advantage over a monaural listening system. Although there is a sense of direction it is by no means sufficiently well defined to permit reliable estimates of source bearing. There is, however, some advantage with respect to the ability to recognize a localized source as existing separately from the diffuse sources responsible for the general background noise. The binaural system, in other words, has a greater recognition differential than the monaural system. This aid to discrimination is, perhaps, not entirely independent of such qualities as tone or rhythm but certainly increases the ability of the listener to detect the presence of a discrete source.

The effectiveness of a binaural listening system is greatly increased if it is arranged so that the operator may change the direction of the axis of symmetry. This may be done in a number of ways. In either an acoustic or an electroacoustic system the two submerged receiving points may be

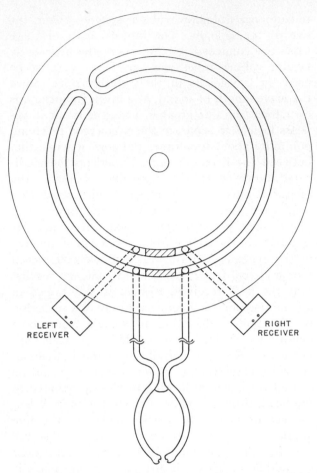

FIG. 7B-1. BINAURAL COMPENSATOR. Arrangement of adjustable-length air paths for altering the phase of sounds from a common source brought separately to the two ears of an observer.

trained mechanically about a vertical axis. In an acoustic system the lengths of the tubes leading to the ears may be adjusted so as to introduce phase delays in the air paths which compensate for differences in the water paths and thus acoustically steer the axis of symmetry to some desired bearing. In an electroacoustic system the same effect can be achieved by means of electric delay networks. By adjusting the system so that the total travel times from a given source to the ears are equal it is possible to determine the bearing of the source with considerable accuracy and also to increase the ability of the observer to detect the presence of a weak signal. The determination of bearing is made simply by adjusting the system until the apparent position of the sound source is that associated by the listener with a source for which there are no unequal delays. This index condition is established by connecting both earpieces, through identical paths, to a common

pickup unit. Actually it is necessary for most listeners to relocate their individual zero index points at frequent intervals during the determination of a single bearing. The improvement in recognition differential characteristic of a trainable binaural system is associated with the effect, familiar to everyone, which makes moving objects more conspicuous than motionless objects.

Binaural systems were used extensively during World War I. They were largely displaced by other forms of directive system during World War II. This appears to have been due largely to the distrust of subjective psychoacoustic phenomena as compared with precise objective measurements. It is certainly true that any application of the binaural effect involves an extensive training program. It is, nevertheless, a fact that the binaural effect makes it possible to utilize this same subjective psychoacoustic phenomena to supplement more objective effects and thus to extend by a worthwhile increment any limiting value of recognition differential set by purely objective methods. The question is not, in other words, one of competition between objective and subjective observations but one of combining the two to attain a result achievable by neither alone. Because of the possibilities in this direction it is felt that it is justified to examine the characteristics of binaural systems in some further detail.

The system used during World War I combined variable acoustic delays with electroacoustic reception. The general arrangement of this system is shown in Fig. 7B-1. The hydrophones were of a carbon microphone type having high sensitivity, but also high circuit noise; they required a simple polarizing-current supply circuit but no amplification. The headphones were connected to the listener's ears through acoustic paths the lengths of which were adjustable by means of an instrument known as a **binaural compensator.** The moving element of this is a circular plate in which are cut two ducts, concentric with the axis of rotation of the plate, and covering arcs of somewhat more than half a circumference. These ducts are joined at both ends of the arc to form a single endless duct. The moving plate rests on a fixed plate carrying two plugs which block each of the circular portions of the duct. As one plate is rotated with respect to the other the total length of duct on one side of the plugs increases while that on the other decreases. These ducts form parts of the acoustic paths between headphones and ears and hence permit the lengths of these paths to be altered at will. For any source not equidistant from the two hydrophones the difference in path length in the compensator may be made equivalent in magnitude and opposite in sign, as measured by signal delay time, to the difference in length of the water paths. Under this condition the source will appear to be at the listener's characteristic index point. The amount of compensation required to bring the apparent source to this position is thus a measure of the actual bearing of the source as measured by its deviation from the axis of symmetry of the system.

There is always an ambiguity in reading the bearing angle of a source when using a single compensated pair of binaural hydrophones. This is because there are always two bearings for which the differences in path length are equal. The compensator scale is marked to read both of the bearings corresponding to any given adjustment. If readings are taken on two or more hydrophone pairs, using a compensator calibrated to indicate bearing relative to some common reference bearing, the correct bearing is given by that scale reading which is repeated. The reason for this will be clear from the diagram of Fig. 7B-2; this shows the correct bearing by solid arrows and the false bearings by dotted arrows. This situation does not arise when listening on a single binaural pair which is trained mechanically. The correct bearing here is given by that side of the dual scale for which the change in scale reading is consistent with the apparent motion of the binaural image as the system is trained through the index position.

Although the binaural effect permits the recognition differential of a given signal-noise combination to be improved it does not, of itself, result in any real discrimination against interfering noise. The only discrimination is that due to the ability of the listener to concentrate his attention on a signal having apparent directionality and thus to be less distracted by noise having none. This somewhat intangible discrimination may be combined with the more definite discrimination obtainable with directional hydrophones. This is accomplished simply by substituting directional hydrophones, or hydrophone systems, for the nondirectional receiving pairs. Applications which have been made of this principle have used either a pair of long multispot arrays, or a pair of line hydrophones, for the two binaural elements. In such systems the separation of the effective

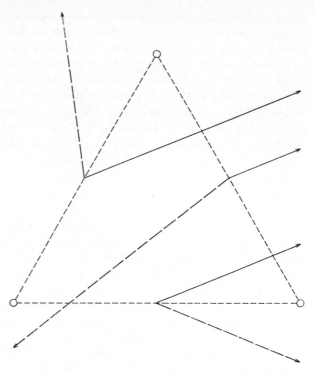

FIG. 7B-2. BINAURAL ARRAY. In a triangular array of hydrophones each pair, when used binaurally, gives one true and one false bearing. The true bearing is that which is the same for all pairs.

centers of the binaural receiving pair is generally increased considerably beyond the distance corresponding to normal separation of the ears. It is often that distance which results when the two hydrophone systems are placed end-to-end, in which case it is the distance between effective centers and is approximately the length of either system. The directivity of the hydrophone systems improves the signal-to-noise ratio, in the usual manner, by discriminating against noise sources on bearings which deviate from the major response axis. This improvement is independent of and in addition to any advantage which may result from the binaural effect. The two therefore combine to give a greater improvement in recognition differential than would be obtained with either alone. In the same manner the fact that the signal intensity passes through a maximum, due to hydrophone directivity, at the instant when it reaches the characteristic index point of the listener tends to increase the bearing accuracy obtainable. In one system in which each of the binaural receivers was a multispot array some 25 ft long the bearing accuracy of a single reading was approximately 0.2 degrees.

In the systems thus far described the binaural

effect has been due to phase alone. Any variations in amplitude as functions of direction have appeared equally in the two receiving systems and have contributed nothing to the binaural effect. It is possible to introduce amplitude variations in such manner that they simulate the screening action of the head, as it occurs in normal listening to air-borne sounds, and thus to duplicate more nearly the conditions responsible for the binaural effect to which we are normally accustomed. This is accomplished by the simple expedient of setting the two directional elements, forming the binaural pair, at a slight angle so that their major response axes are no longer parallel. The response of the element which is nearer the source may thus be made greater at the same time that the delay time between it and the source is made less. By proper choice of angle, for a given directivity pattern, the relative amplitude and the relative phase may be made to show concurrent variations which bear the same relation to each other as those determined by the screening of the head and by the separation of the ears as we listen normally in air.

The validity of this reasoning has been con-

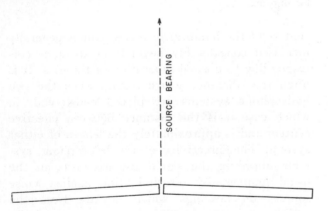

FIG. 7B-3. BINAURAL SYSTEM. An arrangement of directional hydrophones in which variations in both phase and amplitude are employed simultaneously to give an enhanced binaural effect over a wide range of sonic frequencies.

firmed by experiment. Using two 3-foot line hydrophones, end-to-end, it has been found that the binaural effect is more pronounced if their axes make an angle of about 5 degrees, as they lie in a horizontal plane, than if they are parallel. It is obvious that the correct relations between phase variations and amplitude variations are obtained only for a source on the side of the assembly for which the major response axes do

not cross. The proper position is shown in the diagram of Fig. 7B-3. If the source is on the opposite side of the assembly the variations in amplitude, as the system is rotated, will be of opposite sign from those which should accompany the variations in phase. The fact that each of these variations contributes to the binaural effect is strikingly evidenced by the existence, under these conditions, of two binaural images, one moving in one direction and one in the other. The predominance of the phase effect at low frequencies and of the amplitude effect at higher frequencies is also demonstrated by the fact that the image which moves in the correct direction, as determined by the actual bearing of the source and by the direction of rotation of the array, appears to be of lower frequency than the image which moves in the wrong direction.

In systems in which directional hydrophones, or hydrophone systems, are connected to form a binaural pair there are three distinct effects which contribute to the recognition differential. One is the actual, objective, discrimination against interference sources on bearings other than that of the sound source. This may be evaluated quantitatively by the directivity index of the hydrophones. One is due to any quality difference, such as rhythm or tone, which may exist between the signal and the interference. One is the impression of direction, due to the binaural effect, which permits the listener to direct his attention to the signal and to disregard, to some extent, the interference which appears to come from other directions. This effect may be enhanced by imparting an apparent motion to the binaural image due to the signal. These last two effects are subjective and are not as easily measured as is the objective directional discrimination. There is almost no reliable data as to the improvement in recognition differential which may be credited to the binaural effect. There is, however, some evidence to indicate that it may be comparable with the improvement due to pronounced quality differences.

7B-4 Ultrasonic Listening

Under normal circumstances, direct-listening operations are most effective when using receiving equipment responsive over some band of frequencies lying within the sonic region. There are, however, occasions when it may be desirable to employ frequency bands in the ultrasonic region. One example of this is found in certain torpedo-detection systems. Because of the high source level of the signal in the ultrasonic region, and because of the much greater directivity index of the transducer in this region, the signal-to-noise ratio may be actually higher than at lower frequencies. Since it is, in many cases, unnecessary to detect an approaching torpedo at long ranges, the high attenuation coefficient corresponding to these frequencies does not impair this signal differential appreciably.

The example just cited represents a case in which the optimum listening band, as determined by the maximum value of actual signal differential, is wholly outside the band associated with normal hearing. In other situations the optimum band may be partially within the audible range but may fail to be at the most suitable location as determined by the ability of the ear to identify the signal. In both of these situations, therefore, it is necessary to translate the signal received by the hydrophone to a position on the frequency scale where it may most easily be detected by the ear. This may be accomplished by means of a simple heterodyne receiver in which the electric output of the hydrophone is modulated by a locally generated carrier of suitable frequency. The desired signal is then obtained by selecting an appropriate sideband from the output of the modulating system. Such heterodyne converters are similar in principle to those familiar to all communication engineers. Their only unusual feature is that in some cases the input and output signal bands may overlap. This requires that balanced modulators be used for suppressing the input signal, thereby preventing its appearance in the output circuit. Since the carrier frequency may also fall in the audible range it, too, is generally suppressed by the use of balanced circuits.

One effect of translating the components of a signal to a lower position on the frequency scale is to alter its spectrum level characteristic. For example, the band between 20 and 25 kc/sec represents about one frequency logit in its normal position. If this band is translated by replacing each component by one having a frequency 19.5 kc/sec lower it will occupy the portion of the spectrum between 0.5 and 5.5 kc/sec; this represents approximately 10 fl. If the original spectrum level characteristic has a slope of −2 db/fl the total change in level will be 2 db. Assuming the signal to be translated by a linear system the total change in level of the derived signal will be

this same amount. In its new position, the spectrum level characteristic will not be a straight line if plotted against the logarithm of the frequency. The curves of Fig. 7B-4 show the spectrum level characteristic of the original and the derived signals for the conditions assumed above.

It is obvious that any change in the slope of the spectrum level characteristic accompanying translation on the frequency scale applies to the interference as well as to the signal. Any signal differentials computed on the basis of spectrum level

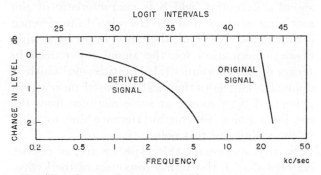

FIG. 7B-4. SIGNAL TRANSLATION. The spectrum-level characteristics of a direct-listening signal normally occupying a band of ultrasonic frequencies before and after translation, by heterodyning, to a band of equal absolute width in the sonic region.

characteristics applying to any given frequency band are, therefore, unaltered as a result of frequency translations.

7-C THE SONAR EQUATION FOR DIRECT LISTENING

Any attempt to arrive at a quantitative estimate of the performance of a direct-listening system is confronted by certain obstacles. The factors which influence this performance and the manner in which they affect it may be described with some assurance; unfortunately the magnitudes of some of these factors, particularly those which are under the control of an enemy, can seldom be ascertained. Complete quantitative solutions are therefore rarely possible. An examination of the functional relation between the several pertinent factors will, however, serve to indicate the general direction in which to look for optimum performance. Although it would be of great advantage to know exactly how good—or how bad—this performance is likely to be we shall often have to content ourselves with deriving as much information as possible from such data as may be available. The methods described in this section are intended to serve as guides in this endeavor.

7C-1 The Derivation of the Direct-Listening Equation

The most significant measure of the performance of direct-listening equipment, from the standpoint of its ultimate use, is the range at which a signal source may be detected, or at which reliable observations may be made of its bearing. This range is identified with the marginal value of signal differential, which is characteristic of the receiving system and of the signal-interference combination. We shall, therefore, begin by setting down an equation for the signal differential in terms of the fundamental quantities on which it depends. This equation will be based on a signal generated by a source at some distance from the receiving point and on interference due to noise in the vicinity of this point.

In any analysis of this type we are, of course, concerned with the actual responses of the hydrophone to the signal and to the interference. It will be sufficient, and more convenient, however, if we express these responses in terms of **equivalent plane waves** in the medium. An equivalent plane wave has been described (Art. 2A-9) as a plane wave of such intensity that, approaching a nondirectional hydrophone along a single bearing, it would produce the same response therein as that actually produced.

The actual signal will, in practically all cases, arrive at the hydrophone in the form of plane waves. These will have a level, at the receiving point, which is equal to their index level reduced by the propagation loss of the water path.

The interfering noise is assumed to result from energy arriving from many directions. Many of the sources of this noise may be in close proximity to the hydrophone. It is, therefore, made up of many waves, not all of which are plane. If this interfering energy has uniform directional distribution (Art. 4F-1) its apparent plane wave level is equal to its equivalent plane wave level, as it would be measured by a directional hydrophone, reduced by the directivity index of the actual hydrophone. If the energy is not uniformly distributed (Art. 4F-2) the level of the actual interference must be reduced by the effective directivity index.

The two levels here in question may be either spectrum levels or band levels. In the first case they will apply to a single common frequency; in the second they will usually apply to a single common frequency band. When dealing with band levels the effective directivity index is that quantity which measures the resultant effect of the directional discrimination of the receiving system, determined as described in Art. 4F-2.

The value of the signal differential is, by definition, the difference between the levels of the apparent plane waves representing the signal and the interference. It is, therefore,

$$\Delta L_{s/n} = (L_s - N_w) - (L_n - N_{DI}) \quad (7C\text{-}1)$$

where

$\Delta L_{s/n} =$ the signal differential, being the difference between the levels of the signal and of the interference as they exist in the receiving system (db)

$L_s =$ the index level of the signal, on the bearing of the receiving point (db//1 joule/cm²·cyc, or db//1 watt/cm²)

$L_n =$ the equivalent plane wave level of the interfering noise at the receiving point (db//1 joule/cm²·cyc, or db//1 watt/cm²)

$N_w =$ the propagation loss of the water path between the signal source and the receiving point (db)

$N_{DI} =$ the effective directivity index of the hydrophone system (db)

This equation may be regarded as a list, in symbolic notation, of those factors which determine the value of the signal differential, as this quantity appears in direct listening. It does, however, have all the properties of a true equation. It may be designated as the **direct-listening equation**. It is one of a series of so-called **sonar equations**. Other sonar equations apply to echo-ranging systems and to communication systems.

7C-2 The Figure of Merit of Direct-Listening Systems

As the first step toward evaluating the maximum range at which a direct-listening system may be expected to give acceptable performance we may solve the direct-listening equation for the propagation loss of the water path between the sound source to be observed and the location of the receiving hydrophone. We thus obtain

$$N_w = L_s - L_n + N_{DI} - \Delta L_{s/n} \quad (7C\text{-}2)$$

When the signal differential, $\Delta L_{s/n}$, appearing in this equation has the minimum acceptable value the propagation loss given by the equation is the maximum tolerable loss. This maximum tolerable propagation loss is known as the **figure of merit** of the system. An equation such as this, in which the maximum propagation loss for which a given sonar system will give acceptable performance is expressed as the resultant value of levels, level differentials, and transmission losses associated with that system, will be spoken of as a **figure-of-merit equation.**

We now have two equations for the propagation loss of the water path over which a sonar system may be operated. One is the figure-of-merit equation described above. The other is a propagation loss equation, such as Eq. (3A-19), in which the transmission loss of this water path is expressed as a function of the length of path and of frequency. These two equations may be considered as a simultaneous pair. Their solution, which is effected by eliminating the transmission loss common to both, results in an expression for the maximum range at which acceptable performance may be obtained.

The figure of merit of a given sonar equipment, expressed as a transmission loss measured in decibels, is, in many ways, a more significant measure of the performance capabilities of that system than the actual range at which the performance becomes marginal under some given set of conditions. Unless the propagation loss corresponding to a single observed range is known a knowledge of this range is of little help in estimating the range to be expected under other conditions. If performance were to be evaluated directly, and solely, in terms of range it would be necessary to measure each system under a variety of conditions and to treat the resulting data statistically. If, however, information is available as to the maximum propagation loss under which acceptable performance may be expected it is possible to translate this loss into terms of range by means of statistical data already available. All of the information which has been accumulated regarding the propagation loss of the ocean may, in other words, be used in predicting the performance of any sonar system provided only that a single determination of its figure of merit has been made. In many situations a reliable measurement of figure of merit is more easily made than is even a single determination of operating range.

Such measurements will be discussed more fully later.

The use of the concept of figure of merit provides an ideal means for studying the relative performance capabilities of sonar equipments. It is difficult to observe the operating ranges of two different equipments under identical conditions. It is even more difficult to observe the operating ranges of a single equipment, before and after some modification, under conditions which are sufficiently similar to make any observed change in range a reliable measure of the change in actual performance capability effected by the modification. These difficulties are overcome if performance is expressed in terms of a figure of merit which may be significantly related to range. Accurate comparisons of the relative performance capabilities of equipments tested in widely separated locations, and at widely separated times are easily made by this method.

The figure of merit of a sonar equipment is also of utility to the equipment designer. By considering the resultant value of the terms appearing in the figure-of-merit equation it is possible to evaluate the performance to be expected of some contemplated design in terms of a single quantity. This quantity may, in turn, be expressed as a function of any of several significant design parameters. In this way optimum values for these parameters may be selected.

Two methods are available for computing the operating range corresponding to a given figure of merit. In some cases it is desired to compute the range to be expected under known or postulated environmental conditions. For this purpose the propagation loss equation used must be one which is known to apply under these particular circumstances. For other problems the relation between range and loss given by an accepted nominal propagation loss equation is more useful. Ranges computed by such an equation are representative of those likely to be encountered in many actual situations. They also have the advantage of possessing that stability, essential in a measurement standard, without which a comparative study of various system arrangements would be impossible.

In a similar manner each of the terms appearing in the figure-of-merit equation may sometimes be given specific absolute values. In many cases, however, definite absolute values for these terms are not known. This is certainly true of the index level of the signal when considering the possibility of detecting a sound source of unknown characteristics. It is often equally difficult to assign reliable values to other terms in this equation. Noise interference is often of uncertain magnitude. It also varies greatly with respect to both the frequency distribution and the directional distribution of its energy. Uncertainties as to directional distribution are accompanied by uncertainties as to the value of the effective directivity index. Finally, the allowable value of signal differential depends upon the character of both the signal and the interference and may vary in an unpredictable manner. Fortunately these uncertainties do not prevent the figure-of-merit equation from having considerable utility. As with the propagation loss equation, much may be accomplished by the use of nominal values. As with range, nominal values of signal level, of noise level, of directivity index, and of signal differential are the most suitable for comparing various proposed system arrangements or adjustments.

In actual situations it is sometimes possible to determine the value of a group of terms appearing in the figure-of-merit equation without being able to evaluate each term individually. This is particularly true of the difference, $L_n - N_{DI}$, between the level of the interfering noise and the value of the effective directivity index. As shown by Eq. (4F-25), this difference is the apparent plane wave level of the interference as it would be measured by the directional hydrophone of a given sonar system in a given situation. If this apparent plane wave level is measured in terms of the known response of the given hydrophone to a plane wave signal reaching it along its maximum response axis, full account is taken of the directional distribution of the interference and of the effect of this distribution on the directivity index. In the majority of practical problems knowledge of this apparent plane wave level is of greater significance than knowledge of the noise level and of the directivity index considered individually. Apparent plane wave level may usually be measured directly with little difficulty.

In problems having to do with estimates of the performance of some contemplated system it is generally preferable to use accepted nominal values for the individual terms. For the interference, levels as given by Fig. 2C-1 may be appropriate. For the directivity index, values computed by a formula such as that of Eq. (4F-41)

give a direct indication of the effect of the design constants of the hydrophone.

Another significant grouping of terms is given by the sum of the apparent plane wave level of the interference and the minimum acceptable value of signal differential. When the figure-of-merit equation is solved for this sum there results

$$L_n - N_{DI} + \Delta L_{s/n} = L_s - N_w \qquad (7C-3)$$

The terms on the right represent the index level of the signal reduced by the maximum tolerable propagation loss. The sum on the left is thus seen to be equal to the level of the **minimum acceptable signal.**

A measurement of the level of the minimum acceptable signal provides one of the simplest methods for determining the figure of merit of a given sonar equipment. For this measurement an artificial signal is introduced electrically in the output circuit of the hydrophone. Signals for this purpose may be conveniently generated by a phonographic recording of an appropriate acoustic signal, obtained under conditions which make it possible to exclude interference and to measure the level at the position of the recording hydrophone. Such a signal may be introduced into the hydrophone circuit, at a low level, when the hydrophone is in some specified environment. This may be done so as to simulate, in a realistic manner, the signal from a given target on a given bearing. The level of the signal is then increased slowly until it is detected by an observer. Since the level of the introduced signal may be known a direct measurement of the level of the minimum acceptable signal is obtained. To express this level in terms of acoustic waves reaching the hydrophone position it is necessary, of course, to know the response of the hydrophone.

The signal to be used in such a measurement is obtained under conditions which make it possible to know its true index level. The difference between this known index level and the measured minimum acceptable level is, as may be seen by Eq. (7C-2), the figure of merit of the system applying to the particular noise conditions under which the observation was made. The figure of merit of a sonar system is, indeed, often described as this difference between the index level of the signal to be observed and the minimum level at which an acceptable observation is possible.

Measurements of the minimum acceptable signal level may be used to establish the value of minimum acceptable signal differential for some given equipment corresponding to some given type of sound source and to some given type of interference. It is evident from an inspection of Eq. (7C-3) that a value for minimum acceptable signal differential is obtained by subtracting a measured apparent plane wave level of interference from a simultaneously measured minimum acceptable signal.

7C-3 Relations Between Range and Frequency

In the two simultaneous equations discussed in the preceding article transmission loss and frequency are the common variables. In the propagation loss equation range appears as an independent parameter. In the figure-of-merit equation there are several parameters. For our present purposes we shall assume that the signal level and the noise level vary as logarithmic functions of frequency. At any frequency, therefore, either may be expressed by an equation of the form

$$L = L_0 + n \lgt \frac{f}{f_0} \qquad (7C-4)$$

where L_0 is the level at some reference frequency, f_0, and n is the exponent showing the power of the frequency to which the acoustic intensity, or intensity per unit band, is proportional. If we assume the transducer dimensions to be held constant, as frequency is varied, the directivity index may be expressed by an equation of this same form. We shall also assume that the minimum allowable value of signal differential is either expressed by an equation of this form or, as is often the case, that it is independent of frequency. Under these assumptions the figure-of-merit equation may be written as

$$N_w = (N_w)_0 - \Sigma n \lgt f_0 + \Sigma n \lgt f \qquad (7C-5)$$

The term $(N_w)_0$ appearing here represents the algebraic sum of the values of the signal level, the noise level, the directivity index, and the minimum acceptable signal differential at the reference frequency, f_0. The quantity Σn is the algebraic sum of the corresponding exponents. It is thus evident that the figure of merit is a function of frequency, and that the signal level, the noise level, the directivity index, and the minimum acceptable signal differential at a specified reference frequency may be considered as constant parameters. In the case of the directivity index this is equiv-

alent to making the size of the transducer a parameter.

If we eliminate the propagation loss from this pair of simultaneous equations we are left with an equation of the form

$$2 \lgt S + (Af + Bf^2)S + 60$$
$$= (N_w)_0 - \Sigma n \lgt f_0 + \Sigma n \lgt f \qquad (7C-6)$$

This equation may be solved for the maximum range, considered as a function of frequency, at which the signal differential obtained by the postulated system under the postulated conditions may be expected to have the minimum acceptable value. In this case the quantities making up the term $(N_w)_0$, the quantities f_0 and Σn, and the coefficients appearing in the attenuation loss terms are fixed constants.

Since the relation between range and frequency is here given by a transcendental equation the desired solution will usually be obtained by graphical methods. The process is the familiar one for finding the solution to a pair of simultaneous equations, the two equations in this case being the propagation loss equation and the figure-of-merit equation. Since transmission loss and frequency are the variables common to these two equations the propagation loss given by the propagation loss equation and the figure of merit given by the figure-of-merit equation are each plotted as a function of frequency against a common pair of loss-frequency coordinates. The resulting curves may be described as a **propagation loss characteristic** and a **figure-of-merit characteristic.** The propagation loss characteristic is drawn with some specified value of range as a parameter. The figure-of-merit characteristic might, in a similar manner, be plotted for specified values of signal level, noise level, directivity index, and signal differential as parameters. In many cases, however, absolute values for these individual quantities are not known. For such cases it is necessary, and proper, to assume some value for the resultant figure of merit, applying to a specified reference frequency, and to assume a slope for the figure-of-merit characteristic based on nominal values for the slopes of the characteristics showing the manner in which the individual quantities vary with frequency. These assumptions correspond to assigning values to the quantities $(N_w)_0$ and Σn appearing in Eq. (7C-6). Any intersection of the figure-of-merit characteristic and the propagation loss characteristic gives a pair of loss-frequency values which is a solution to the simultaneous equations in question. The value of frequency given by the abscissa of such a point of intersection, and the value of range corresponding to the parameter of the propagation loss characteristic represent a solution to the equation, Eq. (7C-6), which has been derived by eliminating the transmission loss from this pair of equations.

A series of range-frequency values satisfying a given equation may be obtained by plotting a family of propagation loss characteristics, having range as a parameter, and reading the values corresponding to the intersections with this family of a given figure-of-merit characteristic. A plot of range-frequency values obtained in this manner may be described as a **range-frequency characteristic.** The parameters of this curve are those associated with the figure-of-merit characteristic used in its derivation.

This process may be continued and a family of range-frequency characteristics derived by plotting a family of figure-of-merit characteristics and a family of propagation loss characteristics against a common pair of loss-frequency coordinates. In this case some one of the parameters associated with the figure-of-merit characteristics will be assumed to be the variable parameter applying to the curves of the derived family. It has already been noted that it is often impossible to assign specific absolute values to the individual parameters of the figure-of-merit equation. It is, however, possible to assume that any one of these parameters may change by a specified amount. Consider, for example, a family of figure-of-merit characteristics drawn as parallel lines separated by loss intervals of six decibels. Such an interval may represent a six-decibel change in the acceptable value of signal differential, a six-decibel change in the index level of the signal to be detected, a six-decibel change in the noise level in the vicinity of the hydrophone, or a six-decibel change in the directivity index of the hydrophone. This last change would correspond to a change in transducer area of four to one. In any case the derived range-frequency characteristics will show the change in operating range which would accompany one of these changes in the system or in the conditions under which it is operated. They will show, furthermore, the manner in which the consequences of such an assumed change vary with frequency.

The graphs of Fig. 7C-1 show the manner in which a single range-frequency characteristic may be derived from a family of propagation loss characteristics and a single figure-of-merit characteristic. In laying off these characteristics the nominal propagation loss formula of Eq. (3A-19) has been used for the propagation loss characteristics. These characteristics have been drawn for range intervals of two range logits. In drawing the figure-of-merit characteristic it has been assumed that the minimum acceptable signal differential is $\Delta L_{s/n} = 0$ db, that this differential is independent of frequency, and that the remaining system parameters have such values that this minimum acceptable signal differential occurs at a frequency of $f_0 = 3$ kc/sec when the sound source is at a range of $S_0 = 10$ kyd. From the propagation loss characteristic applying to this range it is seen that this assumption corresponds to a resultant figure of merit, at the reference frequency, of $(N_w)_0 = 86$ db. It is, however, unnecessary to know this value to draw the figure-of-merit characteristic. All that is required is that it shall pass through the 3-kc/sec point on the 10-kyd propagation loss characteristic. No specific values are assumed for the absolute magnitudes of parameters other than the minimum acceptable signal differential. It is, however, assumed that, whatever their absolute magnitudes may be, the signal level characteristic has a slope of -2 db/fl, the noise level characteristic has a slope of $-5/3$ db/fl, and the directivity index characteristic has a slope of $+2$ db/fl. This last assumption is equivalent to assuming a transducer the active elements of which occupy a finite area. In accordance with these assumptions the figure-of-merit characteristic is drawn with a slope of $\Sigma n = (-2) -(-5/3) + (+2) = +5/3$ db/fl. The range-frequency characteristic derived from this figure-of-merit characteristic and these propagation loss characteristics is shown as the curve marked $\Delta L_{s/n} = 0$ db on the graph of Fig. 7C-2.

A family of range-frequency characteristics obtained by adding other figure-of-merit characteristics to the graph of Fig. 7C-1 is also shown by Fig. 7C-2. The figure-of-merit characteristics used for this derivation have been separated by six-decibel intervals. The several curves of the resulting range-frequency characteristic family have been marked with values of signal differential which differ by this amount. This implies that all other parameters remain unchanged. The characteristics shown would, however, apply

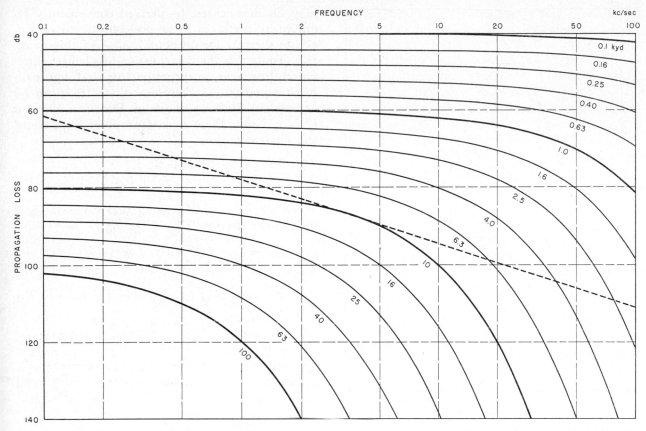

FIG. 7C-1. FIGURE-OF-MERIT CHARACTERISTIC. A loss-frequency diagram, showing the propagation loss of a water path in the sea, and the figure of merit of a direct-listening sonar system, as functions of frequency, with the length of the water path as a parameter, used for the graphical solution of simultaneous equations for propagation loss and figure of merit.

equally well if the same resultant change in the figure of merit were due to a change in signal level, a change in noise level, or a change in transducer size.

It might, at first sight, appear that characteristics for which the absolute magnitudes of the individual parameters are unknown would be of little practical value. It is, however, unnecessary to assign absolute values to these parameters to find the direction in which to alter controllable variables in order to effect an improvement in performance, or to show the effect on performance of some change in environmental conditions. The situation here is analogous to the mapping of contour lines for a hill without knowing the height above sea level; the utility of such lines in indicating the shape of the hill is in no way impaired because of the lack of an absolute reference point.

In drawing the curves of Figs. 7C-1 and 7C-2 the levels assumed have been spectrum levels and the directivity index has been assumed to be that which, at any frequency, would be obtained either

in terms of the powers of sinusoidal waves or of the powers per unit band of continuous waves. In the actual operation of direct-listening equipment frequency bands of finite width are usually employed. Characteristics derived in the manner described may be used for examining the performance of systems receiving energy throughout some finite band. For example, from Fig. 7C-2 it may be seen that acceptable performance may be expected under the postulated conditions when the source is at a range of 8 kyd, provided the listening band lies between the frequencies marked as f_a and f_b. It is also evident that if some source generating a signal of low level is undetected until it is at a range of 4 kyd the chances of detection would be greatest if the listening band were to be somewhere between the frequencies marked f_c and f_d.

The variable parameter of the family of range-frequency characteristics shown in Fig. 7C-2 may be considered as being the actual value of signal differential. In this case the range shown as a

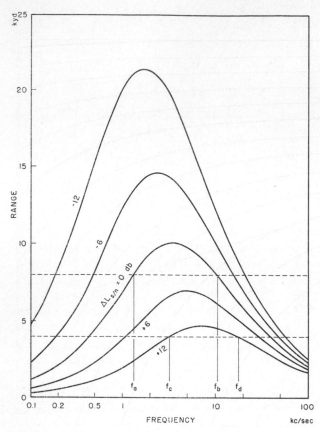

FIG. 7C-2. CONSTANT SIGNAL DIFFERENTIAL CONTOURS. Values of the operating range of a direct-listening system as a function of frequency, with signal differential as a parameter, obtained by the solution of simultaneous equations for propagation loss and figure of merit.

may, in most cases, be derived conveniently by graphical methods it is possible to solve Eq. (7C-6) directly for an actual value of this quantity. To do this the transmission loss is first eliminated from the propagation loss and figure-of-merit equations as these equations are given by expressions such as those of Eqs. (3A-19) and (7C-2). Using these equations there is obtained the single equation

$$2 \lg S + (Af + Bf^2)S + 60$$
$$= L_s - L_n + N_{DI} - \Delta L_{s/n} \quad (7C-7)$$

When this is solved for the actual value of signal differential the result is

$$\Delta L_{s/n} = L_s - L_n + N_{DI} - 2 \lg S$$
$$- (Af + Bf^2)S - 60$$

But, by combining equations of the form of Eq. (7C-4),

$$L_s - L_n + N_{DI} = (N_w)_0 + (\Delta L_{s/n})_0 + \Sigma n \lg \frac{f}{f_0}$$

function of frequency would be the actual range at which this signal differential would be obtained. It is possible to convert the information given by these curves to a family of curves showing actual values of signal differential as a function of frequency with actual values of range as the variable parameter. The pairs of differential-frequency values represented by a single curve of this family correspond to pairs lying along a single propagation loss curve of Fig. 7C-1, rather than to pairs lying along a single figure-of-merit curve, as was the case in deriving the family of Fig. 7C-2. A family of curves showing signal differential as a function of frequency, with range as a parameter, derived from the curves of Fig. 7C-1 in this manner, is shown in Fig. 7C-3. Since the range intervals of Fig. 7C-1 each correspond to two range logits the intervals between the differential-frequency curves of Fig. 7C-3 are separated by this same range interval.

Although signal differential characteristics of the type described in the preceding paragraph

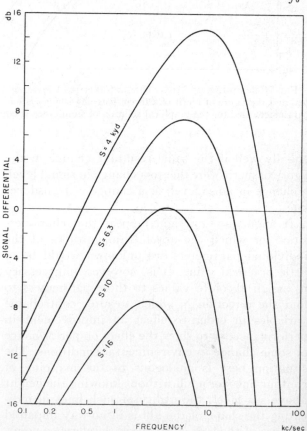

FIG. 7C-3. CONSTANT RANGE LOCI. Values of the signal differential of a direct-listening system as a function of frequency, with range as a parameter, obtained by the solution of simultaneous equations for propagation loss and figure of merit.

Consequently,

$$\Delta L_{s/n} = (\Delta L_{s/n})_0 + N_k - 2 \lgt S$$
$$- (Af + Bf^2)S + \Sigma n \lgt f \quad (7\text{C-}8)$$

where

$$N_k = (N_w)_0 - 60 - \Sigma n \lgt f_0$$
$$= 2 \lgt S_0' + (Af_0 + Bf_0^2)S_0 - \Sigma n \lgt f_0 \quad (7\text{C-}9)$$

Given this equation it is possible to compute directly the value of signal differential as a function of range and frequency for a value of the remaining parameters having some postulated absolute magnitude which varies with frequency in such manner that the slope of the figure-of-merit characteristic, as measured in decibels per frequency logit, has some postulated constant value.

It is evident from an inspection of the loss-frequency diagram of Fig. 7C-1 that the shape of range-frequency characteristics, or of characteristics showing signal differential as a function of frequency, which may be derived therefrom are greatly influenced by the slope of the figure-of-merit characteristics. It is, indeed, evident that such derived characteristics will pass through maximum values, as in Figs. 7C-2 and 7C-3, only when the figure-of-merit characteristic has a positive slope. If this characteristic has a constant loss value, or if it has a negative slope, range will increase and signal differential will decrease, with increasing frequency, throughout the entire region for which such a slope is maintained. Figure-of-merit characteristics having negative slopes are by no means uncommon. Whenever the slope of a figure-of-merit characteristic is positive, however, a characteristic showing range as a function of frequency, or a characteristic showing signal differential as a function of frequency, will, in general, pass through a maximum value. The frequency at which such a maximum occurs is usually of major significance to those interested in the design and operation of sonar equipment. The value of this optimum frequency may be determined by analytical methods.

Although a transcendental expression such as Eq. (7C-6) may not be solved to give range as an explicit function of frequency it may be differentiated with respect to frequency. It may also be differentiated with respect to the logarithm of frequency. Since the slope of the figure-of-merit characteristic is given in decibels per frequency logit this may appear to be a more direct approach to the desired result. Actually, the end result is independent of which method is used.

In differentiating with respect to the logarithm of the independent variable the following general formulas are required.

$$\frac{d(\lgt x)}{dx} = \frac{4.343}{x} \quad (7\text{C-}10)$$

$$\frac{d(\lgt x)}{dt} = \frac{4.343}{x} \frac{dx}{dt} \quad (7\text{C-}11)$$

and

$$\frac{d(\lgt x)}{d(\lgt t)} = \frac{t}{x} \frac{dx}{dt} \quad (7\text{C-}12)$$

These relations are derived directly from the fundamental relations of logarithms and of the differential calculus. The last of these three equations states that the slope of a characteristic drawn on log-log paper has, at any value of the independent variable, a slope equal to the product of the slope which would be obtained if the two variables were plotted against linear coordinates multiplied by the ratio of the independent variable to the dependent variable.

On differentiating Eq. (7C-6) with respect to the logarithm to the base $10^{0.1}$ of the frequency there is obtained

$$2 \frac{\lgt S}{\lgt f} + \left[(Af + Bf^2) \frac{dS}{df} \right.$$
$$\left. + (A + 2Bf)S \right] \frac{f}{4.343} = \Sigma n$$

or

$$2 \frac{f}{S} \frac{dS}{df} + \left[(Af + Bf^2) \frac{dS}{df} \right.$$
$$\left. + (A + 2Bf)S \right] \frac{f}{4.343} = \Sigma n \quad (7\text{C-}13)$$

When $\dfrac{dS}{df} = 0,$

as required when the range has its maximum value,

$$(Af + 2Bf^2) \frac{S}{4.343} = \Sigma n \quad (7\text{C-}14)$$

We thus have an explicit relation between the optimum value of frequency and range. From this it is seen that the optimum frequency, for any given range, depends on the slope of the figure-of-merit characteristic but is independent of its absolute magnitude. This does not imply that detection at any given range will be made possible with a given system merely by operating it at the frequency computed by this equation. It does indicate that if detection is desired at a given range, operation at the optimum frequency thus computed will permit detection with a lower figure of merit than would be required at any other frequency.

This is, perhaps, made more evident by differentiating Eq. (7C-8) with respect to the logarithm of frequency and solving for the relation between range and frequency at which the actual value of signal differential is a maximum. The relation obtained by this method is the same as that given by Eq. (7C-14).

These relations may be studied graphically as well as analytically. In deriving a family of range-frequency characteristics by graphical methods it will be recalled that a figure-of-merit characteristic is, in effect, moved progressively downward across a family of propagation loss characteristics. Considering the succession of positions occupied by the figure-of-merit characteristic as constituting a family representing a signal and an interference having fixed spectrum level characteristics and a hydrophone having a fixed directivity index characteristic, the parameter of this family would be the signal differential. Signal differential, in other words, would have a constant value for each position of the figure-of-merit characteristic. The parameter of the family of propagation loss characteristics is range. This, also, is constant for each curve. The range-frequency characteristic derived from the intersections of a figure-of-merit characteristic with the members of a family of propagation loss characteristics may thus be said to be a constant signal differential locus. This locus will have a maximum range value at the point where the figure-of-merit characteristic is tangent to a propagation loss characteristic. In a similar manner the intersections of a single propagation loss characteristic with the members of a family of figure-of-merit characteristics define a constant range locus on a graph showing signal differential as a function of frequency. This locus will have a maximum value of signal differential at a frequency for which the propagation loss characteristic is tangent to a figure-of-merit characteristic. The frequency at which a figure-of-merit characteristic and a propagation loss characteristic are tangent is thus seen to be the optimum frequency for the range given by the propagation loss characteristic, or for the signal differential given by the figure-of-merit characteristic. It is the frequency at which the range identified with a given signal differential is a maximum, or at which the signal differential identified with a given range is a maximum.

From the foregoing it is evident that at the point on a diagram such as that of Fig. 7C-1 which defines an optimum frequency the slopes of the tangent figure-of-merit and propagation loss characteristics are equal. This is in agreement with the relation expressed by Eq. (7C-14). In this expression the term on the right is, by definition, the slope of the figure-of-merit characteristic; the terms on the left give the slope of the propagation loss characteristic.

The graph of Fig. 7C-4 shows the relation between range and optimum frequency expressed by Eq. (7C-14). The three curves shown correspond to three positive values of the slope of the figure-of-merit characteristic. Although the equation by which these curves have been computed was obtained by differentiating the expression for propagation loss, it will be noted that the spreading loss component is without effect on the final result. This loss, being a constant for any assigned range, does not contribute to the value of the derivative. The curves of Fig. 7C-4, therefore,

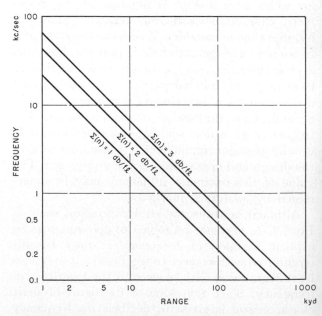

FIG. 7C-4. OPTIMUM FREQUENCY. The optimum operating frequency for a direct-listening system, plotted as a function of range with the slope of the figure-of-merit characteristic as a parameter.

depend only on the manner in which the attenuation loss, the signal level, the noise level, and the directivity index of the hydrophone vary with frequency. They are independent of the absolute magnitudes of these quantities at any given frequency.

The frequency shown by the ordinate of any point on one of these curves is that at which the range corresponding to a signal differential of constant magnitude, derived from a figure-of-merit characteristic having a constant slope, passes through a maximum having the value shown by the corresponding abscissa. Also, at this same frequency the signal differential associated with the same range, derived as a function of frequency from a family of figure-of-merit characteristics of this same slope, will be greater than at any other frequency. It does not follow that at this range and frequency the signal differential considered as a function of range will be greater than at any other range; as range is reduced the signal differential at any frequency is always increased. Neither are these curves to be interpreted as indicating that at any given frequency greater operating ranges are to be obtained with figure-of-merit characteristics of high slope than with those of lesser slope. These curves give no information as to the absolute magnitude of signal differential. They merely indicate the frequency at which the range for a given signal differential has a maximum, or at which the signal differential for a given range has a maximum. This frequency is plotted against either the maximum range or the fixed range, depending upon whether the signal differential or the range is considered the independent variable.

Discretion must be exercised in drawing and interpreting constant signal differential loci, showing range as a function of frequency. It is recognized that all such curves are based on assumptions as to the propagation loss and as to the factors appearing in the figure-of-merit equation. In the curves of Fig. 7C-2, for example, it was assumed that the propagation loss was characterized by a spreading loss which obeys the inverse square law and by an attenuation loss corresponding to the attenuation coefficient given by Eq. (3A-18). The reliability of this equation decreases with decreasing frequency for frequencies below 10 kc/sec. For short ranges and for low frequencies, however, this quantity has little effect on computations such as those here in question since, for this portion of the loss-frequency diagram, propagation loss is due almost entirely to spreading. It is obvious that the existence of shadow zones or of sound channels, resulting from thermal conditions in the medium which are by no means uncommon, will greatly affect the propagation loss characteristics and, through these characteristics, affect the constant signal differential loci. The method of analysis here described, however, permits the consequences of such conditions to be evaluated in terms of practical operating significance. All that is required is that the propagation loss characteristics shall properly represent the conditions in question.

In a similar manner constant signal differential loci must not be extended into regions where assumptions as to the shape of the figure-of-merit characteristic are invalid. Deviations from a constant slope are likely to occur at frequencies less than 1 kc/sec since, below this frequency, the spectrum level characteristics of both signal and interference are likely to depart from the linearity so often found at higher frequencies. The assumption of a linear figure-of-merit characteristic, as expressed in decibels per frequency logit, also becomes invalid for frequencies at which the directivity index of the hydrophone may not be represented by a straight line.

In spite of the many assumptions and restrictions attending the computation of constant signal differential loci much useful information may be obtained from families of curves such as those shown in Figs. 7C-2 and 7C-3. From the curves of 7C-2, for example, it is seen that the range at which a given required signal differential will be obtained is much greater for the two octaves between 2 and 8 kc/sec than for the two octaves between 8 and 32 kc/sec. These curves also suggest that if we wish to detect some source, having the characteristics postulated, at ranges in excess of 15 kyd we shall have the best chance of success if we use a listening band centered somewhere in the neighborhood of 1.8 kc/sec. If, however, the signal from this source is so weak, or the interference so strong, as to make detection at such long ranges impossible, there will be a better chance of detection at a shorter range, such as 4 kyd, if the listening band is raised nearly two octaves.

These curves are somewhat more specific as to the effect of changes in the level of the signal or of the interference, or of changes in the directional discrimination of the hydrophone. These changes, as seen earlier, are definitely related to the intervals between the constant signal differential loci. If, for example, when listening in the vicinity of 2 kc/sec, the interference is reduced by 6 db it is evident that the range associated with a given signal differential will be increased from below 14 kyd to something like 20 kyd. To accomplish this same improvement by changes in the sonar equipment would require that the linear dimensions of the hydrophone be doubled. Conversely, if the level of the signal at a source which might be detected at a range of 8 kyd were to be reduced by 6 db the range at which this source might be detected with equal probability would be reduced to something under 5 kyd.

7C-4 Relations Between Range and Bearing

The preceding articles have considered methods whereby the relations between the operating range of a direct-listening sonar system and frequency may be examined when the sound source to be observed is on the maximum response bearing of the hydrophone. These methods are also applicable to an examination of the relations between operating range and bearing for an acoustic signal of fixed frequency. All that is required is that the deviation loss of the hydrophone be introduced into the direct-listening equation as given by Eq. (7C-2). The effect of deviation loss is to reduce the figure of merit of the equipment, under the conditions postulated in any given problem. We may express this by writing the maximum tolerable propagation loss of the water path between signal source and receiving hydrophone as

$$N_w + N_d = (N_w)_{do} \qquad (7\text{C-}15)$$

where N_d is the deviation loss of the hydrophone for any given bearing. Now for any given value of signal differential the figure of merit of a specified system, operating at a specified fixed frequency, is constant. The relation between propagation loss and deviation loss shown here is, therefore, the same as that discussed in Art. 4D-3 in connection with constant transmission loss contours, or constant signal level contours. The constant value of the sum of the two has, however, now acquired additional significance. Curves derived in the manner illustrated in Fig. 4D-6 are, it is now apparent, constant signal differential contours showing range as a function of bearing for a constant frequency. As such, they are related to the constant signal differential contours of Fig. 7C-2, which show range as a function of frequency for a constant bearing. When drawn in polar coordinates, to the proper scale, a constant signal differential contour, giving range as a function of bearing, defines an area such that if the signal source postulated in computing the figure of merit of the equipment is located at any point of that area the observed signal differential will equal or exceed the signal differential for which the figure of merit was computed. If this signal differential is the minimum acceptable differential the curve represents the boundary separating the area from which acceptable signals will be received from the area from which unacceptable signals will be received.

CHAPTER 8

FUNDAMENTAL FACTORS IN ECHO RANGING

Various features of echo-ranging systems have been considered in earlier chapters of this book. It is the present purpose to examine the interrelations between the several functional elements of these systems and the factors which influence their performance. As a preliminary to this endeavor it will be desirable to investigate certain extensions and modifications of the basic principles pertaining to underwater acoustic signals and to their reception consequent upon the conditions encountered in echo-signal transmission.

8-A THE ECHO-RANGING PROCESS

8A-1 Pulses, Echoes, and Reverberation

Echo-ranging systems function by virtue of the reflection of acoustic energy from some object fully or partially submerged in water. In echo ranging the target observed is caused to act as a secondary source of acoustic energy whereas in direct listening it must be a primary source. It is thus possible by means of echo-signal transmissions to detect the approach or the presence of an otherwise silent target. By measuring the duration of the signal travel time and determining the target bearing it is also possible, from a single observation point, fully to establish the position of a reflecting target, which may or may not be silent. These two applications of echo ranging are frequently combined in a single operation; they do, however, represent two distinct advantages of the echo-ranging system over the direct-listening system. They are, on the other hand, attended by the almost certain risk of disclosing the presence of the observer and possibly his position as well.

The basic operations involved in echo ranging are the transmission of waves of acoustic energy and the subsequent reception of such portions of this energy as may be directed to an observation point by reflection. This differs from the visual observation of an object illuminated by a searchlight, in which the operations of transmission and reception are continuous and are carried out simultaneously. The energy transmitted in echo ranging is, in the elementary system which we shall first consider, generally in the form of a short train of waves of ultrasonic frequency. If the transducer is highly directional the energy of the pulse will be restricted in bearing as well as in time. This brief signal may be of a single frequency (CW); it may be amplitude modulated (AM); or it may be frequency modulated (FM). The outgoing signal is generally known as the **pulse** and the returned signal, after reflection by some given **target**, as the **echo.** Energy returned by reflectors other than that which it is desired to observe is known as **reverberation.** The relation between echo and reverberation is, in some respects, similar to the signal-to-noise ratio and is often the factor which limits the performance of an echo-ranging system.

There are two reasons for using a signal having the form of a pulse of short duration. One is to permit the identification of a specific increment of energy in order that its travel time may be measured. The second is to avoid an acoustical effect in the water analogous to the familiar optical effect which impairs the utility of automobile headlights on a foggy night. In the latter case energy reaching the observer by back-scattering from nearby water droplets interferes with the observation of energy received simultaneously from more distant reflectors. If the transmitted signal is of short duration interference due to acoustic energy back-scattered by nearby objects in the water will also be of short duration and will have subsided before the arrival of energy from a more distant target. The use of individual pulses, on the other hand, limits the rate at which some given area may be scanned in search of a target because of the time required for a pulse to travel along a given bearing for some specified distance and for the echo to return.

8A-2 The Use of Ultrasonic Frequencies

The frequencies of the pulses used in echo ranging are generally in the ultrasonic region. One reason for this is to permit the transducer to have adequate directivity, which requires that certain of its dimensions exceed several wave spaces, without being of prohibitive size. Another advantage is that the spectrum levels of many noises which might interfere with echo reception are lower at these frequencies than at audio frequencies. Operation at ultrasonic frequencies, then, results in higher signal-to-noise ratios, for a given transmitted power, than would be found at lower frequencies. On the other hand, attenuation increases with increasing frequency and may set an upper limit in certain applications of echo ranging. As a rule the frequencies commonly used for echo ranging lie between 5 and 40 kc/sec. For echo sounding and for certain special applications higher frequencies may be desirable.

Although indicators and recorders may be designed to operate directly at ultrasonic frequencies it is desirable to listen to sonar signals as well as to observe them visually. This requires that the electric signal delivered by the transducer be modified in the receiving system so that it is translated from the ultrasonic region to the audio region. Also, by changing the frequencies of the components of an electric wave it is possible to locate those components which it is desired to observe within the pass band of fixed selective circuits. The advantage of such an arrangement is the familiar advantage of the superheterodyne radio receiver.

8A-3 The Functional Arrangement of Echo-Ranging Systems

It would, of course, be entirely possible to set up an echo-detection system in which the echo is not received at the point of origin of the signal wave. Such echoes are frequently heard when a number of vessels are operating echo-ranging equipment in proximity to each other. Were it desired merely to detect the presence of a submerged object the relation between the intensity of the echo from the target and that of the reverberation which obscures it might, in some cases, be improved if the echo were to be received at some point not on the line of initial transmission. Where it is desired to measure ranges, however, the determination of signal travel time would become intolerably complicated unless the signal paths began and ended at a single point.

Because the sending and receiving of echo signals occur at a single place but at different times it is a relatively simple matter to use a single transducer for both. The signal is usually generated as an electric wave of the desired form by electronic circuits. These circuits, including such amplification as may be required, are connected to the transducer for a brief interval during which

the pulse is transmitted. The transducer is then disconnected from the output of the driving system and connected to the input of the receiving system. The directional characteristics of the transducer which confine the energy of the outgoing pulse along some given bearing now restrict the receiving response to this same bearing. Certain consequences of thus confining the transmitting and the receiving response to the bearing of a target have already been considered quantitatively, in a general way, in articles dealing with the reverberation index of transducers.

The driving circuits of echo-ranging systems present no unusual features of which we need take notice at this point. The receiving amplifier, on the other hand, has such a definite influence on the ultimate signal that certain transmission phenomena cannot be fully studied without taking the effect of this circuit into account. We shall, therefore, review here such operational features of echo-ranging receivers as are pertinent to an analysis of the fundamental phenomena involved.

The general arrangement of the receiver-amplifier used in echo ranging is similar to that of the conventional superheterodyne receiver except that the frequency of the intermediate stages, containing the fixed selective circuits, is higher than the frequency of the signal delivered to the input terminals. In spite of this the terminology associated with the radio broadcast receiver has been retained; the wave received from the transducer is known as the r-f signal, the wave passed by the fixed selective circuits as the i-f signal, and the final low-frequency wave as the a-f signal.

The functional schematic of a type of heterodyne receiving circuit which has been in use in echo-ranging systems for many years and which has proved ideally suited to a wide variety of operating requirements is shown in Fig. 8A-1. The so-called r-f stages contain a tuned input circuit which is variable over the range of frequencies for which the circuit is designed. This is generally from 15 to 40 kc/sec. These initial stages supply signal to a modulator, known as the first detector, which also receives a heterodyning current from a variable-frequency oscillator. This oscillator and the input tuned circuits are controlled in unison by a single master frequency dial calibrated to read the frequency of the input electric signal. The first heterodyne oscillator, in a typical circuit, will cover a frequency range of the same absolute extent as that of the r-f circuits but located 60 kc/sec higher on the frequency

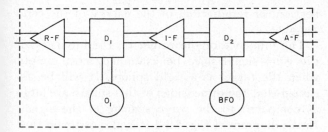

FIG. 8A-1. ECHO-RANGING RECEIVER-AMPLIFIER. The arrangement of the basic functional elements of the circuit for deriving an audio-frequency signal from the ultrasonic electric wave delivered by the transducer.

R-F The r-f amplifier, tunable to ultrasonic frequencies between 15 and 40 kc/sec
D₁ The first detector
O₁ The first oscillator, adjustable to heterodyning frequencies of 75 to 100 kc/sec, or 60 kc/sec above the original ultrasonic signal
I-F The i-f amplifier, containing fixed selective circuits centered at 60 kc/sec
D₂ The second, or beat-frequency, detector
BFO The beat-frequency oscillator, adjustable to 60.8 kc/sec, or 800 cyc/sec above the i-f signal
A-F The audio amplifier, generally containing circuits highly selective at 800 cyc/sec

scale. One of the products of modulation of this heterodyne current and an r-f signal within the range previously indicated may, therefore, be made to have a difference frequency of 60 kc/sec. When the signal is a continuous wave, of single frequency, the i-f signal is a continuous wave of 60 kc/sec; when the signal is made up of a group of sinusoidal components the i-f signal is a group of sinusoidal components in the neighborhood of 60 kc/sec corresponding to the portion of the input wave selected by the tuned circuits of the r-f stages.

Unlike the radio broadcast superheterodyne the receiving amplifier used in sonar systems does not obtain its essential selectivity in the i-f stages. The chief function of the selective circuits of this section of the receiver is to discriminate against unwanted products of modulation generated in the first modulator. Following the i-f stages is a second detector. The oscillator supplying heterodyning current to this circuit operates at 60.8 kc/sec, or 800 cyc/sec above the frequency of the signal delivered by the i-f stages. Modulation of the signal wave by current from this oscillator, then, results in an audio-frequency component of 800 cyc/sec. The function of this second detector and oscillator is to generate the familiar beat-frequency signal required in all systems employing continuous ultrasonic wave transmission.

The audio-frequency signal is amplified in the a-f output stages of the receiver. The interstage coupling circuits of this amplifier provide effective discrimination against interference by components having frequencies near that of the signal. These audio-frequency selective circuits may be connected to have pass bands of different widths. Three are generally provided, one of which is usually so highly selective that the beat frequency must be within a few cycles of the correct value to avoid being rejected. In view of this the beat-frequency oscillator is given sufficient range of adjustment to permit the audio frequency to be located accurately within the pass band of the fixed selective circuits.

The audio-frequency stages of the receiving amplifier are often arranged to have two independent output connections, one going to a loud-speaker and one to the range-measuring indicator or recorder. An auxiliary output is also often provided, through a suitable attenuator, for supplying signal at a proper level to headphones.

The instruments which may be used for the visual observation of the signal or for the measurement of target range have been discussed, in general terms, in Chapter 6. It appears necessary here merely to add that the range-measuring instrument generally includes some mechanism for coordinating the transfer switching of the transducer, the sending of the pulse, and the release of the timing device for measuring the target range.

The purpose of the preceding brief description of the technique of echo ranging has been to establish the nature of the fundamental operations involved and the influence of the several functional elements of the system on these operations. On the basis of this general survey of the environment of our problem we may now proceed to a more detailed discussion of the several factors and processes pertinent to the performance of echo-ranging systems.

8-B THE ECHO SIGNAL

The matters to be discussed in this section are those for which it will be found convenient to focus attention on the echo signal. It will, however, be evident here, as elsewhere in this chapter, that the echo is part of general reverberation and that the two can never be completely separated.

8B-1 Target Strength

The intensity of the echo signal returned by some specific reflecting target which is wholly within the beam of a directional transducer depends upon the total energy falling on the target. Since the target is of fixed dimensions this total energy is proportional to the intensity of the pulse at the target range. The echo signal therefore suffers normal propagation loss on its path from the transducer to the target. On the path from the target back to the transducer the spreading loss is that applying to distance from the target which, being a secondary radiator, is the origin of a new group of diverging rays. The total propagation loss effective for the echo signal is consequently twice the one-way propagation loss of the path between transducer and target; it is not the loss associated with a path of twice this length. The intensity of an echo signal is thus seen to vary with target range in accordance with the relation

$$\operatorname{lgt} \frac{(I_e)_1}{(I_e)_2} = 4 \operatorname{lgt} \frac{S_2}{S_1} + 2a(S_2 - S_1) \quad (8B\text{-}1)$$

where

$(I_e)_1 =$ the intensity of the echo signal returned from a target at a range of S_1 kyd (watt/cm²)

$(I_e)_2 =$ the intensity of the echo signal returned from a target at a range of S_2 kyd (watt/cm²)

$a =$ the attenuation coefficient applying at the frequency of the transmission in question (db/kyd)

When the quantity S_1 is the one yard index distance from a given transducer and S_2 is the range of a given target this equation represents the total propagation loss identified with the water path between transducer and target. This loss is measured by the ratio between an echo intensity, $(I_e)_1$, which has the hypothetical value associated with the target in question assuming it were possible for it to be at a range of one yard, and consequently at the index point, and the intensity, $(I_e)_2$, of the echo actually received. It is necessary to determine the total transmission loss as measured by the ratio between the index intensity, I_p, of the outgoing pulse and the intensity, $I_e = (I_e)_2$, of the returned echo. This total transmission loss, which may be designated as the **echo loss,** is made up of the propagation loss, just discussed, and any loss accompanying the re-

flection, or reradiation, of the energy of the echo signal.

The influence of the target on the intensity of the echo signal may be examined most simply when the target is a rigid sphere. It will be assumed that the dimensions of this sphere are large as compared to the wave spacing of the signal. In the diagram of Fig. 8B-1 it is also assumed that the source is at such a distance from the target that the energy may be considered to arrive at the target as plane waves. Energy traveling along a ray path which coincides with the line from the source, O, to the center of the target, C, therefore strikes the target at the point N with normal incidence and is reflected back along this same path. Energy traveling along a ray path parallel to this line will strike the target at a point P. Let the ray path and the radius of the sphere through this point meet at the angle θ. The reflected ray will leave this point at the angle θ on the other side of the radius, as shown. If, in the diagram, the path of the reflected ray is extended into the interior of the sphere it will meet the line joining the source and the center of the sphere at the point Q. The extended ray path, the line from the source, and the radius through P form the triangle CPQ. From elementary geometry it is evident that this is an isosceles triangle having the base $CP = r$, where r is the radius of the sphere, and the equal angles θ. By trigonometry

$$PQ = CQ = r \frac{\sin \theta}{\sin (\pi - 2\theta)} = r \frac{\sin \theta}{\sin 2\theta} \quad (8B\text{-}2)$$

When θ is small, that is, when the ray path strikes the target in the neighborhood of the point N,

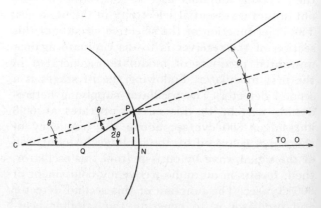

FIG. 8B-1. GEOMETRY OF SPHERICAL TARGET. The geometrical relations establishing the point of apparent reradiation of sound rays reflected by an ideal spherical target.

sin $\theta = \theta$, and sin $2\theta = 2\theta$. In this case

$$CQ = \frac{r}{2} \qquad (8B\text{-}3)$$

This is true for all rays striking the surface of the target in the neighborhood of the ray having normal incidence. All such rays, in consequence, appear to be reradiated from a point halfway between the center and the surface of the sphere on the radius through the source. Rays striking the target at some distance from the point of normal incidence appear to be reradiated from a point nearer to the surface than to the center. Such rays, however, do not return to the neighborhood of the source and hence are of no immediate significance.

Let the intensity of the transmitted pulse at the one yard index point, on the bearing of the target, be represented by I_p and its intensity at the target by I_T. The relation between these two intensities may be expressed in terms of the normal propagation loss suffered by the pulse in traveling between the source and the target as

$$\lgt \frac{I_p}{I_T} = 2\lgt S + aS + 60 \qquad (8B\text{-}4)$$

If the range of the target is large it would be impossible to distinguish between values of I_T at the surface of the target, at the point of apparent reradiation, or at the center of the target; under the inverse square law the last yard of a long path has little effect on the intensity. For the return path, however, this yard is the first yard and has a very important effect on the intensity of the returned signal. Assuming, for the moment, that all of the energy striking the target is reflected the intensity of the echo signal, as it leaves the target surface, is the same as the intensity, I_T, falling on this surface. This point is, as shown by Eq. (8B-3), already at a range of $r/2$ yd, or $r/2000$ kyd, from the point of apparent reradiation. The transmission loss measuring the ratio between the intensity, I_T, of the echo as it leaves the target surface and its intensity, I_e, as it arrives at the transducer from which the signal was originally transmitted is therefore

$$\lgt \frac{I_T}{I_e} = 2\lgt \frac{2000\,S}{r} + a\left(S - \frac{r}{2000}\right) \qquad (8B\text{-}5)$$

The quantity $r/2000$ kyd may be neglected in the term showing the attenuation loss; the effect of its presence in the spreading loss term is by no means negligible. If this quantity is omitted from the attenuation loss the above equation may be written as

$$\lgt \frac{I_T}{I_e} = 2\lgt S + aS + 60 - 2\lgt \frac{r}{2} \qquad (8B\text{-}6)$$

The quantity 60 db appearing in this equation is a dimensional conversion factor which is required because the target radius, r, is given in yards and the range, S, in kiloyards. It is the same quantity which appears in Eq. (8B-4) and other propagation loss formulas involving an index point where, as in the present case, one range is in yards and one in kiloyards.

By adding Eqs. (8B-4) and (8B-6) the transmission loss measuring the ratio between the index intensity of the pulse and the intensity of the returned echo is found to be

$$N_e = \lgt \frac{I_p}{I_e} = \lgt \frac{I_p}{I_T} + \lgt \frac{I_T}{I_e}$$

$$= 4\lgt S + 2aS + 120 - 2\lgt \frac{r}{2} \qquad (8B\text{-}7)$$

This is the resultant transmission loss suffered by the echo signal, or the echo loss, which we are attempting to evaluate. The first three terms represent twice the normal one-way propagation loss of the path between transducer and target. The third term indicates that the resultant loss is less than this propagation loss. The return of the echo from a point more than the one yard index distance from the point of apparent reradiation causes the phenomena accompanying reflection at the target to constitute an effective transmission gain rather than a transmission loss. This transmission gain will be designated as the **target strength.**

From the foregoing it is evident that this target strength is equal to the amount by which the two-way propagation loss between transducer and target exceeds the total echo loss, or that

$$N_{TS} = 2N_w - N_e \qquad (8B\text{-}8)$$

The two-way propagation loss, as already defined, is measured by the ratio between the intensity, $(I_e)_1$, of the echo corresponding to a target range of one yard and the intensity, $(I_e)_S$, of the echo returned from the same target when at a range of S kyd. The target strength is thus

$$N_{TS} = \lg \frac{(I_e)_1}{(I_e)_S} - \lg \frac{I_p}{(I_e)_S} = \lg \frac{(I_e)_1}{I_p} \quad \text{(8B-9)}$$

We may, therefore, define target strength as the difference between the level of the echo corresponding to a target range of one yard and the index level of the outgoing pulse.

The total transmission loss suffered by the echo signal, which has been designated as the echo loss, may now be written as

$$N_e = \lg \frac{I_p}{I_e} = 4 \lg S + 2\,aS + 120 - N_{TS} \quad \text{(8B-10)}$$

where

    N_e = the echo loss or the total transmission loss suffered by an echo signal (db)

    I_p = the index intensity of the outgoing pulse, as measured on the target bearing (watt/cm^2)

    I_e = the intensity of the received echo, considered as a plane wave propagated along the target bearing (watt/cm^2)

    S = the target range (kyd)

    a = the attenuation coefficient applying at the frequency of the transmitted pulse (db/kyd)

    N_{TS} = the target strength of the target (db)

In practice the strength of any given target is usually determined, in accordance with Eq. (8B-8), as the difference between twice the measured one-way propagation loss between a transducer and this target and the measured echo loss. A comparison of Eqs. (8B-7) and (8B-10) shows that if the target were an ideal rigid sphere its target strength would be

$$N_{TS} = 2 \lg \frac{r}{2} \quad \text{(8B-11)}$$

where r is the radius of the sphere in yards. The behavior of an actual target is frequently reported in terms of that of an ideal sphere by substituting the measured value of target strength into this equation and solving for the value of the radius, r, which would make the sphere an equivalent target.

It is not always possible to represent an actual target by an equivalent sphere in this manner. Situations have been found in practice, for example, where the strength of a target, measured in the manner just described, appears not to be constant but to depend upon the distance of the target from the echo-ranging transducer. This is not unreasonable. Consider, for example, the conditions which would exist if the reflecting target were a large plane surface. In this case the echo would appear to originate at an image of the source as far behind the target as the true source is in front of it. The transmission loss between the index point for this image and the actual receiving point, assuming complete reflection at the target, would then be that associated with the distance $2S$, or twice the target range. It would thus be

$$\lg \frac{I_p}{I_e} = 2 \lg (2S) + 2aS + 60$$

$$= 2 \lg S + 2aS + 2 \lg 2 + 60 \quad \text{(8B-12)}$$

If this is substituted into Eq. (8B-10) there is obtained

$$2 \lg S + 2aS + 66$$

$$= 4 \lg S + 2aS + 120 - N_{TS} \quad \text{(8B-13)}$$

whence the target strength is given as

$$N_{TS} = 2 \lg S + 54 \quad \text{(8B-14)}$$

The target strength, in other words, appears here to be 6 db less than the one-way spreading loss between the echo-ranging transducer and the target; it is clearly a function of range.

In practice the value of target strength assigned to some specific target includes the effect of reflectivity as well as the effect of geometry. In fact, the strength which a target would have were it an ideal reflector is a convenient reference against which to measure the actual reflectivity. Measurements made on the basis of the relations given by Eq. (8B-8) include the effect of reflectivity as well as the effect of target dimensions.

From measurements made as indicated above the target strengths of ships in the 5000 to 10,000 ton group have been found to lie between N_{TS} = 5 db and N_{TS} = 20 db. This means that the radii of equivalent ideal spherical targets may be expected to lie between $r = 4$ yd and $r = 20$ yd. The values commonly used in attempting to estimate the order of magnitude of echo intensity

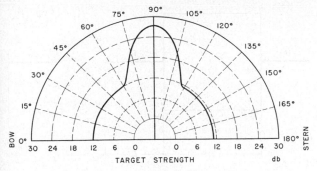

FIG. 8B-2. TARGET STRENGTH. Typical values for the target strength of a submerged submarine as a function of its aspect.

to be expected in some hypothetical situation are $r = 15$ yd, or $N_{TS} = 18$ db. Target strength is almost always a function of the aspect of the target vessel, being greatest when the target's course is perpendicular to the path of the echo signal and least when it is parallel. The curve of Fig. 8B-2 shows typical values for the target strength of a submerged submarine, plotted as a function of its aspect. These values are averaged from the results of many measurements made on several submarines and under varying conditions. In no case is the actual data on a single vessel represented by a curve as smooth as that shown; there is, in fact, considerable variation over the angles for which a constant value of target strength is indicated. The curve given represents statistical averages in the same manner as do curves for propagation loss, for water noise, or for similar variables. It has been verified, with respect to its general character, by measurements made in air using ultrasonic frequencies and scale models so chosen that the relation between target dimensions and signal wave spacing is the same as in the actual case. It has also been checked optically by observing light reflected from a scale model when using point source illumination.

The significance of the magnitudes, both absolute and relative, given by a target strength characteristic, such as that for submarines, is indicated in Fig. 8B-3. Each curve there shown is a constant echo level contour for all points for which there is a constant difference between twice the one-way propagation loss for the range indicated and the target strength, as given by Fig. 8B-2, for the aspect indicated. If echo-ranging equipment, operated under constant conditions, were to move relative to the target along the path represented by a given contour line the echo signal level would be constant; it would change by 6 db

if the transducer were to move from one line to the next.

8B-2 The Effect of Pulse Length— Target Length

There is, of course, a definite relation between the path length occupied by the wave train, or pulse, as measured along the direction of its propagation, and the duration of the time required for it to pass a given point. The ratio of the length of wave train which passes a fixed point during a given time interval is, in fact, the velocity of propagation of the wave by definition. Taking 5000 ft/sec as an approximate value for this velocity it is evident that a transmitting interval of 1 ms corresponds to a pulse length of 5 ft. It is somewhat more accurate to use the value $c = 1.6$ yd/ms.

If the target from which an echo signal is returned were an ideal rigid sphere the time interval during which an echo would be reradiated would be identical with the time interval required for the pulse reaching the target to pass the point of normal incidence; echo and pulse would, then, have the same length. Even were the target an ideal reflecting sphere, however, it is unlikely that the echo would be a true replica of the pulse leaving the transducer because of the almost inevitable distortion due to multiple transmission paths. We have already seen how such paths cause rapid variations in signal level, under steady-state conditions, due to continual variation in path length and the consequent changes in the phase relations between signals arriving over different routes. An echo-ranging pulse is not a steady-state signal and would be distorted by multiple transmission paths even though these were ideally stable. The resultant signal reaching the target would then begin with the pulse arriv-

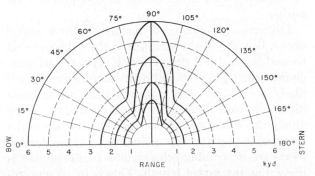

FIG. 8B-3. TARGET STRENGTH. Constant signal contours, plotted as a function of aspect, for 6-db signal level intervals. These curves are based on the same data as Fig. 8B-2.

ing over the path having the shortest transmission time. This would maintain a constant intensity until the arrival of a second pulse, over another path, whereupon the two would combine in a manner determined by their relative amplitudes and phases. The resultant intensity would, in general, differ from the initial intensity, the probability of an increase being the same as that of a decrease. If there were only two paths this new value of intensity would be maintained until the termination of the first pulse when it would again change, this time to a level fixed by the second pulse. If there are more than two paths the manner in which their contributions combine depends upon the length of the original pulse and upon the magnitudes of the differences between the travel times. These latter quantities determine both the intervals during which some given combination of pulses exists and the phase relations applying during those intervals. Actually, as we have already seen, the phase relations are never constant during any interval, no matter how short, but change quite unpredictably due to slight changes in path length.

Regardless of its intensity it is obvious that the total duration of the resultant pulse, as it reaches the target, is equal to the duration of the original pulse, as it left the transducer, plus the difference between the travel times for the fastest and the slowest paths.

All of the effects which act to cause distortion of the signal pulse on its way to the target act also to cause further distortion in the echo signal on its way back to the receiving point. It is not possible here to consider the consequences of these recurrent effects in detail beyond noting that the duration of the echo, as ultimately received, in addition to suffering other modifications, is increased in duration by twice the difference between the travel times of the fastest and slowest paths.

Distortion of the type discussed above would occur, because of the medium, if the echo were returned by an ideal target which repeated without change the signal falling on it. Normal targets are likely to return energy from points at different distances from the source. The distance, measured along the direction of propagation, between the first point and the last point, on a given target, to return detectable echo signals to the source, is known as the **target length.** This is in no way related to the size of the equivalent ideal sphere by which target strength is sometimes evaluated.

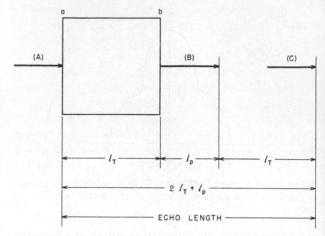

Fig. 8B-4. Echo Length. The relations between target, pulse, and echo lengths. When the pulse is at (A) the front of the echo is leaving (a), when it is at (B) the end of the echo is leaving (b), and when it is at (C) the end of the echo passes (a).

The effect of this finite length of target on the echo signal may be found by correlating the motion of the echo past some fixed reference point and the motion of the pulse, traveling at the same speed, past the target. When the pulse is in the position (A) shown in the diagram of Fig. 8B-4 its leading edge has just arrived at the point on the target, a, which is nearest to the transducer. At this instant the leading edge of the echo is just leaving this point, which will serve as a convenient reference. When the pulse is at (B) its trailing edge is leaving the point on the target, b, farthest from the transducer. The trailing edge of the echo is, therefore, leaving this distant point at the same instant; it must travel the length of the target before it reaches the reference point. While the echo is traveling the target length the pulse will continue in the opposite direction for the same distance. It will arrive at the position shown by (C) as the trailing edge of the echo passes a, the reference point. The time required for the entire echo to pass a fixed point, then, is the same as the time required for the pulse to move from the position shown by (A) to the position shown by (C). It is therefore evident that the length of the path occupied by the echo, which must be equal to this distance, is equal to the length of the pulse falling on the target plus twice the target length.

This relation gives at once a very simple method for determining the effective length of any target. By means of a cathode ray oscilloscope, or similar instrument, it is possible to measure with considerable accuracy the lengths of each of a series of outgoing pulses and of each of the echoes returned in response to them. When these echo lengths are plotted against their corresponding pulse lengths the resulting curve should be a straight line. The target length is one-half the value of the echo length corresponding to zero pulse length.

In certain types of target the echo is reradiated only after repeated reflection within the target. This delays the reradiation by the time required for the signal to travel between the several reflection points. In such cases the **effective target length** is one-half the length of the echo signal which would result from a pulse of zero length, as determined by the variable-pulse method.

The relation between pulse length and target strength may be investigated by considering the situation at some fixed instant as acoustic energy, in the form of a short train of waves, travels away from the transducer along the target. It will be assumed that any beam within which energy may be confined by the transducer is sufficiently broad to cover the target completely with respect to dimensions perpendicular to the direction of propagation. Consider the situation at the instant when the pulse has arrived at a position such as indicated by the solid arrow of Fig. 8B-5. At this instant energy is being reflected back toward the source from each point of the target included within the length of the pulse. Increments of energy which are simultaneously reflected from different portions of the target do not, however, reach the receiving point simultaneously. Consider the energy which, at the instant when the pulse is in the position shown, is passing—or leaving—the reference surface *a-a* on the return trip to the source. At this instant energy carried by the leading edge of the pulse is starting back from points on the surface *b-b* but will not reach the surface *a-a* until some time in the future. On the other hand, energy which was at one time carried by the leading edge but which was turned back by points on the surface *c-c*, halfway between *a-a* and *b-b*, at a time prior to the instant in question has had an opportunity to reach the reference surface. It will, in fact, reach this surface simultaneously with energy carried by the trailing edge of the pulse and will continue its return trip in company with this energy. Similarly, energy once carried by intermediate portions of the pulse, but which has already been reflected from points between *a-a* and *c-c*, will reach the reference surface, *a-a*, at this same instant. It is thus apparent

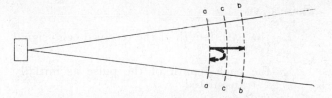

Fig. 8B-5. Effect of Pulse Length on Target Strength. The relations between the path length occupied by a pulse of acoustic energy, the space, *aabb*, from which energy is being reradiated at a given instant, and the space, *aacc*, from which energy will, at some later instant, be received.

that at the particular instant represented by the diagram the energy crossing the reference boundary, *a-a*, is made up of contributions from all points of the target included between the surfaces *a-a* and *c-c*. These increments of energy will continue together and will arrive at the receiving point simultaneously; no other increments of reflected energy will arrive at the same time. It follows that at any instant throughout the duration of the echo resulting from the transmission of a pulse of acoustic energy the energy reaching the receiving point represents the summation of reflections from that portion of the target which is contained between spherical boundaries separated by a linear distance equal to one-half the pulse length. The strength of a given target is therefore proportional to the logarithm of the pulse length used so long as this length is less than twice the target length.

Target strengths reported in an earlier article are based on pulses which are in excess of twice the target length. They consequently correspond to the maximum strengths which the targets in question may exhibit.

The effect of the medium has been shown to increase the duration of the echo signal by twice the difference between the travel times for the fastest and the slowest paths. The effect of the target has been shown to increase the length of path occupied by the echo by twice the target length. The result of combining these effects may be expressed as a summation if they are stated in common terms. The relation between path length and time is, as already noted, given by the velocity of propagation $c = l/T$. Using this equation the increase in echo length due to multiple transmission paths is $2c(\Delta T)$ where (ΔT) is the difference between the transmission times for the fastest and the slowest paths. The length of the path occupied by a received echo is then

$$l_e = l_p + 2c(\Delta T) + 2l_T \qquad (8B\text{-}15)$$

where

l_e = the path length of the received echo signal (yd)

l_p = the path length of the pulse as initially transmitted (yd)

c = the velocity of propagation (yd/sec)

ΔT = the difference between the transmission times of the fastest and the slowest paths between source and target (sec)

l_T = the effective length of the target (yd)

An equivalent summation in terms of time intervals may be obtained by dividing each term in Eq. (8B-15) by c, the velocity of propagation.

Any instrument designed for indicating the ranges of acoustically reflecting targets does so by measuring time intervals. It is calibrated to report any time interval as the length of path which would be traversed twice during that interval by a signal wave traveling at the velocity of sound in water. It would, therefore, report the time required for a pulse or echo signal to pass any fixed point as one-half the length of path actually occupied by that signal. It is thus apparent that if echo signals received by a range-measuring instrument were used to determine the length of some given target, or the difference between the travel times of two ray paths—this time difference being expressed in terms of a range difference—these quantities would be reported correctly. This fact must, indeed, be true since both quantities are related to increments of range which are traversed twice by the echo-ranging signal.

8-C REVERBERATION

Interference with an echo by reverberation in echo ranging is quantitatively quite different from interference with a signal by noise in direct listening. In the latter case the signal and the noise are more or less independent; they come from different sources, and may have different frequency characteristics and different directional distributions. In echo ranging it is often difficult to find any significant difference between the echo and the reverberation. The echo signal is, in fact, merely a component of general reverberation to which special interest is attached. If the target is moving relative to the medium a change in frequency due to the Doppler effect may serve to distinguish the echo from other reflected waves. When there is no target motion the detection of an echo is possible only when the presence of the target causes the level of the total energy reflected to deviate noticeably from the level to be expected if the target were absent. Unless the target alters the total reflectivity encountered by the outgoing pulse it cannot be detected. It is then the acoustical analogue of a white rabbit sitting on a snowbank.

Although we are in almost all cases concerned with the level of the total energy reflected it will often be convenient to consider the echo and the reverberation separately and to refer to the **echo-to-reverberation ratio.** As with signal-to-noise ratio this quantity will be expressed in decibels, and will be designated as the **signal differential.**

One of the major fundamental investigations in the field of acoustics to be undertaken during World War II was a quantitative study of underwater reverberation.[1,2] Like the study of other underwater sounds this involves the analysis, by statistical methods, of the results of many observations. As with underwater sounds, also, it will be possible here to do little more than to review the general conclusions reached and to describe certain quantitative relations which have been found to have considerable practical utility.

8C-1 Sources of Reverberation

We have already seen (Sec. 3-C) that both the surface and the bottom of the ocean reflect acoustic energy. Some portion of this energy is likely to be reflected in such a direction that it returns to the point of observation. Any energy returned in this manner is known either as **surface reverberation** or as **bottom reverberation.** Since these show the same characteristic behavior it will be convenient to refer to them generically as **boundary reverberation.** Much of the energy reaching the starting point as a result of reflection at the boundaries of the medium undergoes more than one reflection on its excursion.

In addition to its boundary surfaces impedance discontinuities are to be found throughout the volume of the ocean itself. These may be due to a variety of causes such as air bubbles occluded by wave action, gas bubbles from decaying vegetation, or living organisms. Frequently these reflectors are of considerable size, as in the case of masses of kelp or of schools of fish. Such large reflectors are to be found at intervals and are usually reported as targets, which, indeed, they are. In addition to these discrete reflectors there are so many minute reflectors in the ocean that no sample is free of them. It is these small reflectors, or **scatterers,** which are responsible for what is known as **volume reverberation.** Scatterers are understood to have dimensions which are small as compared to a signal wave. Each may be considered to act as a point source of secondary radiation.

Although scatterers are found in all parts of the sea they are by no means uniformly distributed. In some locations they are concentrated in layers which vary in thickness and in depth, sometimes moving in a diurnal cycle. Such layers have been shown to be composed of huge colonies of minute marine creatures. The location, size, and movements of these colonies have been studied by echo-sounding equipment, to which the entire depth occupied returns a clearly defined signal. Under some conditions the reverberation due to a layer having a high concentration of scatterers will show the same general characteristics as bottom reverberation.

8C-2 Reverberation Strength

It is invariably found that the reverberation following the transmission of an echo-ranging pulse decreases rapidly during the receiving interval. To say that the reverberation due to a pulse of acoustic energy varies with time is, of course, the same as saying that it varies with the range at which the pulse is reflected. Reverberation suffers from propagation losses in water as do all other forms of acoustic energy.

As a pulse of acoustic energy travels along the beam formed by a directional transducer the intensity, on any bearing, decreases because of the distribution of this energy over an increasing area and also because of the effect of attenuation. This attenuation, it is now evident, is in part accounted for by the energy lost through conversion into reverberation prior to the arrival of the pulse at the point in question. In the absence of other effects, then, the intensity of the outgoing pulse is subject to normal propagation losses. The reverberation returned from any range, however, depends upon the total energy reaching that range rather than upon its intensity; under ideal conditions this total energy is unaffected by geometric spreading but is subject only to the usual effects of attenuation. At any range some small portion of this total energy is reflected by scatterers distributed throughout the volume of the medium there occupied by the pulse. At some instant in the future energy associated with one-half of this volume, as shown in Art. 8B-2, will reach the receiving point and will determine the level of the reverberation at that instant. On the return trip the energy reflected from each scatterer will diverge, generally in accordance with the inverse square law. On the return trip, then, reverberation is subject to both spreading and attenuation losses. The spreading loss for the entire transmission, therefore, is the same as for a single transit of the path; the total attenuation loss is twice that for a single transit.

In measuring reverberation it is recognized that the energy reaching a receiving point does not have the form of a single plane wave, as does the echo from a target, but converges from all directions. The directional distribution of the apparent sources of this energy is, in fact, determined by the directional characteristics of the echo-ranging transducer. In this situation it will be convenient to express the magnitude of the reverberation, at any instant, as the intensity of a plane wave which would produce in a nondirectional hydrophone the same open-circuit voltage as would be produced by the actual reverberation. This is the **equivalent plane wave intensity** applying to a nondirectional hydrophone.

The propagation loss for volume reverberation, which measures the change in the equivalent plane wave intensity of this reverberation as the range from which it is returned increases, is thus given by the equation

$$\lg \frac{(I'_r)_{v1}}{(I'_r)_{v2}} = 2 \lg \frac{S_2}{S_1} + 2a(S_2 - S_1) \quad (8C\text{-}1)$$

where

$(I'_r)_{v1} =$ the equivalent plane wave intensity, as measured with a nondirectional hydrophone, of the volume reverberation returned from a range of S_1 kyd (watt/cm²)

$(I'_r)_{v2} =$ the equivalent plane wave intensity, also as measured with a nondirectional hydrophone, of the volume reverberation returned from a range of S_2 kyd (watt/cm²)

a = the attenuation coefficient applying at the frequency of the transmission in question
(db/kyd)

Although the above relation has been deduced by considering an ideal situation it has been found to represent with considerable accuracy the results of statistical analyses of many actual measurements of the rate of change of the intensity of volume reverberation with time, and hence with range. In many of these measurements the effect of boundary layers was avoided by working in deep water, thus eliminating bottom reverberation, and by directing the transducer beam at a sharp downward inclination, thus eliminating surface reverberation.

As with all propagation loss formulas the smooth curve of intensity as a function of range, which represents the equation graphically, applies to the average value of intensity. The actual intensity at any instant may depart appreciably from this mean value. Moreover, in any single situation, the average intensity there appearing may also deviate from the general average. The equation gives, in other words, an average of many values each of which is itself an average. Thus interpreted Eq. (8C-1) summarizes in a single expression the results of many actual measurements of the propagation loss applying to volume reverberation.

In the case of boundary reverberation the interception of the beam by a reflecting surface results in the deflection of a portion of the total energy of the outgoing pulse. The amount of energy thus diverted increases with increasing range. The total energy from which surface reverberation may be withdrawn, at any instant, consequently decreases with range. This decrease has been found by actual observation to vary approximately as the inverse first power of the range. As with volume reverberation the spreading loss suffered by boundary reverberation on its return trip, in general, follows the inverse square law, thus making the total spreading loss correspond to the inverse cube of the range. Attenuation loss, which is effective in both directions, is the same for boundary reverberation as for volume reverberation and has twice the value associated with a single transit of a given path. The propagation loss for boundary reverberation, as measured by the decrease in equivalent plane wave intensity with increase in range, is thus

$$\lg \frac{(I'_r)_{b1}}{(I'_r)_{b2}} = 3 \lg \frac{S_2}{S_1} + 2a(S_2 - S_1) \quad \text{(8C-2)}$$

where

$(I'_r)_{b1}$ = the equivalent plane wave intensity, as measured with a nondirectional hydrophone, of the boundary reverberation returned from a range of S_1 kyd
(watt/cm²)

$(I'_r)_{b2}$ = the equivalent plane wave intensity, also as measured with a nondirectional hydrophone, of the boundary reverberation returned from a range of S_2 kyd
(watt/cm²)

a = the attenuation coefficient applying at the frequency of the transmission in question.
(db/kyd)

Like Eq. (8C-1) this equation represents a statistical averaging of much experimental data and thus summarizes the conclusions to be drawn therefrom. It will be found useful in many practical problems.

As with the propagation loss suffered by an echo signal, the propagation loss for reverberation identified with the distance between the transducer and some reflecting surface, or volume, at a range $S = S_2$, is obtained by making S_1 equal to the one yard index distance in either of the preceding equations. As before, it is necessary to determine the total transmission loss, as measured by the ratio between the intensity of the outgoing pulse and the intensity of the reverberation returned from the given range.

The losses affecting reverberation at the time of reflection are somewhat more complex than those, represented by target strength, affecting an echo from a single target. In the case of reverberation the energy directed toward the echo-ranging receiver depends upon the number and distribution of the reflectors as well as upon their size, shape, and reflectivity. In general it may be assumed that individual reflectors are relatively small and that the energy which they turn back leaves from a point at a distance from the apparent source of reradiation which is considerably less than the one yard index distance. With respect to this factor, then, it would be expected that the transmission loss due to reflection would have a large positive value. At any instant, however, there will be a large number of such reflectors, distributed, as we have seen, throughout one-half the volume occupied by the transmitted pulse.

The magnitude of the phenomena taking place at the time of reflection may be expressed by a quantity analogous to target strength, as defined in Art. 8B-1. When combined with the propagation loss suffered by reverberation the resulting transmission loss gives the difference between the index level of the outgoing pulse and the equivalent plane wave level of the reverberation returned from some specified range. Although this quantity is likely to be an actual transmission loss, as differentiated from target strength, which is a virtual transmission gain, it will be advantageous to maintain a similarity of expression in the two cases. We shall, therefore, define **reverberation strength** as the difference between the level of a plane wave producing in a nondirectional transducer a response equal to that produced by the reverberation corresponding to a range of one yard from the effective center of the transducer and the index level of the pulse transmitted, on any bearing, by the same nondirectional transducer.

In accordance with the preceding definition the formula for reverberation strength may be written as

$$N_{RS} = \text{lgt} \frac{(I'_r)_1}{I'_p} \qquad (8C-3)$$

where

N_{RS} = the reverberation strength of an acoustic medium (db)

$(I'_r)_1$ = the equivalent plane wave intensity corresponding, by extrapolation, to energy returned as reverberation from a distance of one yard from the effective center of a nondirectional transducer and measured by that transducer (watt/cm²)

I'_p = the index intensity of the pulse transmitted, on any bearing, by the same nondirectional transducer (watt/cm²)

The level of the plane wave which is equivalent, in a nondirectional transducer, to the reverberation corresponding to a range of $S_1 = 1$ yd, as given by this equation, may be substituted into either of the two equations for the propagation loss suffered by the reverberation. This gives the difference between the index level of the pulse sent out, on any bearing, by a nondirectional transducer and the equivalent plane wave level, for that same transducer, of the reverberation returned from a range of $S_2 = S$ kyd. This difference may be written as

$$\text{lgt} \frac{I'_p}{I'_r} = (N_w)_r - N_{RS} \qquad (8C-4)$$

where $(N_w)_r$ is the propagation loss as given either by Eq. (8C-1) or by Eq. (8C-2).

The volume of the space from which reverberation may be received at any instant depends upon the area over which acoustic energy is distributed by the echo-ranging projector and upon the distance along the direction of propagation occupied by the transmitted pulse at some earlier instant. As shown in Art. 8B-2, in connection with the intensity of an echo signal, energy from all points within the volume identified with one-half of this pulse length appears simultaneously at the receiving point. From this it is to be expected that the intensity of reverberation will be directly proportional to pulse length. This conclusion has been verified many times by carefully conducted experiments. Any statement of reverberation strength is, therefore, without significance unless the pulse length is specified. The value of actual reverberation strength effective for a pulse of t seconds duration may be written in terms of a reference reverberation strength, $(N_{RS})_0$, corresponding to a pulse of t_0 seconds duration as

$$N_{RS} = (N_{RS})_0 + \text{lgt} \frac{t}{t_0} \qquad (8C-5)$$

Since the level of reverberation continues to increase indefinitely with increasing pulse length, while the level of an echo from some definite target remains constant after the pulse length has become twice the target length, it is obvious that the echo-to-reverberation ratio decreases after the pulse length has reached this critical value. In other words, as the volume of the medium returning energy to an echo-ranging transducer by reflection becomes larger than is required to include some given target there is a corresponding decrease in the fractional change in the intensity of this returned energy corresponding to the decreased fraction of the total reflectivity represented by the target.

Reverberation strength has been defined in terms of the performance of a nondirectional transducer in order that it may be considered a property of the medium. It would appear in order, then, to include at this point some statement as to the actual magnitudes of reverberation strength found under various conditions. As with other quantities affecting the performance of sonar systems it is impossible here to do more than indicate the order of magnitude of the reverberation strength representing the results of statistically averaged observations under a variety of conditions. For general purposes, then, we may say that the reverberation strength for a 100-ms pulse is likely to have a value in the neighborhood of $N_{RS} = -50$ db. Since this is no more than a nominal value it may be applied to both volume and to boundary reverberation. It is, however, frequently found that boundary reverberation is likely to have a higher reverberation strength than volume reverberation. It has been found, also, that boundary reverberation, which usually predominates during the first portion of an echo-signal transmission, is dependent to a considerable extent on sea state. Reverberation returned from ranges within 1000 yd of an echo-ranging transducer may be expected to increase as much as 30 to 40 db for an increase in wind velocity from 5 miles/hr to 20 miles/hr. For reverberation returned from ranges in excess of 1000 yd the effect of sea state—or of wind velocity—is almost negligible.

In speaking of the energy returned to the point of origin of an echo-ranging pulse it is sometimes the practice to evaluate the effect of the medium as a reflector in terms of a **scattering coefficient,** m. This quantity is defined as the total target area of all scatterers in a unit volume of the medium. It is related to the quantity here defined as reverberation strength by the equation

$$N_{RS} = \lg \frac{ml}{2} \qquad (8C\text{-}6)$$

where l is the length of the echo-ranging pulse in yards. The quantity $\lg m$ is thus seen to be the reverberation strength identified with a pulse having a length of 2 yd.

8C-3 The Effect of Transducer Directivity

The loss given by Eq. (8C-4) is the total transmission loss, or **reverberation loss,** when the transducer is nondirectional. It is required to find the value of this loss as it would be measured for a transducer having specified directional characteristics. The preceding equation is inde-

pendent of the actual projector and hydrophone losses of the nondirectional transducer in terms of which it is derived. It may be applied to a nondirectional transducer which has the same receiving response on any bearing as the given directional transducer has on its maximum response bearing. It also applies when the level of the pulse at the index point, on any bearing, is equal to the level at the index point on the maximum response bearing of the given transducer. Under these conditions the response of the nondirectional transducer corresponds to the reference response specified in the definition of **reverberation index** given in Art. 4F-7. The response of the directional unit is, in this case, less than the response of the reference nondirectional unit by the amount of this index. Now the receiving response of the directional unit on its maximum response axis is, by hypothesis, equal to the response of the reference nondirectional unit on any axis. That is, plane waves of equal intensity would produce equal responses in the two hydrophones. Consequently the equivalent plane wave level, $\lg(I_r/I_{ref})$, of the reverberation from a given range as measured by the directional transducer must be less than the apparent plane wave level, $\lg(I'_r/I_{ref})$, of the reverberation from the same range as measured by the reference nondirectional transducer by the amount of the reverberation index. In other words,

$$\lg I'_r = \lg I_r + N_{RI}$$

This equation is valid only on the assumption that the index intensity of the pulse measured on the maximum response axis of the directional transducer is equal to the index intensity of the pulse measured on any axis of the nondirectional transducer, or that $I'_p = I_p$. These equalities may be substituted into Eq. (8C-4) to give the difference between the index level of the pulse transmitted on the maximum response axis of a directional echo-ranging transducer and the apparent plane wave level of the reverberation returned from a range of S kyd, as measured on this same directional transducer. This difference is

$$\lg \frac{I_p}{I_r} = (N_w)_r + N_{RI} - N_{RS} \qquad (8C\text{-}7)$$

where

$I_p =$ the index intensity of a transmitted echo-ranging pulse as measured on the maximum response axis of a specified directional echo-ranging transducer (watt/cm²)

I_r = the apparent plane wave intensity of the reverberation returned from a range of S kyd as measured on this same directional transducer (watt/cm²)

$(N_w)_r$ = the propagation loss suffered by the type of reverberation in question (db)

N_{RI} = the reverberation index of the given directional transducer (db)

N_{RS} = the reverberation strength of the medium, corresponding to the type of reverberation and to the pulse length (db)

The reverberation index as defined in Art. 4F-7 applies to the case of volume reverberation almost as well as to the hypothetical spherical surface postulated in the definition. In practice few directive beams have an opportunity to expand over a constantly increasing area for an indefinite distance. If the transducer is close to the surface the upper portion of the beam will ultimately be intercepted and the assumptions on which the reverberation index has been computed will cease to be valid. The major portion of the energy sent out by a highly directional transducer may, however, be transmitted in a normal manner for an appreciable range. In such cases the reverberation index is a significant guide to the relative performance of transducers having comparable directional characteristics. It should not be relied upon when the directivity pattern shows much energy in the secondary lobes.

The reverberation index as defined does not apply to situations where reverberation is due largely to boundary reflections. The condition required by the original definition is that energy be reflected, along any bearing, by a surface normal to the direction of propagation. When the directive beam from a submerged transducer encounters either the surface or the bottom of the ocean the angle of incidence is likely to be far from normal. Moreover, the reflecting surface may intercept only a portion of the beam. In general the area returning energy, the intensity distribution over this area, and the receiving response of the transducer to this returned energy all vary with range.

The entire problem of reverberation due to reflection at a boundary is further complicated by bending of the transducer beam by refraction.

In some cases a strong velocity gradient may cause the axis of the beam to strike a surface to which it was parallel at the source. Energy directed back along any ray path at the point of reflection will follow that path all the way back to its source. The effect of refraction may then be described as equivalent to tilting the reflecting surface so that it intercepts the beam at a less oblique angle than would otherwise be found.

From the foregoing it is clear that the relation between boundary reverberation and transducer directivity depends upon many factors fixed by the environment; it is not a unique function of the transducer. This introduces a serious difficulty into the determination of the value of reverberation strength characteristic of any given location or situation. The logical method for evaluating reverberation strength would be to make observations of the index level of the transmitted pulse and of the equivalent plane wave level of the reverberation returned from some known range. This fixes the reverberation loss represented by Eq. (8C-7). The substitution of numerical values for propagation loss and for reverberation index into this equation would, then, be assumed to give a numerical value for reverberation strength. We have, however, just seen that it is quite unlikely that the effective value of reverberation index will be known with any assurance. Fortunately, in many problems it is unnecessary to evaluate the reverberation strength and the reverberation index individually. The difference, $(N_{RS} - N_{RI})$, between these two quantities is, in many cases, more significant than either alone. In view of the analogy between this difference and the apparent plane wave level of noise interference given by Eq. (4F-25) it may logically be designated as the **apparent reverberation strength.** Apparent reverberation strength is seen by Eq. (8C-7) to be equal to the difference between the apparent plane wave level of the reverberation corresponding to a range of one yard, as received on a given directional transducer, and the index level of the pulse transmitted on the maximum response axis of the same transducer. The negative value of this difference is, by definition, the reverberation loss corresponding to a range of one yard, as measured on a given transducer.

Apparent reverberation strength may usually be measured with little difficulty. In general all that is required is to observe the level of the reverberation returned to some given point as a function of time. A typical oscillographic record

FIG. 8C-1. REVERBERATION. Oscillogram showing the time variation in amplitude of reverberation following the transmission of an echo-ranging pulse.

of the voltage generated in an echo-ranging transducer, following the transmission of a short train of sinusoidal ultrasonic waves by that transducer, is shown in Fig. 8C-1. It is obvious from an inspection of this record that the rate at which energy reaches a transducer after reflection by the various impedance discontinuities encountered by the acoustic waves radiated by that transducer decreases with time in an irregular manner. At any instant the magnitude of the deviation from a value representing a simple continuous function of time is, indeed, likely to be comparable with the absolute magnitude of such a function. It is, nevertheless, possible to draw, even on a record such as that shown by Fig. 8C-1, a smooth curve representing average values having a continuously decreasing rate of decay. From such a curve it is possible to compute values of reverberation level which also decrease continuously with time. It is, in other words, possible to draw a smooth curve showing the average value of reverberation level as a continuous function of time. Since, moreover, time is a measure of the range of the reflectors from which this reverberation is directed to the point in question, a curve of reverberation level as a function of range may also be drawn. By referring this reverberation level to the index intensity of the transmitted energy the curve thus drawn represents the value of reverberation loss

as a function of range, as well as the value of reverberation level.

In many cases it will be found that a curve showing smoothed values of reverberation level, derived in the manner described, corresponds closely to the sum of two reverberation intensities, each of which has a level characteristic of constant slope when plotted against a logarithmic scale of time, or of range. It is often possible to represent one of these intensities by a level characteristic having the constant slope of 3 db/Sl known to be typical of boundary reverberation, and one by a level characteristic having the constant slope of 2 db/Sl known to be typical of volume reverberation. This possibility is, of course, limited to ranges which are so short, or to frequencies which are so low, that attenuation losses are negligible compared to spreading losses.

The reverberation loss characteristic of reverberation which may be considered as made up of two such components is shown in Fig. 8C-2. The loss characteristics of the two component intensities may be drawn, with such extrapolation as may be required, to show the reverberation loss corresponding to a range of one yard. The loss

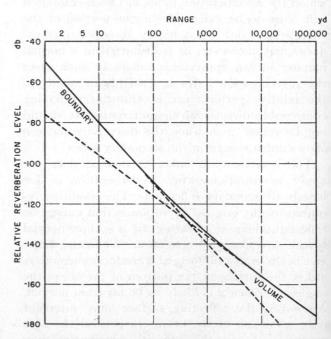

FIG. 8C-2. REVERBERATION LEVELS. The levels of volume reverberation and of boundary reverberation, relative to the index level of the transmitted echo-ranging pulse causing this reverberation, as functions of the range from which the reverberation is returned. The solid line gives the level due to both types of reverberation.

thus indicated by the straight line identified with boundary reverberation is the apparent boundary reverberation strength. The loss similarly indicated by the straight line identified with volume reverberation is the apparent volume reverberation strength. In the example shown the portion of the curve corresponding to ranges less than 200 yd is seen, because of its slope, to be due chiefly to boundary reverberation. The apparent reverberation strength of the surfaces returning this boundary reverberation is $(N_{RS}-N_{RI})_b$ $=-50$ db. The portion of the curve corresponding to ranges greater than 4000 yd appears, for a similar reason, to be due chiefly to volume reverberation. The apparent reverberation strength of the medium returning this reverberation is given by the extrapolated straight line matching this portion of the curve as $(N_{RS}-N_{RI})_v=-76$ db.

Values of reverberation strength obtained as described above serve adequately for many predictions as to the effects of changes in the environment or of changes in the method of operation. For certain types of analytical problem it is advantageous to consider reverberation index and reverberation strength as independent quantities, even though the separate evaluation of their absolute magnitudes may be impossible. It is for this reason that they have been separately defined.

The reverberation loss suffered by a specified type of reverberation may be written as a function of the range from which the reverberation is returned by substituting the appropriate propagation loss, as given by Eq. (8C-1) or Eq. (8C-2), into Eq. (8C-7). In substituting the expressions for propagation loss it is understood that the distance S_1 is to be made equal to the one yard index distance, and that the distance S_2 is to be made equal to the range, S, from which the reverberation is actually returned. Making these substitutions we have, for volume reverberation,

$$(N_r)_v = \lgt \frac{I_p}{(I_r)_v} = 2\lgt S + 2aS + 60$$
$$-(N_{RS}-N_{RI})_v \quad (8C-8)$$

and for boundary reverberation,

$$(N_r)_b = \lgt \frac{I_p}{(I_r)_b} = 3\lgt S + 2aS + 90$$
$$-(N_{RS}-N_{RI})_b \quad (8C-9)$$

where

$(N_r)_v=$ the total transmission loss suffered by volume reverberation, or the volume reverberation loss (db)

$(N_r)_b=$ the total transmission loss suffered by boundary reverberation, or the boundary reverberation loss (db)

$I_p=$ the index intensity of the transmitted echo-ranging pulse, as measured on the maximum response axis of a specified echo-ranging transducer (watt/cm²)

$(I_r)_v=$ the apparent plane wave intensity of the volume reverberation received from some given range, as measured by the specified transducer (watt/cm²)

$(I_r)_b=$ the apparent plane wave intensity of the boundary reverberation received from some given range, as measured by the specified transducer (watt/cm²)

$S=$ the given range (kyd)

$a=$ the attenuation coefficient applying at the frequency of the transmitted pulse (db/kyd)

$(N_{RS}-N_{RI})_v=$ the apparent reverberation strength of the volume reverberation as measured by the specified transducer (db)

$(N_{RS}-N_{RI})_b=$ the apparent reverberation strength of the boundary reverberation as measured by the specified transducer (db)

8C-4 The Reverberation Picture

If the reflectivity of some target is the same as the reflectivity of the portion of the medium which it replaces no detectable echo will be obtained from it. If the reflectivity of the target differs from that of the medium the greater the ratio of the target volume to the total volume from which energy is simultaneously reflected the more prominent will be the echo signal.

The possibility of detecting an echo from a significant target in the presence of reverberation will be found to depend not only on the absolute value of the average level of the reverberation but also on the magnitude of short-time deviations from this average and on the rate at which they occur. The instantaneous value of the reverberation intensity is often spoken of as the reverberation picture. The oscillogram of Fig. 8C-1 shows a typical reverberation picture containing one significant echo. Since the vertical height of the oscillographic trace is proportional to the transducer voltage it is also proportional to the acoustic pressure due to the reverberation; the intensity of the reverberation varies as the square of the variations thus reported. This oscillogram was taken for a transmission at a frequency of 26 kc/sec, in the shallow water of Long Island Sound. It is, however, representative, particularly as to the relative magnitude and frequency of deviations from average value, of the reverberation found in many locations.

8-D THE SONAR EQUATIONS FOR ECHO RANGING

The problems encountered in estimating the performance of echo-ranging equipment, and in appraising the factors which influence it, resemble, in many ways, similar problems having to do with direct listening. The same uncertainties as to the absolute magnitudes of various important quantities are to be found in both cases. The general method of analysis there adopted may, however, be extended to apply to problems encountered in echo ranging.

8D-1 The Derivation of the Echo-Ranging Equations

Situations in which echo ranging is limited by noise interference fall into two main classifications; in one the noise is due to the ship operating the echo-ranging gear or to nearby sources, in the other it is generated by the target. When local noise is the limiting interference the noise level is independent of target range but generally depends to a considerable extent on target bearing. Certain components of own-ship's noise, such as turbulence about the hull and about the transducer, vary little with bearing. Propeller noise, on the other hand, may be so definitely localized that it may be excluded quite effectively, on all bearings more than 20° or so either side of the stern, by a transducer having moderate direc-

tivity. It is often found that the noise level will be higher on bearings which pass through a bow wave than on other bearings except those near the stern. The effects associated with this type of interference approximate closely those observed in direct listening.

Conditions are reversed when target noise is the limiting interference. Here the noise level is directly dependent on target range and is wholly independent of target bearing.

In the following analysis we shall retain the method, adopted in connection with direct listening (Art. 7C-1), of expressing the effective magnitudes of the signal and of the interferences as those of equivalent plane waves in the medium.

The echo loss, N_e, shown by Eq. (8B-10), establishes the difference between the index level of the transmitted echo-ranging pulse and the level of the returned echo. We may, therefore, write the level of a received echo signal as

$$L_e = L_p - N_e = L_p - 2N_w + N_{TS} \quad (8\text{D-}1)$$

The energy thus expressed is usually due to plane waves; no further manipulation is required to express it in terms of equivalent plane waves.

When the limiting interference is due to ownship's noise the interference encountered on any bearing is constant. The level of this interference is understood to apply to energy, contained within the frequency band to which the receiving system is responsive, arriving from all directions. It may be reported as the equivalent plane wave level which would be measured with a nondirectional hydrophone. As in the case of direct listening the apparent plane wave level of this interference for a given directional transducer is obtained by subtracting the effective directivity index of that transducer from the equivalent plane wave level measured with a nondirectional transducer.

As in the case of direct listening, the limiting range at which acceptable performance may be expected of an echo-ranging system is that for which the signal differential has the minimum acceptable value. We therefore write, as for direct listening, a sonar equation in which the signal differential is expressed as the difference between the two plane wave levels described above. This equation, which may be called an echo-ranging equation, is

$$\Delta L_{e/n} = [L_p - 2N_w + N_{TS}]$$
$$- [(L_n)_{\text{loc}} - N_{DI}] \quad (8\text{D-}2)$$

where

$\Delta L_{e/n}=$ the signal differential in echo ranging when self noise, locally generated, is the limiting interference (db)

$L_p=$ the index level of the transmitted pulse, as measured on the maximum response axis of the transducer (db//ref. intensity)

$(L_n)_{loc}=$ the equivalent plane wave level, as measured by a nondirectional hydrophone, of locally generated noise included within the frequency band to which the echo-receiving system is responsive (db//ref. intensity)

$N_w=$ the one-way propagation loss of the water path between the echo-ranging transducer and the echo target (db)

$N_{TS}=$ the target strength of the echo target (db)

$N_{DI}=$ the effective directivity index of the echo-ranging transducer (db)

When target noise is the limiting interference the level of interference is obtained by subtracting the one-way propagation loss between target and receiver from the index level of the target noise. The interference level in this case is, in fact, the level which would be designated as the signal level in the case of direct listening. This interference, like the signal, is usually received as actual plane waves. In these circumstances the signal differential is written as

$$\Delta L_{e/n} = [L_p - 2N_w + N_{TS}]$$
$$- [(L_n)_T - N_w] \qquad (8D\text{-}3)$$

where

$\Delta L_{e/n}=$ the signal differential in echo ranging when target noise is the limiting interference (db)

$(L_n)_T=$ the index level of the noise generated by the target, in the frequency band to which the echo receiver is responsive, as measured on the bearing of the echo-ranging transducer (db//ref. intensity)

When target noise is the predominating interference the echo and the interference originate at a common point and the signal-to-noise ratio

there existing remains unaltered by transducer directivity. It is, of course, advantageous to use a directional transducer, nevertheless; it improves signal-to-noise ratio, as it exists at the target, by concentrating energy associated with the outgoing pulse on the target, and it discriminates against noise from sources other than the target. It is, in fact, largely because of transducer directivity that other noises are reduced sufficiently to leave target noise as the major constituent of interference.

When the reception of an echo signal is obscured by general reverberation the observer usually recognizes the echo only because of a momentary increase in the level of energy returned by reflection. This level is, in practically all cases, varying rapidly and by large amounts about some average value which is decreasing in accordance with one of the reverberation loss formulas. Any echo, to be detected, must cause a greater variation than those normally expected. In view of this situation it would appear logical to study the effect of reverberation on echo signal transmission by attempting to evaluate the observed differential (Art. 6B-1). We have, however, seen that the factors affecting echo intensities are somewhat different than those affecting reverberation intensities. It is, therefore, more convenient to treat them separately as signal and interference. Fortunately there is a unique relation between observed differential and signal differential (Fig. 6B-5) which permits conclusions pertaining to one to be translated into terms of the other. We shall, therefore, continue to use signal differential as a measure of the performance of an echo-ranging system when reverberation is the limiting interference.

The volume reverberation loss, $(N_r)_v$, shown by Eq. (8C-8), establishes the difference between the index level of the pulse and the level of the equivalent plane wave representing the volume reverberation returned from some given range. When volume reverberation is the limiting interference the signal differential is the difference between the level of the equivalent plane wave representing the echo, as given by Eq. (8D-1), and the level of the equivalent plane wave representing the reverberation, obtained by subtracting the reverberation loss as given by Eq. (8C-8) from the index level of the pulse. It is, therefore,

$$\Delta L_{e/r}=[L_p-2N_w+N_{TS}]$$
$$-[L_p-N_{spr}-2N_{attn}+(N_{RS}-N_{RI})_v] \quad (8D\text{-}4)$$

where

$\Delta L_{e/r}$ = the signal differential in echo ranging when volume reverberation is the limiting interference (db)

N_{spr} = the spreading loss of the water path between the echo-ranging transducer and the echo target (db)

N_{attn} = the attenuation loss of this same water path (db)

$(N_{RS} - N_{RI})_v$ = the apparent reverberation strength for volume reverberation as measured by a given directional transducer (db)

When boundary reverberation is limiting, the equation for signal differential is the same as that given above except for the reverberation loss, which now has the value given by Eq. (8C-9). It is thus written as

$$(\Delta L_{e/r})_b = [L_p - 2N_w + N_{TS}]$$
$$- \left[L_p - \frac{3}{2} N_{spr} - 2N_{attn} + (N_{RS} - N_{RI})_b \right]$$
$$(8D-5)$$

where

$(\Delta L_{e/r})_b$ = the signal differential in echo ranging when boundary reverberation is the limiting interference (db)

$(N_{RS} - N_{RI})_b$ = the apparent reverberation strength for boundary reverberation as measured by a given directional transducer (db)

It is generally true that the reverberation index applying to the case of volume reverberation will not be the same as that applying to boundary reverberation. The use of the apparent reverberation strength, which has been described earlier, takes due account of these differences.

8D-2 Figures of Merit of Echo-Ranging Systems

The employment of a figure of merit is as helpful in the design and operation of echo-ranging systems as it is with direct-listening systems. As in the case of direct listening, a figure of merit for an echo-ranging system may be obtained by solving one of the echo-ranging equations, as given in the preceding article, for the propagation loss between transducer and target and finding the maximum tolerable value of this loss, corresponding to the minimum acceptable value of signal differential. We shall first examine the equation thus obtained when the limiting interference is that due to the noise field in the vicinity of the echo-ranging transducer.

On solving Eq. (8D-2) for the one-way propagation loss between the transducer and the target there is obtained

$$N_w = \frac{1}{2}[L_p - (L_n)_{loc} + N_{DI} + N_{TS} - \Delta L_{e/n}] \quad (8D-6)$$

It is to be noted that the apparent plane wave level of the interference, given by the difference $L_n - N_{DI}$, is here the same as in the direct-listening equation. It will also be noted that whereas the index level of the signal was a unique property of the source to be detected, in the case of direct listening, it is now a property of the sonar equipment. The one quantity which now measures a unique property of the target is its target strength.

An important difference between the direct-listening equation and the echo-ranging equation applying to local interference has to do with the minimum detectable signal. In the case of direct listening, it will be recalled, the difference between the index level of the signal and the minimum detectable level of the signal is equal to the maximum tolerable propagation loss between source and receiver. In echo ranging when local noise is the limiting interference this difference is equal to the total transmission loss suffered by the echo signal during its round trip from transducer to target and back to the transducer. This total loss is twice the one-way propagation loss between transducer and target less the target strength of the target. It may be written as

$$2N_w - N_{TS} = L_p - (L_n)_{loc} + N_{DI} - \Delta L_{e/n} \quad (8D-7)$$

The observation of the level of the minimum detectable signal provides as convenient a method for measuring a figure of merit for an echo-ranging system as for a direct-listening system. The method is, in fact, even more direct in echo ranging than it is in direct listening; in the former case the index level of the signal, as well as its minimum detectable level, may be measured at the transducer. Assumptions as to the index level of the signal, which are often required in direct listening, are unnecessary in echo ranging. In many practical problems involving the performance capabilities of echo-ranging systems it is convenient to use this directly measured difference between the index level of the signal and its minimum detectable level as a figure of merit. In addition to the directness with which it may be measured this quantity has the advantage of being expressed, as shown by Eq. (8D-7), by an equation in which those terms which represent properties of the sonar system are separated from those which represent properties of the medium and of the target. In making this statement it is understood that the noise interference is due largely to the vessel carrying the echo-ranging equipment and may, therefore, be said to be a property of the system in the sense that it is somewhat under the control of those responsible for the operation of the system. Although it may be advantageous to separate the terms of the echo-ranging equation in the manner described it is not possible, by this means, to avoid the necessity for either knowing or assuming the value of the target strength of the echo-ranging target. Unless the magnitude of this quantity is known no grouping of terms will make it possible to predict the range corresponding to a given echo-ranging equation.

In problems of the type described in the preceding chapter, where it is desired to investigate the relation between frequency and operating performance, and where it is necessary to solve a pair of simultaneous equations, one of which gives the propagation loss of the water path as a function of range and frequency, it is more convenient to use the maximum tolerable one-way propagation loss as the figure of merit. This loss is expressed by Eq. (8D-6) when the signal differential has its minimum acceptable value. For a given system operated at a given frequency this one-way loss may be derived from the measured difference between the index and minimum detectable levels of the signal as one-half the value obtained by adding the target strength of the target to this difference. When studying the relations between operating range and system design parameters this figure of merit is usually considered a function of frequency. Its value may be plotted graphically as a figure-of-merit characteristic on a loss-frequency diagram, together with propagation loss characteristics, as was done in Fig. 7C-1. To plot such a figure-of-merit characteristic it is necessary to know, or to assume, a slope for the characteristics corresponding to the individual terms appearing on the right of Eq. (8D-6). The absolute magnitudes of these terms may be un-

known at any given frequency. The resultant value of the figure-of-merit characteristic then represents the sum of a number of terms each having the form shown in Eq. (7C-4). In echo ranging, as in direct listening, it is possible to study the effect of an assumed change in some factor without knowing the absolute magnitude of that or related factors.

When target noise is the interference limiting an echo-ranging operation the maximum tolerable propagation loss, an expression for which is obtained by rearranging terms in Eq. (8D-3), is

$$N_w = L_p - (L_n)_T + N_{TS} - \Delta L_{e/n} \quad \text{(8D-8)}$$

This maximum tolerable propagation loss, like the losses given by Eqs. (7C-2) and (8D-6) for direct-listening systems and for echo-ranging systems in which the limiting interference is self noise, may be used as a figure of merit of the system. The equation expressing this figure of merit, like the previous equations, may be combined with an equation expressing propagation loss as a function of range and frequency to form a simultaneous pair from which the relation between operating range and frequency may be derived. As with the two previous equations, this expression does not give a figure of merit which is dependent solely on the sonar equipment. The expression for the direct-listening system, given by Eq. (7C-2), includes the index level of the target noise; the expression for the maximum tolerable propagation loss when the performance of an echo-ranging system is limited by self noise, as given by Eq. (8D-6), includes the target strength of the target; the present expression includes both of these quantities.

In the case of echo ranging when self noise is the limiting interference it was shown by Eq. (8D-7) that a figure of merit could be defined which was independent of the target. This figure of merit was the total transmission loss suffered by the echo signal, or the difference between the index level of the transmitted pulse and the level of the minimum detectable signal. In the present case this difference is seen to be

$$2N_w - N_{TS} = L_p - (L_n)_T + N_w - \Delta L_{e/n} \quad \text{(8D-9)}$$

It is here a function both of the index level of the target noise and of the propagation loss between target and transducer. A measured value of minimum detectable signal, and a known or postulated value of target strength does not now lead to a value for the permissible one-way propagation loss. The total transmission loss is, in the present case, neither a unique property of the equipment nor a directly measurable quantity which may be related to operating range. The desired figure of merit may, however, be evaluated indirectly.

It has already been noted that a number of the factors appearing in the direct-listening equation appear also in the echo-ranging equations. There is, in fact, a relation between these equations which permits the figure of merit defined by any one of them to be derived from the figures of merit of the other two provided the minimum acceptable signal differential for direct listening is known. For example, if the figure of merit for a given system when used for direct listening, as given by Eq. (7C-2), is subtracted from twice the figure of merit for the same system when used for echo ranging, as given by Eq. (8D-6), the difference is found to be

$$\Delta(N_w) = L_p - L_s + N_{TS} - \Delta L_{e/n} + \Delta L_{s/n} \quad (8D-10)$$

Remembering that the index level, L_s, of the signal in direct listening and the index level, $(L_n)_T$, of target-noise interference in echo ranging are the same quantity it is evident, by comparison with Eq. (8D-8), that this difference is equal to the maximum tolerable propagation loss when echo ranging with target noise as the limiting interference plus the minimum acceptable signal differential for direct listening. It is thus seen that, although the figure of merit of an echo-ranging system operating against target noise as the limiting interference cannot be evaluated in terms of a single measured minimum detectable signal level, it may be evaluated in terms of two such measured levels. In this connection it is to be noted that the quantity $(\Delta L_{e/n} - \Delta L_{s/n})$ appearing in Eq. (8D-10) is the difference between the level of the minimum detectable echo-ranging signal and the level of the minimum detectable direct-listening signal, for a given level of local-noise interference.

In attempting to predict the performance of an echo-ranging system, under either known or postulated conditions, it is necessary to consider the combined effect of self-noise and target-noise interference. In attempting to select an optimum operating frequency, also, it is necessary that both of these sources of interference be taken into account. The use of the figures of merit described in the preceding paragraphs provides a convenient means for examining the limitations imposed on the operation of an echo-ranging system by these two types of interference.

This situation will be discussed in terms of a specific example. In the diagram of Fig. 7C-1 the figure-of-merit characteristic has been drawn for a given sonar system when used for direct listening under certain postulated conditions. We shall now assume that this same system is to be used for echo ranging against the same target. In the case of the use for direct listening, it will be recalled, specific values were not assigned to such quantities as the index level of the signal, the equivalent plane wave level of local interference, or the directivity index of the transducer. The resultant effect of these individual factors was, in that example, embodied in the assumption that the figure-of-merit characteristic passed through the point corresponding to a range of 10 kyd and a frequency of 3 kc/sec. The one absolute magnitude assumed was that of the minimum acceptable signal differential. This was given the value $\Delta L_{s/n} = 0$ db. Slopes were assumed for the characteristics giving the various transmission levels and transmission losses as functions of frequency. The values assumed for these slopes were such that the slope of the resultant figure-of-merit characteristic was $\Sigma n = 5/3$ db/fl.

In examining the use of this same system for echo ranging it will now be assumed that the index level of the transmitted pulse, the target strength of the target, and the minimum acceptable signal differential are such that if the target were silent an acceptable echo signal having a frequency of 3 kc/sec would be received if the target were within a range of 6.3 kyd. The assumptions affecting the slope of the figure-of-merit characteristic passing through the point corresponding to this condition will be that the transducer radiates a constant amount of acoustic power, regardless of the frequency, and that the target strength and the minimum acceptable signal differential are also independent of frequency. Since the total acoustic power radiated is constant, and since it has already been assumed that the directivity index of the transducer increases at the rate of 2 db/fl, the index level of the pulse must increase at this same rate. All other factors affecting the slope of this characteristic have already been specified in connection with the figure-of-merit characteristic for direct listening. We thus have the characteristic giving the index level of the echo-ranging signal with a slope of $+2$ db/fl, the characteristic giving the level of the local-noise interference with a slope of $-5/3$ db/fl, and the characteristic giving the directivity index of the transducer with a slope of $+2$ db/fl. The slope of the resultant figure-of-merit characteristic is, therefore, in accordance with Eq. (8D-6), $\frac{1}{2}(\Sigma n)=17/6$ db/fl. It passes, with this slope, through the range-frequency point already postulated.

No further assumptions are required, or permitted, in drawing the figure-of-merit characteristic which would apply to this system and to this target when echo ranging against target noise in the absence of self noise. As shown by Eqs. (8D-9) and (8D-10) values for this characteristic may be derived by subtracting values given by the direct-listening characteristic from twice the corresponding values given by the echo-ranging characteristic for self noise and adding the minimum acceptable signal differential postulated in drawing the direct-listening characteristic. In the present case this direct-listening signal differential has been assumed to be $\Delta L_{s/n}=0$ db. The desired echo-ranging characteristic is, therefore, drawn as the difference between twice the echo-ranging characteristic already drawn and the direct-listening characteristic already drawn. Figure-of-merit characteristics drawn in accordance with the assumptions described above are shown in Fig. 8D-1. It is to be noted that the point of intersection of the two echo-ranging characteristics falls on the direct-listening characteristic; this is because the signal differential in the case of direct listening has been assumed to be zero.

When figure-of-merit characteristics for these two echo-ranging conditions are superimposed on a family of propagation loss characteristics, as was done in Fig. 7C-1, two other characteristics may be derived. Since the figure-of-merit characteristics have been drawn on the assumption of a constant signal differential these derived characteristics are constant signal differential contours, giving range as a function of frequency, for each of the two types of interference. The two constant signal differential contours obtained in this manner from the figure-of-merit characteristics of Fig. 8D-1 are shown in Fig. 8D-2.

It is at once evident, from either of these graphs, that for any frequency below 10 kc/sec the predominating interference, under the postulated conditions, is target noise; for higher frequencies it is self noise, or local interference. At the frequency where these two curves intersect the two types of interference are equal. The resultant interference when both are present in equal amounts has, as shown by Fig. 2B-3, a level which

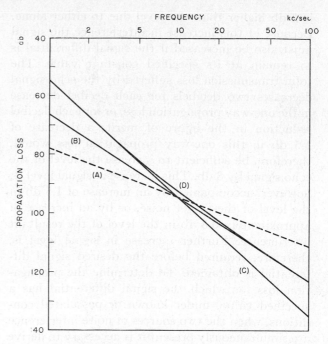

FIG. 8D-1. FIGURE-OF-MERIT CHARACTERISTICS. A loss-frequency diagram showing the figures of merit of a sonar system.

  (A) As used for direct listening
  (B) As used for echo ranging against self-noise interference
  (C) As used for echo ranging against target-noise interference
  (D) As used for echo ranging against both self- and target-noise interference

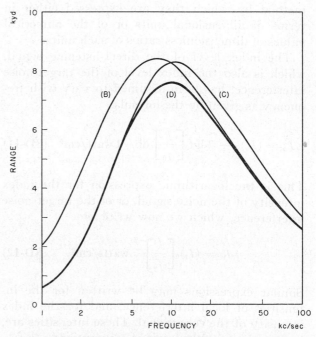

FIG. 8D-2. CONSTANT SIGNAL DIFFERENTIAL CONTOURS. Values of the operating range of a sonar system used for echo ranging, plotted as functions of frequency for a constant signal differential, obtained from the figure-of-merit characteristics of Fig. 8D-1.

is 3 db higher than the level due to either alone. Because of this increase in interference the signal must also be increased if the signal differential is to remain at its specified constant value. The total transmission loss suffered by the echo signal decreases two decibels for each decibel decrease in the one-way propagation loss, or for each decibel reduction in the figure of merit; a decrease of 1.5 db in this one-way propagation loss would, therefore, be sufficient to increase the level of the echo signal by 3 db. This increase in signal level is, however, accompanied by an increase of 1.5 db in the level of the target noise, or by an increase of approximately 0.8 db in the level of the resultant interference. Further increase in signal level is, therefore, required before the desired signal differential is obtained. To determine the propagation loss for which the signal differential has a specified value, under known or postulated conditions, when the two sources of noise interference are simultaneously present it is necessary to derive an exact formula taking account of all factors affecting this loss.

In this situation the factors in question are no longer related by simple multiplication. We must, therefore, abandon the convenient use of the logarithmic method of expressing the values of these factors and return to the more general method by which they are expressed either in terms of dimensional units or of the numerical values of dimensionless ratios of such units.

The index level of the direct-listening signal, which is also the index level of the target-noise interference, has been assumed to vary with frequency as given by the formula

$$L_s = (L_s)_0 - 2 \lgt \left[\frac{f}{f_0} \right] \text{db}//1 \,\text{watt/cm}^2 \quad (8D\text{-}11)$$

This is the logarithmic expression for the index intensity of the noise signal, or of the target-noise interference, which we now write as

$$I_s = (I_s)_0 \left[\frac{f}{f_0} \right]^{-2} \text{watts/cm}^2 \quad (8D\text{-}12)$$

Similar expressions may be written for the intensities of local interference, and for the index intensity of the echo signal. These intensities are, in accordance with previous assumptions,

$$I_n = (I_n)_0 \left[\frac{f}{f_0} \right]^{-5/3} \text{watts/cm}^2 \quad (8D\text{-}13)$$

and

$$I_p = (I_p)_0 \left[\frac{f}{f_0} \right]^{2} \text{watts/cm}^2 \quad (8D\text{-}14)$$

In the case of transmission losses, such as the directivity index of the transducer or the propagation loss of the water path, it is to be remembered that any transmission loss, N, is related to a transmission factor, η, having the properties of an efficiency coefficient, by an expression of the form $N = \lgt 1/\eta$. An example of this is given by Eq. (4F-22) showing the relation between directivity index and directivity factor. In view of this relation it follows that if

$$N_{DI} = (N_{DI})_0 + 2 \lgt \left[\frac{f}{f_0} \right] \quad (8D\text{-}15)$$

$$\eta_D = (\eta_D)_0 \left[\frac{f}{f_0} \right]^{-2} \quad (8D\text{-}16)$$

Similarly, since

$$N_w = \lgt \frac{1}{\eta_w}, \quad 2N_w = \lgt \left[\frac{1}{\eta_w} \right]^{2} \quad (8D\text{-}17)$$

On the basis of these relations the intensity of the received echo signal may be written as

$$I_e = \eta^2{}_w \, \eta_{TS} \, I_p$$
$$= \eta^2{}_w \, \eta_{TS} (I_p)_0 \left[\frac{f}{f_0} \right]^{2} \text{watts/cm}^2 \quad (8D\text{-}18)$$

In the case of target strength it is to be noted that since the target strength is a transmission gain, instead of a transmission loss, it is equal to the logarithm of a transmission factor, instead of to the logarithm of the reciprocal of such a factor, as in previous cases. That is, $N_{TS} = \lgt \eta_{TS}$.

The apparent plane wave intensity of the local-noise interference is, on the basis of assumptions already specified,

$$\eta_D I_n = (\eta_D)_0 (I_n)_0 \left[\frac{f}{f_0} \right]^{-11/3} \text{watts/cm}^2 \quad (8D\text{-}19)$$

The intensity of the received target-noise interference may be written as

$$\eta_w I_s = \eta_w (I_s)_0 \left[\frac{f}{f_0} \right]^{-2} \text{watts/cm}^2 \quad (8D\text{-}20)$$

The ratio of the echo intensity to the resultant intensity of the interference due to the two noise sources acting simultaneously may now be written as

$$\eta_{e/n} = \frac{I_e}{\eta_D I_n + \eta_w I_s} = \frac{\eta^2_w \, \eta_{TS} I_p}{\eta_D I_n + \eta_w I_s} \quad (8D\text{-}21)$$

whence the one-way propagation factor when the two sources of interference are simultaneously effective may be written as

$$(\eta_w)_\Sigma = \frac{\eta_{e/n} I_s \pm \sqrt{(\eta_{e/n} I_s)^2 + 4(\eta_{e/n} \eta_{TS} \eta_D I_n I_p)}}{2(\eta_{TS} I_p)} \quad (8D\text{-}22)$$

It is clearly evident from the form of this expression why it is not possible, in the case of combined self-noise and target-noise interference, to express the propagation loss of the water path between transducer and target as the sum of the logarithms of the numerical values of the several factors which determine its magnitude.

When the target is silent $I_e = 0$ and the preceding equation reduces to

$$(\eta_w)_n = \sqrt{\frac{\eta_{e/n} \eta_D I_n}{\eta_{TS} I_p}} \quad (8D\text{-}23)$$

This relation is the same as that which is expressed in logarithmic form in Eq. (8D-6). When there is no local interference $I_n = 0$ and Eq. (8D-22) becomes

$$(\eta_w)_s = \frac{\eta_{e/n} I_s}{\eta_{TS} I_p} \quad (8D\text{-}24)$$

This is the same as the relation which is expressed logarithmically by Eq. (8D-8).

The amount by which the echo-ranging figure of merit for self-noise interference exceeds the figure of merit for echo ranging when both self-noise and target-noise interference are present is

$$(N_w)_s - (N_w)_\Sigma = \lg t \frac{(\eta_w)_\Sigma}{(\eta_w)_s} \quad (8D\text{-}25)$$

By combining Eqs. (8D-22) and (8D-24) the ratio appearing here may be evaluated as

$$\frac{(\eta_w)_\Sigma}{(\eta_w)_s} = \frac{\eta_{e/n} I_e \pm \sqrt{(\eta_{e/n} I_s)^2 + 4(\eta_{e/n} \eta_{TS} \eta_D I_n I_p)}}{2(\eta_{e/n} I_s)}$$

$$= \frac{1 \pm \sqrt{1 + 4 \dfrac{(\eta_D I_n)(\eta_{TS} I_p)}{\eta_{e/n} I_s^2}}}{2} \quad (8D\text{-}26)$$

A similar expression may be written for the ratio

of the propagation factors applying to target-noise and to resultant-noise interference.

At the frequency where the echo-ranging figures of merit for the two types of noise interference, considered separately, are equal $(\eta_w)_s = (\eta_w)_n$. By combining Eqs. (8D-23) and (8D-24) we have, therefore,

$$\frac{(\eta_{e/n} I_s)^2}{(\eta_{TS} I_p)^2} = \frac{\eta_{e/n} \eta_D I_n}{\eta_{TS} I_p}$$

or

$$\eta_D I_n = \frac{\eta_{e/n} I_s^2}{\eta_{TS} I_p} \quad (8D\text{-}27)$$

When this equality is substituted into Eq. (8D-26) the ratios of the transmission factors measuring the difference between the figure of merit for echo ranging against either type of noise interference alone, at the frequency for which the two types of interference would be equal, and the figure of merit, at this same frequency, when both types of interference are simultaneously present are found to be

$$\frac{(\eta_w)_\Sigma}{(\eta_w)_s} = \frac{(\eta_w)_\Sigma}{(\eta_w)_n} = \frac{1 \pm \sqrt{5}}{2} = 1.618 \quad (8D\text{-}28)$$

Consequently, at this particular point,

$$(N_w)_s - (N_w)_\Sigma = (N_w)_n - (N_w)_\Sigma$$
$$= \lg t \, 1.618 = 2.09 \text{ db} \quad (8D\text{-}29)$$

Values for either of these differences may be computed for frequencies at which they are not equal by means of Eq. (8D-26), or by a similar equation for the ratio $(\eta_w)_\Sigma/(\eta_w)_n$. Values for the echo-ranging figure of merit applying when the two types of noise interference are simultaneously present are then obtained by subtracting these differences from one or the other figures of merit computed when these interferences are considered separately. The resulting figure-of-merit characteristic computed in this manner is shown as Curve (D) of Fig. 8D-1. The constant signal differential contour corresponding to this resultant figure-of-merit characteristic is shown by Curve (D) of Fig. 8D-2.

When the operation of an echo-ranging system is limited by reverberation relations between operating range and the factors which determine it may be obtained by methods analogous to those which have been used in the case of noise interference. In attempting to employ these methods, however, it will be found that the sonar equations may not be solved for a maximum tolerable propagation loss. From Eqs. (8D-4) and (8D-5) it is evident that the signal differential measuring the amount by which the level of the echo exceeds the level of the reverberation is independent of the attenuation loss of the water path. These two equations may, however, be solved for the spreading loss of this path. In the case of Eq. (8D-4), applying to volume reverberation, the solution is

$$N_{\mathrm{spr}} = N_{TS} - (N_{RS} - N_{RI})_v - \Delta L_{e/r} \quad (8D\text{-}30)$$

In the case of Eq. (8D-5), applying to boundary reverberation, the solution is

$$N_{\mathrm{spr}} = 2[N_{TS} - (N_{RS} - N_{RI})_b - \Delta L_{e/r}] \quad (8D\text{-}31)$$

It will be noticed that the spreading losses given by these two equations are both independent of the level of the transmitted pulse. This is, of course, because the pulse level affects both the echo and the reverberation levels equally. These spreading losses are not, however, independent of pulse length because pulse length does not necessarily affect the target strength, N_{TS}, and the apparent reverberation strength, $(N_{RS} - N_{RI})$, equally.

As in the case of the figure-of-merit equations considered earlier, each of these equations may be made one of a pair of simultaneous equations, the other being an equation for spreading loss as a function of range. A pair of simultaneous equations formed in this manner may be solved to give range as a function of frequency in the same manner as that used with the figure-of-merit equations for direct listening and for echo ranging against noise interference. Such a solution may be obtained graphically as in the previous cases. Here, however, the family of propagation loss curves would be replaced by a family of spreading loss curves. These would, in general, be represented simply as straight lines parallel to the frequency axis of the loss-frequency diagram. The graphical method is usually advantageous only when the spreading loss characteristic derived from the echo-ranging sonar equation for reverberation interference is a curved line, as plotted on this same diagram. If this characteristic is a straight line the range-frequency relation may be derived more conveniently in analytical form.

In the pair of simultaneous equations here in question the equation derived from a sonar equation for echo ranging against reverberation ex-

presses spreading loss as a function of frequency. This equation, which may be derived either from Eq. (8D-30) or (8D-31), may be written in the form

$$(N_{\mathrm{spr}})_f = (N_{\mathrm{spr}})_{fo} + \mathrm{lgt}\left[\frac{f}{f_0}\right]^n \quad (8D\text{-}32)$$

Here the reference loss, $(N_{\mathrm{spr}})_{fo}$, is the spreading loss corresponding to a given frequency and to a given range for which the signal differential appearing in the sonar equation for echo ranging against reverberation would have some assigned value. In a similar manner, the spreading loss of the water path is a function of range, independent of frequency. This loss may therefore be written as

$$(N_{\mathrm{spr}})_S = (N_{\mathrm{spr}})_{So} + \mathrm{lgt}\left[\frac{S}{S_0}\right]^m \quad (8D\text{-}33)$$

The desired operating condition exists when the spreading loss of the water path is equal to the spreading loss given by the sonar equation. In this case the spreading loss may be eliminated from Eqs. (8D-32) and (8D-33) and we have

$$S = S_0\left[\frac{f}{f_0}\right]^{n/m} \quad (8D\text{-}34)$$

From the form of this equation it is evident that if range is plotted against frequency, using logarithmic scales for both, the resulting graph will be a straight line. This line represents a constant signal differential locus similar to those shown by Figs. 7C-2 and 8D-2. The value of the exponent, n/m, appearing in the above equation establishes the slope of this locus. Its position on the range-frequency diagram must be such that it passes through the range, S_0, and the frequency, f_0, corresponding to the reference loss. Unfortunately it is rarely possible to assign a value to the exponent, n, appearing in Eq. (8D-32) with as much assurance as was justified either for the direct-listening figure-of-merit characteristic or for the characteristics applying to echo ranging against noise interference. In many problems it is usual to assume that both target strength and reverberation strength are independent of frequency and that the reverberation index increases with increasing frequency at the same rate as does the directivity index. For the usual echo-ranging transducers, therefore, we would use $n = 2$ in the case of volume reverberation, and $n = 4$ in the case of boundary reverberation. A nominal value for the exponent in Eq. (8D-33), giving spreading loss as a function of range, would be $m = 2$. Under these assumptions, therefore, a range limited by volume reverberation would be directly proportional to frequency; a range limited by boundary reverberation would be proportional to the square of the frequency.

In practice volume reverberation and boundary reverberation are generally present at the same time. Their combined effect may be examined by a method which is similar, in principle, to that used for the combined effect of local-noise and target-noise interference. In any situation the difference between the apparent reverberation strength of volume reverberation and the apparent reverberation strength of boundary reverberation will have a value which is, in general, a function of frequency. Such functional dependence, if it exists, will usually be attributable to differences in the manner in which the reverberation index of the transducer for volume reverberation and the manner in which its reverberation index for boundary reverberation vary with frequency.

Assuming, for the moment, that these two indexes do not vary alike we shall adopt some given frequency, f_0, as a reference frequency. The reverberation strength for volume reverberation then has, at this frequency, the reference value $(N_{RS} - N_{RI})_{vo}$. The reverberation strength for boundary reverberation has, at this same frequency, the reference value $(N_{RS} - N_{RI})_{bo}$. At this reference frequency, then, the level for the volume reverberation returned from any range, written as a function of the spreading and attenuation losses for that range in accordance with the relation given by Eq. (8C-8) will be

$$(L_r)_v = L_p - N_{spr} - 2N_{attn}$$
$$+ (N_{RS} - N_{RI})_{vo} \qquad (8D\text{-}35)$$

In a similar manner the level for boundary reverberation may be written, in accordance with Eq. (8C-9), as

$$(L_r)_b = L_p - \frac{3}{2} N_{spr} - 2N_{attn}$$
$$+ (N_{RS} - N_{RI})_{bo} \qquad (8D\text{-}36)$$

At this reference frequency there will, in general, be some range for which these two levels will be equal. For this range and frequency a reference spreading loss, which is obtained by taking the difference between these two equations, is found to be

$$(N_{spr})_0 = 2[(N_{RS} - N_{RI})_{bo} - (N_{RS} - N_{RI})_{vo}] \qquad (8D\text{-}37)$$

We shall now assume that the apparent reverberation strengths each vary with frequency in such manner that

$$(N_{RS} - N_{RI})_v = (N_{RS} - V_{RI})_{vo} - n_v \lgt (f/f_0) \qquad (8D\text{-}38)$$

and

$$(N_{RS} - N_{RI})_b = (N_{RS} - N_{RI})_{bo} - n_b \lgt (f/f_0) \qquad (8D\text{-}39)$$

Under these conditions Eqs. (8D-30) and (8D-31) may be written as

$$(N_{spr})_v = N_{TS} - \Delta L_{e/r} - (N_{RS} - N_{RI})_{vo}$$
$$+ n_v \lgt (f/f_0)$$

and

$$(N_{spr})_b = 2[N_{TS} - \Delta L_{e/r} - (N_{RS} - N_{RI})_{bo}$$
$$+ n_b \lgt (f/f_0)] \qquad (8D\text{-}40)$$

When these two losses are equal

$$(N_{spr})_v = (N_{spr})_b$$
$$= (N_{spr})_0 + 2(n_v - n_b) \lgt (f/f_0) \qquad (8D\text{-}41)$$

and

$$(2n_b - n_v) \lgt (f/f_0)$$
$$= 2(N_{RS} - N_{RI})_{bo} - (N_{RS} - N_{RI})_{vo}$$
$$- N_{TS} + \Delta L_{e/r} \qquad (8D\text{-}42)$$

In many actual situations $n_v = n_b = 2$ db/fl. In this case the characteristics showing these two losses on the loss-frequency diagram will cross at the loss, $(N_{spr})_0$, given by twice the difference between the two apparent reverberation strengths, as evaluated at the reference frequency. The frequency at which this crossing occurs is given by Eq. (8D-42). The characteristic applying to volume reverberation passes through the point thus established with the slope $n_v = 2$ db/fl. The characteristic applying to boundary reverberation passes through this same point with the slope $2 n_b = 4$ db/fl. These slopes are in agreement with the relations given by Eqs. (8D-30) and (8D-31). It remains to determine the resultant characteristic corresponding to the combined volume and boundary reverberation.

By methods analogous to those used in deriving Eq. (8D-21) it is possible to derive a quadratic equation relating spreading factor to factors associated with target strength, apparent volume reverberation strength, apparent boundary reverberation strength, and to the ratio of echo intensity to resultant reverberation intensity. The solution of this equation yields an expression for spreading factor analogous to that for propagation factor given by Eq. (8D-22). Finally, expressions may be derived for the ratios of the spreading factor when both types of reverberation are present concurrently to the spreading factor when either type is considered separately. At the frequency computed by Eq. (8D-42) these two ratios are equal. Their value indicates that the maximum tolerable spreading loss, for given known or postulated conditions, when both types of reverberation are considered simultaneously is 4.18 db less than it would be, for the same value of signal differential, if either type of reverberation were absent. It is to be noted that this difference between the resultant loss-frequency characteristic and the characteristic applying to either type of reverberation considered separately is twice the difference computed for analogous conditions when considering the combined effect of local-noise and target-noise interference.

By means of the relations described in the foregoing paragraphs it is possible, on the basis of certain information or assumptions as to the apparent reverberation strengths of volume reverberation and boundary reverberation, to arrive at a loss-frequency characteristic applying to their combined effect on an echo-ranging operation. When such a characteristic is plotted on a loss-frequency diagram together with the straight lines, parallel to the frequency axis, which represent spreading loss characteristics for various ranges it is possible to derive constant signal differential contours applying to echo-ranging operations which are limited by reverberation. These contours may be plotted on a range-frequency diagram as were the contours shown in Fig. 7C-2. Constant signal differential contours derived and plotted in this manner are shown in Fig. 8D-3. These contours have been drawn for the reverberation conditions illustrated in Fig. 8C-2 on the assumption that $n_v = n_b = 2$ db/fl. This is equivalent to assuming that the transducer remains of constant size as the frequency of the transmitted echo-ranging pulse is altered. Since the slopes of the two characteristics showing apparent reverberation strength as functions of frequency are equal, the two spreading loss characteristics, as drawn on the loss-frequency diagram, cross at that loss which, as required by Eqs. (8D-37) and

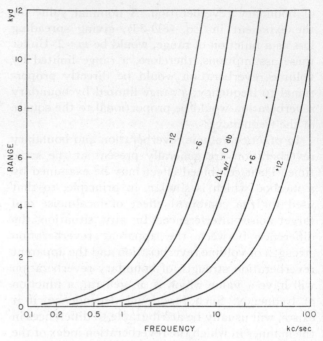

FIG. 8D-3. CONSTANT SIGNAL DIFFERENTIAL CONTOURS. Values of the operating range of an echo-ranging system as limited by reverberation, plotted as functions of frequency for 6-db signal differential increments. The combined effects of volume and boundary reverberation are included in the computation of these contours.

(8D-41), is twice the difference between the apparent reverberation strengths at the reference frequency. This loss is, therefore, $(N_{spr})_0 = 2(76 - 50) = 52$ db. It is further assumed that when the signal differential is $\Delta L_{e/r} = 0$ db this loss occurs at a frequency of 1 kc/sec. These assumptions determine the position of the resultant loss characteristic on the loss-frequency diagram. From Eq. (8D-42) it is evident that an increase of 6 db in the signal differential has the effect of moving this loss characteristic 3 fl in the direction of higher frequencies. The constant signal differential contours shown in Fig. 8D-3, which are separated by 6-db intervals, have been computed graphically in this manner. These contours are designated as corresponding to fixed increments of 6 db in signal differential. From Eq. (8D-42) it is evident, however, that the effect of a 6-db increase in signal differential is the same as the effect of a 6-db reduction in target strength. The intervals between contours may, therefore, be interpreted as due to either of these causes.

A notable characteristic of constant signal differential contours for echo ranging against reverberation is the manner in which they indicate that the range of acceptable operation increases indefinitely with increasing frequency. Such increase cannot, of course, be utilized in practice because a point will ultimately be reached at which reverberation is replaced by noise as the limiting interference. A comparison of the manner in which noise and reverberation affect echo-ranging operations may be made by drawing signal differential contours for both on a single range-frequency diagram. Were it not for the difficulty of assigning realistic values to the minimum acceptable signal differential, over the region where both noise and reverberation are simultaneously effective in obscuring a desired echo signal, it would be possible to arrive at a signal differential contour taking into account the four types of interference represented by the four sonar equations for echo ranging. In view of the many assumptions which would be required in order to compute such a characteristic, however, it appears more profitable to limit efforts in this direction to the separate examination of noise interference and reverberation interference, and to a simple comparison of the results obtained in the two cases.

8D-3 Relations Between Range and Bearing

The effect of transducer directivity on the signal differential when the bearing of an echo-ranging target is not on the maximum response axis of the transducer may be described quantitatively by means of constant signal differential contours, showing range as a function of bearing, similar to those shown in Art. 7C-4 in connection with direct listening.

When noise is the limiting interference a constant signal differential contour is identical with a constant loss contour, as in direct listening. By definition a point moving along a constant loss contour receives a signal of constant intensity from a fixed transducer; a source of constant intensity moving along such a line causes a constant response in a fixed transducer. It therefore follows that an echo-ranging target moving along such a line receives a signal of constant intensity from an echo-ranging transducer, acts as a secondary source of constant intensity, and thus causes a constant response to the echo signal. The response to noise is also constant, either because it comes from sources fixed in position with respect to the transducer or because it comes from a source moving along a constant loss contour. If signal and interference both remain constant the signal differential must remain constant. Regardless of

whether the limiting interference is noise generated in the immediate vicinity of the echo-ranging transducer or noise generated by the target, the sum of the one-way propagation loss between transducer and target and the deviation loss of the transducer is constant. When the interference is due to self noise this constant is equal to one-half the figure of merit; when the interference is due to target noise this constant is equal to the figure of merit. In either case the value of the constant depends upon the fixed signal differential for which the contour line in question is to be drawn, on the index level of the echo-ranging pulse, on the level of the interfering noise, on the target strength, and on the directivity index of the transducer. As in similar situations occurring in direct listening, we can rarely determine the absolute magnitude of this quantity but must content ourselves with studying the effects of changing it from one fixed value to another. The method of finding pairs of range-angle values corresponding to a given constant value of an expression such as this has been described in Art. 4D-3.

In a diagram made up of a family of constant loss—or constant signal level—contours the loss interval between lines is equal to the change in the one-way propagation loss of the water path corresponding to the range increment between the two lines as measured along any bearing crossing them. The decrease in the level of a signal received from the transducer by a point moving from one such line to another, or the decrease in the response of the transducer to a source moving from one such line to another, is given directly by the value of the loss interval between the two lines. The decrease in the response of a fixed transducer to an echo from a target moving from one such line to another is, consequently, equal to twice the loss interval between the two lines. When interference is due to own-ship's noise its level is constant, regardless of target range or of target bearing deviation, and any change in echo signal level results in an equal change in signal differential. The **signal differential interval** between contours is, then, in this case, equal to twice the loss interval. When interference is due to target noise any change in total loss, corresponding to the interval between two contour lines, results in an equal change in noise level. The change in noise level thus offsets one-half the change in signal level and the signal differential interval is now equal to the loss interval.

When the limiting interference is due to reverberation rather than to noise the level of interference, at any instant, is independent of the target bearing deviation. However, the instant at which the echo returns, and thus the instant at which the reverberation interferes with its reception, does vary with the range of the target. The level of reverberation interference, then, varies as the target moves along a constant loss contour and the signal differential is not constant. This situation may be met by properly introducing the deviation loss into Eqs. (8D-4) and (8D-5). In either case the deviation loss of the transducer acts both to reduce the level of the transmitted pulse and the receiving response of the transducer to the returned echo. In the case of volume reverberation, therefore, we have

$$N_{\mathrm{spr}} + 2N_d = (N_{\mathrm{spr}})_{do} \qquad (8D\text{-}43)$$

and in the case of boundary reverberation

$$N_{\mathrm{spr}} + 4N_d = (N_{\mathrm{spr}})_{do} \qquad (8D\text{-}44)$$

The computation of the desired pairs of range-angle values may be carried out graphically in the manner illustrated in Fig. 4D-6. Now, however, instead of obtaining the range values from the normal propagation loss for water we use the spreading loss, which is independent of frequency.

Constant signal differential contours for volume reverberation and for boundary reverberation, which have been computed by this method, are shown in Fig. 8D-4. The transducer on which these computations were based is a circular piston, having a diameter of 5λ. A curve for noise interference is also shown so that constant signal differential contours applying to reverberation interference and to noise interference may be compared. Each curve of Fig. 8D-4 has been plotted for the constant, but arbitrary, value of signal differential assumed to exist for a target at a range of 2000 yd along the acoustic axis. The absolute value of signal differential corresponding to one of the lines of this figure is in no way related to the absolute value of differential corresponding to any other line. The curves of this figure permit a comparison of the four types of interference insofar as the effect of deviation loss in the transducer is concerned.

In the case of reverberation interference the intervals between members of a family of constant signal differential contours are related to spreading loss, instead of to normal propagation loss as

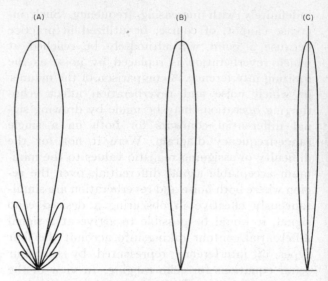

FIG. 8D-4. CONSTANT SIGNAL DIFFERENTIAL CONTOURS. Contour lines showing the positions of echo-ranging targets, with respect to a circular plate transducer having a diameter of 5λ at 25 kc/sec, for which the signal differential, for any one line, has a constant value.
(A) Interference due to self noise or to target noise
(B) Interference due to volume reverberation
(C) Interference due to boundary reverberation

in the case of noise interference. It can be seen from Eq. (8D-30) that for volume reverberation the signal-differential interval between two given contour lines is equal to the change in spreading loss between these same two lines as measured along any fixed bearing. The signal differential interval for boundary reverberation is shown by Eq. (8D-31) to be equal to one-half the change in spreading loss.

For any location of an echo-ranging transducer the locus of target positions giving a constant signal differential is a surface. It may be generated by rotating a constant signal differential contour line about a suitable axis of symmetry, in the same manner as described in Art. 4D-3 in connection with constant loss contours.

Intersections of constant signal differential surfaces with a vertical plane, generally taken through the axis of symmetry, give vertical contour diagrams. Such diagrams yield important information relative to the effect of depth of submergence, either of the target or of the transducer, on the performance of echo-ranging equipment.

For a given contour line drawn in a vertical plane the positions of target and of transducer may not be interchanged without changing the value of signal differential. This applies particularly to situations in which reverberation is the limiting interference. For a given contour line, originating at a given transducer position, it is assumed that the reverberation strength is independent of target position. If the target were to be held fixed at the origin and the transducer moved along the curve the reverberation intensity would vary with position because of the varying depth, and the line would no longer represent the locus of positions of constant signal differential.

In drawing vertical contour diagrams it is convenient to plot depth in feet and horizontal range in yards, as is done in ray diagrams. This requires that both distances be computed for the true distance, or slant range, S, between transducer and target, and for the deviation angle, β, of the target relative to the reference axis of the transducer. The horizontal range is given in terms of these quantities as

$$S_h = S \cos \beta \text{ yd} \qquad (8D\text{-}45)$$

and the depth as

$$D = 3S \sin \beta \text{ ft} \qquad (8D\text{-}46)$$

An example of the use of vertical contour diagrams is given in Fig. 8D-5. The two curves

shown in this diagram correspond to the following specified conditions. In the absence of any noise it is assumed that the reverberation and target strengths are such that the marginal value of signal differential would occur when the target is at a distance of 3 kyd along the reference axis of the transducer. A constant signal differential contour for volume reverberation is drawn through this point. It is then assumed that, in the absence of reverberation, the level of noise interference is such that the marginal differential would occur for a target position 2 kyd along the reference axis. A second contour line, based on interference due to self noise, is drawn through this point. In any practical situation both types of interference are likely to exist simultaneously; the magnitudes chosen above are typical of frequently encountered conditions. The vertical plane through the acoustic axis of the transducer is seen to be divided into a number of areas by the two contour lines. The only area from which acceptable echo signals may be received is that labeled (A), since this is the only area within the limits set by both curves. In the area (B), which includes the side lobes of the contour lines for noise interference, reception

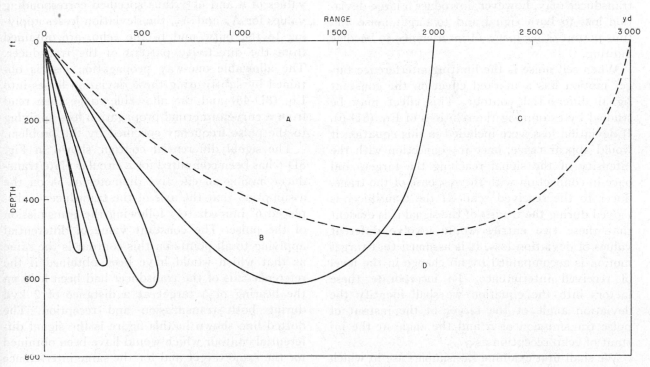

FIG. 8D-5. VERTICAL CONTOUR DIAGRAM. The range, as a function of depth, at which the signal differential has an assumed fixed marginal value for self noise and for volume reverberation, each considered separately. These contours define regions in which:
A. The signal differential is above its marginal value
B. Reception is prevented by reverberation alone
C. Reception is prevented by noise alone
D. Reception is prevented by both noise and reverberation

is prevented by reverberation; in the area marked (C) it is prevented by noise. Outside of these three areas reception is prevented by both noise and reverberation.

8D-4 The Effect of Transducer Motion

Constant signal differential contour lines are especially useful in problems having to do with the rate at which echo-ranging search operations may be carried out. In this connection, contours derived for a transducer which is moved between the transmission of the pulse and the reception of the echo disclose much pertinent information.

For situations in which target noise is the limiting interference motion of the transducer following the transmission of the pulse is without effect on the signal differential. The deviation angle of the target at the time of transmission determines the signal-to-noise ratio at that point. Thereafter signal and noise are propagated along the same path and transducer directivity cannot alter the signal differential. Constant signal differential contours and constant signal level contours are consequently identical in shape when the interference is due solely to target noise. Motion of the transducer may, however, introduce a large deviation loss to both signal and to target noise and thus permit other forms of interference to become limiting.

When self noise is the limiting interference target motion has a marked effect on the constant signal differential contour. This effect may be studied by examining the relations of Eq. (8D-6). If deviation loss were included in this equation it would appear twice, once in connection with the intensity of the signal reaching the target, and once in connection with the response of the transducer to the received echo. If the transducer is moved during the transit of the signal it is evident that these two entries would involve different values of deviation loss. It is assumed that target motion is accompanied by no change in the level of received interference. To incorporate these factors into the equation we shall identify the deviation angle of the target at the instant of pulse transmission as α and the angle at the instant of echo reception as γ.

We shall first examine the simple case in which the transducer is moved by a fixed angular displacement immediately following the transmission of the pulse and then left in its new position throughout the remainder of the operating cycle. This is the so-called "ping-train-listen" technique.

For this case Eq. (8D-6) would be written as

$$N_w = \tfrac{1}{2}[L_p - (L_n)_{\text{loo}} + N_{DI} + N_{TS}$$
$$- \Delta L_{e/n} - N_\alpha - N_\gamma] \quad (8D\text{-}47)$$

The allowable one-way propagation loss between transducer and target is thus

$$N_w = (N_w)_0 - \tfrac{1}{2}(N_\alpha + N_\gamma). \quad (8D\text{-}48)$$

The reference loss, $(N_w)_0$, is the usual figure of merit of the equipment. It is, therefore, the propagation loss identified with the maximum range at which acceptable operation may be expected when the target is held on the maximum response axis of the transducer. This loss may be written in terms of this range as

$$(N_w)_0 = 2 \lg t\, S_0 + aS_0 + 60 \quad (8D\text{-}49)$$

To compute the desired contour line it is necessary to know the values of the constant loss, $(N_w)_0$, characteristic of the problem, and of the angle, $\alpha - \gamma$, through which the transducer is moved following the transmission of the pulse, and to assign a value to the deviation angle, α, at the instant of pulse transmission. From the values of α and of γ thus specified corresponding values for N_α and N_γ, the deviation losses applying to the pulse and to the echo, are obtained from the directivity pattern of the transducer. The allowable one-way propagation loss is obtained by substituting these deviation losses into Eq. (8D-48) and the allowable range then read from a curve of normal propagation loss applying to the pulse frequency specified by the problem.

The signal differential contour shown in Fig. 8D-6 has been computed for a circular plate transducer having an effective diameter of 5λ on the assumption that the axis of the transducer is displaced 6° immediately following the transmission of the pulse. The constant value of differential applying to all points on this contour is the same as that which would have been obtained if the reference axis of the transducer had been held on the bearing of a target at a distance of 2 kyd during both transmission and reception. The dotted line shown in this figure is the signal differential contour which would have been obtained for the same target and for the same interference if the transducer had not been moved; it corresponds, then, to the so-called "ping-listen-train" method of operation. Angular deviations for the "ping-train-listen" contour are shown for the axis bisecting the transmitting and receiving bearings;

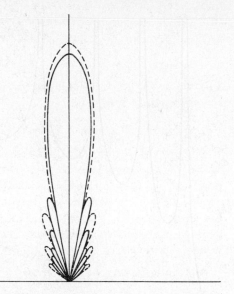

FIG. 8D-6. SIGNAL DIFFERENTIAL CONTOURS. The constant signal differential contour line for the "ping-train-listen" method of operation. The dotted line is the contour for the "ping-listen-train" method.

those for the "ping-listen-train" contour are shown for the fixed bearing of the transducer axis.

If the transducer is in continuous motion the angular displacement introduced during the transit of the echo signal depends upon the range from which this signal is returned. In this case we may rewrite Eq. (8D-47) as

$$N_\gamma = L_p - (L_n)_{100} + N_{DI} + N_{TS} - \Delta L_{e/n}$$

$$- N_\alpha - 2N_w$$

$$= (N_w)_0 - N_\alpha - 4 \lgt S - 2aS - 120 \quad (8D\text{-}50)$$

In terms of the range at which the desired signal differential is obtained when the reference axis of the transducer is on the target bearing during both transmission and reception the value of the constant characteristic of the problem would here be derived as

$$(N_w)_0 = 4 \lgt S_0 + 2aS_0 + 120 \quad (8D\text{-}51)$$

We now have two equations for the deviation loss, N_γ, which must be satisfied simultaneously; one is that given above, where this loss appears as a function of range, the other is that represented by the directivity pattern of the transducer, where it appears as a function of the deviation angle. Both the range and the deviation angle existing at the instant of echo reception are functions of the time interval, t, between the instant of pulse transmission and the instant of echo recep-

tion. Each of the equations might, then, be plotted graphically to show the deviation loss as a function of time. We shall, however, find it more convenient to show it as a function of the angle through which the transducer is displaced. Assuming the transducer to be rotated at the constant angular velocity ω this angular displacement may be designated as ωt. The deviation angle at the instant of echo reception is then

$$\gamma = \alpha - \omega t \quad (8D\text{-}52)$$

The relation between the deviation loss at the instant of reception and the quantity ωt is given by adding a supplementary scale to the directivity pattern of the transducer, in which deviation loss is plotted on rectangular coordinates as a function of deviation angle. The zero point of this supplementary scale of values of ωt must coincide with the point on the scale of values of deviation angle at which $\gamma = \alpha$. Since an increase in the value of ωt results in a decrease in the value of γ it will be convenient to assume that, in the original deviation loss diagram, angular values plotted to the right are negative. The symmetry of this curve permits this to be done without difficulty. The origin will then be moved to the left by the amount α and positive values of ωt laid off to the right of the new origin thus established. The general appearance of this representation of the directivity function is shown at (A) in Fig. 8D-7.

The angular displacement during the time of echo signal travel is given as a function of range by the equation

$$\omega t = 1.25 \, \omega S \quad (8D\text{-}53)$$

where t is in seconds and S is in kiloyards. Using this relation the loss $4 \lgt S + 2aS + 120$ may be plotted as a function of the quantity ωt for the value of attenuation constant, a, corresponding to the pulse frequency specified by the problem in hand. When presented graphically this relation is similar to a normal propagation loss curve, as drawn against a linear range scale. The deviation loss given by Eq. (8D-50) may be shown by this curve as a function of ωt by displacing the origin along the loss axis to the point $-(N_w)_0 + N_\alpha$. Actually, for any given problem, the point $-(N_w)_0$ may be established as a reference; for each assigned value of transmitting deviation angle, α, the position of the origin, effective for that value only, will then be found at the distance N_α above this reference point. The general ap-

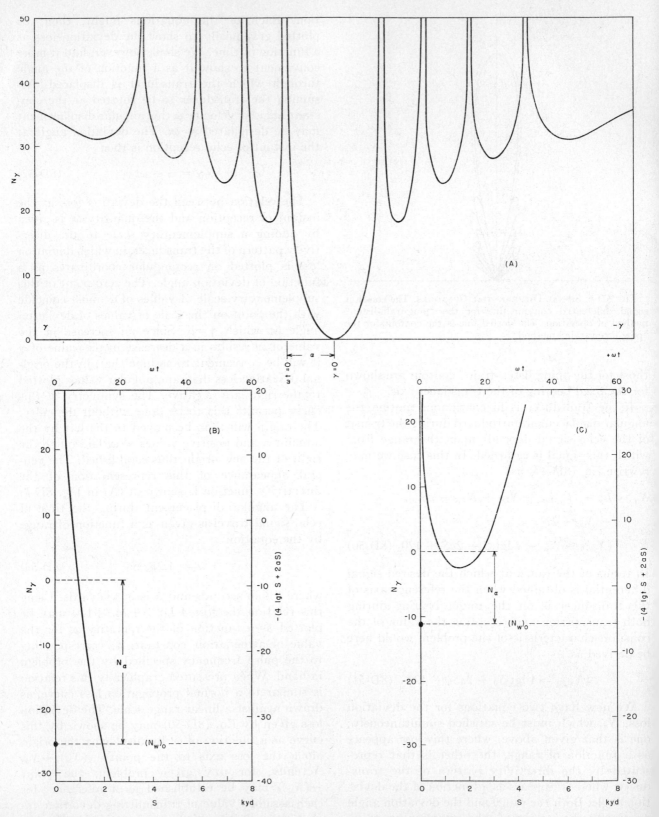

FIG. 8D-7. COMPUTATION OF CONTOUR LINES. Graphical presentations of the functional relations between the deviation loss at the instant of echo reception and the transducer displacement during the interval following the pulse transmission.

(A) As related by transducer directivity
(B) As related by target range when self noise is limiting
(C) As related by target range and reverberation index when volume reverberation is limiting

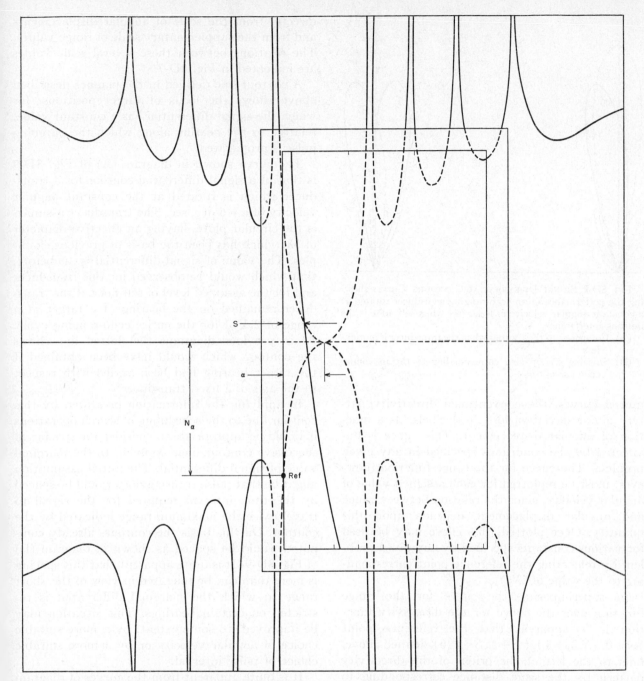

FIG. 8D-8. COMPUTATION OF CONTOUR LINES. A method for obtaining simultaneous solutions to the deviation loss equations applying to target points for which the signal differential is constant.

pearance of this representation of the range function is shown at (B) in Fig. 8D-7.

Given the two curves described above the values of ωt for which the two functions are simultaneously equal are obtained by superimposing one on the other, as indicated in Fig. 8D-8. From the values of ωt given by the intersections the ranges corresponding to any assigned value of transmitting deviation angle may be computed by means of Eq. (8D-53). Values of range may, in fact, be read directly from the graphs by providing a supplementary scale, parallel to the scale of angular displacements used for Curve (B) to which it is related by a constant of proportionality.

This specific method of computation has been proposed because it uses, for one of the two re-

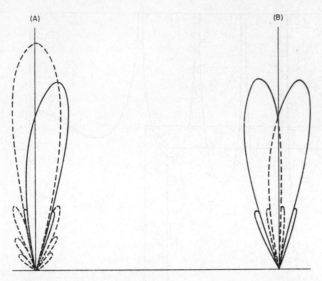

FIG. 8D-9. SIGNAL DIFFERENTIAL CONTOURS. Curves showing the performance of an echo-ranging transducer rotated at a constant angular velocity of 6 deg/sec when self noise is the limiting interference.

(A) Compared to the contour when the transducer is motionless

(B) Showing the spacing corresponding to the maximum echo travel time

quired curves, the conventional directivity pattern giving deviation loss, in decibels, as a function of angular displacement. This curve is unaffected by the conditions specified in any given problem. The curve for the range function, however, must be replotted for each assigned value of angular velocity, since the relation between range and angular displacement depends upon this quantity. Once plotted, this curve may be used for various constants specified by any given problem by relocating the reference point corresponding to the value of $(N_w)_0$.

In superimposing the curve for the range function over the curve for the directivity function it is apparent that the reference point $[\omega t = 0, (N_w)_0 = 4 \lg t\, S + 2aS + 120]$, defined above, falls to the left of the origin of the directivity pattern by the scale distance corresponding to the deviation angle α; it falls below the origin of this pattern by the scale distance corresponding to the deviation loss N_γ. The reference point, in other words, moves along a mirror image of the directivity pattern as a succession of values is assigned to the angle α. The coordinates of the desired contour line may, consequently, be obtained by moving the range curve over the directivity curve in such a manner as to satisfy this condition. Corresponding values of transmitting deviation angle and range may then be read

directly from the scale of angular displacements and from the supplementary scale of range values. The relations between these several scale values are indicated in Fig. 8D-7.

A contour line derived in the manner described above shows the locus of target positions, for which the signal differential has a constant value, relative to the bearing along which the outgoing pulse is propagated.

The curve shown in diagram (A) of Fig. 8D-9 is that of a signal differential contour for a transducer which is rotated at the constant angular velocity of $\omega = 6$ deg/sec. The transducer assumed is the circular plate, having an effective diameter of 5λ, which has been the basis of previous examples. The value of signal differential is, as before, that which would be observed for this transducer and for the assumed level of self noise if the transducer remained on the bearing of a target at a range of 2 kyd for the entire echo-ranging cycle. As in previous diagrams the dotted line shows the contour which would have been obtained if the target bearing had been varied with respect to the axis of a fixed transducer.

In applying the information presented by this contour line to the scheduling of search operations it would be appropriate to consider the spacing of successive contour lines applying to the marginal value of signal differential. The initial assumption might be that pulse transmissions would be spaced by the time interval required for the signal to travel twice the maximum range indicated by the contour. On this basis the contours already computed would be spaced as shown in diagram (B) of Fig. 8D-9. It is quite apparent that this spacing is more than can be tolerated in view of the short range to which the marginal differential is restricted on certain bearings. This situation may be improved, to some extent, by a more suitable choice of angular velocity or by a more suitable choice of pulse interval.

It is quite apparent from the curves of diagram (A), Fig. 8D-9, that motion of a transducer reduces the maximum range at which a given signal differential may be obtained when self noise is limiting. This may be remedied by a modification in the arrangement of the equipment. This requires the use of two transducers, one for transmission and one for reception. These transducers would be mounted on a single shaft so that the reference axis of the receiving unit lags behind the reference axis of the transmitting unit by a fixed amount as they are rotated at a constant angular velocity. In this case the deviation angle at the instant of reception is

$$\gamma = \alpha + \delta - \omega t \qquad (8D\text{-}54)$$

where δ is the fixed angular separation between the axes of the two transducers. This additional factor may be incorporated into the computation described above by increasing the displacement of the origin on the directivity pattern from α to $\alpha + \delta$. This would be represented, in Fig. 8D-8, by displacing the lower directivity pattern to the left, relative to the upper pattern, through the scale distance corresponding to the lag angle.

The curves of Fig. 8D-10 have been computed

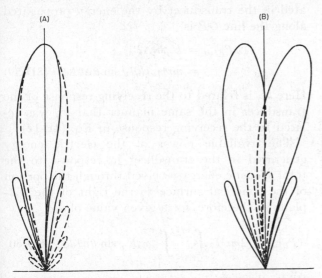

FIG. 8D-10. SIGNAL DIFFERENTIAL CONTOURS. Curves showing the performance of two echo-ranging transducers rotated at 6 deg/sec when separated by 15 deg. The limiting interference is due to self noise.
(A) Compared to the contour of a single motionless transducer
(B) Showing the spacing corresponding to the maximum echo travel time

in this manner for a pair of transducers so spaced that the axis of the receiver reaches the bearing of the transmitting axis in the time required for the signal to travel 2 kyd and back. The angular velocity is 6 deg/sec, as before, making the lag angle $\delta = 15$ deg. It is evident that the maximum range indicated by the contour has been brought back to the reference value applying to a fixed transducer. The spacing corresponding to the signal travel time is, however, now even greater than for a single transducer due to this increased range.

From the relations between the several perti-

nent factors illustrated by these contour curves it is apparent that compromises must be made between them in order to obtain the most satisfactory performance in any given practical problem. The utility of the contour lines as guides in deciding upon these compromises is self-evident.

When the interference limiting the reception of echo-ranging signals is due to reverberation rather than to noise the method for computing the constant signal differential contours of moving transducers requires further consideration. The response of a motionless transducer to reverberation has been described, in Art. 4F-7, in connection with the quantity defined as reverberation index; the response of a moving transducer may be similarly described by making suitable modifications to the factors there considered. These apply specifically to the case of volume reverberation to which we shall, for the moment, confine our attention. As before, we shall hypothecate a uniformly reflecting spherical surface concentric with the transducer. Acoustic energy radiated by the transducer is distributed over this surface, following the transmission of the pulse, in a manner prescribed by the directivity characteristics of the transducer. Energy reflected by the surface is returned toward the transducer, from all points on the surface, with the same relative directional distribution with which it was originally radiated. In the case previously considered the total response to this reflected energy was derived on the basis that the relative response to energy arriving along any bearing was proportional to the relative intensity of that energy. If the transducer is moved between the instant of pulse transmission and the instant when the reflected energy returns this will not be true. Because of this it is no longer possible to represent by a single integration the summation of the contributions to the total response of energy returned from each of the individual incremental areas making up the spherical surface.

The situation which exists when the transducer is in motion may be described by reference to the diagram of Fig. 8D-11, which shows a portion of the hypothetical concentric reflecting surface against a three-dimensional system of rectangular coordinates. It will be assumed that the directivity of the transducer, which is located at the origin of coordinates, is symmetrical about a single acoustic axis which moves in the XY-plane at the constant angular velocity ω.

Consider the point, P, on the arc of a circle

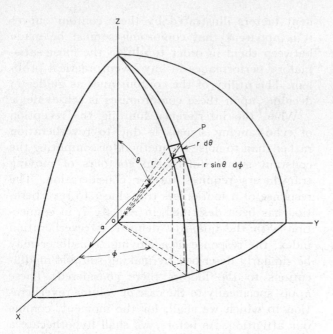

FIG. 8D-11. COMPUTATION OF REVERBERATION INDEX. The geometrical relations involved in computing the response of an echo-ranging transducer to reverberation when the transducer is given a constant angular velocity.

formed by the intersection with the spherical surface of a plane passing through the OZ-axis and making the angle ϕ with the ZX-plane. A line through this point and through the origin makes the angle θ with the OZ-axis. If the plane and the line defining this point are each rotated through incremental angles $\Delta\phi$ and $\Delta\theta$ the incremental surface thus defined will be

$$\Delta A = r^2 \sin \theta \, \Delta\theta \, \Delta\phi \qquad (8D\text{-}55)$$

where r is the constant distance of the spherical surface from the transducer.

If the maximum response axis of the transducer coincides with the OX-axis at the instant of pulse transmission the angle α, between the line OP and the maximum response axis at that instant, is given by the relation

$$\cos \alpha = \cos \phi \sin \theta \qquad (8D\text{-}56)$$

The acoustic intensity at the point P is $I_\alpha = \eta_\alpha I_0$, where η_α is the relative transmitting response and I_0 is the intensity, at the distance r, on the maximum response axis. The relative response, as given by the directivity pattern of the transducer in terms of the deviation angle, α, is seen to be a function of the angles ϕ and θ defining the location of the point P.

The power of the acoustic energy falling on the incremental area defined above is

$$(\Delta P_A)_{\omega t} = \eta_\alpha I_0 \Delta A = r^2 \eta_\alpha I_0 \sin \theta \, \Delta\theta \, \Delta\phi \quad (8D\text{-}57)$$

Some fraction of this energy, having the power $m(\Delta P_A)_{\omega t}$, is reflected by the surface and returned to the transducer along the line OP. If the axis of the transducer has moved by the amount ωt by the time this energy reaches it the line OP will be at the angle γ with the maximum response axis. The magnitude of this angle is given by the relation

$$\cos \gamma = \cos (\phi - \omega t) \sin \theta \qquad (8D\text{-}58)$$

The available power of the electric energy generated in the transducer by the energy propagated along the line OP is

$$(\Delta P_E)_{\omega t} = k'_\gamma m(\Delta P_A)_{\omega t}$$
$$= mr^2 \eta_\alpha k'_\gamma I_0 \sin \theta \, \Delta\theta \, \Delta\phi \quad (8D\text{-}59)$$

Here k'_γ is related to the receiving response of the transducer in the same manner that k'_d was related to the receiving response in Eq. (4F-12).

The available power of the electric energy generated in the transducer in response to the total acoustic energy received through the portion of the spherical surface to the right of the YZ-plane is, therefore, for a given value of ωt,

$$(P_E)_{\omega t} = 2mr^2 I_0 \int_{-\pi/2}^{\pi/2} \int_0^\pi \eta_\alpha k'_\gamma \sin \theta \, d\theta \, d\phi \quad (8D\text{-}60)$$

When the transducer is at rest $\alpha = \gamma$ and $k'_\gamma = k'_\alpha$. The available power in this case is then

$$(P_E)_0 = 2mr^2 I_0 \int_{-\pi/2}^{\pi/2} \int_0^\pi \eta_\alpha k'_\alpha \sin \theta \, d\theta \, d\phi \quad (8D\text{-}61)$$

If we take the ratio of these two available powers we may divide numerator and denominator by k'_0. Then, as shown by Art. 4F-1, $k'_\alpha / k'_0 = \eta_\alpha$, and $k'_\gamma / k'_0 = \eta_\gamma$. The ratio of these two available powers may, therefore, be written as

$$\frac{(P_E)_{\omega t}}{(P_E)_0} = \frac{\displaystyle\int_{-\pi/2}^{\pi/2} \int_0^\pi \eta_\alpha \eta_\gamma \sin \theta \, d\theta \, d\phi}{\displaystyle\int_{-\pi/2}^{\pi/2} \int_0^\pi \eta^2_\alpha \sin \theta \, d\theta \, d\phi} \quad (8D\text{-}62)$$

This is equal to the ratio of the actual response specified by the definition of reverberation factor (Art. 4F-7) as it would be applied to the trans-

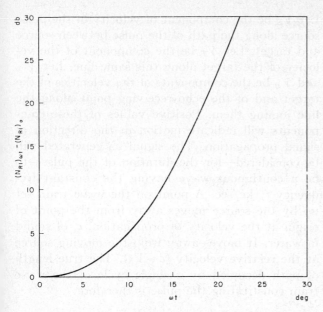

FIG. 8D-12. RELATIVE REVERBERATION INDEX. The increase in the reverberation index of a transducer resulting from motion, plotted as a function of the displacement of the transducer between the time of pulse transmission and the time of echo reception.

ducer response specified by the same definition as applied to the same transducer when at rest. From this ratio, then, since the reference response is the same in both cases, we obtain as the amount by which the reverberation index of a transducer which has been displaced by the ωt from its transmitting position exceeds the index when it remains in this position

$$(N_{RI})_{\omega t} - (N_{RI})_0 = \lgt \frac{(P_E)_0}{(P_E)_{\omega t}} \qquad (8D\text{-}63)$$

Although the computation is somewhat laborious the value of this difference may be obtained by drawing suitable curves for the several functions involved and determining the values of the corresponding integrals by evaluating the areas thus circumscribed. The change in reverberation index may thus be determined as a function of the displacement angle, ωt, between the transmitting and receiving positions of the transducer. The curve of Fig. 8D-12 shows such a graph for the 5λ circular plate transducer which has been the basis of computations of constant signal differential contours for other operating conditions. An equation for the deviation loss at the instant of echo reception may then be derived by rewriting Eq. (8D-30) as

$$N_\gamma = N_{TS} - (N_{RS})_v + (N_{RI})_0 - \Delta L_{e/r} - 60 - N_\alpha$$
$$+ [(N_{RI})_{\omega t} - (N_{RI})_0] - 2\lgt S$$
$$= (N_w)_0 - N_\alpha + [(N_{RI})_{\omega t} - (N_{RI})_0]$$
$$- 2\lgt S \qquad (8D\text{-}64)$$

By writing the equation in this manner it is made evident that the value of reverberation index may be separated into two constituents; one, which may be unknown, may be included in the constant characteristic of a given contour line, the other is the known change in value identified with the angle through which the transducer has been displaced and may be included in the quantity which is a function of range. Values of this quantity, $(N_{RI})_{\omega t} - (N_{RI})_0 - 2\lgt S$, may be plotted as a function of range and, simultaneously, of the angle ωt. By locating the origin of coordinates in the manner described in connection with the graph (B) of Fig. 8D-7 this becomes a graph of the deviation loss, N_γ, corresponding to Eq. (8D-64). The curve of graph (C) of Fig. 8D-7 shows the value of this deviation loss as computed for a circular plate transducer having a diameter of 5λ and rotated at a constant angular velocity of 6 deg/sec.

The curve of Fig. 8D-13 has been computed by the method described above; it gives the constant signal differential contour, when volume reverberation is the limiting interference, corresponding to the conditions there postulated. It is noted

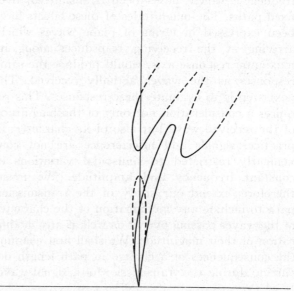

FIG. 8D-13. SIGNAL DIFFERENTIAL CONTOURS. Curves showing the performance of an echo-ranging transducer rotated at 6 deg/sec when volume reverberation is the limiting interference.

that, unlike the effect when self noise is the limiting interference, motion of the transducer increases the maximum range at which a given signal differential may be obtained. This is, of course, because the response to reverberation decreases with displacement of the transducer faster than does the response to the echo signal. It must again be emphasized that long ranges such as those shown by this contour may not always be realized; as in other situations limitations due to other forms of interference are certain to arise before echoes may return from these increased distances. An acceptable value of signal differential, with respect to one form of interference, furnishes no information as to the absolute levels of either signal or interference and hence no information as to the relative level of the signal with respect to other forms of interference. Constant signal differential contours must never be confused with constant signal level contours, although they may be identical under certain conditions.

8-E THE TRANSMISSION AND RECEPTION OF ECHO-RANGING SIGNALS

The transmission losses studied in the preceding sections of this chapter have permitted us to estimate the effect of spreading, of attenuation, and of reflection, insofar as these factors determine the magnitudes of sinusoidal waves of fixed frequency which have been transmitted over fixed paths. The magnitudes of these effects have been expressed in terms of plane waves which, arriving at the receiving transducer along its maximum response axis, would produce the same responses as the waves actually received. The next step is to evaluate these responses. This requires a consideration not only of the magnitude of the received wave but also of its character; in practice, signals and interference are not conveniently restricted to sinusoidal variations of constant frequency and amplitude. We must, therefore, extend our study of the transmission path to include any modification of the character of the waves passing over it as well as any modification of their magnitude. We shall first examine the consequences of a change in path length occurring during the transmission of a signal wave.

8E-1 The Doppler Effect

The effect of motion of the target relative to the source of the pulse and to the point at which the echo is received may be analyzed as follows.

Let $\bar{V}_S$ be the component of velocity of the pulse source along the path of the pulse between source and target. Let V_T be the component of the velocity of the target along this same line. Let V'_T and V_R be the components of the velocities of the target and of the echo receiving point along the line joining them. Positive values of these components will indicate motion in the direction of signal propagation. The signal as generated will be considered—for the duration of the pulse—to be a continuous wave having the constant frequency f_p kc/sec. A point on the wave train set up by the source moves away from the point of origin at the velocity of propagation, c, of sound in water. It moves away from the moving source at the relative velocity $(c - V_S)$. The true length of path occupied by a single cycle of the wave train constituting the pulse is therefore

$$\lambda_p = \frac{(c - V_S)}{f_p} \tag{8E-1}$$

The velocity of this wave train relative to the target is $(c - V_T)$. The time required for a single cycle to pass a point moving at the target velocity is consequently

$$\frac{1}{f_T} = \frac{\lambda_p}{(c - V_T)} \tag{8E-2}$$

and the frequency of the pulse falling on the target is

$$f_T = \frac{(c - V_T)}{\lambda_p} = f_p \frac{(c - V_T)}{(c - V_S)} \tag{8E-3}$$

In the same manner it may be shown that the wave length of the echo signal as reradiated by the moving target is

$$\lambda_e = \frac{(c - V'_T)}{f_T} \tag{8E-4}$$

and that the frequency of the echo signal as received by the moving receiving point is

$$f_e = \frac{(c - V_R)}{\lambda_e} = f_T \frac{(c - V_R)}{(c - V'_T)}$$
$$= f_p \frac{(c - V_T)(c - V_R)}{(c - V_S)(c - V'_T)} \tag{8E-5}$$

This equation is rigorous and quite general. It may, in fact, be applied when the transmitting and receiving points are not the same, in which case the differences between V_S and V_R and between V_T and V'_T may be large. In all practical situations, where the echo is received by the same transducer as that from which the pulse is transmitted, these differences are small. If the transducer has a large component of velocity perpendicular to the target bearing the angles between the pulse path and the courses of source and target may differ detectably from those between the echo path and these courses. It is only by changes in these angles that significant changes may occur in the components of transducer and target velocities parallel to the signal paths. For all practical problems there will be a negligible error in assuming that $V_R = - V_S$ and that $V'_T = - V_T$. On this assumption the ratio between the received and transmitted frequencies is

$$\frac{f_e}{f_p} = \frac{c^2 - c(V_T - V_S) - V_S V_T}{c^2 + c(V_T - V_S) - V_S V_T} \qquad (8E-6)$$

Beyond this point it is customary to make two simplifying approximations. The first is that the term $V_S V_T$ may be neglected in both the numerator and the denominator of the fraction on the right in the above equation. A nominal value for the velocity of sound in water is 2900 knots. The quantity c^2 is therefore somewhere in the neighborhood of 10,000 times as large as $V_S V_T$ and the assumption is amply justified. If this term is omitted the preceding equation becomes

$$\frac{f_e}{f_p} \approx \frac{c - (V_T - V_S)}{c + (V_T - V_S)} \qquad (8E-7)$$

The quantity $(V_T - V_S) = \Delta V$ is the rate of change of separation between the transducer and the target. It is generally called the range rate in tactical problems. Making this substitution in the last equation and solving for the fractional change in frequency there is obtained

$$\frac{f_p - f_e}{f_p} \approx \frac{2(\Delta V)}{c + \Delta V} \qquad (8E-8)$$

The second of the two approximations is now made by assuming that ΔV may be neglected in the denominator of the right-hand fraction. This would be quite proper if we were dealing with electromagnetic waves, where the velocity of propagation is of an entirely different order of magnitude from the relative velocity of a physical target. It may introduce a detectable error in sonar problems where the velocity of propagation is more nearly comparable with the range rate. This error may, in some cases, be as much as one

percent. The relation generally used for computing the change in frequency in an echo signal due to the Doppler effect is, however, derived on the basis of this approximation as

$$f_p - f_e \approx f_p \frac{2(\Delta V)}{c} \qquad (8E-9)$$

This equation shows that, since the velocity of propagation may here be regarded as constant, the change in frequency is proportional to the product of the source frequency and the range rate. When the change in frequency is expressed in cycles per second, the source frequency in kilocycles per second, and the range rate in knots, the factor of proportionality is known as the **Doppler constant** for echo transmission. When f_p and f_e are in kilocycles per second the change in frequency is $\Delta f = 1000(f_p - f_e)$ cyc/sec. The velocity of propagation may be assigned the nominal value of $c = 2900$ knots. The substitution of these equalities into Eq. (8E-9) gives the nominal value of the Doppler constant for echo transmission, which appears as the numerical coefficient in the relation

$$\Delta f = 0.69 \, f_p(\Delta V) \qquad (8E-10)$$

where

$\Delta f =$ the change in frequency suffered by an echo signal during its transmission to a target and back to the point at which it originated (cyc/sec)

$f_p =$ the frequency of the transmitting source (kc/sec)

$\Delta V =$ the range rate, or rate of change of the distance of the target from the echo-ranging transducer (kt)

$0.69 =$ the Doppler constant for echo transmission (cyc/kt·kc)

If the original signal is a complex wave the frequency changes in each sinusoidal component may be computed by means of this relation. By making approximations and conversions in Eq. (8E-3) which are similar to those made above in Eq. (8E-6) it may be shown, as is to be expected, that the Doppler constant for direct, one-way transmission is one half the value of that for two-way echo transmission, its value being 0.345 cyc/kt·kc.

In any installation of echo-ranging equipment

the frequency of the pulse generated by the source may be maintained at some known value. With the source frequency fixed the range rate becomes the only remaining independent variable in the equation for the change in frequency due to the Doppler effect. This change in frequency is therefore a direct measure of the range rate, the two quantities being directly proportional to each other. If, in addition to the instrument for indicating target range, some means is provided for indicating the change in the frequency of the echo signal it is possible to obtain quantitative data as to both range and range rate from a single echo signal transmission. Several instruments have been developed for this purpose.

When an echo-ranging transducer is in motion all waves returned to it by reflection are shifted in frequency by the Doppler effect. The change in frequency of reverberation, as well as of the echo from a well defined target, measures the motion of the transducer relative to the reflector. In the case of general reverberation, however, this relative velocity, ΔV, appearing in Eq. (8E-10) is not the same for all increments of energy sent out by the transducer. Since this relative velocity is a function of the angle between the motion of the transducer and the bearing along which the echo signal is propagated it must vary throughout the beam within which a directional transducer concentrates the energy. The reverberation returned to a moving transducer in response to a single-frequency pulse is thus made up of a group of sinusoidal components occupying a narrow band of frequencies. Consider, for example, the case of volume reverberation. The range rate determining the frequency displacement of a component of this reverberation is $(\Delta V)_\phi = V_S \cos \phi$ where V_S is the speed of the transducer and ϕ is the angle between the transducer course and the bearing along which that particular component is transmitted. To obtain some idea of the order of magnitude of the effects involved assume that $V_S = 20$ knots, that $f_p = 25$ kc/sec, and that the directional beam of the transducer is such that the major portion of the acoustic energy is contained within a beam corresponding to a 20° cone. If the axis of this beam is trained perpendicular to the course of the transducer, then, ϕ varies from 80° to 100°. From Eq. (8E-10) the change in frequency resulting from these conditions is

$$\Delta f = 0.69 f_p(\Delta V) = (345)(\cos \phi)$$

When $\phi = 80°$, $\cos \phi = 0.174$ and $\Delta f = (345)(0.174)$

$= 60.0$ cyc/sec. When $\phi = 100°$, $\cos \phi = -0.174$ and $\Delta f = -60.0$ cyc/sec. The reverberation, under these conditions, is thus seen to be made up of components occupying the frequency band between 24,940 and 25,060 cyc/sec. As the axis of the directive beam is trained forward the band occupied by the reverberation is displaced to a higher position on the frequency scale and, at the same time, reduced in width. When the beam is trained directly along the course of the transducer the angle ϕ varies from 0° to 10°. For the same speed and source frequency as before, then, the change in frequency for energy transmitted along the axis of the beam, where $\phi = 0°$, is $\Delta f = (345)(1)$ $= 345$ cyc/sec. At the edge of the beam, where $\phi = 10°$ and $\cos \phi = 0.985$, $\Delta f = 340$ cyc/sec.

Whenever a moving vessel engages in echoranging operations in shallow water where there are strong currents its velocity relative to the water will differ from its velocity relative to the bottom. In such circumstances components of volume and of surface reverberation will differ in frequency from those of bottom reverberation.

If a reflecting target is motionless in the water the frequency of the echo which it returns will be identical with that of the reverberation from the neighboring medium. If the target has a component of velocity along the line of signal propagation, however, its range rate will differ from that of the nearby medium by the amount of this component. The change in frequency of the echo signal will, as a result, differ from the change in the frequency of the reverberation by the same ratio as that between the corresponding range rates. The difference between these two changes in frequency is a direct measure of the magnitude and sign of the component of target velocity along the line of signal transmission. If the target is moving away from an echo-ranging vessel going in the same direction its range will be closing less rapidly than that of the medium. The frequency of the echo will therefore be raised less than that of the reverberation and will be of lower frequency. If the target is moving away from an echo-ranging vessel going in the opposite direction its range will be opening more rapidly than that of the medium, the echo frequency will be lowered more than that of the reverberation, and, again, the echo will be of lower frequency. In the same manner it may be shown that when the target is moving toward the transducer the echo will be of higher frequency than the reverberation regardless of whether the range is opening or closing. When the echo is of higher frequency than the reverberation it is said to have an **up Doppler.** This indicates that the target has a component of velocity toward the transducer but tells nothing about either the sign or magnitude of the total range rate. Similarly, when the echo is of lower frequency than the reverberation it is said to have a **down Doppler;** it indicates a component of target motion away from the transducer which, as before, may be moving in the same direction or in the opposite direction as the target.

The change in frequency of an echo signal, due to the Doppler effect, may be troublesome as well as helpful. Whenever the response of any element of the receiving system is sharply selective the Doppler shift may carry the signal outside the limits where acceptable performance is obtainable. It will be recalled from the discussion of the electric impedance of transducers (Art. 4C-3) that the ratio of the acoustic power delivered to the water at the resonance frequency, f_0, to the power delivered when the frequency is changed by the amount Δf is given to a close approximation by Eq. (4C-27). This may be written to show the reduction in the level of the total acoustic power delivered to the water as

$$(L_A)_0 - (L_A)_x = \lgt \left[1 + \left(2Q \frac{\Delta f}{f_0} \right)^2 \right] \quad (8E-11)$$

In developing this formula it was assumed that the electric current delivered to the transducer terminals was held constant as the frequency was changed. For small changes in frequency the total terminal resistance will not show a large change; a relation which is true for a condition of constant current is then approximately true for a condition of constant electric power input. In this case the reduction in acoustic level indicated by the equation will be equal to the increase in the efficiency loss of the transducer when used as a projector. It is one of the axioms of transducer theory that the efficiency loss applying to transmission in one direction is equal to the available power loss applying to transmission in the other. The reduction in level shown by the equation is therefore equal to the increase in available power loss of the transducer when used as a hydrophone. For a transducer of constant effective area Eq. (4G-10) shows that any change in available power loss is equal to a concurrent change in hydrophone loss. We may thus write the increase in hydrophone loss accompanying a

departure from the resonance frequency of the transducer as

$$(N_H)_x - (N_H)_0 = \lgt \left[1 + \left(2Q \frac{\Delta f}{f_0} \right)^2 \right] \quad (8E-12)$$

Assume, now, that this transducer is used for the transmission and reception of echo-ranging signals and that the frequency, f_p, of the transmitted pulse is accurately adjusted to the resonance frequency, f_0, of the transducer. In the above equation, under these conditions, the hydrophone loss $(N_H)_0$ is the loss which would be encountered by an echo from a target at a constant distance from the transducer. The hydrophone loss $(N_H)_x$ is the loss which would be encountered by an echo from this same target, when at the same distance, if its range rate were ΔV. For the fractional change in frequency appearing in this equation we may write

$$\frac{\Delta f}{f_0} = \frac{\Delta f}{f_p} = 0.00069(\Delta V) \quad (8E-13)$$

This is derived from Eq. (8E-10) by expressing both the change in frequency and the initial frequency in cycles per second, in conformity with the notation used in Eq. (4C-27). The increase in hydrophone loss due to the Doppler effect is thus given in terms of the dissipation constant, Q, of the transducer and of the range rate, ΔV, of the target as

$$(N_H)_x - (N_H)_0 = \lgt \left[1 + (0.00138 Q \Delta V)^2 \right] \quad (8E-14)$$

This reduction in hydrophone response represents an equal reduction in the level of the response of the echo-ranging system to the signal returned from a distant target. The magnitude of this reduction may be appreciable. Consider, for example, a transducer having a dissipation constant of $Q = 80$, a value which may easily be obtained in transducers designed for high efficiency at a single frequency. For a target having a range rate of $\Delta V = 20$ kt the reduction in response is

$$(N_H)_x - (N_H)_0 = \lgt \left[1 + (2.208)^2 \right]$$
$$= \lgt 5.88$$
$$= 7.5 \text{ db}$$

Although a reduction in receiving response is not, in itself, necessarily harmful it is generally accompanied by a serious impairment in performance. In many cases selectivity has been provided in order to discriminate against interfering noise having frequencies different from that of the signal. If the signal is shifted in frequency it moves away from the point at which it would have been received most advantageously leaving the benefits associated with this point to those noise components the frequencies of which are in the neighborhood of the nominal signal frequency. The reduction in signal level is therefore accompanied by an equal reduction in the signal differential. When it is remembered that a loss of 10 db in signal differential is equivalent to a reduction of some 35 percent in the range of possible detection of a marginal echo signal it will be understood that this situation is one of much concern in the operation of echo-ranging equipment.

When the interference is due to reverberation the consequences of a Doppler shift in frequency are not always as serious as when it is due to noise. If the major component of the range rate comes from the motion of the echo-ranging vessel the shift in frequency will be about the same for the interference as for the signal. In such circumstances the reduction in response is nearly the same for both, and the signal differential ratio is not greatly altered. When the target is the chief contributor to the range rate the shift in signal frequency is correspondingly larger than that of the interference and the consequences are similar to those suffered with interfering noise. This is the situation existing when a submerged submarine attempts to echo range on a high-speed target; it explains why such attempts are not always successful, even at relatively short ranges.

8E-2 The Relation Between Pulse Length and Band Width

The duration of an echo signal is quite as important as its frequency in determining the response of a highly selective receiving system. An increase in selectivity is accompanied by an increase in the time required for the response to reach a constant magnitude following the application of a constant driving force. For any selective element, in other words, a definite **build-up time** must elapse before its response reaches its nominal steady-state value. If the duration of the pulse is less than this critical value the maximum value reached by the response will be less than the value corresponding to steady-state conditions.

The quantitative relations of interest in this connection may be examined for the case of a simple resonant system. In accordance with the established principles of electrical engineering the amplitude of the current flowing in a resonant electric system t seconds after the application of a sinusoidal driving voltage having a frequency equal to the resonance frequency of the system is

$$(i_{pk})_x = (i_{pk})_{\max}(1 - \epsilon^{-\alpha t}) \qquad (8E\text{-}15)$$

Here $(i_{pk})_{\max}$ is the peak value of the steady-state current and α is the time constant of the system. Now it may be shown that the value of this time constant is given in terms of the dissipation constant, Q, and the resonance frequency, f_0, of the system as

$$\alpha = \frac{\pi f_0}{Q} \qquad (8E\text{-}16)$$

But from Eq. (4C-10) the dissipation constant is expressed in terms of the difference, Δf, between the quadrantal frequencies, at which the steady-state currents are $\frac{1}{2}\sqrt{2}$ times the resonance current, as $Q = f_0/\Delta f$. The time constant of the system is thus $\alpha = \pi(\Delta f)$. If, now, we arbitrarily place $t = 1/\Delta f$ the current at the end of this time is seen to be

$$(i_{pk})_x = (i_{pk})_{\max}(1 - \epsilon^{-\pi})$$
$$= 0.957(i_{pk})_{\max} \qquad (8E\text{-}17)$$

This may be stated in words by saying that in a time interval, $t = 1/\Delta f$, which is the reciprocal of the width of the steady-state response characteristic of the resonant system, as measured between its quadrantal points, the amplitude of the response will reach 95.7 percent of its steady-state value. From this, and from similarly derived relations for the responses of systems having bandpass elements, such as filters, is derived the convenient rule that the pass band of any selective system used for the reception of pulses of short duration must equal, in cycles per second, the reciprocal of the pulse duration, as measured in seconds. Applying this rule to a one millisecond pulse, for example, it is seen that the receiving system must be responsive over a band having a width of one kilocycle per second.

8E-3 Continuous Wave Echo Signals

All of the previous discussions of echo signals have been predicated on the assumption that the initial pulse, for the short period during which it is being transmitted, is a continuous wave having a constant amplitude and a single frequency.

This is the method usually followed in analytical studies since pure sinusoidal variations lead to the simplest and, at the same time, to the most useful solutions. The behavior of a system transmitting waves having a continuous spectrum may, as we have seen on several occasions, be deduced from its behavior to sinusoidal waves. The ideal single-frequency wave is, however, of more than academic interest in echo ranging; it represents very closely the actual signal employed in all continuous wave (CW) systems.

In an earlier section of this chapter it was noted that the frequency of the continuous wave echo signal is generally in the ultrasonic region and that the received echo signal is converted, by heterodyning, to a signal of audible frequency. As we saw earlier the process used is, in effect, a combination of the superheterodyne and the beat-frequency methods. One of the important features of this situation is the manner in which the various derived electric signal waves are affected by Doppler shifts in the frequency of the received acoustic signal.

The displacement of the frequency of a signal wave from the point of maximum response of a resonant transducer, because of the Doppler shift, has been examined in a preceding article. This effect reappears in the selective circuits of the initial stages of the receiver-amplifier, where the electric signal is of the same ultrasonic frequency as the acoustic echo signal. Here, as in the resonant transducer, the shift in frequency reduces the response to the signal without altering that to the noise and thus lowers the signal-to-noise ratio. In receivers of the usual design, however, the selectivity of the r-f stages is rarely sufficient to cause great harm in this respect.

The product of modulation delivered to the fixed selective circuits of the i-f stages by the first detector has a frequency which is the difference between the frequencies of the first heterodyne oscillator and of the ultrasonic echo signal. Although in this simple case the consequences of this are fairly obvious it will later be found convenient to express this and associated facts symbolically. For this purpose the following notation will be adopted.

f_e = the frequency of the acoustic echo signal in the water and of the electric signals in the transducer and in the r-f stages of the receiver-amplifier (kc/sec)

f_{if} = the frequency of the electric signal in the i-f stages (kc/sec)

f_{af} = the frequency of the electric signal in the a-f stages (kc/sec)

f_{hf} = the frequency of the heterodyne wave generated by the first oscillator (kc/sec)

f_{bf} = the frequency of the heterodyne wave generated by the second oscillator (kc/sec)

Nominal values of the frequencies of the signal waves, or the values which the frequencies of these waves would have were there no Doppler shift, are indicated by writing their symbols as indicated above. The values to which these frequencies are shifted because of the Doppler effect, or their actual values, are indicated by writing the symbols with primes, as f'.

In this notation the frequency of the signal delivered by the first heterodyne detector to the i-f stages is, as stated above,

$$f'_{if} = f_{hf} - f'_e \qquad (8E\text{-}18)$$

For a given range rate the change in frequency of the echo signal due to the Doppler effect is, as shown by Eq. (8E-10), proportional to the nominal frequency of this signal. In other words,

$$f'_e - f_e = kf_e \qquad (8E\text{-}19)$$

whence the actual value of the echo-signal frequency is

$$f'_e = (1 + k)f_e \qquad (8E\text{-}20)$$

The coefficient k appearing in these equations is the constant of proportionality and is given by the product of the Doppler coefficient and the range rate. When the range rate, ΔV, is in knots this coefficient may be written as $k = 0.00069 \, (\Delta V)$. Thus defined it is dimensionless and gives the difference frequency in kilocycles per second when the echo-signal frequency is in kilocycles per second.

The substitution of Eq. (8E-20) into Eq. (8E-18) gives

$$f'_{if} = f_{hf} - (1 + k)f_e$$
$$= (f_{hf} - f_e) - kf_e \qquad (8E\text{-}21)$$

or, since $f_{if} = f_{hf} - f_e$,

$$f'_{if} = f_{if} - kf_e \qquad (8E\text{-}22)$$

Any given change, kf_e, in the frequency of an acoustic echo signal in the water, and hence of the electric signals in the transducer and in the r-f stage of the receiver-amplifier, is thus shown to be accompanied by a change of the same absolute magnitude, but of opposite sign, in the frequency of the signal delivered to the i-f stages by the first heterodyne detector.

The effect of the frequency displacement in the i-f stages is, in general, to reduce the signal-to-noise ratio in the same manner as in resonant transducers and in the r-f selective circuits. It will be noted, however, that in this case the percentage change in frequency is less than for waves of echo-signal frequency in the inverse ratio of the nominal frequencies of these two signals; it may, therefore, be from one half to less than one quarter of the percentage change in the r-f signal frequency. Since the change in response due to selectivity is a function of the percentage change in frequency rather than of the absolute change the Doppler shift in the frequency of the electric signal in the i-f stages is of relatively minor importance, although by no means to be neglected.

The condition just described is, in effect, reversed in the audio stages of the receiver-amplifier. The frequency of the output of the second detector, as delivered to the audio amplifiers, is the difference between the frequencies of the signal received from the i-f stages and the heterodyning wave received from the beat oscillator. This may be written, in the notation specified for this purpose, as

$$f'_{af} = f_{bf} - f'_{if}$$
$$= f_{bf} - (f_{hf} - f'_e)$$
$$= f'_e - (f_{hf} - f_{bf}) \qquad (8E-23)$$

The resultant effect of the two heterodyning processes is seen, from this equation, to be equivalent to beating the r-f signal directly against a heterodyning wave having the frequency $(f_{hf} - f_{bf})$. This frequency, being the difference between the waves from the two heterodyning oscillators, is at the control of the equipment operator. It is given a value, by the normal adjustment of the system, equal to the difference between the nominal frequency of the echo signal, which is the frequency of the pulse as delivered to the transducer by the driving circuits, and the frequency desired for the audio signal.

By substituting the actual frequency of the echo signal, as given by Eq. (8E-20), into Eq.

(8E-23) the actual frequency of the audio signal is found to be

$$f'_{af} = (1 + k)f_e - (f_{hf} - f_{bf}) \qquad (8E-24)$$

or, since $f_{af} = f_e - (f_{hf} - f_{bf})$,

$$f'_{af} = f_{af} + kf_e \qquad (8E-25)$$

As with the signal in the i-f stages the absolute value of the frequency shift in the audio signal is the same as the absolute value of the shift in the original acoustic signal, although the signs of the two changes are now alike. The ratio of the percentage changes in the frequencies of the two signals is, as before, equal to the inverse ratio of their nominal values. Now, however, the percentage change in the frequency of the derived signal, because of its lower value, is greater than the percentage change in frequency suffered by the acoustic signal in the water. Depending upon the original pulse frequency, or the nominal value of the echo-signal frequency, the percentage shift in the derived audio signal may be from twenty to fifty times the percentage shift in the echo signal.

The perceptibility of any change in frequency depends more upon its percentage value than on its absolute value. To the extent that the heterodyne method of reception used with CW echo signals increases the percentage value of the change in frequency due to the Doppler effect it improves the perceptibility of this change. Using the value 21 cyc/kt·sec, the amount by which a 30 kc/sec signal is shifted, it is seen that if an echo target has a component of motion along the path of the echo signal of 3 kt the difference between the frequencies of the echo and of the reverberation is approximately 60 cyc/sec. This corresponds to a percentage difference between the two of 0.2 percent and would hardly be perceptible, even if it were to occur at an audible frequency. In the derived audio signal, however, the change in frequency, being of the same absolute magnitude as in the ultrasonic wave, becomes a 7.5-percent change. This is readily detected by ear when the response is presented in audible form. A change of this percentage value may also be measured with considerable accuracy by instruments calibrated to read directly in terms of range rate.

Quite apart from disclosing quantitative information as to target motion a difference in frequency between the echo and the reverberation results in a most advantageous improvement in recognition differential. As an observer listens for an echo signal in the absence of this frequency difference there is little to distinguish it from the reverberation except a change in the level of the total energy received. Although it is sometimes possible for a listener with long experience to recognize an intangible quality difference between an echo from a discrete target and general reverberation the recognition differential thus obtained cannot be relied upon in practice. It will also be remembered that the rapid irregular variations in the level of the reverberation require that the signal produce a considerable change in the level of total energy before it becomes at all conspicuous. The recognition differential is, in fact, appreciably more than zero in such situations. The difference between the frequencies of the echo and of the reverberation resulting from target motion therefore gives a much needed characteristic by which to discriminate between them. For this difference to be of useful magnitude, however, its percentage value must be increased by a large factor over the value applying to the ultrasonic waves. Such an increase is obtained as a result of the heterodyne method of receiving CW signals. By this means the audible response to the echo from a moving target has a different pitch from the general reverberation and at once attracts the attention of the listener. The consequent improvement in recognition differential is often as much as 10 to 15 db.

The release of information as to target motion and the improvement in recognition differential obviously represent most useful attributes of the Doppler effect. It is equally obvious from the foregoing that these advantages may be realized, in the practical operation of sonar equipment, only through a virtual enhancement of the effect such as that resulting from the heterodyne method for receiving CW signals. Unfortunately, the disadvantages associated with Doppler shifts in frequency are correspondingly increased by this process.

On the debit side the magnified Doppler shift appearing in the audio wave derived by heterodyning a CW signal carries the depreciation of the signal-to-noise ratio, always consequent on displacing the signal from the frequency of maximum response, to a new order of magnitude. In view of the high selectivity available in the a-f stages of the receiver-amplifier, and of the magnitude of the frequency displacements which occur there, it is apparent that the injury to the signal-to-noise ratio is many times greater than in other parts of

the system. It may, in fact, be sufficient to destroy all possibility of signal detection and must be overcome by proper adjustment and operation of the equipment.

One solution to this problem is to reduce the discrimination of the a-f circuits. If these are broadened sufficiently the signal level may be restored, but only at the cost of an increased noise level due to the increased number of noise components to which the system responds. When noise is the predominant interference this effort may accomplish little. If reverberation is the limiting factor it may be reasonably successful. All components of the interference are then within —or near—the original pass band and little additional energy will be admitted as this band is widened.

When there is a high range rate due largely to the echo-ranging vessel it is possible to use the frequency of the reverberation as a guide to the readjustment of the frequency of one or both of the heterodyne oscillators. An adjustment which brings the reverberation within the pass band of the selective circuits may be assumed to bring the signal into close proximity, at least, to this band. This method may be followed, using nearby reverberation as a reference, even though the critical signal-to-interference is fixed by noise rather than by reverberation. It is often employed by patrol craft searching for a submerged submarine. The limiting interference is generally self noise. It is, of course, possible, once a target has been discovered, to readjust the system so as to restore a damaged signal-to-noise ratio. Signal-to-reverberation ratios may also be improved if there is sufficient target motion to give an adequate frequency differential. This does not solve the problem, however; the optimum adjustment is required before the target is detected rather than after.

When target motion is the major factor in fixing the range rate reverberation gives no clue as to the suitability of any system readjustment. This is the situation when a submarine attempts to determine the range of a fast-moving surface vessel. In this case the signal-to-interference ratio suffers, because of the Doppler effect, regardless of whether the interference is noise or reverberation. Here, also, operation of the equipment is often limited, for reasons of security, to a single echo transmission and the adjustments must be preset, without experimenting, to the condition for best performance. It is standard practice, in the operation of a submarine echo-ranging equipment, to use the a-f circuits giving the maximum width to the frequency response band. A signal displaced by the Doppler effect may then be included; a higher noise level will certainly result. Although information as to range rate would be valuable to a submarine it is undoubtedly true that the disadvantages inherent in Doppler shifts in frequency more than offset their potential advantages; it is unwise to increase the amount of data carried by a signal if, in so doing, the chances of its reception are seriously jeopardized.

It is generally considered to be astute engineering, whenever a given method of operation results in unfavorable performance, to try the opposite method. In the present case difficulties have arisen because the Doppler shift moves the signal away from a frequency of maximum response while the interference is left free to create the greatest possible hindrance to detection. The reverse procedure would be to make the response at the nominal frequency of the signal a minimum, instead of a maximum; any change in frequency due to the Doppler effect would then be an improvement. This calls for the use of circuits in which suppression is restricted to a narrow band of frequencies rather than to all frequencies outside this band. The method is by no means impractical. The conditions required for its success are that the interference be due to reverberation and that target motion introduce a suitable frequency difference between echo and interference. When these conditions are met the system may be so adjusted that the reverberation falls within the narrow suppression band and therefore produces little response. The response to the echo, which falls outside this band because of the difference in Doppler shift due to target motion, is thus relatively higher than to the interference and the signal-to-interference ratio is correspondingly elevated. The circuits by which selective discrimination may be provided against interference restricted to a known narrow frequency band are described as **reverberation-suppression filters.** Their use is open to the obvious objection that the echo from a motionless target is left at the frequency of minimum response. It therefore enjoys no advantage over the reverberation and may be reduced below a background noise which would otherwise have caused little interference. These circuits cannot be recommended for use by submarines, in spite of the large frequency differential due to the target motion generally present in that application, because of the lack of opportunities to make the necessary initial adjustments and because the limiting interference is more likely to be target noise than reverberation.

In attempting to appraise the significance of the Doppler effect, particularly as it is magnified by the heterodyning of CW signals, two balances must be struck. For one, the possibility of increasing the information obtainable from a given signal must be weighed against an increased risk of obtaining no signal at all. For the other, an increased recognition differential, corresponding to a lowering of the acceptable value of signal index, must be measured against a concurrent lowering of the actual value. The answers to these questions determine whether the emphasis given to it in CW transmissions is to be desired or deplored.

8E-4 Amplitude Modulated Echo Signals

As an alternative to the transmission of ultrasonic CW echo signals it is possible to use an **amplitude modulated** (AM) signal of the same frequency. This requires that the wave generated by the oscillator of the driving system be modulated by a signal wave of audio frequency before being delivered to the transducer. It will be assumed that this audio signal is a single-frequency wave; its nominal frequency will be taken to be 800 cyc/sec, corresponding to that of the signal developed by heterodyning in the CW method.

This AM method of transmission is identical in principle with that used in conventional radio broadcasting. From the results of work in that field it is known that when a high-frequency wave is amplitude modulated by an audio-frequency wave, each being sinusoidal, the resultant wave has three components. One, the unmodulated carrier, is of the same frequency as the original high-frequency wave before modulation. The other two lie at frequencies on either side of this frequency and differ from it by the frequency of the audio signal. These are the upper and the lower side bands; they are generally of lower amplitude than the unmodulated carrier. All three of these components are usually transmitted as the AM signal. It is also known that if the unmodulated carrier and either side band are impressed, after transmission to a receiving system, on a circuit element having a nonlinear response one of the components in the resulting output will have a frequency equal to their difference. It has, therefore, the same frequency as that of the audio wave used for modulation prior to transmission, and constitutes a portion of the audio signal recovered, or detected, by demodulation. The total audio signal is obtained by combining the products of demodulation of each of the side bands by the unmodulated carrier. This process is identical in principle with that used for the reception of radio broadcast transmissions. It differs from the beat-frequency method of reception used with CW signals only in that it is carried out in duplicate and that the heterodyning wave, in this case the unmodulated carrier, is transmitted from the sending apparatus instead of being generated in the receiving apparatus. This wave is, therefore, now exposed to the same transmission effects as the remainder of the signal, of which it may be considered a part.

Physical evidence of the similarity between the two methods of reception is given by the fact that it is possible to use the same detector for both. The receiver-amplifier described in Art. 8A-3 may be used for the reception and demodulation of AM signals with no other change than shutting down the beat-frequency oscillator previously used to supply the heterodyning wave to the second detector. No alteration is required in the operation or in the adjustment of any of the preceding elements of the receiving system; the several components of the AM signal are amplified in the r-f stages, translated in frequency in the first detector, and again amplified in the i-f stages, exactly as was the single component CW signal.

The effects of Doppler shifts on the components of an AM wave during transmission and reception, and on the audio signal recovered from it, may be analyzed by the same method as that used in the preceding article. When this is done it is found that the effect of Doppler shifts on the frequency of an audio signal developed in the receiver-amplifier by demodulation from an AM echo signal is to displace it by the product of its own nominal value, the Doppler coefficient, and the range rate of the target from which it is reflected. The shift is, in other words, the same as would have occurred if the audio signal had been transmitted over the given path in its original form instead of having been conveyed by means of an ultrasonic AM wave. Audio signals derived from AM transmissions, therefore, do not exhibit the greatly enhanced Doppler shifts shown to be characteristic of CW transmissions. In terms of the audible reproduction of this signal the change

in pitch of an echo which has traveled to a target and back through the water is less than in an equivalent audible signal which traveled to the same target and back through the air. The ratio of the percentage values of the shifts in these two cases is, as shown by Eq. (8E-9), equal to the inverse ratio of the velocities of propagation in the two media.

Although the use of an AM echo signal does not eliminate Doppler shifts it has avoided their very considerable magnification which accompanies the use of CW transmissions. For a CW echo signal of 30 kc/sec, it will be recalled, the shift in the 800 cyc/sec audio signal is 21 cyc/sec·kt. For an AM echo signal it is 0.56 cyc/sec·kt. In the first case the magnitude of the shift is independent of the frequency of the audio signal; in the second it is independent of the frequency of the ultrasonic wave by which this signal is carried.

Because of the small Doppler shift in the frequency of the final audio-frequency signal resulting from the use of an amplitude modulated echo-ranging transmission the width of the pass band of the audio amplifier of the receiver may be reduced significantly with respect to the width required with a CW transmission. In general this leads to an improvement in the signal differential existing in this portion of the system. The relative widths of the pass bands in the two cases is not, however, a direct measure of this improvement. In the case of the CW receiver the relative magnitudes of the components making up the final system output are essentially the same as the relative magnitudes of the components from which they are derived, as measured at the receiver input. This is not true in the case of the AM receiver. Here, in the absence of a signal, the noise appearing in the audio-frequency portion of the receiver is produced by intermodulation between components of the ultrasonic noise admitted by the so-called r-f circuits. Any pair of components differing in frequency by a frequency falling within the pass band of the audio-frequency circuit will, as a result of intermodulation, produce a component in this pass band. Any such pair will, therefore, contribute to the noise interference. The level of noise interference, as observed in the output of the receiver in the absence of a signal, is thus seen to depend on the widths of the r-f and i-f pass bands as well as on the level of the received noise. Because it is generated as a result of intermodulation the change in level of the resultant interference accompanying a change in the level of the received interference will, in general, be twice the change in the level of the received interference. The level of the interference appearing in the output of an AM receiver usually rises with the appearance of the signal, since the components of the signal provide additional energy for the demodulation of the noise already present. This increase is, however, concurrent with the reception of the signal and does not, as a rule, tend to make its detection more difficult.

In the case of amplitude modulated transmissions the final signal, like the final interference, is the result of intermodulation between energy components entering the receiver at its input terminals. The power of the final signal is, therefore, usually proportional to the square of the power of the signal as measured at these input terminals.

In view of these differences between the responses of the CW and the AM receivers it is evident that the relative widths of the pass bands of the audio circuits of the two is not a direct measure of the relative magnitudes of the interference. In many situations where comparative trials of the two methods of transmission have been made it has been found that the amplitude modulated transmission has given superior performance.

8E-5 Frequency Modulated Echo Signals

Experience in radio broadcast engineering has demonstrated that **frequency modulated** (FM) transmissions have certain marked advantages over AM transmissions. The nature of the FM signal and the properties of the FM detector combine to give a system which responds adequately to its own signal but which is relatively unresponsive to the usual forms of interfering energy. The nature of the FM signal also permits the use of a type of receiving system in which the magnitude of the received signal has relatively little effect on the magnitude of the derived audio signal. It would appear, then, that FM transmission offers an ideal method of overcoming the two most troublesome difficulties of echo ranging; namely, the high levels of interference and the large and frequent changes in transmission loss. Unfortunately certain quantitative differences between conditions attending the transmission of electromagnetic waves through the ether and the transmission of audio waves through the water are such that this promise is not fulfilled.

The experimental work on which the above conclusion is based was carried out during an investigation of methods for underwater communication by means of voice modulated ultrasonic waves. Many of the fundamental tests were, however, made with single-frequency audio signals and are directly applicable to conditions representative of echo-signal transmissions.

The transmitting end of the experimental system included a standard echo-ranging transducer fed by a driving circuit in which was developed a frequency modulated wave having a center frequency of 26 kc/sec. This wave was modulated by a single frequency of 750 cyc/sec in such a manner that the deviation, at maximum signal amplitude, was 3 kc/sec. Oscillographic records made of the output of the driver as delivered to the transducer showed it to have the constant amplitude, characteristic of FM signals, on which the limiting action of the receiver depends. It is, of course, this independence of amplitude on audio signal which permits the limiting circuit to deliver a constant amplitude signal to the detector regardless of variations in transmission loss. The receiving system contained limiter and discriminator circuits, as found in all FM receivers, which were carefully designed to meet the anticipated conditions and which were shown by laboratory tests to satisfy the specified requirements with an adequate margin.

In spite of the fact that both the discriminator and the limiter functioned almost ideally over a wide range of operating values, and that the system exhibited ideal characteristics under laboratory conditions, the performance was anything but ideal for signals transmitted through water. In fact, the overall transmission of the system, under normal operating conditions, was characterized both by excessive noise and by extremely variable signal levels. One phenomenon frequently observed was that the noise appeared to increase whenever the carrier was modulated. This seemed to indicate that it must result from a distortion of the transmitted signal. To verify this point a high-speed oscillograph using a cathode ray tube and a continuously moving film was set up on the receiving vessel. With this instrument records were made of the electric wave delivered at the output terminals of the receiving transducer when a sinusoidal signal of constant frequency and amplitude was impressed at the signal input terminals of the transmitting system. The facts disclosed by these oscillograms, of which those reproduced in Fig. 8E-1 are typical, were most enlightening. Although it was known that the electric wave impressed upon the transducer at

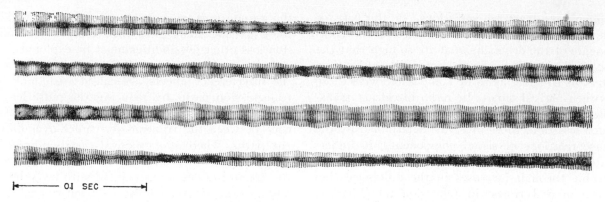

|←——— 0.1 SEC ———→|

FIG. 8E-1. FREQUENCY-MODULATED SIGNALS. Oscillograms showing the distortion resulting from transmission through the ocean of an ultrasonic wave which was originally frequency-modulated by a sinusoidal signal.

the sending end contained negligible amplitude modulation it is clear from the traces that the distortion suffered by the signal during transmission through the water resulted in the appearance of a considerable amount of amplitude modulation by the time it reached the receiver. The sharp, closely spaced spurs appearing in the oscillogram correspond to the envelope of this amplitude modulation. All records showed the amount of amplitude modulation to be extremely variable; in the samples here reproduced intervals may be found where the percentage amplitude modulation changes from a negligible amount to something like 50 or 60 percent in the space of a few milliseconds. This interpretation of the oscillograms is completely confirmed by other tests; whenever frequency modulated waves were transmitted the signals received at a distance could be demodulated successfully in a standard AM receiver. In fact it soon became evident that far better signal responses could be obtained with the standard echo-ranging receiver-amplifier than were possible with the FM receiver.

Once the effects described were recognized the explanation was not far to seek. It is, of course, true that every signal wave, regardless of its character, suffers some distortion during transmission, since the ideal transmitting medium exists only in the region of pure mathematics. Frequency modulated signals are no exception to this rule. In the case of radio-frequency broadcasting, however, the amount of this distortion is such as to cause little injury to the derived signal, as is evidenced by the high fidelity for which FM broadcasting systems are renowned. This is not true of signals transmitted through the water. A careful scrutiny of the actual conditions existing in the two cases discloses reasons for this differ-

ence. Certain of the characteristics of an FM signal, notably its constant amplitude, require the preservation of certain phase relations between the several components of which the signal is constituted. These phase relations are inevitably disturbed during transmission, largely as a result of interference between components traveling by different paths. In the case of a radio-frequency wave modulated by an audio-frequency signal the time intervals between arrivals over these different paths are so short as to be entirely negligible in comparison with the time intervals defining these essential phase relations. In the case of underwater transmission, however, the time intervals between arrivals over different paths are many times greater than those encountered in radio transmission. The difference is, in fact, measured by the difference between the speeds of propagation in the two cases: one may conveniently be expressed in feet per second and one in miles per second. In the case of underwater transmissions, therefore, the disturbance of phase relations in the wave becomes so great as completely to destroy those relations which are necessary in order for the amplitude to be independent of the modulation. One consequence of this is the appearance of amplitude modulation. When impressed upon an FM receiver these distortions produce prohibitive amounts of spurious audio frequency as well as variations in the level of the recovered signal.

This deduction as to the cause of the signal impairment observed when attempting underwater transmission by means of FM signals is supported by the results of attempts to transmit television signals by means of FM waves. Here the intervals between arrival times over multiple paths are the same as in the case of radio-frequency broadcast transmissions. In the case of television, however, the frequencies of the components of the original signal are so high that the phase relations between them are defined by time intervals so short as to be comparable with those between arrival times. In radio broadcast transmission the intervals between arrival times are much less than those intervals determined by the phase relations of signal components; in underwater transmission these intervals become comparable through increases in the differences between arrival times; in television they become comparable through reductions in the intervals determined by the phase relations. In either of the last two transmission systems the injuries suffered by the signal are sufficient completely to destroy the advantages enjoyed by the first.

8E-6 Methods of Reducing Transmission Variability

The general nature and magnitude of the variations in transmission loss appearing in the water path between any two points in the ocean, as manifest by the variations in a single-frequency signal transmitted over that path have been discussed briefly in Chapter 3. The time variations of signal amplitude, in one representative situation, are illustrated by the oscillograms reproduced in Fig. 3A-7. The effect of these variations on the performance of echo-ranging systems is one of considerable importance. Periods of high transmission loss are, of themselves, generally of short duration, as may be seen from the oscillograms. Should the transmission of an echo-ranging pulse coincide with such a period, however, the damage may have lasting consequences. At best an impaired transmission is represented by a loss of time corresponding to an entire cycle of operation, which may be several seconds. In the case of search operations by a patrol craft this may be the only transmission assigned to the bearing of an approaching enemy submarine; the failure due to a momentary high transmission loss, which is identified by no effect except the loss of the echo signal, may thus prevent the discovery of the target before it takes offensive action. In the case of an attempted range measurement by a submerged submarine a momentary hiatus in transmission may prevent the submarine from obtaining the desired information but will not prevent the transmission from disclosing its presence to the enemy. Since the use of FM transmission appears to offer no immediate prospect of stabilizing the response of an echo-ranging system against these normal short-time variations in transmission loss other possibilities must be explored.

It is, of course, theoretically possible to avoid he interference effects associated with multiple transmission paths by reducing the pulse length to a point where its duration is less than the difference between the transmission times over different paths. There are practical disadvantages to this scheme, however. For one thing, it reduces the amount of energy associated with the echo, at any instant, to that reflected from a length of target equal to one half the pulse length. This has the effect of greatly reducing the target strength. This is accompanied by a simultaneous reduction in reverberation strength and may not greatly impair the signal differential in cases where reverberation is the limiting interference. When noise is the limiting interference, however, the signal differential is reduced almost in proportion to the reduction in pulse length.

Abnormally high transmission losses are the result of interference between signal components arriving over different paths with nearly equal amplitudes and nearly opposite phases. When destructive interference exists, for transmission between a given pair of points, at some given frequency it is prima facie evidence that it would not exist, at that particular instant and for that particular pair of points, at some neighboring frequency. This suggests at once that a solution to the difficulty is to transmit a signal containing two or more single-frequency components; if one of them happens to annul itself at least one of the others is likely to find conditions favorable. Although this conclusion is so self-evident as hardly to require experimental verification it has been confirmed by oscillographic records such as those reproduced in Fig. 8E-2. These records were made immediately following the transmission reported by Fig. 3A-7. Transmission was between the same two vessels, both of which were anchored in quiet water at a considerable distance from shore. Except for the inevitable short-time variations in transmission loss, with which we are here concerned, the conditions under which the two signals were transmitted were the same. The signal reported by Fig. 3A-7 was a sinusoidal wave having a frequency of 26 kc/sec. The signal reported by Fig. 8E-2 was made up of two components separated in frequency by 80 cyc/sec and having an average frequency of 26 kc/sec. The amplitudes recorded by the oscillograph, in each case, are

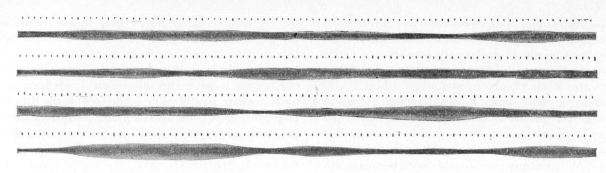

|←—1.0 SEC—→|

FIG. 8E-2. MULTIPLE-COMPONENT SIGNALS. Oscillograms showing the time variation in amplitude of an ultrasonic signal having two sinusoidal components the frequencies of which are 25.96 kc/sec and 26.04 kc/sec.

those of the electric voltages at the output terminals of the receiving transducer. It is quite evident that in the case of the dual-frequency signal there is no time at which there is complete cancellation, as there was with the single-frequency signal. In fact, the total variation in signal amplitude is now something of the order of 18 db. The assumption that either of the individual components of the dual-frequency signal may disappear exactly as the single-frequency signal disappeared may be verified with little trouble. If the beat-frequency oscillator of the receiver-amplifier is disabled there will be developed in the second detector, by intermodulation between the two components of the received signal, a derived component having a frequency equal to the 80-cyc/sec difference between their individual frequencies. This product of intermodulation, however, must vanish if either one of the source components vanishes. Observations proved that it did, indeed, pass through complete extinction even more frequently than did the single-frequency signal. It is clear, then, that a multifrequency signal, considered as a whole, will show far less variability than does the conventional CW signal. To realize this advantage, however, it is necessary that the receiving system respond to each component separately.

This last restriction immediately raises a question as to the effect of transmission variations on AM echo signals. Actually, as far as variability is concerned, the derived audio signal in this case varies very much as the unmodulated carrier varies; whenever the carrier vanishes there will be no derived signal produced as the result of intermodulation in the second detector. The two side bands, on the other hand, behave much as a dual-frequency signal behaves; if either side band is received it is sufficient, with the carrier, to produce the desired audio-frequency signal. Actual

experience, which shows that the variability of an AM echo signal is little different than that of a CW signal, confirms this conclusion. The fact remains, however, that both the CW and the AM methods of transmission leave much to be desired in the way of transmission stability.

A driving circuit capable of generating a signal having a number of coexistant sinusoidal components is, naturally, more complicated than one generating a single component. A practical solution to this problem is to arrange the driver to generate what is, in effect, a signal having a single component the frequency of which sweeps rapidly through a succession of values. The performance in this case may be described in various ways. It may be said that for any given transmission path there will be, at any instant, some value of frequency for which the transmission loss is a maximum, due to destructive interference. The frequency of the component for which this condition exists varies continuously in a random manner. If the variation in signal frequency is more rapid than the variation in the frequency of maximum loss this loss will be effective for only a portion of the pulse. Actually, if the signal frequency varies in any manner the chance that it will coincide with the maximum-loss frequency for any considerable portion of the pulse is very remote. Signals which change in frequency throughout the pulse transmission, then, are less likely to show wide variations in magnitude, at any receiving point, than signals of constant frequency.

Provision has been made for this method of transmission, known as **sweep-frequency modulation,** in practically all echo-ranging systems in use during World War II. The frequency of the signal wave is generally swept from 400 cyc/sec below the nominal frequency to 400 cyc/sec above for a pulse of normal duration. In practice it has been found that sweep modulated transmissions are not necessarily more successful than CW transmissions under all conditions. Quite apart from a possible reduction in variability they are often of great advantage when reverberation is the limiting interference. Here, in some cases, the use of sweep modulation gives the signal-interference combination a recognition differential which is much higher than that applying to a CW transmission. In the reverberation energy arriving from different distances will have different frequencies and the interference will tend not to have a clearly defined tone. The echo, on the other hand, may exhibit a characteristic clear chirp which gives it unusual prominence. This is

by no means universally true, however. It is, therefore, common practice for a sonar operator to compare the performance of the two types of transmission at intervals and to use whichever one seems to give the more sharply defined signals. Sweep modulation interferes with the interpretation of a Doppler shift in frequency as an indicator of target motion and is never used during attack operations by surface craft.

REFERENCES

1. C. F. Eyring, R. J. Christensen, and R. W. Raitt, "Reverberation in the Sea," *JASA*, Vol. 20, pp. 462–475, July, 1948.
2. L. N. Liebermann, "Reflections of Underwater Sound from the Sea Surface," *JASA*, Vol. 20, pp. 498–503, July, 1948.

CHAPTER 9

ADDENDA

In the two years which have passed since the first printing of this book the techniques of applied underwater acoustics have moved steadily away from the slide rule toward the electronic computer. This is not simply because the computer has become increasingly available; it is because sonar systems capable of meeting present requirements have moved beyond the boundaries which it was once necessary to postulate in order to devise workable models for our problems. When sonar was young it was possible to restrict attention to a few variables. The relations between these were easily established on the assumption that all other significant factors were constant. These assumptions were not unjustified; within the scope of our initial interest variations in many quantities could properly be ignored. Until experience had matured, good judgment led us to adhere to systems having simple configurations. These could be rigorously defined and their performance accurately predicted. For these systems it was possible to formulate generalized relations between design constants and performance characteristics without which progress in the techniques of sonar would have been impossible.

To meet present and future operating requirements it is now necessary to look outside the restricted regions governed by these simple and convenient rules. The models representing our present concepts are becoming more complex and the variables which influence their behavior more numerous. Studies of the performance of these more complex models require computations which can be made only by the high-speed computer. Where it was once possible to derive a convenient general relationship by evaluating some relatively simple integral, it is now necessary to carry out extensive point-by-point summations. These apply to particular situations which must be specified in great detail. It is difficult and dangerous to draw general conclusions from the results of such computations. It is, nevertheless, necessary to employ general relationships in planning their programs. It seems paradoxical that while the methods we now employ are more general in their application than those which served so well in the past, the results obtained by these methods are more specific.

The material contained in this chapter has been added in an effort to make the book more useful to those having to meet current problems relating to underwater acoustics.

9-A THE MEASUREMENT OF WAVES HAVING CONTINUOUS SPECTRA

Throughout the foregoing chapters of this book the magnitudes of waves having continuous spectra have been expressed in terms of power or of acoustic intensity when dealing with frequency bands of finite width, and in terms of power per unit band or intensity per unit band when dealing with magnitude considered as a function of frequency. This is in conformity with the familiar conventions of the elementary calculus of continuously variable quantities. It is not the method commonly employed.

It is the contention of many working in underwater acoustics that "pressure is a more basic quantity than energy." It is often asserted that pressure is the quantity usually measured, while energy may be measured only with great difficulty. The validity of these statements will not be argued here; their consequences, however, cannot be ignored.

One of the early efforts toward standardizing the units and terminology of underwater acoustics was to select a quantity to be used as a reference for the transmission levels of acoustic energy. The first choice was acoustic pressure. The magnitude originally selected was 0.0002 microbars. It was subsequently concluded that one microbar would have been more suitable. Both magnitudes are in wide use at the present time. The relation of these reference quantities to those measured as rates of energy flow are discussed in Art. 2B-3.

Pressure is a convenient and reliable measure of the magnitude of sinusoidal acoustic waves. Difficulties arise when attempts are made to use it with waves having continuous spectra. It is, of course, possible to measure the acoustic pressure due to energy having a continuous spectrum and occupying a given frequency band. This pressure is not, however, the sum of the pressures due to the energies occupying component portions of this band. As shown in Art. 2A-9, the pressure of a number of sinusoidal waves is the square root of the sum of the squares of the pressures of the individual waves. Similarly, the pressure due to the energies in a number of contiguous frequency bands is the square root of the sum of the squares of the pressures due to the energies in each. For energy having a continuous spectrum, therefore, the rate of change of pressure with increase in band width is not a unique function of the frequency at which the energy of an incremental band is added. It depends also upon the extent of the original band and on the manner in which the energy within this band is distributed. It is for this reason that the "pressure spectrum level," at a given frequency, of a wave having continuously distributed energy is defined by the **American Standard Acoustical Terminology**[1] in terms of the pressure for a band having a finite width of one cycle per second, instead of in terms of pressure per unit band. Unfortunately, the pressure for some given band may not be computed as the sum of these unit band pressures.

The decision to use the pressure of a band of finite width as a measure of wave magnitude, considered as a function of frequency, was a decision to refrain from using the calculus in problems related to energy having a continuous spectrum. If we are to examine the relations between continuously distributed acoustic energy and the characteristics of the media and systems by which this energy is propagated and transformed the simple processes of differentiation and integration are tools to which we must have unimpeded access. One method of obtaining this access is to express wave magnitudes in terms of such units as power per unit band and intensity per unit band, as was done in the original chapters of this book. Another is by using the quantities discussed in this section. It must be understood that these quantities have not been selected arbitrarily; they are those required by the basic laws of calculus if we are to deal with wave amplitudes, as well as with rates of flow of wave energy.

9A-1 The Measurement of Wave Amplitude

To obtain a measure of some magnitude associated with energy continuously distributed throughout some frequency band it is necessary to know the rate at which that magnitude varies with frequency. It is, in other words, necessary to know the frequency derivative of that magnitude at all points in the band. This quantity may then be integrated with respect to frequency, between the limiting boundaries of the band, to obtain the desired resultant magnitude.

The derivative of any function of a given variable with respect to that variable is, by the fundamental concept of the calculus, the limit approached by the ratio of an increment of the function to the corresponding increment of the variable as the increment of the variable approaches zero. In the situation now before us the independent variable is frequency band width. The function of this variable is acoustic pressure. Consider the portion of the spectrum shown graphically in Fig. 9A-1. Here f_o and f are the frequencies bounding a band of width $\Delta f = f - f_o$. The boundary f_o will be assumed to be fixed. The boundary f will be assumed to be variable. It is with this boundary, therefore, that rates of change of band pressure with change in band width are to be associated.

Let p be the rms pressure due to the acoustic energy in the band of width Δf. Now let the variable boundary be moved from f to $f + \delta f$, and let the rms pressure due solely to the acoustic energy in this band of incremental width δf be δp. By the laws governing the summation of acoustic pressures the pressure for the band between f_o and $f + \delta f$ is $\sqrt{p^2 + (\delta p)^2}$. The increase in band pressure resulting from the increase in band width taking place at the frequency f is consequently $\sqrt{p^2 + (\delta p)^2} - p$. This is equal to the increment of pressure δp only when $p = 0$, or when $\Delta f = 0$. The rate of change of pressure with increasing band width, as a function of frequency, is then, in general

$$\frac{dp}{df} = \operatorname*{Lim}_{\delta f \to 0} \frac{\sqrt{p^2 + (\delta p)^2} - p}{\delta f} \qquad (9A\text{-}1)$$

It is evident that this derivative is not a unique measure of the wave amplitude at a given frequency; it depends on the pressure due to the energy in a frequency band having a specified fixed boundary and on the manner in which this energy is distributed. It is further evident that, given the rate of change of pressure with increasing band width as a function of the varying boundary of the band, the other boundary being fixed, the only band pressures which may be computed by inte-

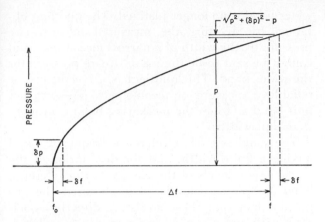

FIG. 9A-1. ACOUSTIC PRESSURE FOR VARYING FREQUENCY BAND. The acoustic pressure due to energy having a uniform distribution in frequency as a function of the portion of this energy included in a frequency band of varying width.

gration are those for bands having the postulated fixed boundary.

Some idea of the relation between the pressure due to the energy in a frequency band of infinitesimal width, which may be added to the energy in an adjoining band, and the change in pressure accompanying this addition may be obtained by an inspection of Fig. 9A-1. The curve there drawn shows the pressure for the band between f_o and f as a function of the frequency f, the frequency f_o being fixed. This pressure has been computed for uniformly distributed energy. The pressure for an incremental band of constant width is, therefore, independent of the location of this band. It is evident that although the pressure for an incremental band of constant width is constant the change in pressure accompanying a change in width of this constant amount is not constant. It depends on the frequency of the fixed boundary as well as on the frequency of the incrementally varying boundary. The magnitude of a change in pressure, in other words, depends on the width of the changing band as well as on the magnitude of the change in this width.

It is also evident from the curve of this figure that the rate of change of pressure for a band of infinitesimal width with change in this infinitesimal width cannot be used as a unique measure of wave amplitude, considered as a function of frequency. It can, in fact, be shown for any distribution of energy, as well as for the distribution postulated in computing the curve, that the limit approached by the quotient $\delta p/\delta f$ as δf approaches zero is infinite. This is confirmed by the slope of the curve at the origin.

Let us now examine the relations which exist between varying **mean-square acoustic pressure** and varying band width. For this we let p^2 be the mean-square pressure for the band of width Δf, and δp^2 the incremental mean-square pressure for the band of incremental width δf. Since mean-square pressures add directly the mean-square pressure for the band from f_o to $f+\delta f$ is $p^2+\delta p^2$, and the increase in mean-square pressure is $p^2+\delta p^2-p^2=\delta p^2$. It is, in other words, exactly equal to the incremental mean-square pressure of the added incremental band. The rate of change of mean-square pressure with increasing band width is thus

$$\frac{dp^2}{df} = \operatorname*{Lim}_{\delta f \to 0} \frac{\delta p^2}{\delta f} \qquad (9A\text{-}2)$$

The derivative in this case is independent of the total band width and of the manner in which energy is distributed therein. It is a unique measure of the wave energy at the point on the spectrum at which an incremental element of spectrum is added to the original frequency band. If this derivative is known as a function of frequency over any portion of the spectrum the mean-square pressure for any band within that portion may be computed at once by integrating between the limits of that band. There are no restrictions as to the location of either limit. This important measure of wave amplitude is the **mean-square pressure per unit band.**

These facts were clearly recognized by those who formulated the American Standard definition for "pressure spectrum level." As already noted the reference quantity used for this level is stated to be an rms sound pressure. It is, nevertheless, mean-square pressure which appears in the instructions for measuring and computing this level. These instructions appear under definition 1.340 of the **American Standard Acoustical Terminology,** as approved 31 July 1951 by the American Standards Association and the Acoustical Society of America. They read,

Since in practice it is necessary to employ filters having an effective band width greater than 1 cycle per second, the pressure spectrum level is in general a computed quantity. For a sound having a uniform distribution of energy, the computation can be made as follows: Let L_{ps} be the desired pressure spectrum level, p be the effective pressure measured through the filter system, p_o be the reference sound pressure, Δf be the effective band width of the filter system (see 3.220), and $\Delta_o f$ be the reference band width (1 cycle per second), then

$$L_{ps} = 10 \log_{10} \left[\frac{p^2/\Delta f}{p^2{}_o/\Delta_o f} \right]$$

All computations today being made of pressure spectrum level, as derived from data obtained by measurement, are made in accordance with these instructions. There is no question as to their validity. The significance of the results obtained, however, requires further attention.

It is evident that the quantity $p^2/\Delta f$ appearing in the instructions quoted above is, in fact, the mean-square pressure due to the energy in a frequency band having the specified reference width of one cycle per second. The computation of this mean-square pressure by dividing the mean-square pressure of a wider band by the width of this wider band is valid only for "a sound having a uniform distribution of energy." Throughout any frequency band in which acoustic energy is uniformly distributed the mean-square pressure per unit band, dp^2/df, is constant. This may be seen to be true by differentiating the acoustic intensity as given by Eq. (2A-33). This shows that

$$\frac{dI}{df} = \frac{1}{\rho c} \frac{dp^2}{df} \qquad (9A\text{-}3)$$

Since the specific acoustic conductance, $1/\rho c$, is constant the mean-square pressure per unit band, dp^2/df, must be constant when the intensity per unit band, dI/df, is constant, or when the acoustic energy is uniformly distributed in frequency. When the mean-square pressure per unit band is constant throughout some measured band $p^2/\Delta f$ is not only the mean-square pressure in a frequency band having a finite width of one cycle per second, it is also the measure of this constant mean-square pressure per unit band. That is

$$\{p^2/\Delta f\} = \{dp^2/df\} \qquad (9A\text{-}4)$$

The braces appearing in this equation are used, in accordance with conventions of the Quantity-Calculus,[9] to indicate that the equality applies only to the measures of two quantities. The quantities cannot be equal since they are of unlike dimensions.

It should be noted that as our interest expands to include waves of very low frequency the measurement bands which we employ may well have widths which are much less than one cycle per second. The unit band for which we undertake to compute the pressure is now wider than the band measured. The assumption of a constant mean-square pressure per unit band throughout this wider band is no longer justified. The quotient obtained by dividing the measured mean-square pressure by the width of a narrow measuring band cannot be said to be the mean-square pressure for the wider band. This quotient is, nevertheless, as reliable a measure of mean-square pressure per unit band as when the measuring band is of more than unit width.

The emphasis on a reference frequency band having a finite width, and the description of the transmission levels of the energy in this reference band as "pressure levels," has obscured the important fact that these levels are directly associated with mean-square pressure per unit band. For problems dealing with continuously distributed energy this is a more useful quantity than the pressure for a band of finite width. One quantity can be integrated to compute the pressure in a given band, the other cannot.

It is fortunate that the measures of these two quantities are the same under conditions of practical significance. Data reported in terms of one may, in consequence, be used for computations which require the other. The formula for pressure spectrum level, as given by the **American Standard Acoustical Terminology**, may be extended to include mean-square pressure per unit band, which is the quantity required in the computation of band pressures. In accordance with Eq. (9A-4) we may write

$$L_{ps} = 10 \log_{10} \left[\frac{p^2/\Delta f}{p^2{}_o/\Delta_o f} \right] = \lg t \frac{(dp^2/df)}{(dp^2/df)_o} \qquad (9A\text{-}5)$$

Here

L_{ps} = the pressure spectrum level of continuously distributed acoustic energy, computed for a band one cycle per second wide centered on a specified frequency, said to be in decibels relative to a reference rms pressure of one microbar

p = the measured rms pressure due to acoustic energy in a given frequency band (μb)

p_o = the reference rms acoustic pressure, usually one microbar

Δf = the width of the frequency band used for measuring, usually several cycles per second

$\Delta_o f$ = the width of the reference frequency band, having a finite width of one cycle per second

(dp^2/df) = the constant mean-square pressure per unit band, throughout the band measured, due to the given acoustic energy ($\mu b^2 \cdot sec/cyc$)

$(dp^2/df)_o$ = a reference mean-square pressure per unit band, preferably one microbar-squared-second per cycle

When the reference mean-square acoustic pressure per unit band is

$$(dp^2/df)_o = 1 \ \mu b^2 \cdot sec/cyc$$

the mean-square pressure per unit band, at any frequency within the measured band, is computed from the reported pressure spectrum level, L_{ps}, derived from this measurement as

$$dp^2/df = (10^{0.1})^{L_{ps}} \ \mu b^2 \cdot sec/cyc \qquad (9A-6)$$

It is the simplicity of this relation which makes the specification of unit mean-square pressure per unit band as the reference mean-square pressure per unit band so desirable.

The mean-square pressure per unit band computed as described above is understood to apply to any frequency in a band having a width of several cycles per second. When used in computations requiring integration, however, this quantity is treated as a function of the mid-frequency of such a band. If the mean-square pressure per unit band due to the acoustic energy in the frequency band between f_a and f_b is thus known the mean-square pressure due to the total energy in the band may be computed as the definite integral

$$p^2_{\Delta f} = \int_{f_a}^{f_b} \frac{dp^2}{df} \, dt \qquad (9A-7)$$

The relations discussed above in connection with acoustic waves apply, in general, to electric waves as well. When dealing with electric waves, however, it should be noted that the direct translation between **mean-square voltage per unit band,** or **mean-square current per unit band,** and transmission level is of doubtful validity. In the case of acoustic waves it is permissible to assume that the specific acoustic conductance has a fixed value throughout any frequency band of interest. The assumption of a constant electric impedance is by no means justified. To speak of a change in transmission level accompanying a change in frequency without taking due account of any concurrent change in impedance is to ignore the basic significance of transmission level, or of transmission loss. When dealing with the amplitudes of waves carrying electric energy continuously distributed in frequency we must make use of the concept of mean-square voltage per unit band, and of mean-square current per unit band. To relate these quantities with transmission level, however, is to risk certain confusion. The transmission losses of systems carrying these waves, and the transmission levels of these waves, should be measured only in terms of rates of energy flow.

9A-2 The Interpretation of Transducer Response

Definitions for the transmitting and receiving responses of sonar transducers are given in Art. 4D-1 in terms of the electric power and the acoustic intensity of sinusoidally varying waves. The responses thus measured are then shown to be related in a similar manner to the power per unit band of electric waves and the intensity per unit band of acoustic waves having continuous spectra. Other transducer responses, as reported in Art. 4G-2, are defined by the **American Standard Acoustical Terminology**[1]. These responses are in terms of the voltage and current of electric waves and the pressure of acoustic waves. In practice these responses are measured by means of waves having sinusoidal variations. Like responses measured in terms of rates of energy flow these amplitude responses may be extended to waves having continuous spectra.

It is evident from the preceding article that when dealing with the responses of electroacoustic transducers to waves having continuous spectra it will be desirable to express amplitude, considered as a function of frequency, in terms of mean-square values. For convenience let us consider specifically a response measured by the quotient obtained by dividing the open-circuit rms voltage of the sinusoidal electric waves generated in a hydrophone by the free-field rms pressure of the sinusoidal acoustic waves, of the same frequency, received by the hydrophone. It is obvious that if the value of this quotient is known a response measured by the quotient obtained by dividing the mean-square voltage by the mean-square pressure of these same sinusoidal waves is obtained at once by squaring. That is, if $(e/p) \sim$ volts/μb is the response as originally measured, using sinusoidal waves, the response expressed in terms of the mean-square amplitudes of these waves is

$$\frac{e^2}{p^2} = \left(\frac{e}{p}\right)_\sim^2 \text{ volts}^2/\mu b^2 \qquad (9A-8)$$

We may now consider waves having continuous spectra and occupying a narrow frequency band which includes the frequency of these sinusoidal waves. Let δe^2 be the mean-square voltage of the electric waves in this narrow band and let δp^2 be the mean-square pressure of the acoustic waves in the same band. As the incremental width, δf, of this band approaches zero the waves occupying it become more nearly sinusoidal. For a band of zero width they would be ideally sinusoidal were it not that, having continuous spectra, they would then be of zero amplitude. Let us cause the width, δf, of this narrow frequency band to approach zero by causing its boundaries to approach some specified frequency included between them. As the width of the band approaches zero the mean-square voltage and the mean-square pressure also approach zero. Their quotient, however, approaches the quotient of the finite mean-square voltage and the finite mean-square pressure observed, at this same specified frequency, for sinusoidally varying waves. It is assumed that the hydrophone response, which is measured by these quotients, is independent of energy levels in the neighborhood of this frequency.

Now it is evident that if mean-square voltage and mean-square pressure each approach zero as the width of the band approaches zero the mean-square voltage approaches zero as the mean-square pressure approaches zero. The limit approached by the quotient of these two variables is the derivative of the mean-square voltage with respect to the mean-square pressure. We may, therefore, write

$$\operatorname*{Lim}_{\delta f \to 0} \frac{\delta e^2}{\delta p^2} = \frac{de^2}{dp^2} = \left(\frac{e}{p}\right)_\sim^2 \qquad (9A-9)$$

The square of the receiving response of a hydrophone, at any frequency, as given by the quotient obtained by dividing the rms voltage of generated sinusoidal electric waves by the rms pressure of received acoustic waves, is thus seen to be equal to the derivative of the mean-square voltage of continuous spectrum electric waves taken with respect to the mean-square pressure of continuous spectrum acoustic waves. By the elementary laws of the calculus, then

$$\left(\frac{e}{p}\right)_\sim^2 = \frac{de^2}{dp^2} = \frac{de^2/dt}{dp^2/df} \qquad (9A-10)$$

In other words, the square of this same receiving response is equal to the quotient obtained by dividing the mean-square voltage per unit band of the continuous spectrum electric waves by the mean-square pressure per unit band of the continuous spectrum acoustic waves.

Other transducer responses, both transmitting and receiving, applying to waves having continuous spectra may be related to corresponding responses measured, in the usual manner, with waves having sinusoidal variations. Responses measured in terms of mean-square amplitudes per unit band are of considerable utility whenever it is desired to compute the amplitude of the resultant response of an electroacoustic transducer to energy having a continuous spectrum and occupying some specified frequency band of finite width. This application may be illustrated by continuing with the specific voltage response used in deriving the relations given above.

Let us assume that a hydrophone has a known receiving voltage response $(e/p)_\sim$ volts/μb, measured by means of sinusoidal waves. This is known as a function of frequency throughout the frequency band between f_a and f_b. It is understood that although measurements are made at a number of frequencies separated by finite intervals the response is considered to be known for any frequency in the band in question.

Let the mean-square pressure per unit band of the acoustic energy received by the hydrophone, at any frequency in the specified band, be (dp^2/df) $\mu b^2 \cdot$sec/cyc. The response of the hydrophone as measured in terms of mean-square voltage per unit band and mean-square pressure per unit band is related to the known response by Eq. (9A-10). To find the open-circuit mean-square voltage per unit band generated in the hydrophone, as a function of frequency, it is necessary simply to multiply the mean-square pressure per unit band of the received acoustic waves by the square of the corresponding hydrophone response. This open-circuit mean-square voltage per unit band is, therefore,

$$\frac{de^2}{df} = \frac{de^2/df}{dp^2/df} \frac{dp^2}{df} = \left(\frac{e}{p}\right)_\sim^2 \frac{dp^2}{df} \qquad (9A-11)$$

The open-circuit mean-square voltage generated in the hydrophone by the total acoustic energy received in the specified frequency band may now be computed as

$$e^2{}_{\Delta f} = \int_{f_a}^{f_b} \frac{de^2}{df} df$$

$$= \int_{f_a}^{f_b} \left(\frac{e}{p}\right)^2_\sim \frac{dp^2}{df} df \text{ volts}^2 \qquad (9A\text{-}12)$$

9A-3 The Significance of Impedance

To conclude this discussion of waves having continuous spectra it remains to establish the connection between wave amplitudes and rates of energy flow. For sinusoidal waves this coupling is effected through the concept of impedance. This same impedance may be used for a similar purpose with waves having continuous spectra.

Throughout the earlier chapters of this book, as in all elementary treatments of impedance, this quantity is defined in terms of waves having sinusoidal variations. It is invariably measured by means of such waves. As we shall see, however, impedances measured with sinusoidal waves may be used for computations having to do with continuous spectra waves. This is another example of the family relationship between impedance and transducer response. For convenience the following discussion will be in terms of electric impedance.

The absolute magnitude of the electric impedance of a circuit in which a sinusoidally varying voltage is accompanied by a sinusoidally varying current is measured by the quotient obtained by dividing the rms value of this voltage by the rms value of this current. That is

$$|Z| = \left(\frac{e}{i}\right)_\sim \qquad (9A\text{-}13)$$

As in the derivation of Eq. (9A-9) we may now assume that these sinusoidal waves are replaced by waves having continuous spectra. For a narrow frequency band, which includes the frequency of the sinusoidal waves, the incremental mean-square voltage will be δe^2, and the incremental mean-square current δi^2. As the limits of this frequency band approach the frequency of the sinusoidal waves the incremental width of the band, δf, approaches zero. The incremental magnitudes of the mean-square voltage and mean-square current also approach zero. At the same time they become more nearly sinusoidal and

their quotient approaches the square, $(e/i)_\sim{}^2$, of the quotient observed with sinusoidal waves. Here, as in Art. 9A-2, frequency band width is an independent variable which, as it approaches zero, causes two dependent variables to approach zero simultaneously. We therefore write

$$\operatorname*{Lim}_{\delta f \to 0} \frac{\delta e^2}{\delta i^2} = \frac{de^2}{di^2} = \left(\frac{e}{i}\right)^2_\sim \qquad (9A\text{-}14)$$

From this it follows at once that

$$|Z|^2 = \left(\frac{e}{i}\right)^2_\sim = \frac{de^2}{di^2} = \frac{de^2/df}{di^2/df} \qquad (9A\text{-}15)$$

It is thus evident that, at any given frequency, the impedance at the terminals of a circuit receiving electric waves having a continuous spectrum is measured by the square root of the quotient obtained by dividing the mean-square voltage per unit band of these waves by their mean-square current per unit band, both being for the given frequency.

In a similar manner we find a relation between the impedance of a circuit and measures of the energy and amplitude of continuous spectrum waves impressed on that circuit. We begin here with the familiar relation, $P = i^2R$, between the power, P, and current, i, of sinusoidal waves, and the resistance, R, of the circuit. We then consider the power and the mean-square current of continuous spectra waves for a frequency band of incremental width and allow the width of this band to approach zero. Since this causes the power and the mean-square current to approach zero simultaneously we have

$$R = \left(\frac{P}{i^2}\right)_\sim = \frac{dP}{di^2} = \frac{dP/df}{di^2/df} = \frac{U}{di^2/df} \qquad (9A\text{-}16)$$

Here $U = dP/df$ is the power per unit band, at the frequency in question, as defined in Art. 2A-11.

The resistance, R, is usually known, as a function of frequency, from measurements made by using sinusoidal waves. The mean-square current per unit band may be measured, also as a function of frequency, by observations made with filters having narrow pass bands, in the same manner that mean-square acoustic pressure is measured. Knowing these two quantities throughout the frequency band between f_a and f_b the power measuring the rate of energy flow for continuous spectrum waves in that band is computed as

$$P_{\Delta f} = \int_{f_a}^{f_b} U\, df = \int_{f_a}^{f_b} R\, \frac{di^2}{df}\, df \quad (9A\text{-}17)$$

The relations expressed by Eq. (9A-15) show that the quotient obtained by dividing the mean-square voltage per unit band of waves having a continuous spectrum by the mean-square current per unit band of these waves is equal to the quotient obtained by dividing the mean-square voltage by the mean-square current of sinusoidal waves at the same terminals and frequency. Now the voltage and current of the sinusoidal waves have a definite phase relation, determined by the phase angle of the impedance of the circuit. This phase angle is not without significance when dealing with the waves having continuous spectra. For sinusoidal electric waves the voltage and current are related to the power by a **power factor.** This power factor is measured by the cosine, $\cos \psi$, of the phase angle of the circuit, which, in turn, is measured by the quotient obtained by dividing the resistance of the circuit by the absolute magnitude of its impedance. The derivation of these relations is discussed in Art. 2A-6, although in terms of acoustic waves rather than of electric waves.

From the known relation between power factor, resistance, and impedance, and the relations given by Eqs. (9A-15) and (9A-16), we obtain at once the relation between power factor and the significant measures of waves having continuous spectra. These relations are

$$\cos^2 \psi = \frac{R^2}{|Z|^2} = \frac{(dP/df)^2}{(de^2/df)(di^2/df)} \quad (9A\text{-}18)$$

or, in a form analogous to the familiar expression $P = ei \cos$,

$$U = \sqrt{(de^2/df)(di^2/df)}\, \cos \psi \quad (9A\text{-}19)$$

Here

$U = dP/df$
= the average power per unit band, at some specified frequency, measuring the rate of flow of electric energy having a continuous spectrum (joule/cyc)

(de^2/df) = the mean-square voltage per unit band of the waves carrying this electric energy (volt²·sec/cyc)

(di^2/df) = the mean-square current per unit band of these same waves, at the same frequency (amp²·sec/cyc)

$\cos \psi = R/|Z|$
= the power factor of the circuit receiving this electric energy, as measured at the same frequency, by means of sinusoidal waves. (watt/volt·amp)

In this case the power measuring the rate of energy flow for electric waves having a continuous spectrum and occupying a frequency band of finite width is computed as

$$P_{\Delta f} = \int_{f_a}^{f_b} U\, df$$

$$= \int_{f_a}^{f_b} \sqrt{(de^2/df)(di^2/df)}\, \cos \psi\, df \quad (9A\text{-}20)$$

Other relations between the rates of energy flow and the amplitudes of waves having continuous spectra may be formulated for both electric and acoustic waves. In many cases these may be written at once by analogy with expressions given above. For example, the intensity per unit band of acoustic waves having a continuous spectrum is given in terms of the mean-square pressure per unit band of these waves and of the specific acoustic conductance of the medium through which they are propagated as

$$J = \frac{dp^2/df}{\rho c}\, 10^{-7} \quad (9A\text{-}21)$$

where

J = the free-field acoustic intensity per unit band, at a given frequency, of acoustic waves having a continuous spectrum (joule/cm²·cyc)

(dp^2/df) = the mean-square pressure per unit band, at the same frequency, of these same waves (μb²·sec/cyc)

$1/\rho c$ = the specific acoustic conductance of the medium, considered independent of frequency (spec acous mho)

In this case the acoustic intensity of these waves for a frequency band between f_a and f_b is

$$I_{\Delta f} = \int_{f_a}^{f_b} J \, dj$$

$$= \frac{10^{-7}}{\rho c} \int_{f_a}^{f_b} \frac{d\bar{p}^2}{df} \, df \ \text{watts/cm}^2 \qquad (9A\text{-}22)$$

The dangers of using wave amplitudes, rather than rates of energy flow, as reference quantities for transmission levels have been under discussion for many years. The practice appears, unfortunately, to have become firmly established in many areas, including underwater acoustics. Levels so reported are said to be measures of acoustic pressure, or of electric voltage. When dealing with continuous spectra waves, these levels are designated as "spectrum levels." Their reference quantities are frequency-dependent measures of wave amplitude. Since a quantity which might be described as "pressure per unit band" is without significance the concept of the pressure due to energy in a finite band of unit width has been devised to serve in its place. From the discussions of this section it is apparent that, although this concept is not without validity it has little utility. The measures of wave amplitude, considered as functions of frequency, which must be used when dealing with waves having continuous spectra are the mean-square amplitudes of these waves. These are the only quantities which may be integrated to yield the amplitudes of waves carrying energy continuously distributed throughout frequency bands of finite width. These required mean-square amplitudes may be computed directly from transmission levels referred to a rate of energy flow. This is accomplished by means of relations expressed in terms of impedance. This property of a medium or system transmitting wave energy may be easily measured using sinusoidal waves, and has rigorously established relations to the energy and amplitude of waves having continuous spectra. There appears to be no justification, therefore, for perpetuating such a concept as that of the pressure due to the energy in a frequency band having a width of one cycle per second.

9-B EFFECT OF EARTH'S CURVATURE ON SOUND PROPAGATION

Of the many devices which have helped in the application of underwater acoustics few have been more idealized, and at the same time more fruitful, than the model of the ocean used for computing the paths traveled by sound energy. Every naval officer participating in underwater operations now carries this model constantly in mind. Its behavior is as significant a factor in his decisions as the weather.

In view of the importance of a true understanding of the manner in which sound energy is distributed in the ocean it is desirable to inspect this model from time to time. We must know the extent to which deviations of its form from the form of the real ocean are accompanied by deviations in its performance. In the past the close resemblance between the behavior of the model and of the real ocean has demonstrated the adequacy of the model. The need for renovation, however, appears imminent.

We are far from prepared, at the moment, to replace our old model by a completely new one. We may, nevertheless, study the effect of a minor revision. Specifically, we may examine the consequences of giving our model a spherical shape, which more nearly resembles the real ocean than does the simpler flat model.

Fortunately the errors introduced by the assumption of a flat earth are by no means as serious when dealing with sound waves in the ocean as when dealing with electromagnetic waves above it. Sound waves are not, in general, unable to enter the region behind a fixed horizon. On meeting such a medium boundary they are reflected back into the water to be propagated along paths which return to a similar boundary at a more remote point. As a result energy is propagated through the medium as through a duct. In other situations sound waves propagated in the vicinity of a surface at which the velocity of propagation is a minimum are refracted along paths which cross and recross this surface. Such surfaces act as virtual wave guides, regardless of whether they are plane or spherical. It is thus evident that, as a result of either reflections or of refractions, sound energy may be propagated through the body of the ocean as it curves along the surface of the earth much as it would be propagated if this surface were flat. It is, nevertheless, desirable that we be able to appraise the magnitude of any errors which may result from the assumption of a flat earth.

The flat model postulates a series of contiguous layers bounded by plane surfaces, nominally parallel to the ocean surface. In each of these layers the velocity of propagation is constant for any plane surface parallel to these boundaries. This velocity varies in such manner that its rate of change with depth is constant throughout any given layer. Each layer, in other words, is characterized by vertical velocity gradients of one constant magnitude, and having directions which are parallel. To take account of the curvature of the earth's surface this model must be modified in two respects. The surfaces of constant velocity of propagation, including the boundary surfaces, must become concentric spheres, having their common center at the center of the earth. The constant velocity gradients must be directed along the radii of these spherical surfaces, instead of along parallel lines. This revised model, no less than the one which it replaces, represents a highly idealized ocean. The step toward a complete generalization is a short one.

In completing this modified model it will be convenient to adopt, as the nominal radius of the spherical surface representing the surface of the real ocean, a length of $7 \cdot 10^6$ yds $= 2.1 \cdot 10^7$ ft. The radius of the real ocean, at the equator is $2.0926 \cdot 10^7$ ft.

9B-1 The Computation of Ray Paths

In carrying out computations based on the model now postulated we shall measure positive radial distances from the center of the spherical surfaces. A positive velocity gradient is, therefore, one for which the velocity of propagation increases with increasing distance from the center, and hence with decreasing depth. In conformity with this convention the angle of inclination at any point on a ray path will be measured in a counter clockwise direction from the normal to the radius through that point, the normal lying to the right of the radius.

The radial gradient for any constant gradient spherical shell of our new model may be written as

$$g = \frac{dc}{dr} \qquad (9\text{B-1})$$

where

$g =$ the constant radial velocity gradient (1/sec)

$c =$ the velocity of propagation over a spherical surface in the constant gradient shell (ft/sec)

$r =$ the radius of this spherical surface (ft)

When this expression is integrated there is obtained

$$r = \frac{c}{g} + R \qquad (9\text{B-2})$$

where

$R =$ the radius of the spherical surface at which the velocity of propagation would be zero, provided the constant gradient continued to this surface (ft)

The length of this radius, which is as characteristic of a constant gradient spherical shell, or constant gradient layer, as its gradient, may be computed from Eq. (9B-2) provided the velocity and radius for any point are known. When the gradient, g, and the zero velocity surface radius, R, are known the velocity for the terminus of any other radius within the layer is given at once as

$$c = g(r - R) \qquad (9\text{B-3})$$

Perhaps the most important lesson to be learned from a study of our curved earth model is that the form of Snell's law which underwater acoustics borrowed from optics, and which has governed the computation of many ray paths in the past, is not sufficiently general for our present use. As formulated for optical systems this law prescribes the change in the angle of inclination of a ray path at a point in the boundary between two media having constant but unlike velocities of propagation. It has been demonstrated that the relation between inclination and velocity of propagation is the same when applied to separated points on a ray path in a single medium having a constantly changing velocity of propagation provided the gradients of this velocity lie everywhere along parallel straight lines. This enabling condition is not satisfied in the curved earth model, where the gradients are radial.

This matter has been admirably dealt with by Freehafer[2] in connection with electromagnetic waves. From the results of this work, and from a consideration of the specific situation now postulated, the required relation is found to be

$$\frac{\cos \theta_1}{\cos \theta_2} = \frac{c_1}{c_2} \frac{r_2}{r_1} \qquad (9\text{B-4})$$

where

$\theta_1 =$ the angle of inclination of a given ray path at a spherical surface at which the velocity of propagation has the constant value c_1 and for which the radius is r_1 (deg)

$\theta_2 =$ the angle of inclination of this same ray path at a spherical surface, concentric with the first, at which the velocity of propagation has the constant value c_2 and for which the radius is r_2 (deg)

In the medium to which this relation applies all ray paths lie in planes through the common center of the concentric spherical surfaces. Ray diagrams computed by the formulas to be given below show the paths of sound rays in such planes.

It is evident that the assumption of a flat model corresponds to the assumption that the radii now postulated are of infinite length. In this case $r_2/r_1 = 1$ and Eq. (9B-4) reduces to Eq. (3B-1).

In a medium where the velocity gradients are everywhere radial any sound ray which is not reflected is characterized by a constant having the dimensions of time. This constant is

$$t_o = \frac{r}{c} \cos \theta = \frac{r_o}{c_o} \qquad (9B\text{-}5)$$

where

t_o = a ray constant characteristic of a given ray path in a medium where the velocity gradients are everywhere radial
    (sec)

r = the radius of a constant velocity spherical surface crossed by the given ray path
    (ft)

c = the velocity of propagation at any point of this surface
    (ft/sec)

θ = the angle of inclination of the ray path at its intersection with this surface
    (deg)

r_o = the radius of a constant velocity spherical surface at which the angle of inclination of the ray path is $\theta = 0°$
    (ft)

c_o = the velocity of propagation at any point on the surface of radius r_o
    (ft/sec)

This ray constant, t_o, is unchanged as the ray passes from one layer of constant radial gradient to another. It is also unchanged when the ray is reflected from a surface perpendicular to the radius through the reflection point.

It will be recalled that in a medium where the velocity gradients are everywhere parallel any ray path is characterized by a vertex velocity, at which its angle of inclination is $\theta = 0°$. This is the maximum velocity to be found at any point through which the ray may pass. No such maximum velocity exists for a ray in a medium where the gradients are radial. The velocity of propagation at any point where the inclination is $\theta = 0°$ is not fixed but has a value which is proportional to the distance from the center of the constant velocity spherical surface. The ray constant, t_o, is now the significant constant for the ray as it passes from one constant gradient layer to another.

Having one constant characteristic of a given ray path in a medium where the velocity gradients are radial, and another characteristic of a given constant gradient layer in such a medium, we now obtain a third constant, characteristic of the given ray in the given layer. By substituting the value of the velocity of propagation, c, as given by Eq. (9B-3), into Eq. (9B-5) this constant is obtained as the product

$$g t_o = \frac{r}{r - R} \cos \theta \qquad (9B\text{-}6)$$

Any sound ray for which a path is to be computed is usually specified in terms of its angle of inclination at its source. The constant velocity of propagation, c_s, and the radius, r_s, of the spherical surface through the source point must also be known or postulated. Points on the path of a ray thus specified may be selected by designating suitable increments of radial distance, equivalent to increments of depth. These will be chosen, as in Art. 3B-9, so that some of their junction points fall on boundaries at which there is a change in gradient. Within each constant gradient layer increments of depth will be chosen to provide an adequate number of points for computation and plotting.

If it is known, or expected, that a ray path will become horizontal in any layer the radius at which this will occur is

$$r_o = \frac{g t_o R}{g t_o - 1} \qquad (9B\text{-}7)$$

as may be seen by making $\theta = 0°$ in Eq. (9B-6). This radius should be made the terminus of the series of selected depth intervals.

Having a number of postulated radial lengths the velocities of propagation characteristic of the spherical surfaces passing through their terminals may now be computed. This is done by finding the change in velocity, $\Delta c = g(\Delta r)$, which takes place in each layer, and adding, consecutively, to the source velocity.

To find the points at which the given ray path crosses the several postulated levels it is necessary to find, first, the angles of inclination at these levels. When high-speed computers are used these angles may be computed to the required precision by Eq. (9B-6), where all quantities except the inclination, θ, are now known.

For computations using a desk calculator it may be more convenient to use a relation analogous to that of Eq. (3B-25), by which incremental changes in the cosine of the angle of inclination, which need be known to a relatively low percentage accuracy, are added to values of the cosine, which must be known to a much greater percentage accuracy. For the curved model this relation is

$$\cos \theta_n = \cos \theta_m + gt_o R \frac{r_n - r_m}{r_m r_n} \qquad (9B-8)$$

The angle of inclination at each level is now found by means of trigonometric tables. Since we are dealing here with small changes in large quantities it will be necessary to use seven-place tables. It is desirable that interpolations be carried to 0.00001°.

The next step is to find the polar angle of the radius through the point of intersection of the ray path with each of the levels. To do this we first differentiate the radius to each of these points with respect to the corresponding angle of inclination, using the relation of Eq. (9B-6). This gives

$$dr = \frac{-r \sin \theta}{gt_o - \cos \theta} d\theta \qquad (9B-9)$$

For the moment we may select any convenient radial direction as a reference direction for the measurement of polar angle, as shown in Fig. 9B-1. From the diagram of this figure it is evident by inspection that

$$dr = r \tan \theta \, d\phi \qquad (9B-10)$$

where

$\phi =$ the polar angle between the radius through some specified point on a given ray path and a radius chosen to have a reference direction
(rad)

This angle is given a positive sign by measuring polar angles in a clockwise direction. This is desirable since it leads to distances which are measured to the right of the source, as is customary.

The changes in polar angle which occur in any constant gradient layer may now be computed. To do this it will be found convenient to select as the reference direction, for any one constant gradient layer, the direction of the radius through the point at which the ray path would have an

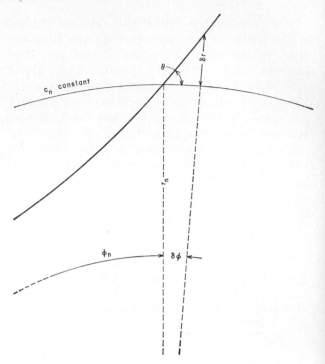

Fig. 9B-1. Computation of Ray Paths. The relations between inclination and radial distance for a ray path in a medium where constant velocity loci are concentric spherical surfaces.

inclination of $\theta = 0°$ if the constant gradient condition were sufficiently extended. This avoids the introduction of a constant of integration. The polar angle, ϕ_n, between this reference direction and the radius through the intersection of the ray path with a specified spherical surface, having the radius r_n, is obtained as the definite integral taken between 0 and θ_n, where θ_n is the angle of inclination at the surface in question. To express the result of this integration conveniently we let $gt_o = a$, and then let

$$A = \frac{2a}{\sqrt{a^2 - 1}}, \quad \text{and} \quad B = \frac{\sqrt{a^2 - 1}}{a - 1}$$

The desired polar angle is then

$$\phi_n = \theta_n - A \arctan \left(B \tan \frac{\theta_n}{2} \right) \qquad (9B-11)$$

By means of this relation the polar angle for each of the several selected levels may be computed. It must be remembered that a different reference direction is used with each constant gradient layer.

Having determined the changes in polar angle taking place in a given layer the relative positions of the corresponding points on the given ray path in that layer are known in terms of polar coordinates. It will be more convenient to plot these points against rectangular coordinates. The origin of these coordinates may be taken to coincide with the source of the ray path, the Y-axis, in the negative direction, coinciding with the radius through this source. The component of an increment of path length between two consecutive points, as measured in the X-direction, is

$$\Delta X = r_n \sin \phi_n - r_m \sin \phi_m \qquad (9B\text{-}12)$$

In a similar manner the incremental change in Y is

$$\Delta Y = r_n \cos \phi_n - r_m \cos \phi_m \qquad (9B\text{-}13)$$

Attention is again called to the fact that the polar angle, ϕ, is the same for the end of one increment of path and the beginning of the next except when the junction falls on a spherical surface bounding two layers having constant radial gradients of unlike magnitude.

Although these equations bear a superficial resemblance to Eqs. (3B-23) and (3B-24) the two pairs must not be confused.

A curve representing the surface of the ocean may be plotted against the same rectangular coordinates as the ray paths. For this

$$x = 7 \cdot 10^6 \sin \phi \text{ yd}$$
$$y = 2.1 \cdot 10^7 \cos \phi \text{ ft} \qquad (9B\text{-}14)$$

where

$\phi =$ the polar angle between the radius through the source point, at the origin, and the point (x, y) (rad)

The change in the horizontal component of the distance between any two points on the ray path, separated by the polar angle $\Delta\phi$, as measured along the surface of the ocean, is

$$\Delta S = 7 \cdot 10^6 (\Delta\phi) \text{ yd} \qquad (9B\text{-}15)$$

The radius here used is the nominal radius of the earth postulated for this curved model of its oceans.

As might be expected, the differences between ray paths computed for the flat model and for the curved model are small. For a ray leaving its source with a given inclination the horizontal component, measured along the ocean surface, of the distance to the point at which the ray reaches a given depth will not be the same for the two.

The manner in which the velocity of propagation varies between the two depths determines which of the two distances will be the greater. In general, this is of little significance; if a ray path having one source inclination reaches a given receiving point on one model the same receiving point may usually be reached on the other by a change in source inclination so small as to be negligible. This is not always true. For example, consider the limiting ray in a deep isothermal surface layer. The source inclination of this ray in the curved model will be slightly greater than in the flat model, but the ray will return to the surface at a point nearer the source. In other words, a limiting point reached by direct transmission on the flat model will not be reached by any direct path on the curved model. It can also be shown that the location of some point where ray paths come to a focus will be different on the two models. Where the existence of a focal point requires that the ocean depth exceed some definite value there will be situations where this focus will be found on one model and not on the other.

In general, we may conclude that differences in the paths of sound rays computed for the two models will be less than those due to uncertainties in our knowledge of the real ocean. The computed differences do not reach significant magnitudes except for ray paths of considerable length. For these long ray paths variations in velocity of propagation with depth which may be known for a source point and for a receiving point cannot be expected to apply to all intermediate points. Before dismissing the curved model as introducing a needless complication, however, we must examine the question of travel time along a ray path connecting two given points.

9B-2 The Computation of Travel Time

The computation of the time required for sound energy to travel along a given ray path is made for the curved model in much the same manner as that commonly used for the plane model. In either case an expression is developed for the component of velocity normal to the boundaries of the constant gradient layers. This component may be expressed as a function of depth, or, in the present case, of change in radius. The time required for a sound wave to travel the length of ray path included between two given levels is then determined by integrating the reciprocal of this normal component of velocity between these two levels. In the case of the curved model the normal component lies along a radius. It may be written as

$$c_{\text{rad}} = c \sin \theta = \frac{r \sin \theta \cos \theta}{t_o} \qquad (9B\text{-}16)$$

The time required for the sound wave to travel the length of path between the boundaries of a given layer is thus

$$\Delta T = t_o \int_{r_{\text{in}}}^{r_{\text{out}}} \frac{dr}{r \sin \theta \cos \theta} \qquad (9B\text{-}17)$$

It will be convenient to carry out this integration in terms of the angle of inclination, rather than in terms of the radius. Making this change of variable, we find that the travel time becomes

$$\Delta T = - t_o \int_{\theta_{\text{in}}}^{\theta_{\text{out}}} \frac{d\theta}{\cos \theta (a - \cos \theta)}$$

$$= \frac{1}{g} \left[\frac{1}{\sqrt{a^2 - 1}} \arcsin \left(\frac{a \cos \theta - 1}{a - \cos \theta} \right) \right.$$

$$\left. - \log_e \tan \left(\frac{\pi}{4} + \frac{\theta}{2} \right) \right]_{\theta_{\text{in}}}^{\theta_{\text{out}}} \qquad (9B\text{-}18)$$

The corresponding expression applying to the plane surface model differs from this only by the absence of the term containing $a = gt_o$.

For one particular example, where a ray path was returned to the surface at a range of approximately 70,000 yd as a result of refraction, having reached a depth of approximately 17,000 ft, the time required to reach a given point on the surface differed by approximately 0.1 percent for the two models. In this example the ray in the flat model reached a depth some 200 ft greater than the maximum depth for the curved model. The ray for the flat model was, therefore, somewhat longer than for the curved model. Since, for an appreciable portion of this length, the velocity of propagation was greater the percentage difference between the travel times proved to be less than the percentage difference between the distances traveled.

With travel time, as with the location of ray paths, it appears that in many cases where an idealized model is used for studying the manner in which sound energy is propagated through the ocean the added labor of using a curved model is not justified. Whenever it is expected that the greater resemblance of the curved model to the real ocean may be significant computations may be made by means of the relations described above.

9-C DIRECTIONAL RESPONSE OF TRANSDUCERS

In Chapter 4, on sonar transducers, directional response has been discussed almost exclusively in terms of transducers having some form of symmetry which has made it possible to develop simple expressions for relative response or for directivity factor. Many of the transducers or transducer arrays now coming into use do not satisfy these ideal restrictive conditions. It is no longer possible to compute the directivity patterns or the directivity factors of all transducer systems of interest by simple substitutions in convenient formulas. Instead, it is necessary to turn to the high-speed computer. The general question of directivity must, therefore, be re-examined in a search for more useful guides than the limited formulas previously available.

9C-1 The Product Theorem

The product theorem, related to the resultant response of arrays of directional electroacoustic transducers, is mentioned in Art. 5A-4. In view of the increasing utility of this theorem it appears desirable to consider somewhat more rigorously the limits within which it may be employed. There are two basic conditions which must be satisfied in order that the product theorem may be valid.

Condition 1: Assume an array of directional electroacoustic transducers in which the magnitude and phase of the response of each transducer, for some given frequency, is identically the same for any bearing as the response of each of the others for that bearing.

Condition 2: Assume, also, that when transmitting acoustic energy each transducer is characterized by a single point, or transmitting acoustic center, from which this energy appears to radiate regardless of the direction in which it is propagated, or, that when receiving acoustic energy each transducer is characterized by a single point, or receiving acoustic center, at which incident plane waves of this energy have a phase relative to the phase of the resulting electric waves which is independent of the direction in which the acoustic waves are propagated.

Product Theorem: For an array of directional electroacoustic transducers which, at some given frequency, satisfy the postulated conditions the resultant relative response, for any bearing, is the product of the relative response of one of the directional transducers and the relative response which the array would have if made up of nondirectional transducers having acoustic centers located at the points occupied by the acoustic centers of the directional transducers.

The first condition may be stated more briefly, although with the loss of specific detail, by saying that the array must be built of identical transducers identically oriented. Particular attention must be given to the second condition. It is, of course, evident that if the individual directional transducers do not have fixed acoustic centers there will be no fixed points at which to locate the individual elements of the hypothetical array of nondirectional transducers.

In practice, as noted in Art. 5A-4, the maximum response axis of the hypothetical array of nondirectional transducers and the maximum response axes of the directional transducers of the actual array will usually have the same direction. Whenever this is true the resultant relative response of the array of directional elements will also be a maximum for this direction and will be of unit magnitude. The product theorem is not restricted to systems satisfying this condition. It may be used equally well, provided the necessary conditions are satisfied, when the component responses have their maximum values at separated bearings. In such cases, however, there will be no bearing for which the response computed by the product theorem is unity. It will then be necessary to find the maximum value of this computed response and to normalize all responses by dividing by this value. When the maximum response bearings of the hypothetical array of nondirectional elements and of a single directional element do not coincide the maximum response bearing of the actual array will not coincide with either; its direction may usually be conveniently established by graphical methods.

9C-2 Apparent Plane Wave Magnitudes

The apparent plane wave intensity per unit band of the acoustic energy received by a directional transducer from all directions, but at a single specified frequency, is defined in Art 4F-2. The distinction between an **apparent plane wave** magnitude and an **equivalent plane wave** magnitude is that the latter is a unique property of the acoustic energy existing at a given point, whereas the former is dependent both on the directional distribution of this energy and on the directional response characteristics of the transducer by which it is received.

The concept of an apparent plane wave magnitude is not restricted to the intensity per unit band, at a specified frequency, of acoustic energy having a continuous spectrum. It applies also to the intensity of acoustic energy having some definite distribution throughout some specified frequency band and to the intensity of sinusoidal waves having a specified frequency. The apparent plane wave intensity of sinusoidal waves of given frequency arriving over many bearings is a convenient quantity by which to measure reverberation, which may be considered either as sinusoidal waves or as waves occupying some frequency band.

The concept of apparent plane wave magnitude is not restricted to energy propagated over many bearings. Since the energy thus measured is not assumed to be uniformly distributed the case of energy associated with a single bearing is not excluded.

Relations between the relative receiving response of a sonar transducer, for a specified bearing and frequency, and significant characteristics of the transducer, of the received acoustic waves, and of the generated electric waves are given by Eq. (4D-4). This equation was derived by combining equations for the receiving response, as given by Eq. (4D-2), for the specified bearing and for the reference bearing. The complete equation, for the case of sinusoidal waves, would be written as

$$\eta'_d = \frac{\mu'_d}{\mu'_{do}} = \frac{P'_d}{I'_d} \frac{I'_{do}}{P'_{do}} \qquad (9\text{C-}1)$$

The relation $\eta'_d = P'_d/P'_{do}$ shown in Eq. (4D-4) results from having postulated (page 158) that the acoustic waves received over the specified and reference bearings be of equal intensity, or that $I'_d = I'_{do}$. We may, however, alter the intensity of the waves received over the reference bearing until $P'_{do} = P'_d$. The value to which this intensity has now been adjusted is the apparent plane wave intensity of the waves received over the given bearing. In this case

$$(I'_d)_{\text{app}} = I'_{do} = \eta'_d I'_d \qquad (9\text{C-}2)$$

or, the apparent plane wave intensity of sinusoidal acoustic waves of given frequency reaching a directional sonar transducer along any given bearing is the product of the actual intensity of these waves and the relative receiving response of this transducer for this bearing.

Similarly, for waves having a continuous spectrum,

$$(J'_d)_{\text{app}} = \eta'_d J'_d \qquad (9\text{C-}3)$$

or, the apparent plane wave intensity per unit band, at a specified frequency, of acoustic waves having a continuous spectrum and reaching a directional sonar transducer along any given bearing is the product of the actual intensity per unit band of these waves at this frequency and of the relative receiving response of this transducer at this bearing.

Many problems dealing with the reception of acoustic energy having a continuous spectrum are simplified by making use of these relations. In general, as shown in Art. 9A-2, computations carried out in terms of the intensity per unit band of waves having a continuous spectrum make use of transducer characteristics measured in terms of the intensities of sinusoidal waves.

9C-3 Basic Equation for Directivity Factor

Formulas for the directivity factor of two specific types of sonar transducer are developed in Art. 4F-1. Each of these types has a three-dimensional directivity pattern which may be generated by rotating a two-dimensional pattern about an axis of acoustic symmetry. For one this axis coincides with the maximum response bearing; for the other it is perpendicular to a plane which is the locus of maximum response bearings. It is desirable to have a formula for directivity factor which is not restricted to such ideal situations.

The desired formula will be derived in terms of acoustic energy reaching a receiving system as plane waves having a continuous spectrum and having, at some given frequency, a magnitude which is the same for all bearings. Since, as shown in Art. 4D-1, the relative transmitting response of a reversible transducer is numerically equal to its relative receiving response, the formula thus derived may also be used for transmitting directivity factor.

The geometry of the situation now confronting us is shown in Fig. 8D-11. In accordance with this diagram an incremental area of a spherical surface concentrically surrounding the system receiving acoustic energy is given in terms of the azimuth angle, ϕ, and of the colatitude angle, θ, as

$$\delta A = r^2 \sin \theta \, \delta\theta \, \delta\phi \qquad (9C\text{-}4)$$

For a point on this spherical surface the intensity per unit band and per unit area of the acoustic energy later reaching the receiving system along the bearing of the element is dJ'_d/dA. This quantity is measured in joules/cm$^4 \cdot$cyc. In accordance with the postulated condition that the

received acoustic energy shall be uniformly distributed in bearing this intensity per unit band and per unit area is understood to be a constant. The apparent plane wave intensity per unit band and per unit area of this acoustic energy is, as may be seen by differentiating the apparent plane wave intensity given by Eq. (9C-3),

$$\frac{(dJ'_d)_{\text{app}}}{dA} = \eta'_d \frac{dJ'_d}{dA} \qquad (9C\text{-}5)$$

The apparent plane wave intensity per unit band of the total acoustic energy reaching the receiving system over all bearings is

$$(J'_d)_{\text{app}} = \int_A \frac{(dJ'_d)_{\text{app}}}{dA} \, dA$$

$$= r^2 \frac{(dJ'_d)_{\text{act}}}{dA} \int_0^{2\pi} \int_0^{\pi} \eta'_d \sin \theta \, d\theta \, d\phi \quad (9C\text{-}6)$$

It has been shown in Art. 4F-2 that the receiving directivity factor of a sonar transducer, at a specified frequency, may be defined as the quotient obtained by dividing (1) the apparent plane wave intensity per unit band, at the specified frequency and as measured by the given transducer, of acoustic energy reaching this transducer with constant magnitude on all bearings by (2) the equivalent plane wave intensity per unit band of this same acoustic energy. In the present case the equivalent plane wave intensity per unit band of the received acoustic energy, as it would be measured by a nondirectional transducer, is computed by assuming a constant relative receiving response, $\eta'_d = 1$, in the preceding equation. This gives

$$(J'_d)_{\text{equi}} = r^2 \frac{(J'_d)_{\text{act}}}{dA} \int_0^{2\pi} \int_0^{\pi} \sin \theta \, d\theta \, d\phi$$

$$= 4\pi r^2 \frac{(dJ'_d)_{\text{act}}}{dA} \qquad (9C\text{-}7)$$

Consequently, dividing Eq. (9C-6) by Eq. (9C-7), in accordance with this definition, the desired receiving directivity factor is found to be

$$(\eta'_D)_f = \frac{1}{4\pi} \int_0^{2\pi} \int_0^{\pi} \eta'_d \sin \theta \, d\theta \, d\phi \quad (9C\text{-}8)$$

This is a more general expression for directivity factor than those given by Eqs. (4F-5) and (4F-6), It may be used for computing the directivity factor of a transducer or array having any known three-dimensional directivity pattern. In many cases the relative response, as a function of bearing, will then be determined by the product theorem. Since the component responses must be multiplied together before integration it is evident that the directivity index of an actual array of directional elements is not the sum of the indexes of a hypothetical array of nondirectional elements and of a single directional element. It is sometimes inferred that the product theorem justifies this method of computing the directivity index of a complex transducer system. This inference is unjustified and its embodiment in a working rule can lead to serious error. Perhaps the greatest danger of this rule is its occasional appearance of truthfulness.

The formula for directivity factor given by Eq. (9C-8) calls for a summation over a complete spherical surface. In many practical cases, because of symmetry, this may be restricted to one half, one quarter, one eighth, or even to one sixteenth of the spherical surface. This may be possible even though the three-dimensional pattern cannot be generated by rotating a two-dimensional pattern.

It is noted that when a three-dimensional pattern may be generated by rotating a two-dimensional pattern the specific formulas of the earlier chapters may be derived from the more general formula now presented. To demonstrate this for the case where the maximum response axis coincides with the axis of acoustic symmetry let OZ, of Fig. 8D-11, be the axis of acoustic symmetry. The deviation angle is then $\beta = \theta$, and the relative response, η_d, is independent of the azimuth angle, ϕ. In this case Eq. (9C-8) reduces to Eq. (4F-5). Or, consider a transducer having an axis of acoustic symmetry perpendicular to a plane locus of maximum response bearings, and, again, having a three-dimensional pattern which may be generated by rotating a two-dimensional pattern. Here we let OZ be the axis of acoustic symmetry and the XY-plane the locus of maximum response bearings. The deviation angle is now $\beta = (\pi/2) - \theta$. Consequently, $\sin \theta = \cos \beta$ and Eq. (9C-8) reduces to Eq. (4F-6).

9C-4 Transducer Directivity and Reverberation

The relation between the directional characteristics of a sonar transducer and its response to reverberation have been discussed in the original chapters of this book. Formulas applying to the case of **volume reverberation** have been developed in Art. 4F-7 for two special cases. These, like related formulas for directivity factor, are restricted to transducers having three-dimensional directivity patterns which may be generated by rotating two-dimensional patterns. By methods analogous to those used in deriving Eq. (9C-8) a formula having more general utility, being independent of restrictions as to pattern symmetry, may be developed. This general formula is

$$\eta''_D = \frac{1}{4\pi} \int_0^{2\pi} \int_0^{\pi} \eta_d \, \eta'_d \sin \theta \, d\theta \, d\phi \quad (9C-9)$$

where

η''_D = the reverberation factor for volume reverberation applying to a transducer system at a common transmitting and receiving point (a numeric)

η_d = the relative transmitting response of this system for a given bearing (a numeric)

η'_d = the relative receiving response of this system for the same bearing (a numeric)

θ = the colatitude angle of the given bearing (rad)

ϕ = the azimuth angle of this bearing (rad)

Formulas for the **reverberation factor** of a sonar transducer which apply to **surface reverberation,** considered as a unique property of the transducer, do not exist. For volume reverberation it is possible to devise a model for the transducer and ocean in which all factors except those associated with the transducer are constant. This is not possible for surface reverberation. Here the response of the transducer to reverberation returned from the ocean surface, or from the ocean bottom, is as much a function of the location and orientation of the transducer, with respect to these surfaces, as of its directional characteristics.

Although it will not be a unique characteristic of a transducer it is, nevertheless, possible to define a factor of significance when dealing with surface reverberation. This factor combines the qualities of the reverberation factor, characteristic of the transducer, and of the reverberation strength factor and propagation loss factor characteristic of its environment. We thus define the surface **reverberation loss factor** as the ratio of (1) the apparent plane wave intensity of acoustic energy which has been transmitted, by a specified transducer located at a specified point with a specified orientation, as a pulse of sinusoidal waves having a specified frequency and duration, has later been re-directed from points making up an extensive surface, and, finally, been received at a specified instant, measured from the termination of the pulse transmission, by a specified transducer located at the same or at another specified point with a specified orientation to, (2) the index intensity of the transmitted pulse as measured on the maximum response axis of the transmitting transducer. The measure of this loss factor may be written as

$$\eta''_r = \frac{(I_r)_{\text{app}}}{(I_p)_{do}} \qquad (9\text{C-}10)$$

To examine the quantities which must be taken into account in evaluating a surface reverberation loss factor it will be assumed that the surface at which the acoustic energy is redirected is a plane surface, and that the location of the receiving transducer is the same as that of the transmitting transducer. These restrictions provide a model having a convenient simplicity and, at the same time, a practical significance.

It has been shown[3] that the acoustic energy returned to its point of origin as reverberation is, in fact, redirected by scatterers distributed throughout a layer which may extend to some depth below the surface. For a full understanding of all factors affecting surface reverberation it would be necessary to know the distribution, acoustical properties, and motions of these scatterers. Their resultant effect, however, may be measured in terms of a single scattering coefficient considered as a property of a plane ocean surface. Computations which assume the same situation when using this coefficient as that assumed when measuring it will lead to valid conclusions as to reverberation magnitudes. Due care must, of course, be taken properly to relate the variability of the scattering layer to the variability of the coefficient.

Consider a directional sonar transducer located D yd below the ocean surface, and having some specified orientation relative to that surface. This transducer is assumed to transmit a pulse of sinusoidal acoustic waves for a time interval of τ sec. Energy returned to the position occupied by this transducer at a given instant T sec after the termination of the transmission of this pulse will have been in transit for intervals varying from T sec to $T+\tau$ sec. Consequently, when the velocity of propagation is c yd/sec, this energy will appear to have been scattered from points at distances between $cT/2$ yd and $c(T+\tau)/2$ yd from the source point, as shown in Fig. 9C-1. The circular loci of

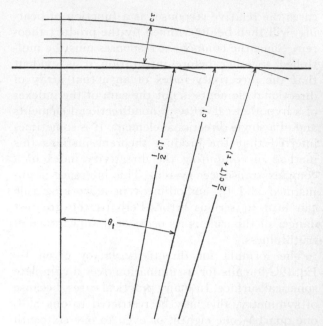

FIG. 9C-1. GEOMETRY OF AREA RETURNING SURFACE REVERBERATION. The circular loci bounding an area from which reverberation, due to back-scattering from the ocean surface, is received at its original source point at a given instant following the transmission of an echo-ranging pulse of given duration.

points at these two distances bound the area from which scattered energy is received at a single instant T sec after the termination of the pulse transmission. An expression for an incremental element of this area may be written as a function of time and of azimuth angle. As may be seen by inspection of Fig. 9C-2,

$$\delta x = \frac{c}{\sin \theta}\, \delta t, \quad \text{and} \quad \delta y = ct \sin \theta\, \delta\phi,$$

hence

$$\delta A = \delta x\, \delta y = c^2 t\, \delta t\, \delta\phi \qquad (9\text{C-}11)$$

The area from which energy reaches the source point at time T is therefore

$$A = c^2 \int_{T/2}^{(T+\tau)/2} \int_0^{2\pi} t\, d\phi\, dt \qquad (9\text{C-}12)$$

The intensity of the energy reaching an incremental area of scattering surface may be computed as the product of three quantities. It is

$$I_i = \eta_w\, \eta_d\, (I_p)_{do} \qquad (9\text{C-}13)$$

where

$I_i =$ the incident intensity of the acoustic energy falling on an incremental area

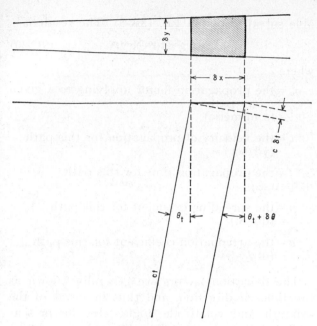

Fig. 9C-2. Geometry of Incremental Area of Scattering Surface. The relations between an incremental element of ocean surface returning reverberation to the source of an echo-ranging pulse and variables of which this element is a function.

of scattering surface (watt/cm²)

$(I_p)_{do}$ = the index intensity of the transmitted pulse as measured on the maximum response axis of the transmitting transducer (watt/cm²)

η_d = the relative transmitting response, or deviation factor, for that bearing of this transducer which is determined by the direction of the ray path connecting the transducer and the incremental area (a numeric)

η_w = the propagation factor for this path at the instant for which the computation is made (a numeric)

The measure of the energy back-scattered by this incremental area toward the source point will be expressed as the **intensity per unit area** of scattering surface, as measured at the index point on this ray path at unit distance from the scattering surface. This intensity per unit area is proportional to the intensity of the incident energy. It may, therefore, be computed as the product of this incident intensity and a **scattering coefficient,** k_s, which may be measured in reciprocal square yards. The index intensity per unit area of scat-

tering surface for an incremental area of this surface reached by a ray path having a given direction relative to the transducer is, therefore,

$$\left(\frac{dI_s}{dA}\right)_d = k_s I_i$$

$$= k_s\, \eta_w\, \eta_d\, (I_p)_{do} \qquad (9C\text{-}14)$$

When the scattering coefficient is measured in reciprocal square yards it is obvious that the intensity per unit area is measured in watts per square centimeter and per square yard (watt/cm²·yd²).

It has been shown by Urick and Hoover[4-8] that the back-scattering coefficient, here given the symbol k_s, is a function of the inclination of the path along which energy reaches and leaves the scattering surface and of sea state. It appears probable that it varies with frequency as well, although adequate data on this point are not yet available.

The intensity per unit area of the energy reaching the source point from the incremental element of scattering surface is measured as the product of the intensity per unit area at the index point on the path joining the area and the source point and the propagation factor for this path. This intensity per unit area of the received energy is thus

$$\left(\frac{dI_r}{dA}\right)_d = \eta_w \left(\frac{dI_s}{dA}\right)_d$$

$$= k_s\, \eta_w^2\, \eta_d\, (I_p)_{do} \qquad (9C\text{-}15)$$

Finally, the apparent plane wave value of the intensity per unit area of the received energy is obtained, as shown by differentiating Eq. (9C-2), by multiplying the actual intensity per unit area of the energy received along the bearing in question by the relative receiving response, η'_d, or deviation factor, of the receiving transducer applying to this bearing. This apparent plane wave intensity per unit area of the received reverberation is

$$\left(\frac{dI_r}{dA}\right)_{app} = \eta'_d \left(\frac{dI_r}{dA}\right)_d$$

$$= k_s\, \eta_w^2\, \eta_d\, \eta'_d\, (I_p)_{do} \quad (9C\text{-}16)$$

We may now integrate this apparent plane wave intensity per unit area, which must be known as a function of time and of azimuth angle, over the surface area from which energy reaches the common source and receiving point at time

T. This gives the apparent plane wave intensity, $(I_r)_{\text{app}}$, of this energy at this time. We then compute the surface reverberation loss factor as

$$\eta''_r = \frac{(I_r)_{\text{app}}}{(I_p)_{do}}$$

$$= c^2 \int_{T/2}^{(T+\tau)/2} \int_0^{2\pi} k_s \, \eta^2{}_w \, \eta_d \, \eta'_d \, t \, d\phi \, dt \quad (9C\text{-}17)$$

This expression is a precise statement of the relations existing, at a given instant, under the postulated conditions. It is by no means a general statement applying to all situations. By restricting attention to the special case where the received reverberation is measured at the original source point the problem has been greatly simplified. Even though it is far from being completely general the relations here formulated apply to the major portion of all present sonar systems. It is, indeed, possible to impose further limitations with profit.

Perhaps the first of these results from specifying that a single transducer be used for both transmission and reception. In this case the relative transmitting response and the relative receiving response are equal, for a given frequency, and the product of the two deviation factors, η_d and η'_d, appearing under the integral sign is the square of either.

A second simplification occurs when the three-dimensional directivity of the single transducer is symmetrical with respect to the vertical through the source point, and independent of azimuth angle. Under this condition the reverberation loss factor is expressed as a single integral with time as the independent variable. It is then written as

$$\eta''_r = 2\pi c^2 \int_{T/2}^{(T+\tau)/2} k_s \, \eta^2{}_w \, \eta^2{}_d \, t \, dt \quad (9C\text{-}18)$$

We now return to the more general case, as expressed by Eq. (9C-17). The only factors appearing under the integral sign which are functions of azimuth angle are the deviation factors. The surface reverberation loss factor may therefore be written as

$$\eta''_r = c^2 \int_{T/2}^{(T+\tau)/2} k_s \, \eta^2{}_w \, t \left[\int_0^{2\pi} \eta_d \, \eta'_d \, d\phi \right] dt \quad (9C\text{-}19)$$

There are three functions of time to be considered here. Although the propagation factor is usually expressed as a function of distance it may be written as a function of time by making suit-

able substitutions in Eq. (3A-5). The result is

$$\eta_w = (ct)^n (10^{0.1})^{-a(ct)} \quad (9C\text{-}20)$$

where

$\eta_w =$ the propagation factor applying to a given ray path
(a numeric)

$c =$ the velocity of propagation for this path
(yd/sec)

$t =$ the propagation time for this path
(sec)

$n =$ the spreading exponent for this path
(db/Sl)

$a =$ the attenuation coefficient for this path
(db/yd)

The deviation factors are generally known as functions of direction, and thus in terms of the azimuth and colatitude angles. In the present situation there is a simple relation between time and colatitude angle, namely,

$$D = ct \cos \theta \quad (9C\text{-}21)$$

where

$D =$ the perpendicular distance between the point at which the pulse is transmitted and the surface reverberation received and the plane surface from which this reverberation is assumed to be returned
(yd)

$\theta =$ the colatitude angle of the ray path along which this reverberation is transmitted and received
(deg)

Given this relation the integral

$$\int_0^{2\pi} \eta_d \, \eta'_d \, d\phi \quad (9C\text{-}22)$$

may be evaluated as a function of time.

Such information as we have regarding the backscattering coefficient, k_s, is in terms of the angle of inclination at the scattering surface and of wind velocity. Designating the angle of inclination as α the relation between this angle and the colatitude angle, θ, is

$$\theta = \frac{\pi}{2} - \alpha \quad (9C\text{-}23)$$

The relation between colatitude angle and time has already been given in Eq. (9C-21).

There is not, unfortunately, complete agreement as to the manner in which the energy back-scattered from the ocean surface should be reported. Widely used data are reported in terms of a "scattering strength," measured in decibels. This quantity is defined as $S = 10 \log_{10} (I_s/I_i)$, where I_s is the intensity of the back-scattered energy at a distance of one yard from an element of surface having the area dA. This area is, however, described as having a magnitude of one square yard. The intention here appears to be similar to that which led to defining pressure spectrum level in terms of the acoustic pressure due to the energy in a frequency band having a finite width of one cycle per second, as discussed in Art. 9A-1. As with pressure spectrum level, the quantity now required must be one which may be integrated. This is not possible with quantities measured in decibels. In the present case the only quantity which can yield an acoustic intensity when integrated with respect to area is an intensity per unit area, the derivative of intensity with respect to area. As in the case of pressure spectrum level, a quantity reported as the intensity due to the energy back-scattered from an element of surface having a finite area of one square yard is, in fact, a measure of the index value of the intensity per unit area, (dI_s/dA) watt/cm$^2 \cdot$yd^2, introduced in Eq. (9C-14).

Once these relations are understood it is a simple matter to derive values of the scattering coefficient, k_s, used here from data reported in terms of the "scattering strength," S. Since the measure of the intensity, I_s, appearing in the definition of this scattering strength is also a measure of the required intensity per unit area, (dI_s/dA), it follows that $S = 10 \log_{10} k_s$, or that

$$k_s = (10^{0.1})^S \qquad (9C-24)$$

The extent to which the several functions of time appearing in Eq. (9C-19) may vary during some interval equal to one half the pulse duration depends upon a number of factors. This variation may be examined in terms of a particular situation. As an example, we postulate a linear transducer having a length of six wave intervals. This is mounted 500 yd below the ocean surface with its axis horizontal. The locus of maximum response axes is, therefore, a vertical plane. At any instant the major portion of the energy associated with a single pulse falls on two equal areas of scattering surface; one dimension of these is determined by the directivity of the transducer and one by the duration of the pulse. These areas move outward, in opposite directions, from a point directly over the transducer.

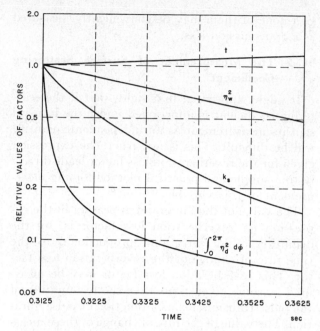

FIG. 9C-3. FACTORS AFFECTING SURFACE REVERBERATION. The relative variability of factors appearing in the integrand of Eq. (9C-19) during a time interval defining the area contributing to reverberation received at a given instant.

For a transducer at this depth the trailing end of the transmitted pulse reaches the ocean surface 0.3125 sec after the termination of the pulse transmission. At this time all of the pulse has reached the surface. The reverberation reaching the transducer 0.625 sec after the termination of transmission is the first sample to contain contributions from the whole pulse. To evaluate the surface reverberation loss factor for this instant due to a pulse duration of $\tau = 0.1$ sec we must evaluate the integral given in Eq. (9C-19) from $T/2 = 0.3125$ sec to $(T+\tau)/2 = 0.3625$ sec. During this interval the factors of the integrand vary as shown in Fig. 9C-3. Since we are interested in the relative variability of these factors, rather than in their absolute magnitudes, the measure of each has been normalized relative to its initial value.

From an inspection of the curves of this figure it is evident that all factors vary by a significant amount. As reverberation continues there is a decrease in the amount by which each factor varies during the interval set by the limits of integration. In general, however, it may be said that none of these factors may be considered as a constant except for pulses of very short duration, or for reverberation occurring some time after energy is first received from the scattering surface. Since these factors must all remain under the integral sign none of them may be conveniently measured as a transmission loss.

9C-5 The Measurement of Surface Scattering Coefficient

It might appear, at first sight, that if the scattering coefficient is imprisoned under the integral sign its measurement as an independent quantity will be difficult. This is not true. The expression given for the reverberation loss factor leads directly to a simple and practical method for the measurement of this variable.

The value of the integrand appearing in the expression for reverberation loss factor is, by the definition of an integrand, proportional to the time rate of change of the reverberation loss factor. This reverberation loss factor may be measured at some given time after the termination of the pulse transmission as a function of pulse duration. The value of the rate of change of these measured values as determined for a pulse of zero duration leads at once to the value of the integrand. Since all factors in this integrand except the scattering coefficient are known, or may be evaluated, the coefficient may be evaluated.

In practice a number of pulses, of unlike duration, would be transmitted and the response of the hydrophone receiving energy back-scattered from the ocean surface recorded by some suitable oscillograph. It is well known that the envelopes of oscillograms showing this reverberation are far from being smooth curves. From them, however, it is possible to draw smooth curves which represent average values of received energy. It is, in fact, possible to draw a reasonably acceptable curve from the record obtained from a single pulse. In so doing use is made of magnitudes recorded at all times in arriving at a statistically averaged value for any one time. The usual types of oscillograph present a record of magnitudes of acoustic pressure, rather than of acoustic intensity. It is, therefore, convenient to plot the square root of the reverberation loss factor as a function of time, rather than to plot the factor as such a function. Curves showing the square root of the reverberation loss factor as a function of time for three values of pulse duration are shown in Fig. 9C-4. These curves are those which would be obtained with the transducer, transducer location, and scattering coefficient previously specified. From such curves it is possible to read values, as indicated by lettered points, from which to compute reverberation loss factor as a function of pulse

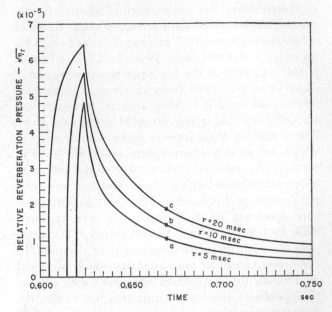

FIG. 9C-4. COMPUTATION OF SCATTERING COEFFICIENT. Curves showing the changes in acoustic pressure due to surface reverberation as a function of time and of the duration of the echo-ranging pulse.

length for some selected value of transmission time. A curve obtained in this manner from the data presented in Fig. 9C-4 is plotted in Fig. 9C-5. This curve is drawn to pass through the origin. The slope of this curve at the origin is a measure of the time derivative of the reverberation loss factor. The quotient obtained by dividing this derivative by the square of the velocity of propagation is the integrand sought.

All factors in this integrand except the scattering coefficient are assumed to be known, as functions of time, for a given transducer in a given location. The value of the scattering coefficient is thus easily determined. Since this value is established for a given time, in a situation having a known geometry, the angle between the reverberation paths and the scattering surface is also known. The value of the coefficient as a function of angle is thus established.

This method has several advantages. Data as to scattering coefficient may be obtained for a range of values of path angle from a relatively small number of pulse transmissions. Each transmission provides information as to all angles beginning with the normal to the surface and continuing to the angle of the longest path over which measurable energy is received.

Measurements may be made by any transducer, without restriction as to its directional characteris-

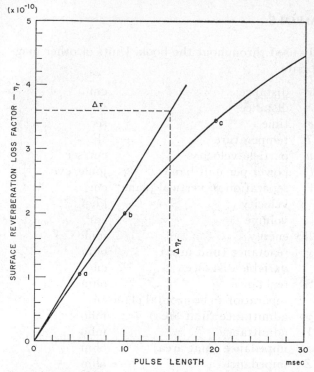

FIG. 9C-5. COMPUTATION OF SCATTERING COEFFICIENT. A graphical method of estimating the magnitude of the integrand in Eq. (9C-19), and hence of measuring the backscattering coefficient. Lettered points correspond to those of Fig. 9C-4.

tics. It has, in fact, been found that values of scattering coefficient may be isolated from measurements of reverberation which, when made, were believed to be significant only for a particular operating situation. Values thus isolated may be applied to the computation of the reverberation to be expected when other transducers are used in other locations.

REFERENCES

1. Sectional Committee Z24, *American Standard Acoustical Terminology* (American Standards Association, Inc., New York, July 31, 1951), p. 11.
2. J. E. FREEHAFER, *Propagation of Short Radio Waves*, Radiation Laboratory Series, Vol. 13, Sec. 2.3 (McGraw-Hill Book Company, Inc., New York, 1951).
3. R. W. RAITT, "Sound Scatterers in the Sea," *J. Mar. Res.*, Vol. 7, No. 3, November, 1948.
4. R. J. URICK and H. L. SAXTON, "Surface Reflection of Short Supersonic Pulses in the Ocean," *JASA*, Vol. 19, pp. 8–12, January, 1947.
5. L. N. LIEBERMANN, "Reflection of Underwater Sound from the Sea Surface," *JASA*, Vol. 20, pp. 498–503, July, 1948.
6. C. F. EYRING, R. J. CHRISTENSEN, and R. W. RAITT, "Reverberation in the Sea," *JASA*, Vol. 20, pp. 462–475, July, 1948.
7. C. ECKART, "The Scattering of Sound from the Sea Surface," *JASA*, Vol. 25, pp. 566–570, May, 1954.
8. R. J. URICK, "The Backscattering of Sound from a Harbor Bottom," *JASA*, Vol. 26, pp. 231–235, March, 1954.
9. M. LANDOLT, *Grandeur, Mesure et Unité* (Office International de Librairie, Bruxelle 1947/Editions Dunod, Paris, 1947).

SYMBOLS USED FOR PHYSICAL QUANTITIES

BASIC SYMBOLS

The dimensional units shown here are those normally used throughout the book. Units of other magnitudes are, however, used when they are more appropriate.

a	acceleration	cm/sec²
	attenuation coefficient	db/kyd
A	area	cm²
	a numerical coefficient	
b	susceptance (unit area)	mho
B	susceptance	mho
	a numerical coefficient	
c	velocity of propagation	cm/sec
C	chart constant	rad/in²
d	diameter	cm
D	depth	ft
e	voltage	volt
E	modulus of elasticity	dyne/cm²
f	frequency	cyc/sec
F	Fechner ratio	numeric
	force	dyne
g	conductance (unit area)	mho
	velocity gradient	1/ft
G	conductance	mho
H	height	ft
	magnetic field intensity	oersted
i	electric current	amp
I	acoustic intensity	watt/cm²
j	$\sqrt{-1}$	imaginary
J	acoustic intensity per unit area	joule/cm²·cyc
k	a constant	numeric
K	a constant	numeric
	square root of band ratio	numeric
l	length	cm
L	transmission level	db//1 watt/cm²
m	mass	gm
M	number of frequency logits	fl
n	any integer	numeric
	spreading exponent	numeric
N	transmission loss	db
p	acoustic pressure	μb
P	power	watt
Q	circuit figure of merit	numeric
r	radius	cm
	resistance (unit area)	ohm
R	resistance	ohm

s	distance	cm
S	distance	yd
t	time	sec
T	temperature	°F
u	particle velocity	cm/sec
U	power per unit band	joule/cyc
V	separation in vertical plane	cm
	velocity	knot
	volume	cm³
W	energy	joule
x	reactance (unit area)	ohm
	variable distance	cm
X	reactance	ohm
	separation in horizontal plane	cm
y	admittance (unit area)	mho
Y	admittance	mho
z	impedance (unit area)	ohm
Z	impedance	ohm
α	angular deviation	deg
β	angular deviation	deg
γ	angular deviation	deg
δ	an increment	a prefix
Δ	a difference	a prefix
η	efficiency, or transmission factor	numeric
θ	inclination, or colatitude angle	deg
	phase angle	rad
λ	wave length	cm/cyc
μ	permeability (magnetic)	numeric
	transmitting response	1/cm²
μ'	receiving response	cm²
ξ	particle displacement	cm
ρ	density	gm/cm³
ρc	specific acoustic impedance	spec. acous. ohm
σ	condensation	numeric
Σ	a sum	a prefix
ϕ	azimuth angle	deg
	phase angle	rad
ψ	phase angle, or phase factor	rad
ω	angular velocity of phasor	rad/sec

SUBSCRIPTS

a	air		act	actual
	an initial value		adj	adjusted
A	acoustic		app	apparent

402

attn	attenuation		n	noise
aver	average			a final value (with angles of inclination)
avl	available		N	a number (with layers of constant velocity gradient)
b	blocked (with impedances)			
	boundary reverberation (with intensities, transmission losses, and transmission levels)		o	reference value
			0	origin
			obs	observed
	a final value		oct	octave
C	capture (with areas)		out	output
	compensated (with angles)		p	pulse
crit	critical		P	parallel (with resistance, inductance, and capacitance)
d	direct			
	directionally dependent			projector, sonar (with transmission loss)
D	directivity			applying to a specified point
DI	directivity index		pk	peak
dis	dissipation		r	reflected
e	echo			reverberation
E	electric		R	receiver
EA	electroacoustic		rb	reverse blocked
eff	efficiency		ref	reference
EM	electromechanical		rf	reverse free
e/n	echo-to-noise		rfl	reflection
equi	equivalent		rgn	recognition
e/r	echo-to-reverberation		RI	reverberation index
f	free (with impedances)		RS	reverberation strength
	frequency dependent		s	signal
F	spectrum		S	source
FM	figure of merit		s/n	signal-to-noise
g	generated		shd	shaded
gm	geometric mean		SI	spectrum index
h	horizontal		spr	spreading
H	hydrophone		sys	system
i	incident		t	transmitted
I	measures intensity		T	target
in	input		tan	tangent
insn	insertion		tdr	transducer
inst	instantaneous		tfr	transfer
IR	incremental response index		th	thermal
J	measures intensity per unit band		TS	target strength
k	a constant value		tsn	transition
K	an absolute temperature value		U	measures power per unit band
l	loaded		v	vertical
L	load			volume reverberation (with intensities, transmission losses, and transmission levels)
loc	local, or self, noise			
m	motional (with impedances)			
	an initial value (with angles of inclination)		V	vertex (velocity of propagation)
M	mechanical		w	water
	a number (with layers of constant velocity gradient)		x	a variable value
			Y	admittance
MA	mechanoacoustic		z	zone
max	maximum		Z	impedance
min	minimum		Δ	difference
mut	mutual		Σ	resultant

LOGARITHMS TO THE BASE $10^{0.1}$

LOGARITHMS OF NUMBERS LESS THAN ONE

Number	0	1	2	3	4	5	6	7	8	9	Avg. Diff.
0.100	−10.000	−9.996	−9.991	−9.987	−9.983	−9.978	−9.974	−9.970	−9.965	−9.961	4
0.101	−9.957	−9.952	−9.948	−9.944	−9.940	−9.935	−9.931	−9.927	−9.923	−9.918	
0.102	−9.914	−9.910	−9.905	−9.901	−9.897	−9.893	−9.888	−9.884	−9.880	−9.876	
0.103	−9.872	−9.867	−9.863	−9.859	−9.855	−9.851	−9.846	−9.842	−9.838	−9.834	
0.104	−9.830	−9.825	−9.821	−9.817	−9.813	−9.809	−9.805	−9.801	−9.796	−9.792	
0.105	−9.788	−9.784	−9.780	−9.776	−9.772	−9.767	−9.763	−9.759	−9.755	−9.751	
0.106	−9.747	−9.743	−9.739	−9.735	−9.731	−9.727	−9.722	−9.718	−9.714	−9.710	
0.107	−9.706	−9.702	−9.698	−9.694	−9.690	−9.686	−9.682	−9.678	−9.674	−9.670	
0.108	−9.666	−9.662	−9.658	−9.654	−9.650	−9.646	−9.642	−9.638	−9.634	−9.630	
0.109	−9.626	−9.622	−9.618	−9.614	−9.610	−9.606	−9.602	−9.598	−9.594	−9.590	
0.10	−10.000	−9.957	−9.914	−9.872	−9.830	−9.788	−9.747	−9.706	−9.666	−9.626	42
0.11	−9.586	−9.547	−9.508	−9.469	−9.431	−9.393	−9.355	−9.318	−9.281	−9.245	38
0.12	−9.208	−9.172	−9.136	−9.101	−9.066	−9.031	−8.996	−8.962	−8.928	−8.894	35
0.13	−8.861	−8.827	−8.794	−8.761	−8.729	−8.697	−8.665	−8.633	−8.601	−8.570	32
0.14	−8.539	−8.508	−8.477	−8.447	−8.416	−8.386	−8.356	−8.327	−8.297	−8.268	30
0.15	−8.239	−8.210	−8.182	−8.153	−8.125	−8.097	−8.069	−8.041	−8.013	−7.986	28
0.16	−7.959	−7.932	−7.905	−7.878	−7.852	−7.825	−7.799	−7.773	−7.747	−7.721	26
0.17	−7.696	−7.670	−7.645	−7.620	−7.595	−7.570	−7.545	−7.520	−7.496	−7.471	25
0.18	−7.447	−7.423	−7.399	−7.375	−7.352	−7.328	−7.305	−7.282	−7.258	−7.235	24
0.19	−7.212	−7.190	−7.167	−7.144	−7.122	−7.100	−7.077	−7.055	−7.033	−7.011	22
0.20	−6.990	−6.968	−6.946	−6.925	−6.904	−6.882	−6.861	−6.840	−6.819	−6.799	21
0.21	−6.778	−6.757	−6.737	−6.716	−6.696	−6.676	−6.655	−6.635	−6.615	−6.596	20
0.22	−6.576	−6.556	−6.536	−6.517	−6.497	−6.478	−6.459	−6.440	−6.421	−6.402	19
0.23	−6.383	−6.364	−6.345	−6.326	−6.308	−6.289	−6.271	−6.253	−6.234	−6.216	19
0.24	−6.198	−6.180	−6.162	−6.144	−6.126	−6.108	−6.091	−6.073	−6.055	−6.038	18
0.25	−6.021	−6.003	−5.986	−5.969	−5.952	−5.935	−5.918	−5.901	−5.884	−5.867	17
0.26	−5.850	−5.834	−5.817	−5.800	−5.784	−5.768	−5.751	−5.735	−5.719	−5.702	16
0.27	−5.686	−5.670	−5.654	−5.638	−5.622	−5.607	−5.591	−5.575	−5.560	−5.544	16
0.28	−5.528	−5.513	−5.498	−5.482	−5.467	−5.452	−5.436	−5.421	−5.406	−5.391	15
0.29	−5.376	−5.361	−5.346	−5.331	−5.317	−5.302	−5.287	−5.272	−5.258	−5.243	15
0.30	−5.229	−5.214	−5.200	−5.186	−5.171	−5.157	−5.143	−5.129	−5.114	−5.100	14
0.31	−5.086	−5.072	−5.058	−5.045	−5.031	−5.017	−5.003	−4.989	−4.976	−4.962	14
0.32	−4.949	−4.935	−4.921	−4.908	−4.895	−4.881	−4.868	−4.855	−4.841	−4.828	13
0.33	−4.815	−4.802	−4.789	−4.776	−4.763	−4.750	−4.737	−4.724	−4.711	−4.698	13
0.34	−4.685	−4.672	−4.660	−4.647	−4.634	−4.622	−4.609	−4.597	−4.584	−4.572	13
0.35	−4.559	−4.547	−4.535	−4.522	−4.510	−4.498	−4.486	−4.473	−4.461	−4.449	12
0.36	−4.437	−4.425	−4.413	−4.401	−4.389	−4.377	−4.365	−4.353	−4.342	−4.330	12
0.37	−4.318	−4.306	−4.295	−4.283	−4.271	−4.260	−4.248	−4.237	−4.225	−4.214	12
0.38	−4.202	−4.191	−4.179	−4.168	−4.157	−4.145	−4.134	−4.123	−4.112	−4.101	11
0.39	−4.089	−4.078	−4.067	−4.056	−4.045	−4.034	−4.023	−4.012	−4.001	−3.990	11
0.40	−3.979	−3.969	−3.958	−3.947	−3.936	−3.925	−3.915	−3.904	−3.893	−3.883	11
0.41	−3.872	−3.862	−3.851	−3.840	−3.830	−3.820	−3.809	−3.799	−3.788	−3.778	10
0.42	−3.768	−3.757	−3.747	−3.737	−3.726	−3.716	−3.706	−3.696	−3.686	−3.675	10
0.43	−3.665	−3.655	−3.645	−3.635	−3.625	−3.615	−3.605	−3.595	−3.585	−3.575	10
0.44	−3.565	−3.556	−3.546	−3.536	−3.526	−3.516	−3.507	−3.497	−3.487	−3.478	10
0.45	−3.468	−3.458	−3.449	−3.439	−3.429	−3.420	−3.410	−3.401	−3.391	−3.382	10
0.46	−3.372	−3.363	−3.354	−3.344	−3.335	−3.325	−3.316	−3.307	−3.298	−3.288	9
0.47	−3.279	−3.270	−3.261	−3.251	−3.242	−3.233	−3.224	−3.215	−3.206	−3.197	9
0.48	−3.188	−3.179	−3.170	−3.161	−3.152	−3.143	−3.134	−3.125	−3.116	−3.107	9
0.49	−3.098	−3.089	−3.080	−3.071	−3.063	−3.054	−3.045	−3.036	−3.028	−3.019	9

Multiplication of a number by 10^{-n} requires that $-10n$ be added to its logarithm.

LOGARITHMS TO THE BASE $10^{0.1}$

LOGARITHMS OF NUMBERS LESS THAN ONE

Number	0	1	2	3	4	5	6	7	8	9	Avg. Diff.
0.50	−3.010	−3.002	−2.993	−2.984	−2.976	−2.967	−2.958	−2.950	−2.941	−2.933	9
0.51	−2.924	−2.916	−2.907	−2.899	−2.890	−2.882	−2.874	−2.865	−2.857	−2.848	8
0.52	−2.840	−2.832	−2.823	−2.815	−2.807	−2.798	−2.790	−2.782	−2.774	−2.765	8
0.53	−2.757	−2.749	−2.741	−2.733	−2.725	−2.716	−2.708	−2.700	−2.692	−2.684	8
0.54	−2.676	−2.668	−2.660	−2.652	−2.644	−2.636	−2.628	−2.620	−2.612	−2.604	8
0.55	−2.596	−2.588	−2.581	−2.573	−2.565	−2.557	−2.549	−2.541	−2.534	−2.526	8
0.56	−2.518	−2.510	−2.503	−2.495	−2.487	−2.480	−2.472	−2.464	−2.457	−2.449	8
0.57	−2.441	−2.434	−2.426	−2.418	−2.411	−2.403	−2.396	−2.388	−2.381	−2.373	8
0.58	−2.366	−2.358	−2.351	−2.343	−2.336	−2.328	−2.321	−2.314	−2.306	−2.299	7
0.59	−2.291	−2.284	−2.277	−2.269	−2.262	−2.255	−2.248	−2.240	−2.233	−2.226	7
0.60	−2.218	−2.211	−2.204	−2.197	−2.190	−2.182	−2.175	−2.168	−2.161	−2.154	7
0.61	−2.147	−2.140	−2.132	−2.125	−2.118	−2.111	−2.104	−2.097	−2.090	−2.083	7
0.62	−2.076	−2.069	−2.062	−2.055	−2.048	−2.041	−2.034	−2.027	−2.020	−2.013	7
0.63	−2.007	−2.000	−1.993	−1.986	−1.979	−1.972	−1.965	−1.959	−1.952	−1.945	7
0.64	−1.938	−1.931	−1.925	−1.918	−1.911	−1.904	−1.898	−1.891	−1.884	−1.878	7
0.65	−1.871	−1.864	−1.858	−1.851	−1.844	−1.838	−1.831	−1.824	−1.818	−1.811	7
0.66	−1.805	−1.798	−1.791	−1.785	−1.778	−1.772	−1.765	−1.759	−1.752	−1.746	7
0.67	−1.739	−1.733	−1.726	−1.720	−1.713	−1.707	−1.701	−1.694	−1.688	−1.681	7
0.68	−1.675	−1.669	−1.662	−1.656	−1.649	−1.643	−1.637	−1.630	−1.624	−1.618	6
0.69	−1.612	−1.605	−1.599	−1.593	−1.586	−1.580	−1.574	−1.568	−1.561	−1.555	6
0.70	−1.549	−1.543	−1.537	−1.530	−1.524	−1.518	−1.512	−1.506	−1.500	−1.494	6
0.71	−1.487	−1.481	−1.475	−1.469	−1.463	−1.457	−1.451	−1.445	−1.439	−1.433	6
0.72	−1.427	−1.421	−1.415	−1.409	−1.403	−1.397	−1.391	−1.385	−1.379	−1.373	6
0.73	−1.367	−1.361	−1.355	−1.349	−1.343	−1.337	−1.331	−1.325	−1.319	−1.314	6
0.74	−1.308	−1.302	−1.296	−1.290	−1.284	−1.278	−1.273	−1.267	−1.261	−1.255	6
0.75	−1.249	−1.244	−1.238	−1.232	−1.226	−1.221	−1.215	−1.209	−1.203	−1.198	6
0.76	−1.192	−1.186	−1.180	−1.175	−1.169	−1.163	−1.158	−1.152	−1.146	−1.141	6
0.77	−1.135	−1.129	−1.124	−1.118	−1.113	−1.107	−1.101	−1.096	−1.090	−1.085	6
0.78	−1.079	−1.073	−1.068	−1.062	−1.057	−1.051	−1.046	−1.040	−1.035	−1.029	6
0.79	−1.024	−1.018	−1.013	−1.007	−1.002	−0.996	−0.991	−0.985	−0.980	−0.975	5
0.80	−0.969	−0.964	−0.958	−0.953	−0.947	−0.942	−0.937	−0.931	−0.926	−0.921	5
0.81	−0.915	−0.910	−0.904	−0.899	−0.894	−0.888	−0.883	−0.878	−0.872	−0.867	5
0.82	−0.862	−0.857	−0.851	−0.846	−0.841	−0.835	−0.830	−0.825	−0.820	−0.814	5
0.83	−0.809	−0.804	−0.799	−0.794	−0.788	−0.783	−0.778	−0.773	−0.768	−0.762	5
0.84	−0.757	−0.752	−0.747	−0.742	−0.737	−0.731	−0.726	−0.721	−0.716	−0.711	5
0.85	−0.706	−0.701	−0.696	−0.691	−0.685	−0.680	−0.675	−0.670	−0.665	−0.660	5
0.86	−0.655	−0.650	−0.645	−0.640	−0.635	−0.630	−0.625	−0.620	−0.615	−0.610	5
0.87	−0.605	−0.600	−0.595	−0.590	−0.585	−0.580	−0.575	−0.570	−0.565	−0.560	5
0.88	−0.555	−0.550	−0.545	−0.540	−0.535	−0.531	−0.526	−0.521	−0.516	−0.511	5
0.89	−0.506	−0.501	−0.496	−0.491	−0.487	−0.482	−0.477	−0.472	−0.467	−0.462	5
0.90	−0.458	−0.453	−0.448	−0.443	−0.438	−0.434	−0.429	−0.424	−0.419	−0.414	5
0.91	−0.410	−0.405	−0.400	−0.395	−0.391	−0.386	−0.381	−0.376	−0.372	−0.367	5
0.92	−0.362	−0.357	−0.353	−0.348	−0.343	−0.339	−0.334	−0.329	−0.325	−0.320	5
0.93	−0.315	−0.311	−0.306	−0.301	−0.297	−0.292	−0.287	−0.283	−0.278	−0.273	5
0.94	−0.269	−0.264	−0.259	−0.255	−0.250	−0.246	−0.241	−0.237	−0.232	−0.227	5
0.95	−0.223	−0 218	−0.214	−0.209	−0.205	−0.200	−0.195	−0.191	−0.186	−0.182	5
0.96	−0.177	−0.173	−0.168	−0.164	−0.159	−0.155	−0.150	−0.146	−0.141	−0.137	4
0.97	−0.132	−0.128	−0.123	−0.119	−0.114	−0.110	−0.106	−0.101	−0.097	−0.092	4
0.98	−0.088	−0.083	−0.079	−0.074	−0.070	−0.066	−0.061	−0.057	−0.052	−0.048	4
0.99	−0.044	−0.039	−0.035	−0.031	−0.026	−0.022	−0.017	−0.013	−0.009	−0.004	4

$$10^{0.1} = 1.2589254+$$
$$\text{lgt } N = \log_{10}{0.1} N = 10 \log_{10} N = 4.343 \log_e N$$

LOGARITHMS TO THE BASE 10$^{0.1}$

LOGARITHMS OF NUMBERS GREATER THAN ONE

Number	0	1	2	3	4	5	6	7	8	9	Avg. Diff.
1.00	0.000	0.004	0.009	0.013	0.017	0.022	0.026	0.030	0.035	0.039	4
1.01	0.043	0.048	0.052	0.056	0.060	0.065	0.069	0.073	0.077	0.082	
1.02	0.086	0.090	0.095	0.099	0.103	0.107	0.112	0.116	0.120	0.124	
1.03	0.128	0.133	0.137	0.141	0.145	0.149	0.154	0.158	0.162	0.166	
1.04	0.170	0.175	0.179	0.183	0.187	0.191	0.195	0.199	0.204	0.208	
1.05	0.212	0.216	0.220	0.224	0.228	0.233	0.237	0.241	0.245	0.249	
1.06	0.253	0.257	0.261	0.265	0.269	0.273	0.278	0.282	0.286	0.290	
1.07	0.294	0.298	0.302	0.306	0.310	0.314	0.318	0.322	0.326	0.330	
1.08	0.334	0.338	0.342	0.346	0.350	0.354	0.358	0.362	0.366	0.370	
1.09	0.374	0.378	0.382	0.386	0.390	0.394	0.398	0.402	0.406	0.410	
1.0	0.000	0.043	0.086	0.128	0.170	0.212	0.253	0.294	0.334	0.374	42
1.1	0.414	0.453	0.492	0.531	0.569	0.607	0.645	0.682	0.719	0.755	38
1.2	0.792	0.828	0.864	0.899	0.934	0.969	1.004	1.038	1.072	1.106	35
1.3	1.139	1.173	1.206	1.239	1.271	1.303	1.335	1.367	1.399	1.430	32
1.4	1.461	1.492	1.523	1.553	1.584	1.614	1.644	1.673	1.703	1.732	30
1.5	1.761	1.790	1.818	1.847	1.875	1.903	1.931	1.959	1.987	2.014	28
1.6	2.041	2.068	2.095	2.122	2.148	2.175	2.201	2.227	2.253	2.279	26
1.7	2.304	2.330	2.355	2.380	2.405	2.430	2.455	2.480	2.504	2.529	25
1.8	2.553	2.577	2.601	2.625	2.648	2.672	2.695	2.718	2.742	2.765	24
1.9	2.788	2.810	2.833	2.856	2.878	2.900	2.923	2.945	2.967	2.989	22
2.0	3.010	3.032	3.054	3.075	3.096	3.118	3.139	3.160	3.181	3.201	21
2.1	3.222	3.243	3.263	3.284	3.304	3.324	3.345	3.365	3.385	3.404	20
2.2	3.424	3.444	3.464	3.483	3.503	3.522	3.541	3.560	3.579	3.598	19
2.3	3.617	3.636	3.655	3.674	3.692	3.711	3.729	3.747	3.766	3.784	18
2.4	3.802	3.820	3.838	3.856	3.874	3.892	3.909	3.927	3.945	3.962	17
2.5	3.979	3.997	4.014	4.031	4.048	4.065	4.082	4.099	4.116	4.133	17
2.6	4.150	4.166	4.183	4.200	4.216	4.232	4.249	4.265	4.281	4.298	16
2.7	4.314	4.330	4.346	4.362	4.378	4.393	4.409	4.425	4.440	4.456	16
2.8	4.472	4.487	4.502	4.518	4.533	4.548	4.564	4.579	4.594	4.609	15
2.9	4.624	4.639	4.654	4.669	4.683	4.698	4.713	4.728	4.742	4.757	15
3.0	4.771	4.786	4.800	4.814	4.829	4.843	4.857	4.871	4.886	4.900	14
3.1	4.914	4.928	4.942	4.955	4.969	4.983	4.997	5.011	5.024	5.038	14
3.2	5.051	5.065	5.079	5.092	5.105	5.119	5.132	5.145	5.159	5.172	13
3.3	5.185	5.198	5.211	5.224	5.237	5.250	5.263	5.276	5.289	5.302	13
3.4	5.315	5.328	5.340	5.353	5.366	5.378	5.391	5.403	5.416	5.428	13
3.5	5.441	5.453	5.465	5.478	5.490	5.502	5.514	5.527	5.539	5.551	12
3.6	5.563	5.575	5.587	5.599	5.611	5.623	5.635	5.647	5.658	5.670	12
3.7	5.682	5.694	5.705	5.717	5.729	5.740	5.752	5.763	5.775	5.786	12
3.8	5.798	5.809	5.821	5.832	5.843	5.855	5.866	5.877	5.888	5.899	11
3.9	5.911	5.922	5.933	5.944	5.955	5.966	5.977	5.988	5.999	6.010	11
4.0	6.021	6.031	6.042	6.053	6.064	6.075	6.085	6.096	6.107	6.117	11
4.1	6.128	6.138	6.149	6.160	6.170	6.180	6.191	6.201	6.212	6.222	10
4.2	6.232	6.243	6.253	6.263	6.274	6.284	6.294	6.304	6.314	6.325	10
4.3	6.335	6.345	6.355	6.365	6.375	6.385	6.395	6.405	6.415	6.425	10
4.4	6.435	6.444	6.454	6.464	6.474	6.484	6.493	6.503	6.513	6.522	10
4.5	6.532	6.542	6.551	6.561	6.571	6.580	6.590	6.599	6.609	6.618	10
4.6	6.628	6.637	6.646	6.656	6.665	6.675	6.684	6.693	6.702	6.712	10
4.7	6.721	6.730	6.739	6.749	6.758	6.767	6.776	6.785	6.794	6.803	9
4.8	6.812	6.821	6.830	6.839	6.848	6.857	6.866	6.875	6.884	6.893	9
4.9	6.902	6.911	6.920	6.929	6.937	6.946	6.955	6.964	6.972	6.981	9

Multiplication of a number by 10^n requires that 10n be added to its logarithm.

LOGARITHMS TO THE BASE 10⁰·¹

LOGARITHMS OF NUMBERS GREATER THAN ONE

Number	0	1	2	3	4	5	6	7	8	9	Avg. Diff.
5.0	6.990	6.998	7.007	7.016	7.024	7.033	7.042	7.050	7.059	7.067	9
5.1	7.076	7.084	7.093	7.101	7.110	7.118	7.126	7.135	7.143	7.152	8
5.2	7.160	7.168	7.177	7.185	7.193	7.202	7.210	7.218	7.226	7.235	8
5.3	7.243	7.251	7.259	7.267	7.275	7.284	7.292	7.300	7.308	7.316	8
5.4	7.324	7.332	7.340	7.348	7.356	7.364	7.372	7.380	7.388	7.396	8
5.5	7.404	7.412	7.419	7.427	7.435	7.443	7.451	7.459	7.466	7.474	8
5.6	7.482	7.490	7.497	7.505	7.513	7.520	7.528	7.536	7.543	7.551	8
5.7	7.559	7.566	7.574	7.582	7.589	7.597	7.604	7.612	7.619	7.627	8
5.8	7.634	7.642	7.649	7.657	7.664	7.672	7.679	7.686	7.694	7.701	7
5.9	7.709	7.716	7.723	7.731	7.738	7.745	7.752	7.760	7.767	7.774	7
6.0	7.782	7.789	7.796	7.803	7.810	7.818	7.825	7.832	7.839	7.846	7
6.1	7.853	7.860	7.868	7.875	7.882	7.889	7.896	7.903	7.910	7.917	7
6.2	7.924	7.931	7.938	7.945	7.952	7.959	7.966	7.973	7.980	7.987	7
6.3	7.993	8.000	8.007	8.014	8.021	8.028	8.035	8.041	8.048	8.055	7
6.4	8.062	8.069	8.075	8.082	8.089	8.096	8.102	8.109	8.116	8.122	7
6.5	8.129	8.136	8.142	8.149	8.156	8.162	8.169	8.176	8.182	8.189	7
6.6	8.195	8.202	8.209	8.215	8.222	8.228	8.235	8.241	8.248	8.254	7
6.7	8.261	8.267	8.274	8.280	8.287	8.293	8.299	8.306	8.312	8.319	6
6.8	8.325	8.331	8.338	8.344	8.351	8.357	8.363	8.370	8.376	8.382	6
6.9	8.388	8.395	8.401	8.407	8.414	8.420	8.426	8.432	8.439	8.445	6
7.0	8.451	8.457	8.463	8.470	8.476	8.482	8.488	8.494	8.500	8.506	6
7.1	8.513	8.519	8.525	8.531	8.537	8.543	8.549	8.555	8.561	8.567	6
7.2	8.573	8.579	8.585	8.591	8.597	8.603	8.609	8.615	8.621	8.627	6
7.3	8.633	8.639	8.645	8.651	8.657	8.663	8.669	8.675	8.681	8.686	6
7.4	8.692	8.698	8.704	8.710	8.716	8.722	8.727	8.733	8.739	8.745	6
7.5	8.751	8.756	8.762	8.768	8.774	8.779	8.785	8.791	8.797	8.802	6
7.6	8.808	8.814	8.820	8.825	8.831	8.837	8.842	8.848	8.854	8.859	6
7.7	8.865	8.871	8.876	8.882	8.887	8.893	8.899	8.904	8.910	8.915	6
7.8	8.921	8.927	8.932	8.938	8.943	8.949	8.954	8.960	8.965	8.971	6
7.9	8.976	8.982	8.987	8.993	8.998	9.004	9.009	9.015	9.020	9.025	6
8.0	9.031	9.036	9.042	9.047	9.053	9.058	9.063	9.069	9.074	9.079	5
8.1	9.085	9.090	9.096	9.101	9.106	9.112	9.117	9.122	9.128	9.133	5
8.2	9.138	9.143	9.149	9.154	9.159	9.165	9.170	9.175	9.180	9.186	5
8.3	9.191	9.196	9.201	9.206	9.212	9.217	9.222	9.227	9.232	9.238	5
8.4	9.243	9.248	9.253	9.258	9.263	9.269	9.274	9.279	9.284	9.289	5
8.5	9.294	9.299	9.304	9.309	9.315	9.320	9.325	9.330	9.335	9.340	5
8.6	9.345	9.350	9.355	9.360	9.365	9.370	9.375	9.380	9.385	9.390	5
8.7	9.395	9.400	9.405	9.410	9.415	9.420	9.425	9.430	9.435	9.440	5
8.8	9.445	9.450	9.455	9.460	9.465	9.469	9.474	9.479	9.484	9.489	5
8.9	9.494	9.499	9.504	9.509	9.513	9.518	9.523	9.528	9.533	9.538	5
9.0	9.542	9.547	9.552	9.557	9.562	9.566	9.571	9.576	9.581	9.586	5
9.1	9.590	9.595	9.600	9.605	9.609	9.614	9.619	9.624	9.628	9.633	5
9.2	9.638	9.643	9.647	9.652	9.657	9.661	9.666	9.671	9.675	9.680	5
9.3	9.685	9.689	9.694	9.699	9.703	9.708	9.713	9.717	9.722	9.727	5
9.4	9.731	9.736	9.741	9.745	9.750	9.754	9.759	9.763	9.768	9.773	5
9.5	9.777	9.782	9.786	9.791	9.795	9.800	9.805	9.809	9.814	9.818	5
9.6	9.823	9.827	9.832	9.836	9.841	9.845	9.850	9.854	9.859	9.863	4
9.7	9.868	9.872	9.877	9.881	9.886	9.890	9.894	9.899	9.903	9.908	4
9.8	9.912	9.917	9.921	9.926	9.930	9.934	9.939	9.943	9.948	9.952	4
9.9	9.956	9.961	9.965	9.969	9.974	9.978	9.983	9.987	9.991	9.996	4

lgt π = 4.971
lgt e = 4.343

LOGARITHMS TO THE BASE 10⁰·¹

NUMBERS HAVING NEGATIVE LOGARITHMS

Loga-rithms	0	1	2	3	4	5	6	7	8	9	Avg. Diff.
−0.0	1.0000	0.9977	0.9954	0.9931	0.9908	0.9886	0.9863	0.9840	0.9817	0.9795	23
−0.1	0.9772	0.9750	0.9727	0.9705	0.9683	0.9661	0.9638	0.9616	0.9594	0.9572	22
−0.2	0.9550	0.9528	0.9506	0.9484	0.9462	0.9441	0.9419	0.9397	0.9376	0.9354	22
−0.3	0.9333	0.9311	0.9290	0.9268	0.9247	0.9226	0.9204	0.9183	0.9162	0.9141	21
−0.4	0.9120	0.9099	0.9078	0.9057	0.9036	0.9016	0.8995	0.8974	0.8954	0.8933	21
−0.5	0.8913	0.8892	0.8872	0.8851	0.8831	0.8810	0.8790	0.8770	0.8750	0.8730	20
−0.6	0.8710	0.8690	0.8670	0.8650	0.8630	0.8610	0.8590	0.8570	0.8551	0.8531	20
−0.7	0.8511	0.8492	0.8472	0.8453	0.8433	0.8414	0.8395	0.8375	0.8356	0.8337	19
−0.8	0.8318	0.8299	0.8279	0.8260	0.8241	0.8222	0.8204	0.8185	0.8166	0.8147	19
−0.9	0.8128	0.8110	0.8091	0.8072	0.8054	0.8035	0.8017	0.7998	0.7980	0.7962	18
−1.0	0.7943	0.7925	0.7907	0.7889	0.7870	0.7852	0.7834	0.7816	0.7798	0.7780	18
−1.1	0.7762	0.7745	0.7727	0.7709	0.7691	0.7674	0.7656	0.7638	0.7621	0.7603	18
−1.2	0.7586	0.7568	0.7551	0.7534	0.7516	0.7499	0.7482	0.7464	0.7447	0.7430	17
−1.3	0.7413	0.7396	0.7379	0.7362	0.7345	0.7328	0.7311	0.7295	0.7278	0.7261	17
−1.4	0.7244	0.7228	0.7211	0.7194	0.7178	0.7161	0.7145	0.7129	0.7112	0.7096	16
−1.5	0.7079	0.7063	0.7047	0.7031	0.7015	0.6998	0.6982	0.6966	0.6950	0.6934	16
−1.6	0.6918	0.6902	0.6887	0.6871	0.6855	0.6839	0.6823	0.6808	0.6792	0.6776	16
−1.7	0.6761	0.6745	0.6730	0.6714	0.6699	0.6683	0.6668	0.6653	0.6637	0.6622	15
−1.8	0.6607	0.6592	0.6577	0.6561	0.6546	0.6531	0.6516	0.6501	0.6486	0.6471	15
−1.9	0.6457	0.6442	0.6427	0.6412	0.6397	0.6383	0.6368	0.6353	0.6339	0.6324	15
−2.0	0.6310	0.6295	0.6281	0.6266	0.6252	0.6237	0.6223	0.6209	0.6194	0.6180	14
−2.1	0.6166	0.6152	0.6138	0.6124	0.6109	0.6095	0.6081	0.6067	0.6053	0.6039	14
−2.2	0.6026	0.6012	0.5998	0.5984	0.5970	0.5957	0.5943	0.5929	0.5916	0.5902	14
−2.3	0.5888	0.5875	0.5861	0.5848	0.5834	0.5821	0.5808	0.5794	0.5781	0.5768	13
−2.4	0.5754	0.5741	0.5728	0.5715	0.5702	0.5689	0.5675	0.5662	0.5649	0.5636	13
−2.5	0.5623	0.5610	0.5598	0.5585	0.5572	0.5559	0.5546	0.5534	0.5521	0.5508	13
−2.6	0.5495	0.5483	0.5470	0.5458	0.5445	0.5433	0.5420	0.5408	0.5395	0.5383	12
−2.7	0.5370	0.5358	0.5346	0.5333	0.5321	0.5309	0.5297	0.5284	0.5272	0.5260	12
−2.8	0.5248	0.5236	0.5224	0.5212	0.5200	0.5188	0.5176	0.5164	0.5152	0.5140	12
−2.9	0.5129	0.5117	0.5105	0.5093	0.5082	0.5070	0.5058	0.5047	0.5035	0.5023	12
−3.0	0.5012	0.5000	0.4989	0.4977	0.4966	0.4955	0.4943	0.4932	0.4920	0.4909	11
−3.1	0.4898	0.4887	0.4875	0.4864	0.4853	0.4842	0.4831	0.4819	0.4808	0.4797	11
−3.2	0.4786	0.4775	0.4764	0.4753	0.4742	0.4732	0.4721	0.4710	0.4699	0.4688	11
−3.3	0.4677	0.4667	0.4656	0.4645	0.4634	0.4624	0.4613	0.4603	0.4592	0.4581	11
−3.4	0.4571	0.4560	0.4550	0.4539	0.4529	0.4519	0.4508	0.4498	0.4487	0.4477	10
−3.5	0.4467	0.4457	0.4446	0.4436	0.4426	0.4416	0.4406	0.4395	0.4385	0.4375	10
−3.6	0.4365	0.4355	0.4345	0.4335	0.4325	0.4315	0.4305	0.4295	0.4285	0.4276	10
−3.7	0.4266	0.4256	0.4246	0.4236	0.4227	0.4217	0.4207	0.4198	0.4188	0.4178	10
−3.8	0.4169	0.4159	0.4150	0.4140	0.4130	0.4121	0.4111	0.4102	0.4093	0.4083	10
−3.9	0.4074	0.4064	0.4055	0.4046	0.4036	0.4027	0.4018	0.4009	0.3999	0.3990	9
−4.0	0.3981	0.3972	0.3963	0.3954	0.3945	0.3936	0.3926	0.3917	0.3908	0.3899	9
−4.1	0.3890	0.3882	0.3873	0.3864	0.3855	0.3846	0.3837	0.3828	0.3819	0.3811	9
−4.2	0.3802	0.3793	0.3784	0.3776	0.3767	0.3758	0.3750	0.3741	0.3733	0.3724	9
−4.3	0.3715	0.3707	0.3698	0.3690	0.3681	0.3673	0.3664	0.3656	0.3648	0.3639	8
−4.4	0.3631	0.3622	0.3614	0.3606	0.3597	0.3589	0.3581	0.3573	0.3565	0.3556	8
−4.5	0.3548	0.3540	0.3532	0.3524	0.3516	0.3508	0.3499	0.3491	0.3483	0.3475	8
−4.6	0.3467	0.3459	0.3451	0.3443	0.3436	0.3428	0.3420	0.3412	0.3404	0.3396	8
−4.7	0.3388	0.3381	0.3373	0.3365	0.3357	0.3350	0.3342	0.3334	0.3327	0.3319	8
−4.8	0.3311	0.3304	0.3296	0.3289	0.3281	0.3273	0.3266	0.3258	0.3251	0.3243	8
−4.9	0.3236	0.3228	0.3221	0.3214	0.3206	0.3199	0.3192	0.3184	0.3177	0.3170	7

The addition of $-10n$ to the logarithm of a number requires that the number be multiplied by 10^{-n}.

LOGARITHMS TO THE BASE $10^{0.1}$

NUMBERS HAVING NEGATIVE LOGARITHMS

Logarithms	0	1	2	3	4	5	6	7	8	9	Avg. Diff.
−5.0	0.3162	0.3155	0.3148	0.3141	0.3133	0.3126	0.3119	0.3112	0.3105	0.3097	7
−5.1	0.3090	0.3083	0.3076	0.3069	0.3062	0.3055	0.3048	0.3041	0.3034	0.3027	7
−5.2	0.3020	0.3013	0.3006	0.2999	0.2992	0.2985	0.2979	0.2972	0.2965	0.2958	7
−5.3	0.2951	0.2944	0.2938	0.2931	0.2924	0.2917	0.2911	0.2904	0.2897	0.2891	7
−5.4	0.2884	0.2877	0.2871	0.2864	0.2858	0.2851	0.2844	0.2838	0.2831	0.2825	7
−5.5	0.2818	0.2812	0.2805	0.2799	0.2793	0.2786	0.2780	0.2773	0.2767	0 2761	6
−5.6	0.2754	0.2748	0.2742	0.2735	0.2729	0.2723	0.2716	0.2710	0.2704	0.2698	6
−5.7	0.2692	0.2685	0.2679	0.2673	0.2667	0.2661	0.2655	0.2649	0.2642	0.2636	6
−5.8	0.2630	0.2624	0.2618	0.2612	0.2606	0.2600	0.2594	0.2588	0.2582	0.2576	6
−5.9	0.2570	0.2564	0.2559	0.2553	0.2547	0.2541	0.2535	0.2529	0.2523	0.2518	6
−6.0	0.2512	0.2506	0.2500	0.2495	0.2489	0.2483	0.2477	0.2472	0.2466	0.2460	6
−6.1	0.2455	0.2449	0.2443	0.2438	0.2432	0.2427	0.2421	0.2415	0.2410	0.2404	6
−6.2	0.2399	0.2393	0.2388	0.2382	0.2377	0.2371	0.2366	0.2360	0.2355	0.2350	5
−6.3	0.2344	0.2339	0.2333	0.2328	0.2323	0.2317	0.2312	0.2307	0.2301	0.2296	5
−6.4	0.2291	0.2286	0.2280	0.2275	0.2270	0.2265	0.2259	0.2254	0.2249	0.2244	5
−6.5	0.2239	0.2234	0.2228	0.2223	0.2218	0.2213	0.2208	0.2203	0.2198	0.2193	5
−6.6	0.2188	0.2183	0.2178	0.2173	0.2168	0.2163	0.2158	0.2153	0.2148	0.2143	5
−6.7	0.2138	0.2133	0.2128	0.2123	0.2118	0.2113	0.2109	0.2104	0.2099	0.2094	5
−6.8	0.2089	0.2084	0.2080	0.2075	0.2070	0.2065	0.2061	0.2056	0.2051	0.2046	5
−6.9	0.2042	0.2037	0.2032	0.2028	0.2023	0.2018	0.2014	0.2009	0.2004	0.2000	5
−7.0	0.1995	0.1991	0.1986	0.1982	0.1977	0.1972	0.1968	0.1963	0.1959	0.1954	5
−7.1	0.1950	0.1945	0.1941	0.1936	0.1932	0.1928	0.1923	0.1919	0.1914	0.1910	4
−7.2	0.1905	0.1901	0.1897	0.1892	0.1888	0.1884	0.1879	0.1875	0.1871	0.1866	4
−7.3	0.1862	0.1858	0.1854	0.1849	0.1845	0.1841	0.1837	0.1832	0.1828	0.1824	4
−7.4	0.1820	0.1816	0.1811	0.1807	0.1803	0.1799	0.1795	0.1791	0.1786	0.1782	4
−7.5	0.1778	0.1774	0.1770	0.1766	0.1762	0.1758	0.1754	0.1750	0.1746	0.1742	4
−7.6	0.1738	0.1734	0.1730	0.1726	0.1722	0.1718	0.1714	0.1710	0.1706	0.1702	4
−7.7	0.1698	0.1694	0.1690	0.1687	0.1683	0.1679	0.1675	0.1671	0.1667	0.1663	4
−7.8	0.1660	0.1656	0.1652	0.1648	0.1644	0.1641	0.1637	0.1633	0.1629	0.1626	4
−7.9	0.1622	0.1618	0.1614	0.1611	0.1607	0.1603	0.1600	0.1596	0.1592	0.1589	4
−8.0	0.1585	0.1581	0.1578	0.1574	0.1570	0.1567	0.1563	0.1560	0.1556	0.1552	4
−8.1	0.1549	0.1545	0.1542	0.1538	0.1535	0.1531	0.1528	0.1524	0.1521	0.1517	4
−8.2	0.1514	0.1510	0.1507	0.1503	0.1500	0.1496	0.1493	0.1489	0.1486	0.1483	3
−8.3	0.1479	0.1476	0.1472	0.1469	0.1466	0.1462	0.1459	0.1455	0.1452	0.1449	3
−8.4	0.1445	0.1442	0.1439	0.1435	0.1432	0.1429	0.1426	0.1422	0.1419	0.1416	3
−8.5	0.1413	0.1409	0.1406	0.1403	0.1400	0.1396	0.1393	0.1390	0.1387	0.1384	3
−8.6	0.1380	0.1377	0.1374	0.1371	0.1368	0.1365	0.1361	0.1358	0.1355	0.1352	3
−8.7	0.1349	0.1346	0.1343	0.1340	0.1337	0.1334	0.1330	0.1327	0.1324	0.1321	3
−8.8	0.1318	0.1315	0.1312	0.1309	0.1306	0.1303	0.1300	0.1297	0.1294	0.1291	3
−8.9	0.1288	0.1285	0.1282	0.1279	0.1276	0.1274	0.1271	0.1268	0.1265	0.1262	3
−9.0	0.1259	0.1256	0.1253	0.1250	0.1247	0.1245	0.1242	0.1239	0.1236	0.1233	3
−9.1	0.1230	0.1227	0.1225	0.1222	0.1219	0.1216	0.1213	0.1211	0.1208	0.1205	3
−9.2	0.1202	0.1199	0.1197	0.1194	0.1191	0.1189	0.1186	0.1183	0.1180	0.1178	3
−9.3	0.1175	0.1172	0.1169	0.1167	0.1164	0.1161	0.1159	0.1156	0.1153	0.1151	3
−9.4	0.1148	0.1146	0.1143	0.1140	0.1138	0.1135	0.1132	0.1130	0.1127	0.1125	3
−9.5	0.1122	0.1119	0.1117	0.1114	0.1112	0.1109	0.1107	0.1104	0.1102	0.1099	3
−9.6	0.1096	0.1094	0.1091	0.1089	0.1086	0.1084	0.1081	0.1079	0.1076	0.1074	2
−9.7	0.1072	0.1069	0.1067	0.1064	0.1062	0.1059	0.1057	0.1054	0.1052	0.1050	2
−9.8	0.1047	0.1045	0.1042	0.1040	0.1038	0.1035	0.1033	0.1030	0.1028	0.1026	2
−9.9	0.1023	0.1021	0.1019	0.1016	0.1014	0.1012	0.1009	0.1007	0.1005	0.1002	2

LOGARITHMS TO THE BASE $10^{0.1}$

NUMBERS HAVING POSITIVE LOGARITHMS

Loga-rithms	0	1	2	3	4	5	6	7	8	9	Avg. Diff.
0.0	1.000	1.002	1.005	1.007	1.009	1.012	1.014	1.016	1.019	1.021	2
0.1	1.023	1.026	1.028	1.030	1.033	1.035	1.038	1.040	1.042	1.045	2
0.2	1.047	1.050	1.052	1.054	1.057	1.059	1.062	1.064	1.067	1.069	2
0.3	1.072	1.074	1.076	1.079	1.081	1.084	1.086	1.089	1.091	1.094	2
0.4	1.096	1.099	1.102	1.104	1.107	1.109	1.112	1.114	1.117	1.119	3
0.5	1.122	1.125	1.127	1.130	1.132	1.135	1.138	1.140	1.143	1.146	3
0.6	1.148	1.151	1.153	1.156	1.159	1.161	1.164	1.167	1.169	1.172	3
0.7	1.175	1.178	1.180	1.183	1.186	1.189	1.191	1.194	1.197	1.199	3
0.8	1.202	1.205	1.208	1.211	1.213	1.216	1.219	1.222	1.225	1.227	3
0.9	1.230	1.233	1.236	1.239	1.242	1.245	1.247	1.250	1.253	1.256	3
1.0	1.259	1.262	1.265	1.268	1.271	1.274	1.276	1.279	1.282	1.285	3
1.1	1.288	1.291	1.294	1.297	1.300	1.303	1.306	1.309	1.312	1.315	3
1.2	1.318	1.321	1.324	1.327	1.330	1.334	1.337	1.340	1.343	1.346	3
1.3	1.349	1.352	1.355	1.358	1.361	1.365	1.368	1.371	1.374	1.377	3
1.4	1.380	1.384	1.387	1.390	1.393	1.396	1.400	1.403	1.406	1.409	3
1.5	1.413	1.416	1.419	1.422	1.426	1.429	1.432	1.435	1.439	1.442	3
1.6	1.445	1.449	1.452	1.455	1.459	1.462	1.466	1.469	1.472	1.476	3
1.7	1.479	1.483	1.486	1.489	1.493	1.496	1.500	1.503	1.507	1.510	3
1.8	1.514	1.517	1.521	1.524	1.528	1.531	1.535	1.538	1.542	1.545	3
1.9	1.549	1.552	1.556	1.560	1.563	1.567	1.570	1.574	1.578	1.581	4
2.0	1.585	1.589	1.592	1.596	1.600	1.603	1.607	1.611	1.614	1.618	4
2.1	1.622	1.626	1.629	1.633	1.637	1.641	1.644	1.648	1.652	1.656	4
2.2	1.660	1.663	1.667	1.671	1.675	1.679	1.683	1.687	1.690	1.694	4
2.3	1.698	1.702	1.706	1.710	1.714	1.718	1.722	1.726	1.730	1.734	4
2.4	1.738	1.742	1.746	1.750	1.754	1.758	1.762	1.766	1.770	1.774	4
2.5	1.778	1.782	1.786	1.791	1.795	1.799	1.803	1.807	1.811	1.816	4
2.6	1.820	1.824	1.828	1.832	1.837	1.841	1.845	1.849	1.854	1.858	4
2.7	1.862	1.866	1.871	1.875	1.879	1.884	1.888	1.892	1.897	1.901	4
2.8	1.905	1.910	1.914	1.919	1.923	1.928	1.932	1.936	1.941	1.945	4
2.9	1.950	1.954	1.959	1.963	1.968	1.972	1.977	1.982	1.986	1.991	5
3.0	1.995	2.000	2.004	2.009	2.014	2.018	2.023	2.028	2.032	2.037	5
3.1	2.042	2.046	2.051	2.056	2.061	2.065	2.070	2.075	2.080	2.084	5
3.2	2.089	2.094	2.099	2.104	2.109	2.113	2.118	2.123	2.128	2.133	5
3.3	2.138	2.143	2.148	2.153	2.158	2.163	2.168	2.173	2.178	2.183	5
3.4	2.188	2.193	2.198	2.203	2.208	2.213	2.218	2.223	2.228	2.234	5
3.5	2.239	2.244	2.249	2.254	2.259	2.265	2.270	2.275	2.280	2.286	5
3.6	2.291	2.296	2.301	2.307	2.312	2.317	2.323	2.328	2.333	2.339	5
3.7	2.344	2.350	2.355	2.360	2.366	2.371	2.377	2.382	2.388	2.393	5
3.8	2.399	2.404	2.410	2.415	2.421	2.427	2.432	2.438	2.443	2.449	6
3.9	2.455	2.460	2.466	2.472	2.477	2.483	2.489	2.495	2.500	2.506	6
4.0	2.512	2.518	2.523	2.529	2.535	2.541	2.547	2.553	2.559	2.564	6
4.1	2.570	2.576	2.582	2.588	2.594	2.600	2.606	2.612	2.618	2.624	6
4.2	2.630	2.636	2.642	2.649	2.655	2.661	2.667	2.673	2.679	2.685	6
4.3	2.692	2.698	2.704	2.710	2.716	2.723	2.729	2.735	2.742	2.748	6
4.4	2.754	2.761	2.767	2.773	2.780	2.786	2.793	2.799	2.805	2.812	6
4.5	2.818	2.825	2.831	2.838	2.844	2.851	2.858	2.864	2.871	2.877	7
4.6	2.884	2.891	2.897	2.904	2.911	2.917	2.924	2.931	2.938	2.944	7
4.7	2.951	2.958	2.965	2.972	2.979	2.985	2.992	2.999	3.006	3.013	7
4.8	3.020	3.027	3.034	3.041	3.048	3.055	3.062	3.069	3.076	3.083	7
4.9	3.090	3.097	3.105	3.112	3.119	3.126	3.133	3.141	3.148	3.155	7

The addition of $10n$ to the logarithm of a number requires that the number be multiplied by 10^n.

LOGARITHMS TO THE BASE 10$^{0.1}$

NUMBERS HAVING POSITIVE LOGARITHMS

Loga-rithms	0	1	2	3	4	5	6	7	8	9	Avg. Diff.
5.0	3.162	3.170	3.177	3.184	3.192	3.199	3.206	3.214	3.221	3.228	7
5.1	3.236	3.243	3.251	3.258	3.266	3.273	3.281	3.289	3.296	3.304	8
5.2	3.311	3.319	3.327	3.334	3.342	3.350	3.357	3.365	3.373	3.381	8
5.3	3.388	3.396	3.404	3.412	3.420	3.428	3.436	3.443	3.451	3.459	8
5.4	3.467	3.475	3.483	3.491	3.499	3.508	3.516	3.524	3.532	3.540	8
5.5	3.548	3.556	3.565	3.573	3.581	3.589	3.597	3.606	3.614	3.622	8
5.6	3.631	3.639	3.648	3.656	3.664	3.673	3.681	3.690	3.698	3.707	8
5.7	3.715	3.724	3.733	3.741	3.750	3.758	3.767	3.776	3.784	3.793	9
5.8	3.802	3.811	3.819	3.828	3.837	3.846	3.855	3.864	3.873	3.882	9
5.9	3.890	3.899	3.908	3.917	3.926	3.936	3.945	3.954	3.963	3.972	9
6.0	3.981	3.990	3.999	4.009	4.018	4.027	4.036	4.046	4.055	4.064	9
6.1	4.074	4.083	4.093	4.102	4.111	4.121	4.130	4.140	4.150	4.159	9
6.2	4.169	4.178	4.188	4.198	4.207	4.217	4.227	4.236	4.246	4.256	10
6.3	4.266	4.276	4.285	4.295	4.305	4.315	4.325	4.335	4.345	4.355	10
6.4	4.365	4.375	4.385	4.395	4.406	4.416	4.426	4.436	4.446	4.457	10
6.5	4.467	4.477	4.487	4.498	4.508	4.519	4.529	4.539	4.550	4.560	10
6.6	4.571	4.581	4.592	4.603	4.613	4.624	4.634	4.645	4.656	4.667	11
6.7	4.677	4.688	4.699	4.710	4.721	4.732	4.742	4.753	4.764	4.775	11
6.8	4.786	4.797	4.808	4.819	4.831	4.842	4.853	4.864	4.875	4.887	11
6.9	4.898	4.909	4.920	4.932	4.943	4.955	4.966	4.977	4.989	5.000	11
7.0	5.012	5.023	5.035	5.047	5.058	5.070	5.082	5.093	5.105	5.117	12
7.1	5.129	5.140	5.152	5.164	5.176	5.188	5.200	5.212	5.224	5.236	12
7.2	5.248	5.260	5.272	5.284	5.297	5.309	5.321	5.333	5.346	5.358	12
7.3	5.370	5.383	5.395	5.408	5.420	5.433	5.445	5.458	5.470	5.483	13
7.4	5.495	5.508	5.521	5.534	5.546	5.559	5.572	5.585	5.598	5.610	13
7.5	5.623	5.636	5.649	5.662	5.675	5.689	5.702	5.715	5.728	5.741	13
7.6	5.754	5.768	5.781	5.794	5.808	5.821	5.834	5.848	5.861	5.875	13
7.7	5.888	5.902	5.916	5.929	5.943	5.957	5.970	5.984	5.998	6.012	14
7.8	6.026	6.039	6.053	6.067	6.081	6.095	6.109	6.124	6.138	6.152	14
7.9	6.166	6.180	6.194	6.209	6.223	6.237	6.252	6.266	6.281	6.295	14
8.0	6.310	6.324	6.339	6.353	6.368	6.383	6.397	6.412	6.427	6.442	15
8.1	6.457	6.471	6.486	6.501	6.516	6.531	6.546	6.561	6.577	6.592	15
8.2	6.607	6.622	6.637	6.653	6.668	6.683	6.699	6.714	6.730	6.745	15
8.3	6.761	6.776	6.792	6.808	6.823	6.839	6.855	6.871	6.887	6.902	16
8.4	6.918	6.934	6.950	6.966	6.982	6.998	7.015	7.031	7.047	7.063	16
8.5	7.079	7.096	7.112	7.129	7.145	7.161	7.178	7.194	7.211	7.228	17
8.6	7.244	7.261	7.278	7.295	7.311	7.328	7.345	7.362	7.379	7.396	17
8.7	7.413	7.430	7.447	7.464	7.482	7.499	7.516	7.534	7.551	7.568	17
8.8	7.586	7.603	7.621	7.638	7.656	7.674	7.691	7.709	7.727	7.745	18
8.9	7.762	7.780	7.798	7.816	7.834	7.852	7.870	7.889	7.907	7.925	18
9.0	7.943	7.962	7.980	7.998	8.017	8.035	8.054	8.072	8.091	8.110	19
9.1	8.128	8.147	8.166	8.185	8.204	8.222	8.241	8.260	8.279	8.299	19
9.2	8.318	8.337	8.356	8.375	8.395	8.414	8.433	8.453	8.472	8.492	19
9.3	8.511	8.531	8.551	8.570	8.590	8.610	8.630	8.650	8.670	8.690	20
9.4	8.710	8.730	8.750	8.770	8.790	8.810	8.831	8.851	8.872	8.892	20
9.5	8.913	8.933	8.954	8.974	8.995	9.016	9.036	9.057	9.078	9.099	21
9.6	9.120	9.141	9.162	9.183	9.204	9.226	9.247	9.268	9.290	9.311	21
9.7	9.333	9.354	9.376	9.397	9.419	9.441	9.462	9.484	9.506	9.528	22
9.8	9.550	9.572	9.594	9.616	9.638	9.661	9.683	9.705	9.727	9.750	22
9.9	9.772	9.795	9.817	9.840	9.863	9.886	9.908	9.931	9.954	9.977	23

TABLES FOR COMPUTING DIRECTIVITY PATTERNS

VALUES OF FUNCTIONS

ψ rad	$(\sin\psi)/\psi$	$(\sin^2\psi)/\psi^2$	$2\mathcal{J}_1(\psi)/\psi$	$\mathcal{J}_0(\psi)$	ψ rad	$(\sin\psi)/\psi$	$(\sin^2\psi)/\psi^2$	$2\mathcal{J}_1(\psi)/\psi$	$\mathcal{J}_0(\psi)$
0.0	1.000	1.000	1.000	1.000	11.0	−0.091	0.008	−0.032	−0.171
0.5	0.959	0.920	0.969	0.939	11.5	−0.076	0.006	−0.040	−0.068
1.0	0.841	0.707	0.880	0.765	12.0	−0.045	0.002	−0.037	+0.048
1.5	0.665	0.442	0.744	0.512	12.5	−0.005	0.000	−0.026	0.147
2.0	0.455	0.207	0.577	+0.224	13.0	+0.032	0.001	−0.011	0.207
2.5	0.239	0.057	0.398	−0.048	13.5	0.060	0.004	+0.006	0.215
3.0	+0.047	0.002	0.226	−0.260	14.0	0.071	0.005	0.019	0.171
3.5	−0.100	0.010	+0.078	−0.380	14.5	0.064	0.004	0.027	+0.088
4.0	−0.189	0.036	−0.033	−0.397	15.0	0.043	0.002	0.027	−0.014
4.5	−0.217	0.047	−0.103	−0.321	15.5	+0.013	0.000	0.022	−0.109
5.0	−0.192	0.037	−0.131	−0.178	16.0	−0.018	0.000	0.011	−0.175
5.5	−0.128	0.016	−0.124	−0.007	16.5	−0.043	0.002		
6.0	−0.047	0.002	−0.092	+0.151	17.0	−0.057	0.003		
6.5	+0.033	0.001	−0.047	0.260	17.5	−0.056	0.003		
7.0	0.094	0.009	+0.001	0.300	18.0	−0.042	0.002		
7.5	0.125	0.016	0.036	0.266	18.5	−0.019	0.000		
8.0	0.124	0.015	0.059	0.172	19.0	+0.008	0.000		
8.5	0.094	0.009	0.064	+0.042	19.5	0.031	0.001		
9.0	+0.045	0.002	0.055	−0.090	20.0	0.046	0.002		
9.5	−0.008	0.000	0.034	−0.194	20.5	0.049	0.002		
10.0	−0.054	0.003	+0.009	−0.246	21.0	0.040	0.002		
10.5	−0.084	0.007	−0.015	−0.237	21.5	0.022	0.000		
					22.0	0.000	0.000		

MAXIMUM AND MINIMUM VALUES

ψ rad	$(\sin\psi)/\psi$	$(\sin^2\psi)/\psi^2$	ψ rad	$\mathcal{J}_0(\psi)$	$2\mathcal{J}_1(\psi)/\psi$
0.000	+1.000	1.000	0.00	+1.000	+1.000
3.14	0.000	0.000	2.40	0.000	
4.49	−0.217	0.047	3.83	−0.403	0.000
6.28	0.000	0.000	5.14		−0.132
7.72	+0.129	0.017	5.52	0.000	
9.32	0.000	0.000	7.02	+0.300	0.000
10.87	−0.090	0.008	8.42		+0.0645
12.57	0.000	0.000	8.65	0.000	
14.10	+0.071	0.005	10.17	−0.250	0.000
15.7	0.000	0.000	11.62		−0.0400
17.2	−0.058	0.003	11.79	0.000	
18.9	0.000	0.000	13.32	+0.218	0.000
20.3	+0.050	0.002	14.80		+0.0279
			14.93	0.000	

INDEX

413

TRIMMED SIZE: $7\frac{7}{8} \times 10\frac{1}{2}$ Inches
TYPE PAGE: $39\frac{1}{2} \times 56$ Picas
TYPE FACE: Monotype 21E, 25J and 453J
TYPE SIZE: 10 Point on 12
CHAPTER TITLE: 14 Point Baskerville Bold Caps
PAPER: 50 lb. White Winnebago E. F.
CLOTH: Columbia Tanotex #320/2998